SCIENCE

The Art of Sugarcraft

# PIPING

# The Art of Sugarcraft

# PIPING

## NORMA LAVER

Foreword  Mitzie Wilson
Series Editor  Joyce Becker
Photography by Melvin Grey and Graham Tann

**MEREHURST PRESS**
— LONDON —

Published 1986 by Merehurst Press
5 Great James Street
London WC1N 3DA

© Copyright 1986 Merehurst Limited

ISBN 0 948075 10 4

Designed by Carole Perks
Editorial Assistant Suzanne Ellis
Further assistance provided by Trudie Ballantyne, Rachel Lalley
    and Sara Townshend
Cover photograph by Graham Tann
Typeset by Filmset
Colour separation by Fotographics Ltd, London-Hong Kong
Printed by New Interlitho S.p.A., Milan


**ACKNOWLEDGEMENTS**
Norma Laver would like to thank Susan Ashby, June Cooper, Janet
Foster, Nicholas Lodge, Tombi Peck and Jenny Walker for their help
in the preparation of this book. She would also like to thank David,
Alison and Karen Laver, her mother, family and friends for their
encouragement, support and great patience.

The publishers would like to thank the following companies for their
help in the preparation of this book:
Cuisena Cookware Limited
Guy, Paul and Company Limited, Unit B4, A1 Industrial Park,
    Little End Road, Eton Scoton, Cambridgeshire, PE19 3JH
Sugarflair Colours Limited
B.R. Mathews, 12 Gipsy Hill, London SE19 1NN
A Piece of Cake, 18 Upper High Street, Thame, Oxon, OX9 2XE

Companion volumes:
The Art of Sugarcraft — **CHOCOLATE**
The Art of Sugarcraft — **MARZIPAN**
The Art of Sugarcraft — **SUGAR FLOWERS**

# CONTENTS

# NORMA LAVER

It is difficult to believe that Norma Laver only began cake decorating in 1979. An accomplished craftswoman, she enrolled in a beginner's class and she took to this new medium with enthusiasm and delight. Her great talent for sugarart was confirmed when she won the very first competition she entered, just 18 months after her first icing lesson. She has since collected many more awards at national and international levels.

Cake decorating dominates the Laver household. Norma's daughters, Alison and Karen, are both enthusiasts, and even her husband has been known to pick up a piping tube and help finish a cake. Norma is co-owner of a shop specializing in cake decorating equipment and she works as a teaching assistant in a local primary school. She has taught sugarcraft in adult education and she is in great demand to design cakes for brides all over the UK.

Norma takes great pleasure in decorating a cake, but she is happy that the cake will be cut and eaten, gaining satisfaction from this artistic yet functional craft. Norma is an expert in many of the decorating skills and particularly enjoys fine piping. She is well known in the sugarcraft world for her extension work and embroidery.

# FOREWORD

As a keen cake decorator myself, I have found Norma Laver's piping instructions invaluable. The piping on a cake can make or mar your design, and although I have a reasonably steady hand I do find it difficult to get perfect results every time. Now her instructions have taught me where I'm going wrong. There's no need for an amateur attempt at writing Happy Birthday, as the book gives patterns for all your favourite greetings, templates for script and lettering styles, with illustrations to help everyone master the skills.

From basic shell piping, Norma's techniques show how to build up the most intricate of borders, elegant run-out collars, dainty drop lines, curves and the finest extension work. Now I know how to do them all, and although I can't promise you'll reach the same standard as Norma, it only takes practice for you too to become perfect.

My favourite sections of the book must be how to embroider in icing, with patterns to copy, beautiful broderie anglaise, tulle and lace work, too. This book is a delight for beginners and professional cake icers alike.


Mitzie Wilson
Cookery Editor, Woman's Own Magazine

# EQUIPMENT

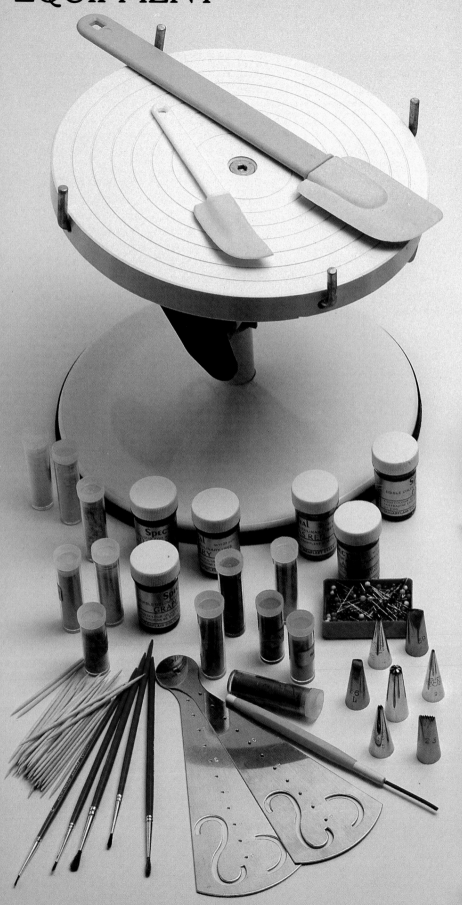

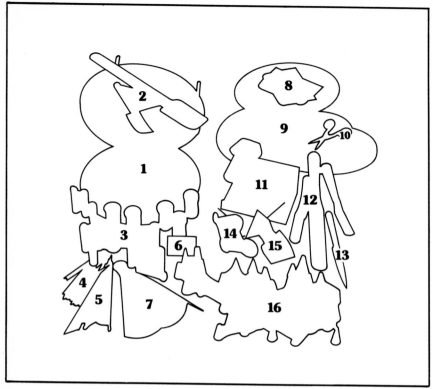

This is a selection of tools and equipment used for piping. Most are ordinary kitchen or household items, while the more unusual tools are available from cake decorating shops and specialist suppliers.

1 Turntable
2 Rubber spatulas for buttercream
3 Paste colours and petal dust
4 Cocktail sticks
5 Paintbrushes
6 Glass-headed pins
7 Scribers
8 Side scrapers
9 Cake boards
10 Scissors
11 Icing bag stand
12 Palette knives
13 Sharp paring knife
14 Icing nails
15 Forms for piping shapes
16 Piping tubes

# EQUIPMENT

Piping tubes come in a variety of qualities and prices but to achieve good results, especially with fine work, the best quality tubes are worth the extra expense. Flower tubes (No56 and 59) are necessary for piped flowers. Basket weave or ribbon tubes are also handy.
No0 and No00 are used for extension work, lace, and other fine work. No1 is used for embroidery and writing. No5 is the first of the stars. These are all useful for borders and edges, or when it is necessary to decorate a cake quickly. The larger stars can be used with buttercream. No23 is a basket tube.
Small palette knives and side scrapers are useful for mixing colour into icing.

For sifting icing sugar use a fine meshed sieve kept for this purpose only.
An electric mixer is useful for beating royal icing.
You will also need greaseproof paper, wax paper and baking parchment.
Colour is brushed onto decorated cakes with various sizes of paint brushes.
A sharp knife is needed for cutting icing bags; scissors are also useful.
A scriber or glass-headed pins are used to mark a design onto an iced cake.
A good turntable, tilting if possible, is important.
An anglepoise lamp provides good light and can be moved easily. It is also useful for drying lace and flood work.

# PIPING BAGS

Well-made piping bags from greaseproof paper or baking parchment are essential for good piping. Paper bags are easier to control than the plastic or metal icing syringes, and they are disposable, so do not have to be cleaned like the plastic or nylon bags.

Piping bags should never be made too large, as they will be difficult to control and the heat from your hand will change the consistency of the icing. Bags for buttercream will need to be larger than those for royal icing. If doing a lot of piping, make several bags before starting to pipe. If piping with different coloured icing or when using different tubes, you will need several bags on hand for each one.

There are different methods for making paper piping bags. The one shown here produces bags which are a good shape and easy to use.

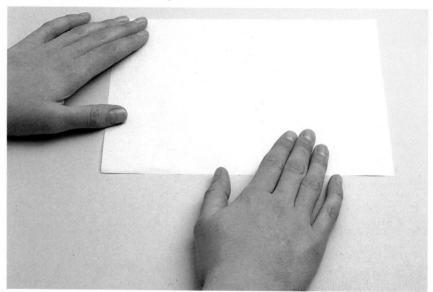

Cut a piece of greaseproof paper twice as long as it is wide.

Fold the paper diagonally. The points will not meet.

Cut along the fold with a sharp
knife to make two right-angle
triangles.

Lay the triangle flat with the right
angle facing you and fold the
corner inwards.

Place the corner on the point of
the right angle, making a cone.

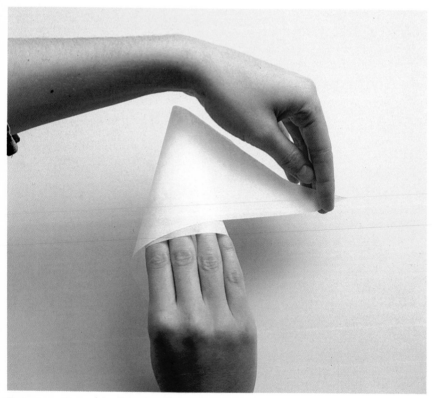

Put your fingers in the cone to
hold it and bring the other corner
over it.

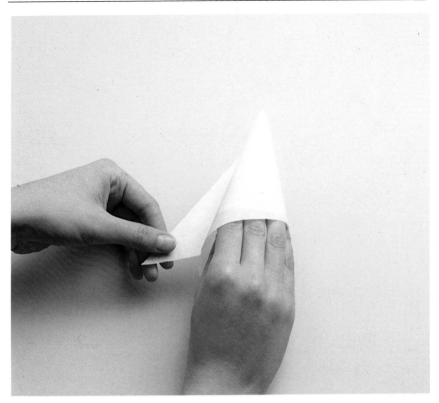

Wrap the corner around the cone
twice so that the points meet.

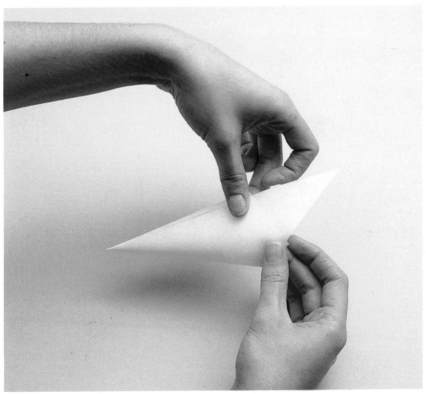

Slide the three points together to
tighten the bag.

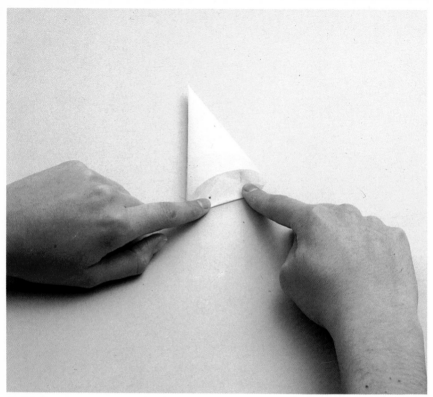

Fold the top point into the bag. If piping without a tube, fill the bag now.

If using a piping tube, cut off the tip of the bag with scissors and insert the tube.

# FILLING THE BAG

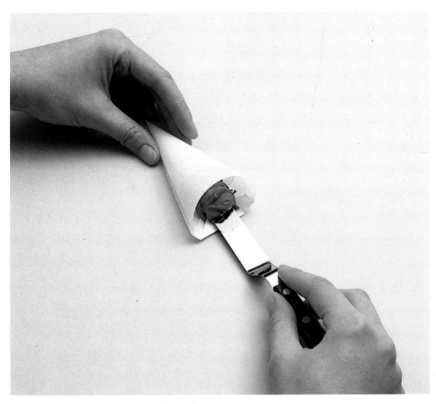

Hold the bag in your hand or place on the table and hold the point. Scoop up some icing with a palette knife and place in the bag.

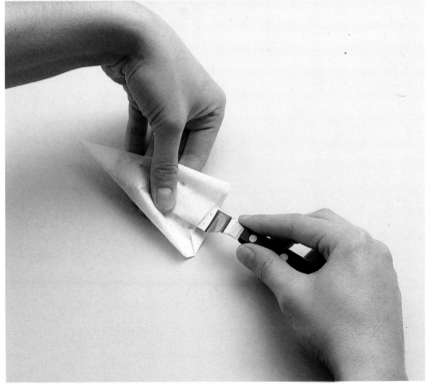

Hold the top of the bag down and gently pull out the palette knife.

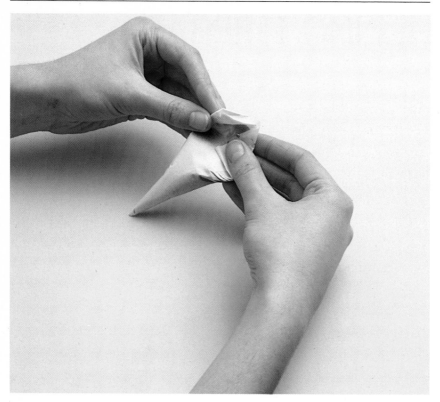

Fold the points of the bag towards the centre.

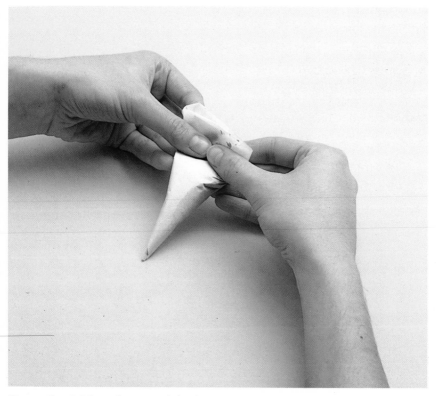

Fasten by folding the top of the bag over twice.

# USING A PIPING BAG

The bag when filled will fit comfortably into one hand. The other is then left free to steady it.

Hold the bag as you would hold a short, very fat pencil, with the thumb and index finger either side and the third finger bent underneath. The fourth and fifth fingers are also bent under. The folded end of the bag will then fit snugly into the hand between the thumb and index finger.

For smaller amounts of icing the bag will not reach as far as the palm, so hold it with the thumb and first two fingers. Always make sure the thumb is on the folded end, keeping the bag firmly closed.

If this position seems uncomfortable at first, persevere, as it enables the most pressure to be applied with the least effort. This is very important if you are piping for a long time.

Pressure is applied by the thumb and first two fingers which are in contact with the bag. Fine movement is also achieved by use of these fingers.

Do not hold the bag with both hands as this restricts movement and control. If two hands are necessary to force the icing through the nozzle, then it is too stiff or has been made incorrectly.

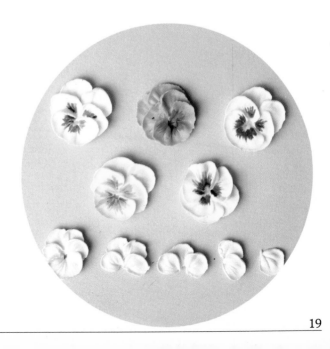

# ICING FOR PIPING

## Royal Icing

200g (7oz/1¾cups) icing
(confectioner's) sugar, sifted
white of 1 large egg
pinch of tartaric acid (cream of
tartar)

Put all the ingredients in a grease-free bowl of an electric mixer. Stir to incorporate, then mix for about 5 minutes on medium.

It is important that all the equipment be clean and free of grease or fat, so unless the mixer is used only for making royal icing, scald all of the equipment and dry before use.

If, when separating the egg white from the yolk, the yolk breaks, discard the white and use another egg. Any trace of fat from the yolk will make the icing flat.

**Colouring royal icing:** Royal icing can be coloured with liquid or paste food colours, but paste colours are preferable because they give a dense colour without altering the consistency of the icing.
When colouring a small amount of icing for piping, put the icing on a side scraper. Add colour and use a palette knife to blend in the colour with a backwards and forwards motion. If colouring a large amount of icing, colour some on a scraper first, then incorporate this into the bowl of icing.
Liquid colours are useful if a colour is to be repeated. Use an eyedropper to add the colour until the desired shade is reached, then record how many drops were added to the amount of icing.

## Buttercream Icing

240g (8oz/2cups) icing
(confectioner's) sugar
60-120g (2-4oz/¼-½cup)
butter, margarine, or white fat
milk or water as required

Cream butter or margarine very well. Add half of the sieved icing sugar gradually, beating well after each addition. Add the rest of the sugar spoonful by spoonful, adding liquid if required alternately, until the mixture is smooth and fluffy and will hold its shape.

Buttercream for piping is best made with about 60g (2oz/¼cup) icing sugar. Add liquid to achieve the right consistency.

When piping with buttercream, the heat of your hand changes the consistency of the icing very quickly, especially when doing basketwork. Minimise this by using a small amount in a small bag, and keep replacing the bags.

# BASKET WEAVE CAKE

For a round cake top or for the lid
of a round basket, pipe lines like
the spokes of a wheel. The basket
work lines will be very short at the
centre and longer at the outside.
Pipe them so that they appear to
go over and under the spokes.

# BASIC PIPING

## Writing tubes

To pipe a straight line work towards your body. Touch the tube to the cake surface and apply light, even pressure, pulling away immediately to avoid making a bulb at the beginning of the line. Lift the tube up and about 3cm (1½in) away from the surface. Keep your eye on the line to be followed. When about 3cm (1½in) from the end of the line, stop the pressure and gently lower the tube into position. With practice you will be able to finish the piped line in exactly the right place.

When piping a line with angles, such as a zigzag, touch the nozzle to the surface of the cake each time you change direction.

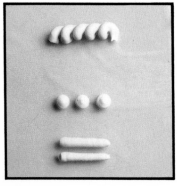

No4 writing tube.

No3 writing tube.

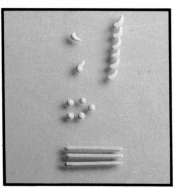

No2 writing tube.

# Star and shell tubes

No6 star tube.

No15 star tube.

No9 star tube.

No12 star tube.

No42 shell tube.

No44 shell tube.

No5 shell tube.

No7 star tube.

No8 star tube.

# Petal and basket-weave tubes

No56 flower or petal tube.

No59 flower or petal tube.

No23 basket weave tube.

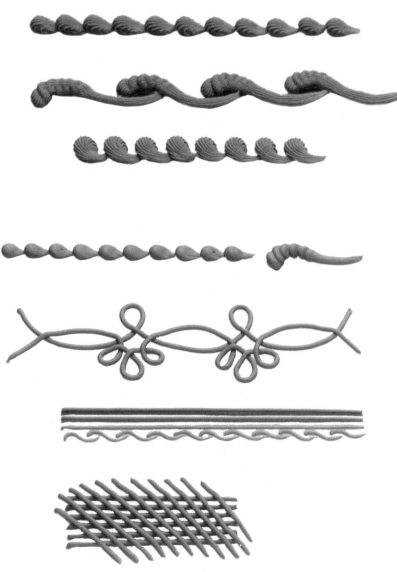

**Top to bottom:** Shells; running scrolls; pulled shells; shells; S scroll; dropline work; straight line work; trellis work.

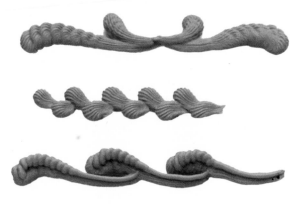

**Top to bottom:** S and C scroll combination with reverse S and C; herringbone; running S scroll with overpiping.

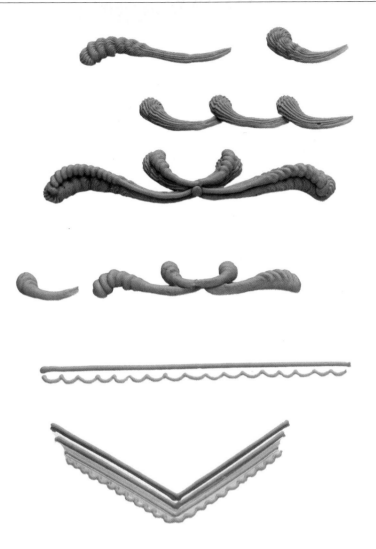

**Top to bottom:** S scroll and C scroll; running C scroll; S and C scroll with overpiping; C scroll and S and C scroll; straight and scallop lines; straight line work.

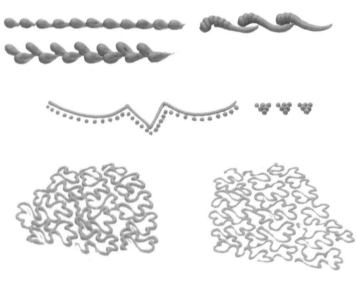

**Top to bottom:** Shells; running S scroll; herringbone; curved lines; petit point lace work; cornelli work.

# CORNELLI WORK CAKE

Cornelli work looks attractive
done in a contrasting colour and
is useful for hiding a poor cake
surface. Cornelli work is simply a
continuous wavy line piped with
a No0 or No1 writing tube. Work
on a small area at a time keeping
the line equidistant from any
others. Bend the line up and
down and from side to side,
varying it all the time. If you find
this difficult, practise by drawing a
line on paper first, and then
piping over it.

Template for Cornelli Work Cake.

Top

Side designs

# BIRDS

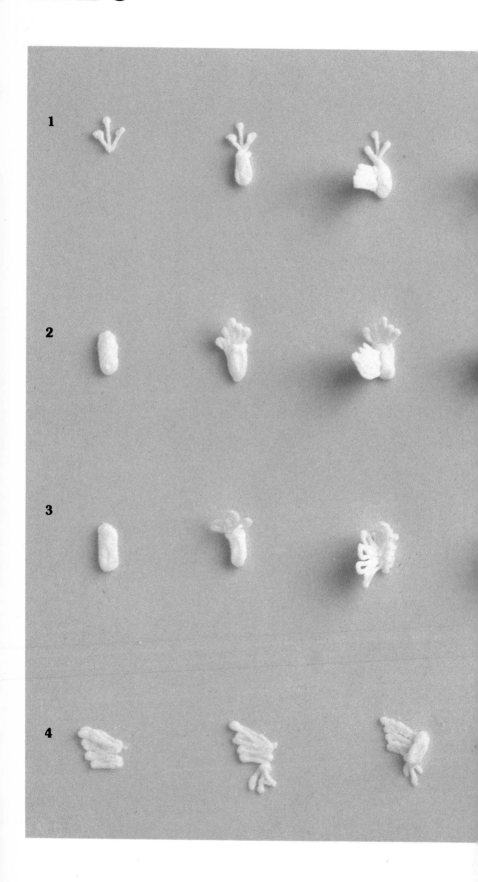

1 With royal icing of piping consistency and a No0 tube, pipe the wings onto wax paper. For some birds you can pipe the tail onto wax paper also. While these are drying pipe the body onto the cake. Start at the tail, increase pressure as you do the body, then decrease pressure towards the neck. Insert the wings. Pipe a bulb to form a round head. When the required size is reached, pull the tube sharply away to form the beak.

2 For this bird, the tail as well as the body is piped onto the cake. Remove the dried wings from the wax paper and insert into the body. Support wings with foam or cotton wool until the royal icing used to stick them on is dry.

3 Make as above, except that the tail is piped separately on wax paper and inserted into the body.

4 Pipe one wing onto wax paper and allow to dry. Pipe the other wing and then the tail directly onto the cake. Pipe body as shown. Insert wing into body. Pipe head and beak.

# PIPING SHAPES OVER A MOULD

Many objects are suitable for this work, and there are many commercial moulds available. If fine work is to be done, the article must be fairly small. The design must be piped freehand.

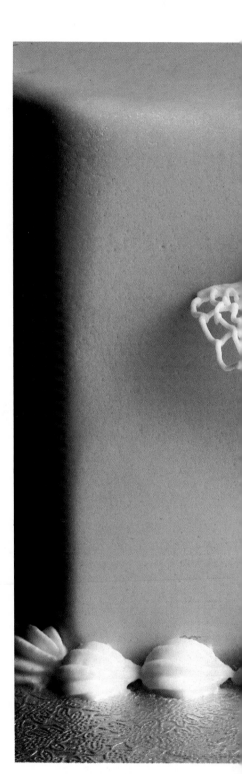

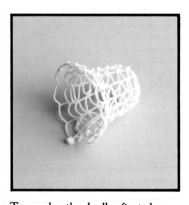

To make the bells, first draw around the base of the bell. Divide this circle into equal sections. Grease the outside of the mould with white fat (shortening). Place the mould on the pattern as a guide for the vertical lines. Pipe the lines from top to bottom, dividing the bell into equal sections. Fill in the spaces with an S-design or freehand flowers or, if the lines are closer together, dots. Make sure the lines touch each other. Leave to dry. When dry, warm the shape slightly to melt the fat and release the filigree shape.

AUTUMN LEAVES
BIRTHDAY CAKE

Happy

Birthday

# RUN-OUT COLLARS WITH BRUSH EMBROIDERY

Trace the designs for the borders and collars, place on a board, cover with wax paper, and pipe the outlines using gold-coloured royal icing and a No1 tube. Flood with soft royal icing and leave to dry. Make four of each design. Colour the leaves with brush embroidery. Flooding the colours with the gold icing first makes them strong so that the deep autumn colours can be added afterwards. Position the borders and collars on the cake and attach with gold royal icing.

# SLEEPING MOUSE CAKE

# GREEN RUN-OUT COLLARS

Trace the designs and make four
top collars and four base collars.
Leave to dry for about two days
before attaching to the cake.

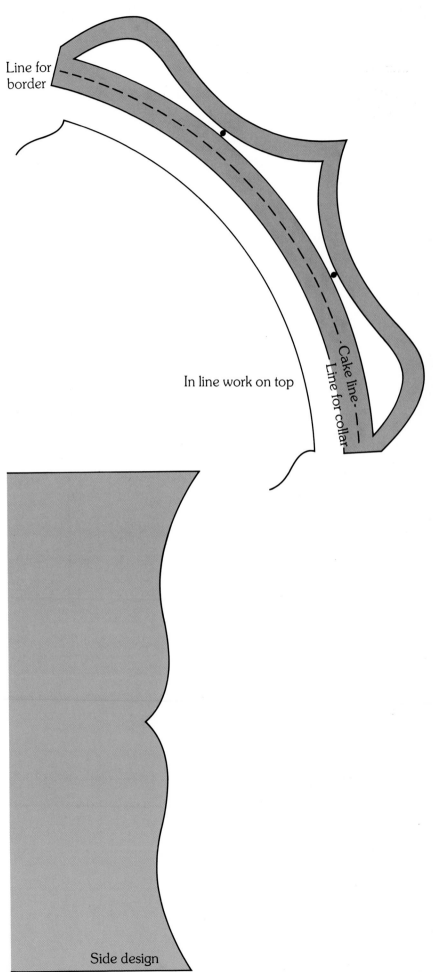

Line for
border

In line work on top

Cake line.
Line for collar

Side design

# RUN-OUT GREENHOUSE

Trace the pattern pieces and place under wax paper. Outline all the pieces with a No1 tube and green royal icing, then flood with soft royal icing. Let dry. Lie the front down and attach door. Pipe a line of royal icing for hinge. Position the door and support with foam rubber until dry.

Attach front to sides and sides to back, making sure the base lines match the plan with angles of 90°. When dry, attach the roof, side pieces and, finally, the top piece.

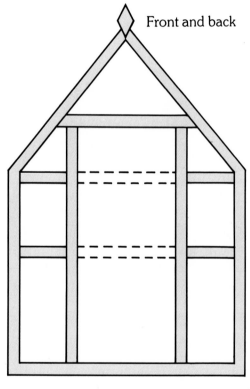

Front and back

Roof top

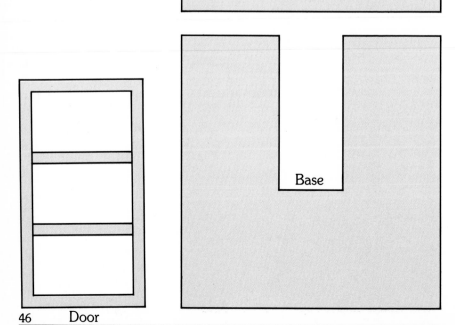

Base

Door

Roof (make 2)

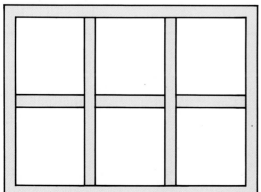

Side (make 2)

# STAR, SHELL AND TASSEL BORDERS

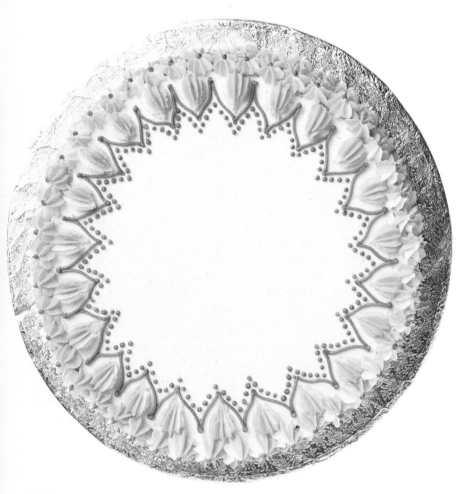

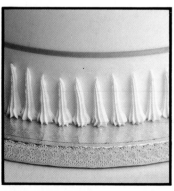

Use a star tube for tassel borders. Lean over the cake and pipe a rosette on the board. Bring the tube up towards you to a height of 3cm (1¼in), decreasing the pressure to make the tassel shape.

If wished, pipe drop loops in different colours from one tassel to the next. Use a fine tube. The design shown here features the four colours in the brush embroidery on the Anemone Cake.

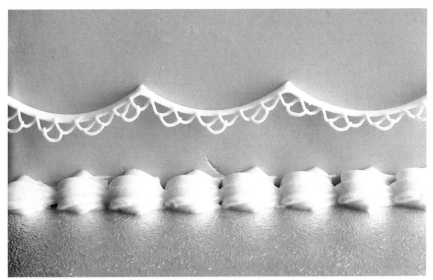

Any shell tube can be used for this technique. Hold the tube at a 45° angle to the cake. Squeeze to form a shell, pull to the right (to the left if you are left-handed) while releasing pressure. Hold the nozzle at this position to pipe the next shell.

The shell border is overpiped with a circle using a No00 tube. Circle scratch line on board.

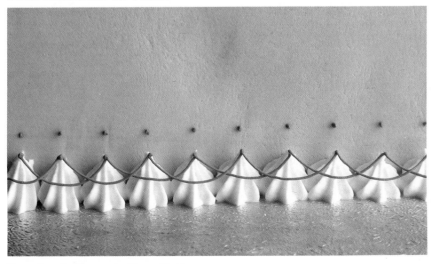

Pipe the shells vertically with the points at the top. Drop loops from the top of alternate points.

# TOP DESIGNS

Designs for the tops of cakes can be piped directly onto the cake, or onto sugarpaste or royal icing plaques. Although a very experienced decorator will be able to pipe some designs freehand, most require a template. An advantage of piping the design onto a prepared plaque is that the plaque can be removed before the cake is cut and saved as a momento or stored for reuse.

Trace the design onto greaseproof or tracing paper, then transfer to the plaque or cake by lightly marking with pins or a scriber.

A simple trellis design piped freehand on a sugarpaste plaque. Pipe the trellis first. When dry, position piped royal icing roses and pipe on the stems and leaves.

The top design for the Sleeping Mouse Cake, which is piped directly onto the surface of the royal-iced cake. Transfer the design to the cake, then begin by piping the leaves which will appear furthest away when the design is finished. Build up the design with pressure piping. Add in detail with a fine tube when the icing is dry.

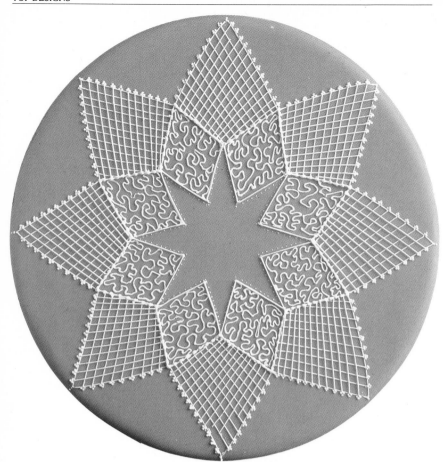

An unusual geometric design piped on a plaque. Use the design here for a pattern, or create a different design with a compass or by tracing different shapes. First, pipe the outlines with a fine tube. Pipe the diagonal lines, first in one direction and then in the other direction. Fill in the sections with cornelli work. Pipe tiny dots around the edge of the star.

This design can be adapted to any cross-stitch pattern from an embroidery book. Mark out the design on graph paper, as shown, then transfer to a sugarpaste plaque or a velvet-covered thin cake card. Pipe the background first, so that the finished design resembles needlepoint embroidery. Pipe the chosen design in cross-stitch.

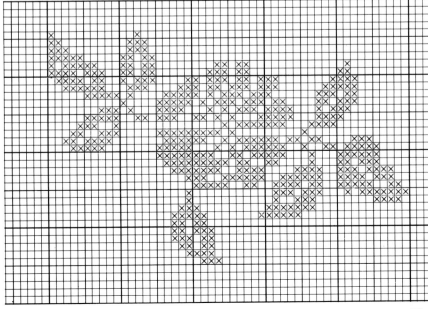

# PIPED ROSES

Use stiff royal icing. Attach wax paper to nail and hold in left hand. Hold the petal tube vertically with the broad end of the tube towards the centre of the nail. Keep the broad end on the paper and lift the narrow end of the tube until the bag is at a 90° angle.

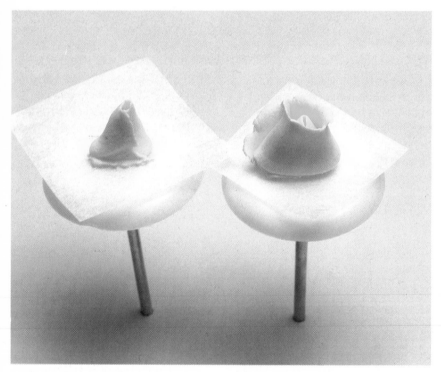

Lift the tube from the paper and turn the nail clockwise to make a cone. When you have made a complete rotation, turn the tube so that it lies flat and pull away.

For the second petal, hold the bag at a 90° angle with the broad end of the tube at the bottom. Begin part way up at the back of the cone, turn the nail clockwise and pipe a band around the cone, lifting and lowering as you go.

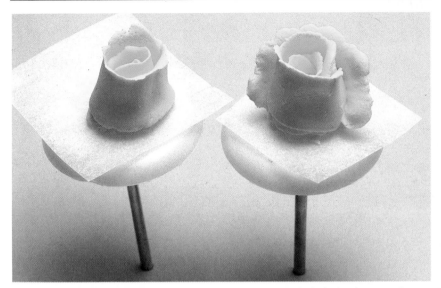

Finish by turning the tube flat and pulling away. For the third petal, repeat as for the second petal

beginning slightly higher up the cone, and starting at the opposite side.

The tube is held horizontal and upsidedown for the fourth petal.

Lift the tube up and turn it over while moving the nail clockwise.

The fifth and sixth petals are made in the same way, each slightly overlapping the one before.

The finished rose.

# MORE PIPED FLOWERS ON NAILS

Use stiff royal icing for all flowers. Attach a small square of wax paper to the nail with royal icing. Keep the square small or it will get in your way.

**Apple blossom:** Pipe as for forget-me-not but finish with piped green dots.

**Forget-me-not:** Place royal icing in the bag, white on the broad side of the tube and blue on the narrow side.

Hold the bag horizontally with the broad side of the tube at the centre of the nail. Squeeze the bag and move your right hand in an anti-clockwise direction while your left hand turns the nail in an anti-clockwise direction. Move through almost one-quarter of a circle. Stop the pressure and finish with a slicing movement towards the centre of the flower. The second and sub-sequent petals overlap the preceding one and the fifth petal is piped over the first. Finish with a small piped yellow dot.

**Pansy:** Pipe the first and second petals as for forget-me-nots. The third petal is in front and just to the left of the first petal. The fourth petal is in front and to the right of the second petal. To make petal five, start halfway over petal four. Pipe a semicircle to finish, halfway over petal three. Paint the markings with food colour.

**Narcissus:** Pipe white petals with the tube flat as for forget-me-not, but move tube out and in again to get the correct length. Pipe the first three petals an even distance apart. Pipe the next three petals in the gaps. Pinch each petal at the end or stroke it with a paintbrush. Pipe the centre with a No1 tube. First pipe the pistil by pulling out a dot in the centre. Then pipe a spiral around it to form the trumpet. Finish with a zigzag line at the top. Paint with orange food colour.

**Primrose:** Use pale yellow royal icing. Follow the instructions for piping the forget-me-not, but halfway around each petal move the nozzle in towards the centre and then out again. When the flowers are dry, paint or petal dust the centres a darker yellow. Pipe a white dot in each centre.

# WIRED PIPED FLOWERS AND BASKET

Use 24-gauge flower wire. Make a hook at one end. Fill a bag fitted with a No4 tube with firm peak royal icing. Insert the hook into the tube and squeeze while withdrawing the wire to coat the hook with icing. Push the hook into the tube a distance equal to the height of the flower you plan to make. Allow to dry. For the rest of the piping use a flower tube. Never insert the wires directly into a cake or use wired flowers on children's cakes.

**Leaves:** Lay a piece of straight wire on wax paper. Fill bag with two shades of green icing and cut the end into a sharp V-shaped point. The more of the bag you slice off, the larger the leaves will be. Pipe a leaf, making sure the tip of the leaf covers one end of the wire. For smooth long leaves, move the tube quickly. For wavy leaves either move the bag slightly from side to side or up and down. Experiment to get different effects.

**Piped basket:** Tape oval pattern to the side of a bottle and tape wax paper over the pattern. Pipe basket work with a No2 tube. Neaten the top edge with piped interlinked S-designs. Pipe a handle over the bottle, also with an interlinked S-design. The

**Carnation:** Hold the wire vertically and the icing bag horizontally with the narrow end of the tube uppermost along the centre. Turn the wire clockwise while applying pressure to the bag and moving the tube up and down. Continue until the flower is the size you require. Dry for a few minutes. Snip the petals with small scissors. Pipe the calyx with a bag cut for making leaves.

**Daisy:** Pipe a short blob onto the wire with a No4 tube. Allow to dry. With a No1 tube pipe a series of pulled dots in yellow to cover the blob.
Fill a small flower tube with white icing. Hold the flower upside-down and pipe the outside petals with an out and in motion.

handle should extend as far around the bottle as the basket extends. When dry, remove the pieces from the bottle and fill basket with flowers arranged in sugarpaste. Stick the handle in place with royal icing.

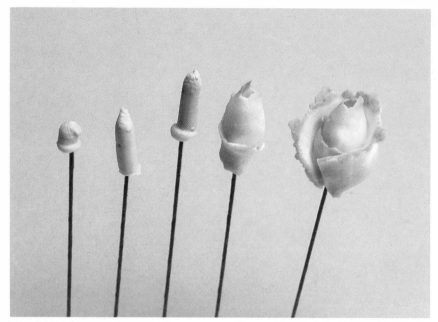

**Yellow rose:** Pipe a long blob on the hook with a No4 tube. With the narrow edge of a flower tube held uppermost hold the icing bag horizontally next to the icing blob. Twist the wire clockwise while applying an even pressure to the bag. Pipe all the way around, then gradually lower the tube to form a bud. Stop the pressure when your fingers have twisted the wire as far as they can.

Pipe the second petal with the narrow end of the tube leaning slightly away from vertical. Pipe around while twisting the bud clockwise. Lift the tube up and then down to complete the turn. Pipe the third petal in the same way, starting opposite the end of the second petal.

For petals four and five, hold the bag horizontally, with the broad end of the tube touching the base of the flower and the narrow end at the left. Your hand should have the palm facing down.

Squeeze while turning your hand holding the bag through 180° and twist the flower clockwise with the other hand. Each petal should overlap the preceding one slightly. Pipe the calyx with a bag cut in a V-shape as for piping leaves.

# COCKTAIL STICK FLOWERS

These flowers will add height to a cake. Stick them straight into the cake. If the cocktail stick forms the stem of the flower, colour it green with food colour before piping. Pipe leaves along the stick starting at the bottom. Add the flowers, which can be copies of real flowers or imaginary ones. For the white or yellow bell flowers, use a No1 tube and make a circular movement to create the bell shape.

**Sunflowers:** Pipe the flowers onto wax paper on a nail, using a small flower tube and stiff yellow icing. Hold the tube at right angles to and almost touching the nail. Squeeze and pull the petal sharply towards the centre. Work a circle of petals leaving a space in the centre. Fill the space with brown dots. When dry stick the flower to a cocktail stick which already has leaves attached.

# LACE

The addition of lace to a cake immediately gives it a delicate look. Lace is the last decoration to go on a cake, as it is very fragile. Always use fresh, well beaten royal icing or the lace will not be strong and will break as soon as it is picked up.

When choosing your design, remember that lace which looks simple may not always be the easiest to do. If it has just a few straight lines any flaws will show, whereas a more complicated design could mask faults.

Place the lace pattern onto a flat surface and masking tape a piece of wax paper over it. A very thin smear of white fat on the wax paper helps to release the dried lace. If the lace has a straight line where it joins the cake, pipe this first, then the rest of the pattern. Always pipe more pieces than you will need to allow for breakages. When dry, the lace should come away easily. A slight movement of the paper should be enough to release the pieces, or use a thin palette knife or a fine brush. Pick up lace with your fingers (it is impossible to do this with tweezers) and attach to the cake with two dots of royal icing per section. This icing should also be fresh, well beaten to full peak or the pieces will not stay in place.

Lace patterns

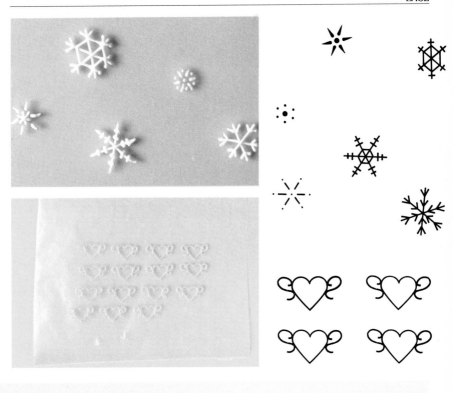

# TWENTY-FIRST BIRTHDAY CAKE

# BASIC EMBROIDERY

Piped embroidery is a series of straight and curved lines, dots, leaf and flower shapes etc, put together in a design.

When doing embroidery on the side of a cake it is much easier if you tilt it away from yourself.

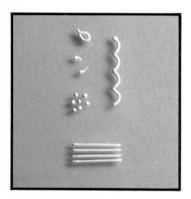

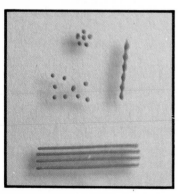

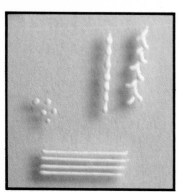

**Dots:** Piped dots should not have points so keep the icing soft. Just touch the tube to the cake surface, apply pressure and stop when the dot is the required size.

**Pulled dots:** Pipe dot then pull the tube away to the side.

**Leaf shape:** Start at the point, curve around and finish neatly. The sides can be curved slightly or more deeply as in a teardrop.

**Flowers:** These can be five dots piped around one dot; pulled dots around one dot; or leaf shapes piped in a circle, pointing in or out.

**Lily of the valley:** For all methods, pipe a stem first. Pipe oval bulbs of icing. Clean the end of the tube, insert into the centre of the bulb and pull downwards sharply. Buds are graduated oval bulbs.

Pipe an oval bulb with three piped dots beneath.

Think of an elephant! Pipe one 'ear' — a pulled curved dot. Pipe the second 'ear' — a reversed curved pulled dot. Then pipe the 'trunk' — squeezed in between the 'ears'. Press towards the cake and then sharply out again.

**Snowdrops:** Pipe three teardrops with a bulb at the top.

# TUBE EMBROIDERY

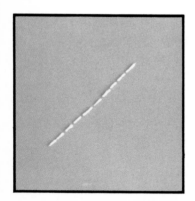

**Running stitch:** Pipe short lines at even intervals.

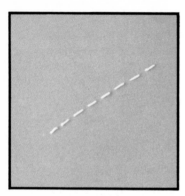

**Back stitch:** As for running stitch but leave much smaller gaps between 'stitches'.

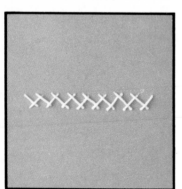

**Herringbone:** Pipe a diagonal line going down from right to left. Pipe a second diagonal line in the opposite direction which crosses the first towards the bottom of the 'stitch'. The third line crosses the second towards the top.

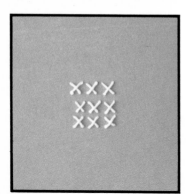

**Cross-stitch:** Pipe two lines of equal length crossing at the centre.

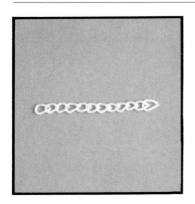

**Chainstitch:** Pipe an open teardrop. Pipe a second open teardrop starting inside the open end of the first.

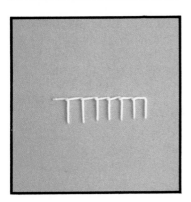

**Stem stitch:** Pipe short strokes in a line, each stroke overlapping the preceding one slightly.

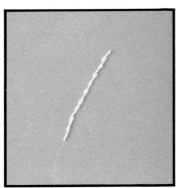

**Buttonhole:** Pipe a line from left to right then down at a right angle. The second stitch starts inside the corner of the first.

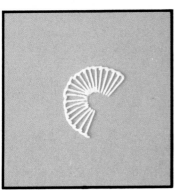

**Buttonhole wheel:** As for buttonhole but the lines are piped to form a circle. Take care that the right angled lines all point towards the centre.

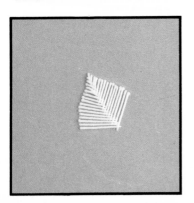

**Fishbone stitch:** This is useful for leaves with a central vein. Start at the outside edge of the leaf and pipe an angled line which just crosses the central vein. Pipe the second stitch from the opposite side to cross the vein from the opposite direction.

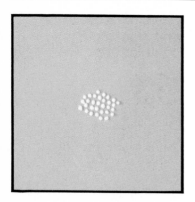

**Seed stitch:** Pipe very small dots close together. This is useful for flower centres.

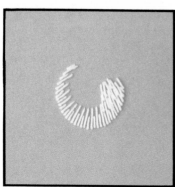

**Long and short stitch:** Pipe a row of long and short lines. The second row is piped to fill in the gaps.

**Feather stitch:** Pipe a small U-shaped line. Start the second stitch just above the centre of the first and pipe in the opposite direction.

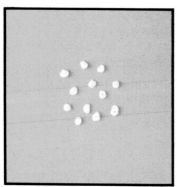

**French knots:** Pipe a small circle. Continue piping to fill in the centre and pull away in an untidy dot.

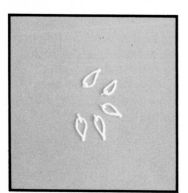

**Lazy daisy:** Pipe a series of leaf shapes to form a flower. Pipe small lines over the rounded ends.

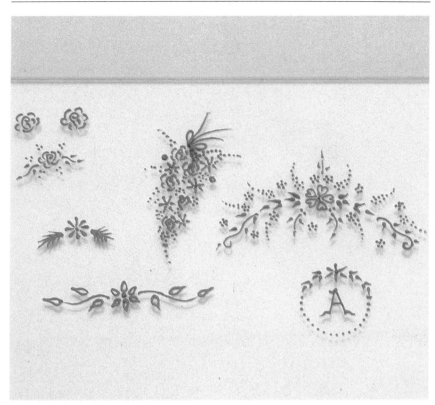

A selection of freehand piped embroidery designs, suitable for side decorations. Flower patterns can be done in a single colour, as shown, or in different coloured icing. For the initial in the circle, copy letters from the typefaces on page 116, or use letters from embroidery patterns or needlework books.

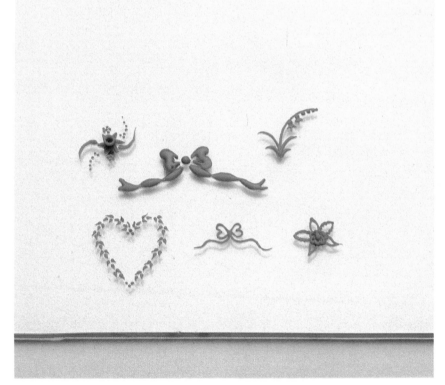

Freehand piped designs featuring bows and flowers. Choose patterns which compliment the overall design of the cake. These patterns could also be used individually to decorate small cakes, petits fours or biscuits.

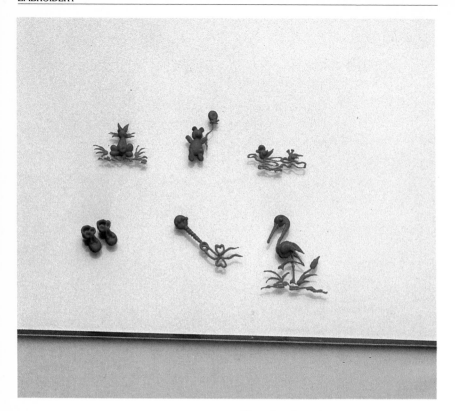

Tiny freehand pressure-piped motifs suitable for side decorations on christening cakes or birthday cakes for young children.

A selection of the embroidery designs which have been used on the cakes featured in this book.

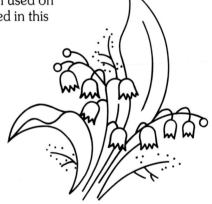

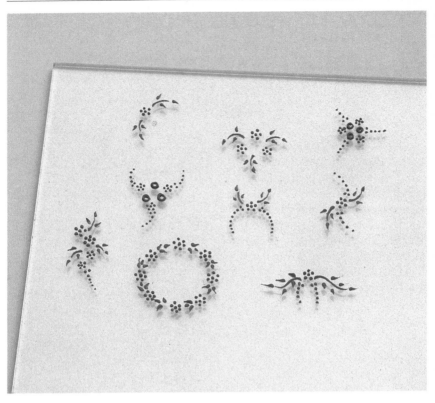

Flower embroidery side designs based on dots and pulled dots.

# TUBE EMBROIDERY PLAQUE

Trace the design and transfer to a prepared rectangular plaque. Have ready several piping bags with fine tubes filled with the different colour icing. Pipe the design following the embroidery stitches. This kind of design can be adapted to use patterns from books on embroidery and other needlework.

# BRODERIE ANGLAISE

This must be done on freshly applied sugarpaste, or sugarpaste which has just skinned, to avoid cracks. The design must be carefully pricked out using a pattern or done freehand. Broderie anglaise can also be done on royal-iced cakes if a sharp scriber is used to make the holes.

Holes are made with the pointed end of a paintbrush, a knitting needle or a special tool. To make oval holes for leaves hold the end of the paintbrush at an angle. Ice around the hole with royal icing.

For coloured embroidery dip the tool into food colouring or petal dust before making the hole. Pipe around the holes using a fine tube and white or coloured icing.

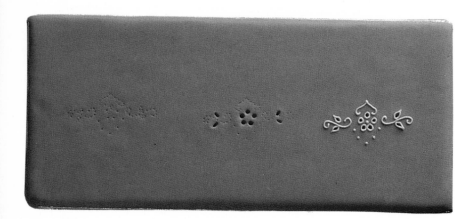

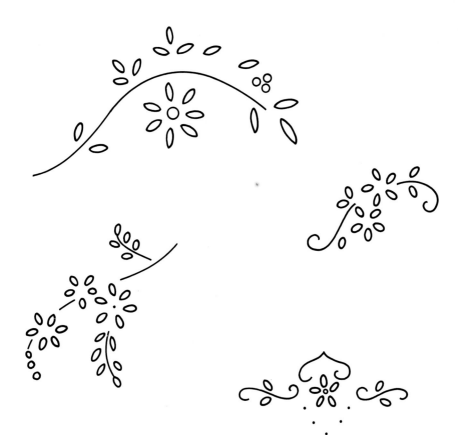

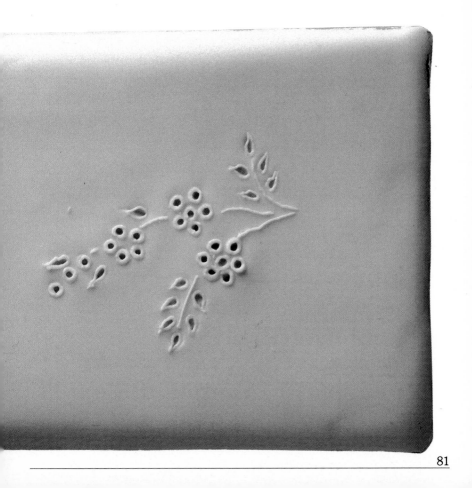

# BRODERIE ANGLAISE PLAQUE

Trace the design and transfer to the prepared plaque, which must be soft enough to insert a tool to make the holes. Pipe the design using a fine tube. The icing can be white, as shown, or coloured.

# BRUSH EMBROIDERY

This embroidery can be done with soft royal icing but you must work quickly to finish before it dries. Adding about 5ml (1tsp) piping gel to a cup of icing slows down the drying and gives a smoother surface. Use a No1 tube for all embroidery, increasing the pressure where more icing is needed. Always start with the part of the design which appears to be the furthest away, to give depth to the finished work.

Pipe the outline, working on a small area at a time. Flood just inside the line. Brush the icing down towards the centre of the flower with a small, flat brush which is slightly damp. Continue with each petal, finishing with the one nearest you.

If you use care, it is not necessary to pipe the outlines first. Pipe the line but increase the pressure at the outer edge where you would usually flood it. Always work down towards the point where the petal or leaf is attached to the plant.

When the brush work is completely dry, pipe in any detail, such as stamens in flowers or veins in leaves, using a fine tube. Place the finished plaque in the centre of a plain iced cake.

Template for the Anemone Cake.

Template for the brush embroidery
plaque shown here.

Template for the brush
embroidery Christmas plaque.

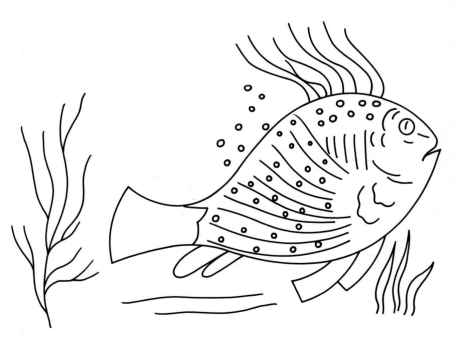

Design for the brush embroidery
fish plaque.

# TULLE WORK POPPIES

Tulle work involves cutting out shaped pieces of tulle, then piping the design with soft peak royal icing. Leave the pieces to dry over a curved surface if necessary, then attach to a plaque or cake with royal icing. Support until dry.

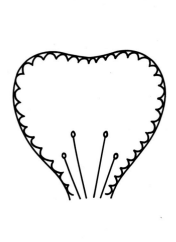

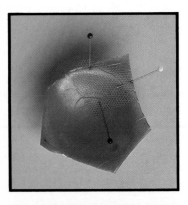

Cut four petals out of red tulle. Pin onto a greased apple tray or press foil into pastry tins and use the foil cups. The petals should be pinned so that the outer edge bends back.

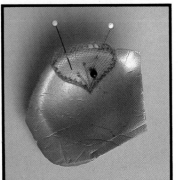

With red royal icing, pipe the design onto the petal and let dry.

**Leaves:** Cut out leaf shapes. Pipe the design and leave to dry flat or over a slightly curved surface. Pipe the stem directly onto the cake and when leaves are dry arrange them along the stem.

Pipe a blob of green royal icing about 5mm (¼in) in diameter onto the cake. Position the first two petals opposite each other. Support with foam or cotton wool. Place the third and fourth petals inside and on top of the first two. Push the petals into the green blob. Support until dry. Push black stamens into the centre blob as shown.

# TULLE WORK KEY

Cut out the key in white tulle and place on a cake board. Cover with wax paper, then pin in position. Pipe the design. When dry, carefully remove from the wax paper, turn over and pipe on the reverse side. Let dry. Attach the key to the top of the 21st birthday cake and support with foam or cotton balls until dry.

# TULLE WORK CRADLE

Cut out tulle according to a pattern. Trace around petal cutters to create your design and pin to a cake board over wax paper. Pipe the design and let dry.

Pipe the tulle base quickly onto wax paper and place over a curved surface, such as a kitchen roll tube. Tape each end to the roll.

When dry, attach one end to the base. Lay the outside of the end down on a flat surface. Pipe a line of royal icing in position. Attach base. Make sure it is level or the cradle will tilt. When dry repeat for the other end.

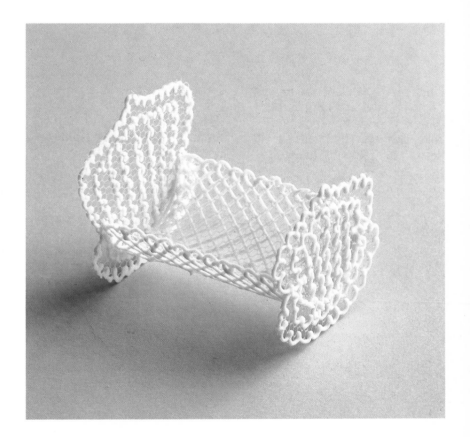

# TULLE EXTENSION WORK

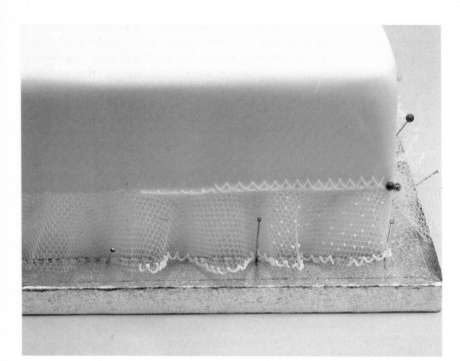

Cut a piece of tulle to the required depth and twice as long as the perimeter or diameter of the cake. Gather so that it fits snugly around the cake. Pin to the surface of the cake, then attach with a snailstrail. Pipe a scallop design at the top and bottom of the tulle, and finish by piping tiny dots on the tulle.

Cut a piece of tulle to the required depth and twice as long as the perimeter or diameter of the cake. Gather so that it fits snugly around the cake. Pin to the surface of the cake, then attach with a snailstrail. Finish off the bottom edge with a snailstrail and the top with scallops. Pipe cornelli work over the tulle.

Mark the design onto the side of the cake. Cut tulle triangles slightly larger than the triangle in the design and pin to the cake. Attach with a snailstrail. Remove the pins when dry and finish off each piece with a snailstrail border. Pipe cornelli work on each triangle.

Pipe the side designs and attach the ribbons first. Cut a piece of tulle to the required depth and twice as long as the perimeter or diameter of the cake. Gather so that it fits snugly around the cake. Pin to the surface, then attach with a snailstrail. Finish off the top with scallops, and pipe two rows of scallops around the bottom. Pipe tiny hearts on the tulle and attach heart lace above it.

# FILIGREE PLAQUE CAKE

# FLOATING FILIGREE PLAQUE

Trace the wren design and place on a board. Cover with wax paper and tape down. Pipe the background using a No00 tube. First pipe a straight line which goes through the centre of the circle. Turn 90° and pipe a second line at right angles to the first. Turn 90° and pipe a third line which is parallel to the first and 2mm (⅛in) away to the right. Turn 90° and pipe to complete the outline. Continue in this way until the grid is complete. Leave to dry.

Pipe the wren onto the grid lines. When dry, carefully remove from the wax paper and place gently onto a prepared circle of 2cm (¾in) cubes on top of the cake. The cubes should be about 1cm (½in) apart. Pipe lines from the edge of the plaque to the cake, carefully removing the cubes as you go. Pipe drop loops from the edge of the plaque, and position narrow lace around the bottom.

# FILIGREE BOX

Do not attempt filigree work on a humid day, as the icing absorbs too much moisture and will not hold its shape. Humidity will also affect the finished article, causing it to bend and, eventually, collapse.

Sections of filigree are piped onto wax paper. If they are to be seen from both sides, when dry turn over and pipe on the reverse side. Using smaller sections with more joins will result in stronger filigree.

Pieces are joined together using royal icing and supported with sugar or stock cubes until dry. Boxes, small blocks of wood, foam or cotton wool can be used for larger items. These supports are used to keep the pieces vertical.

Trace the pattern pieces and put wax paper over them. Pipe the outline of the base. Flood with soft royal icing. Let dry. Pipe two fronts, two sides and four diagonals onto wax paper. Pipe the background with a No00 tube

in an alternating scallop design (like fish scales). Keep the design straight and even. For a quicker design, use a trellis pattern. Pipe the outlines of the birds, flowers and leaves with a No1 tube for contrast, making sure this piping actually touches the background.

Flood the beak, legs, etc and let dry. Carefully release the piped pieces from the wax paper.

Pipe a line of royal icing around the base and join the side pieces. Start at the front and work from side to side, joining pieces at the bottom only. When all the sides are in position, join them together with dots. Support with stock cubes or sugar lumps to ensure sides stay vertical until dry.

Place the top carefully in position and join with dots. If you wish to have the top at an angle, in an open position, support it with cotton wool balls or foam until dry.

Make 2

Top & base (plain)

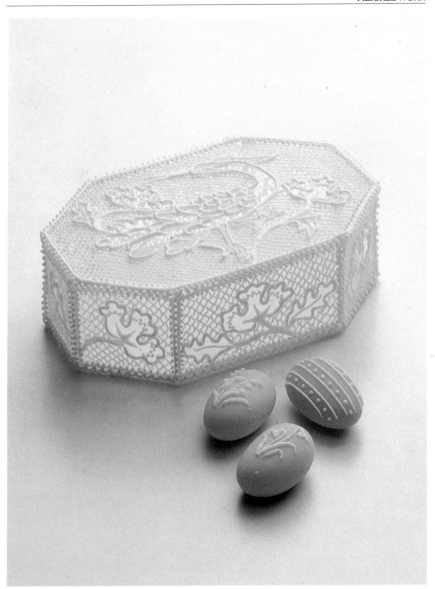

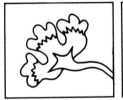

Make 2          Make 2

Use a No0 tube to pipe fine designs onto sugared almonds. Straight or diagonal lines, tiny flowers, birds or animals are all suitable. Similar designs could be piped onto sugar cubes, mints or other small sweets.

# ANGEL CHRISTMAS CAKE

# FILIGREE ANGEL

Pipe the three angel pieces and the lace one or two days in advance, using piping consistency royal icing.

Trace the pattern and place on a flat board. Cover with wax paper taped firmly to the board with masking tape. Pipe the trellis design using a No0 tube and pipe the remaining lines with a No1 tube. Repeat for the other two angels. Let dry. Remove tape to free the wax paper from the board. Carefully pull the paper towards the edges of the board and over the edge using one hand to peel the design away while the other hand holds the paper firm. Turn the paper through 90° and repeat for the other three sides working towards the centre, until the design is free from the paper.

Overpipe on the reverse side, as the angel is seen from all angles. Let dry.

Assembling angel: Take the first angel and pipe a line of icing on the two base points. Position along lines of the circle and support vertically with stock cubes or sugar lumps. Place the other two angels similarly. Join the angels at the centre with crisscrossed lines of icing. Support in position until dry. Pipe a snailstrail or dots along the base to neaten.

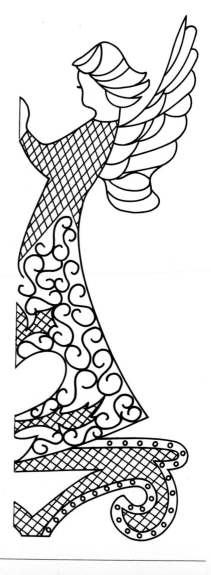

# EXTENSION WORK

Use fresh royal icing and No00 or 0 tube for extension work. Always work with the cake at eye level in a good light. Support your back with a small cushion to help prevent backache.

The first step is to pipe the bridgework, a ridge or bridge of icing piped around the edge of the cake from which the drop lines fall. The bridge is a series of drop loops, each row exactly over the preceding one.

To make a pattern for the bridge, measure a band of greaseproof paper the circumference of the cake, fold into sections and cut to the shape of the extension work. This can be scalloped just at the bottom or at the top and bottom. Put this pattern around the cake and mark the lines with a scriber. The bottom edge should be about 5mm (¼in) above the board. Pipe a snailstrail around the base of the cake with a No0.

Work the bridgework with the cake tilted slightly away from you. Touch the tube to the cake at the highest point of the bridge, pull the tube away from the cake and, maintaining even pressure, move the tube horizontally to the next highest point on the design. Touch tube to the cake again.

Work around the cake. Make sure the first row of bridgework is dry before starting on the second. There should be no gaps between the scallops and the cake. If there are, fill them by painting in soft royal icing with a fine paintbrush. Care must be taken not to pipe each row higher than the one before or an ugly cupped effect will result. Pipe each row exactly over the one preceding, just less than the width of a line.

When the bridge is completely dry, pipe the extension work. Tilt the cake towards you so that the lines fall perpendicularly. Touch the tube to the cake at the top of the design, then pull away immediately, taking care not to get a bulb at the top. Pipe vertical lines just beyond the bridge. Remove the ends with a fine, damp brush. The lines should be parallel and there should not be enough room to pipe another line between the strands.

The simplest form of extension
work is done with a straight top
and scalloped lower bridge.

Another simple method is from a
top line with points, and scallops
at the bottom. Try piping dots
onto the extension work. This is
called hail spotting. Finish off with
a triangle of dots, three at the top,
then two, then one at the bottom.
Pipe a snailstrail at the lower
edge.

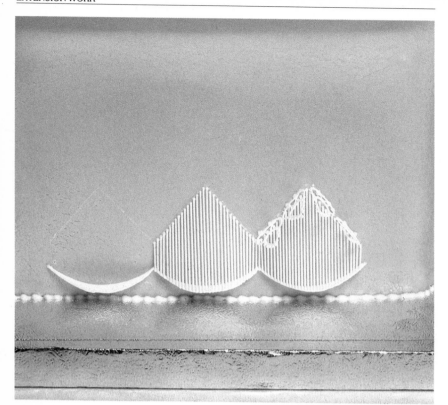

The bridge can be tapered at the sides. Pipe the first line of the bridge over the entire base line, each succeeding line should be piped slightly shorter. Pipe the last line to cover all the other lines. Great care must be taken to make sure each line is shorter by the same amount all around the cake.

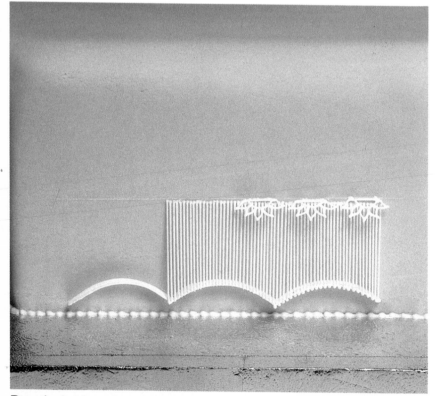

Pipe the bridge when the cake is upsidedown. Attach lace along the top edge and dots along the bottom.

**For double extension with curtain effect,** pipe basic extension work with hail spotting. Then pipe another five lines of bridgework over the first bridge.

Tilt the cake towards you and slightly to one side. Pipe a second layer of lines. Finish off the lower edge with drop loops and pulled dots.

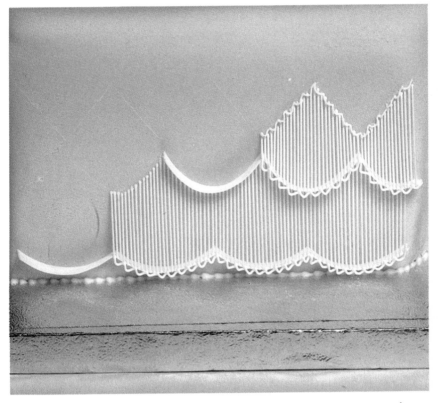

**For double extension work,** pipe the first bridge and drop lines. Then pipe a second bridge as close as possible to the top of the extension work. Add a

second row of extension work. The top and bottom edges are finished with drop loops.

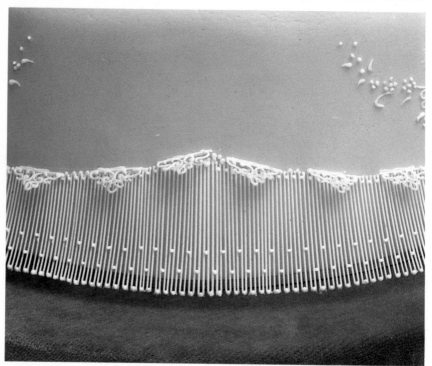

**Extension work without a bridge** is done by piping from a line on the cake to the rim of a cake tin. When the icing is dry, the cake is removed from on top of the tin and the extension work remains unsupported. For a 20cm (8in) round cake, prepare a 23cm (9in) round cake tin by greasing the rim with white fat and place on the turntable. Put a 15cm (6in) upsidedown tin or dummy in the tin, and position the sugarpasted cake centred on it. The bottom of the cake should be about 5mm (¼in) lower than the rim of the tin. Pipe the extension work, taking great care not to knock the tin. Pipe dots to link each alternate line at the lower edge. Pipe more dots 1cm (½in) up the lines to link and strengthen them. Leave to dry. To remove, place a hand at each side of the cake and lift it straight up. Gently lower onto a prepared board.

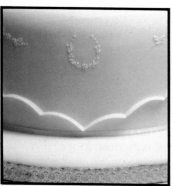

To create the unusual effect of points on the extension work the bridge must be piped with the cake upsidedown. Allow the sugarpaste to dry for at least 48 hours before attempting this or the surface of the cake will be damaged.

# TWO-TIER WEDDING CAKE

Place a sheet of foam or several layers of smooth, soft cloth on a turntable. Carefully pick up the cake with the fingers of both hands spread out and pointing down. Turn the cake over and lower it onto the pad. Pipe the bridge and let dry. Carefully pick the cake up again, turn it the right way up, and lower it onto a prepared board. The extension work is piped with the cake the right way up using a No00 tube.

111

# PRESSURE PIPING

This is a method for building up three-dimensional piped pictures by increasing or decreasing the amount of pressure. Trace the design and transfer it to a cake or plaque. Look at the original and decide which part should appear to be furthest away, and start piping with that part. Use a bag with a No2 tube, then add details with a smaller tube. Build up the picture, increasing the pressure for parts which need to stand out.

# LETTERING TECHNIQUES

Lettering is one of the more problematic aspects of cake decorating, for poor lettering could spoil an otherwise excellent piece of work. Good lettering takes a great deal of practice to achieve.

An experienced decorator will be able to pipe lettering directly onto the cake freehand, but for most people it is best to draw a plan of the cake top and experiment to find the best style, size and position for the letters. The chosen lettering can then be traced and scratched onto the surface of the cake in the correct position before piping.

When piping letters, take care not to form bulbs of icing where lines begin or join. Neaten any ugly joins with a dampened paintbrush. If letters are still imperfect, overpipe the lines with very small dots or a fine snailstrail using a No0 or 00 tube.

When piping on a sugarpasted cake, be careful not to rest your hand on the edge of the cake, as this may spoil the surface. Instead, rest your forearm on a turntable slightly higher than the cake and positioned just to the side.

Piping directly onto the cake with a strong colour can be risky, as the colour will stain the surface, making it difficult to correct mistakes. A better method is to pipe the lettering first in icing to match the basecoat, and then overpipe with the chosen colour icing.

Lettering can also be done with runouts on wax paper and then positioned on the cake with royal icing when dry. This is more suitable for doing numbers or initials than for greetings.

# PLAQUES WITH INSCRIPTIONS

The plaques here are inscribed with the greetings shown on page 118. Prepare sugarpaste plaques, then transfer the chosen lettering. Pipe the lettering. Finish off the plaque with piped flowers or other designs, or pressure pipe figures. If wished, the plaque can be removed before the cake is cut and either saved as a momento or stored and used again.

ABCDEFGH
IJKLMNOPQ
RSTUVW
XYZ

abcdefghijkl
mnopqrstuv
wxyz

12345
67890

ABCDEFG
HIJKLM
NOPQRS
TUVWXYZ

abcdefghij
klmnopqr
stuvwxyz

12345
67890

Happy
Birthday

Welcome
Baby

Merry
Christmas

New Year
Greetings

Happy
Anniversary

# Good Happy Luck Birthday

# Easter Greetings

# Congratulations

# 1234567890

# 1234567890

# 1234567890

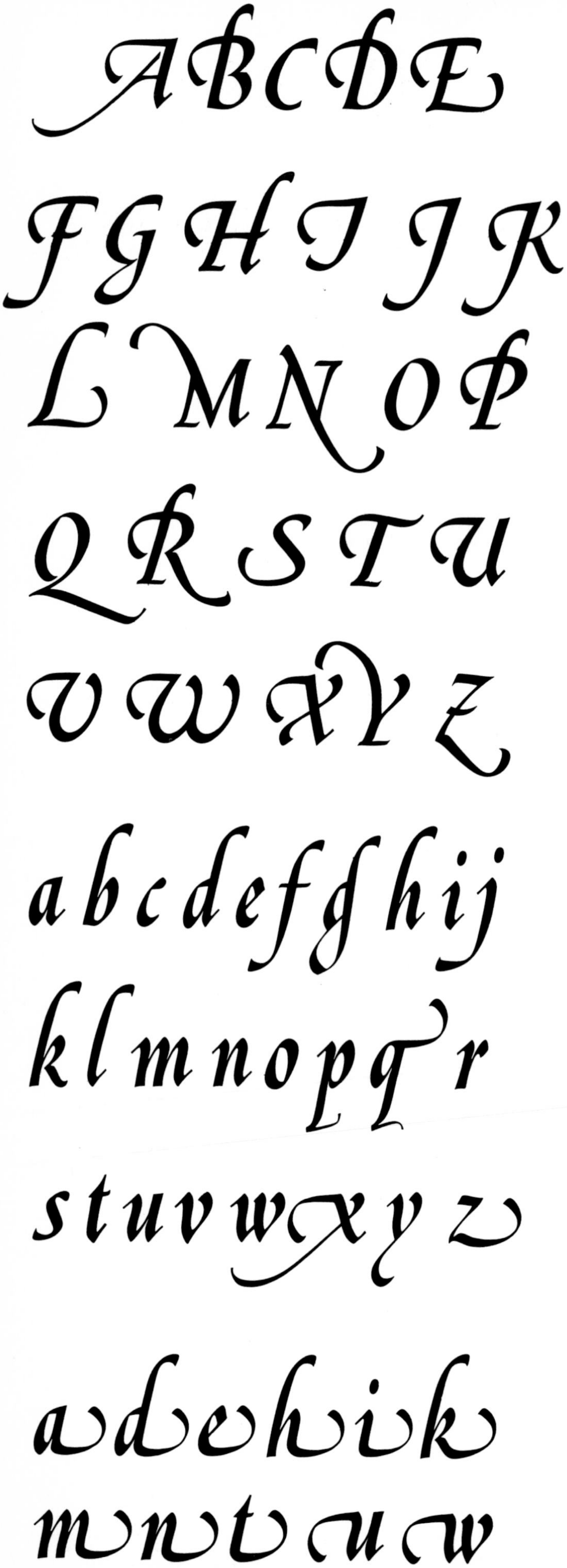

A B C D E

F G H I J K

L M N O P

Q R S T U

V W X Y Z

a b c d e f g h i j

k l m n o p q r

s t u v w x y z

a d e h i k

m n t u w

Template for oblong

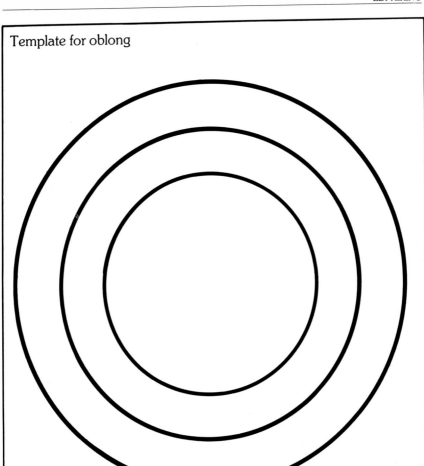

Templates for circles

Template for square

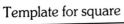

Template for heart

# INSTRUCTIONS FOR CAKES

**Basket weave cake:** Basket work can be done either with plain or basket weave tubes. When covering a square or on the sides of the cake, pipe a vertical line with a plain tube. Pipe horizontally over the top of this line with a basket weave tube. Start 1.5cm (½in) in front of the vertical line and extend to 2cm (¾in) beyond it. Leave a gap the width of the basket weave line, and then pipe another line. Continue in this way until you reach the bottom. Now pipe a second vertical line with the writing tube, parallel to the first and 1.5cm (½in) away. With a basket weave tube, repeat as for previous line but pipe in the gaps. When dry position a ribbon and decorate with piped buttercream roses.

**Cornelli work cake:** Cover the cake with coffee-coloured sugarpaste. Scribe the design onto the cake. With a No0 tube pipe cornelli work with cream-coloured royal icing. Pipe snailstrail around all edges except the flower. Outline the flower with a No1 tube. The centre of the flower is worked with pulled dots and then filled in with dark brown dots. Pipe a dark brown snailstrail all around the outer edge of the design. Work the design on the side of the cake similarly over the ribbon. Pipe a bottom border of cornelli work topped with a dark brown snailstrail. Pipe shells around the bottom edge of the cake. Overpipe each shell with brown S-shapes. Pipe a scratch line on the cake board around each shell.

**Autumn leaves birthday cake:** Make the borders and collars following the instructions on page 40. Coat a 20cm (8in) oval cake with gold-coloured royal icing. Coat an oblong board with the same icing. Attach the ribbons. Position the collars and borders. Neaten the bottom edge with a snailstrail and pipe the inscription.

**Greenhouse cake:** Cover the cake with green sugarpaste. Mark the plan of the greenhouse on the cake. Make the path with grey sugarpaste and mark the tiles. Use brown royal icing for the earth and rough the surface with a palette knife. Position the toothpick tomato plants and lower the greenhouse into place over them. Use grey sugarpaste for the crazy paving, marking the stones in a random pattern. Make the vegetable garden and flower patch and position the fruit and vegetables. Lettuces are made as green 'roses' and carrots are blobs of orange icing with green pulled dots at the top. Tomatoes are red dots.

**Sleeping mouse cake:** This cake would be suitable for either a birthday or a christening. Coat a 20cm (8in) round cake with pale green royal icing, and coat the board with the same icing. Make the top and base collars following the instructions on page 124 45. The template for the top design is on page 51. Pipe the designs on the side. Position the base collars and neaten the edges with a snailstrail. Attach the top collars with royal icing and pipe dots on the inner edge. Place flowers between each collar.

**Twenty-first birthday cake:**
Cover the cake in pale green sugarpaste. Place an oval of pink sugarpaste on top, outline with a pattern of three dots piped in a triangle; two at the bottom and one on top. Pipe lace: long, medium and short. Pipe embroidery onto the cake. Attach ribbon at the bottom and at a distance up the cake equal to the depth of the long lace. Attach the lace, supporting it with foam or cotton balls if necessary. Attach the key to the top with royal icing. Support until dry. An easier way to do the key is to pipe it flat, directly onto the cake.

**Anemone cake:** Cover a round cake with cream sugarpaste. Do the brush embroidery following the template on page 87. Pipe the tassel border in cream and overpipe in colours to match the embroidery.

125

**Filigree plaque cake:** Cover a round cake with pale lilac sugarpaste. Place on an iced cake card and position on a velvet-covered board. Pipe the side designs. Do the extension work without a bridge. Pipe the floating filigree wren plaque and position. Add lace.

**Angel Christmas cake:** Make approximately 40 pieces of snowflake lace (32 pieces will actually be used.) Cover the cake with blue sugarpaste. Pipe shells around the base with a No6 tube.

Mark a circle in the centre of the cake and draw lines to divide into thirds. Pipe snowflakes randomly over the cake either freehand or by first scribing the design onto the cake. Make the angels and position in the centre.

Attach lace in a random pattern to the sides and in the circle around angels on the top of the cake.

**Two-tier wedding cake:** Cover the two oval cakes in cream sugarpaste. Position ribbons and side designs. The pointed extension work has a yellow bridge and white drop lines. Finish off with lace. Make the sugar flower sprays in complimentary colours.

*Love in* ...

# WARRIOR MOON

## MARILYN JORDAN

## A SOLDIER'S SURRENDER

Sarak gazed at her, his eyes soft with an emotion she had never seen there before. "Ah, Phada," he said gently, reaching out his hand to touch her cheek with one long finger, then quickly dropping it to his side. "Do you think I have not come to realize you can do anything you set your mind to?"

"I only wish that were true," she replied with a crooked smile and a shake of her head. "I think you must have gotten too much sun yestercycle, Sarak. Perhaps it addled your brain into concocting this good opinion of me, although I do not deny that I am flattered."

"I do not need to concoct anything when it comes to you, Keeper's apprentice, including my opinion," he grumbled. He sounded as fierce as he always did, but Phada knew he was not truly angry. "You are like a waterfall, able to wear down the hardest stone if given enough time."

"Does that mean I have worn you down, mighty warrior?" Phada asked.

"To a tiny pebble."

# MARILYN JORDAN

# WARRIOR MOON

**LOVE SPELL**  **NEW YORK CITY**

LOVE SPELL®

March 1996

Published by

Dorchester Publishing Co., Inc.
276 Fifth Avenue
New York, NY 10001

The name "Love Spell" and its logo are trademarks of Dorchester Publishing Co., Inc.

Printed in the United States of America.

# WARRIOR

## Moon

# Chapter One

"By the blue moon, Sarak, what are you doing?"

Sarak looked up to find his friend Mizor planted in the doorway, his hands on his hips. "What does it look like I am doing?" he asked as he adjusted the ties of the leather sheath containing his zirconian dagger, settling it more securely around his waist. "I am on duty tonight."

"But you just came back from desert maneuvers."

"Tell that to Dalcor," he said dryly.

Mizor shook his great, shaggy head in disgust. "The man certainly has it in for you," he muttered as he stepped into Sarak's small private quarters and threw himself down on the neatly made-up sleeping pallet in the corner. "I think he is hoping to break you."

"I am sure he would like to dump me into the sea and let the stingfish have me." Sarak shrugged indifferently. "We may both be warriors, but we see things from opposite poles."

9

"Maybe he wants all the Jiboan women for himself." Mizor grinned up at him from his sprawled position, his practically naked body gleaming in the lamplight. Since he was off duty tonight he was wearing only the standard-issue breechcloth. It barely covered the essentials, but of course there were no town women to recoil in shock from his rudely muscular physique.

"He is welcome to them." Sarak threw his friend a disgusted grimace. "For someone who has sworn to protect the virtue of our queen and every other woman in Mesara, I do not know how you can consort with those desert females."

"It is easy. They offer themselves," he said with a smirk. "And most willingly, too, I might add."

"Yes, for a hefty price and the ever-present possibility of disease."

"It is worth it to have a woman tumble you of her own accord."

Sarak grunted. He could not disagree with that particular sentiment.

"I noticed you did not say no the last time they came to the barracks," Mizor added slyly.

"My mind was against it but my body did not seem to want to heed the message."

"The great Sarak. Fallen from his pure status and lusting after women just like the rest of us. Why do you fight against it, my friend? Why not simply enjoy?"

Sarak frowned. He had asked himself that same question a hundred times before but he never got a satisfactory answer. A warrior was forbidden to take a life mate, although not denied the pleasures of the flesh. So why did he often find himself wishing for a woman to desire him for himself and not because he paid her? Such thoughts were crazy, treasonous even, and totally out of the realm of possibility. What decent woman wanted a pallet partner known only for his brute strength and aggressive tendencies? Barracks dwellers were considered animalistic and unrefined by the women of Mesara, good enough to defend the city but rutting bulloxen otherwise.

And why not? he considered thoughtfully. Every last warrior was chosen for dominator service because of aggressive acts committed in his youth. After the third occurrence, the guilty boy was brought before the council and if the queen saw fit, sent to the Warrior Academy for training. Once a sword was placed in his hand there was no turning back, no reprieve. Unless of course he raped—then he was banished to the Uninhabited Island to live the rest of his life away from the community.

Sarak glanced over to discover that Mizor obviously did not expect an answer to his question. The big warrior's attention had been caught by a cloth-bound book that Sarak had hidden beneath the single lana-wool blanket that covered the pallet.

"What is this?" he asked, holding it up with a flourish. "I will wager it is not Hotek's battle strategies."

"No."

Sarak saw no reason to delve into it any further. Mizor could see for himself the title of the treatise on philosophy he had been perusing. Although not forbidden, intellectual pursuits were not encouraged among dominators. Their preferred reading was supposed to include manuals of military tactics and desert survival guides. Hotek's volume was especially recommended, since it related how he had achieved victory over the vicious, warlike Kargans, forcing them to retreat to the southern antipodes, where they had remained ever since. Of course all that had occurred at the dawn of history, thousands of sun orbits ago. The

Mesarans had achieved much since those early, barbaric times.

Still, everything they knew of the mysterious Kargans was contained in that ancient book. It was knowledge Sarak believed should not be cast aside lightly. And yet that was just what was about to happen.

"We have everything we could possibly want," Sarak muttered. "What do the Kargans possess that is so valuable the queen wants to open a trade route with them?"

"We will find out tonight," his friend replied. "Dalcor promised to send a messenger to the barracks with some of the trade goods. By the time that happens, I plan to have a Jiboan woman on each knee."

"Is that all you can think about, maneuvering yourself between some woman's thighs?"

"Why not?" Mizor grinned good-naturedly. "It is as good a place as any and better than most." He wriggled his eyebrows as he pumped his hips a few times in graphic demonstration. "I plan on teaching them my special feint-and-parry technique."

Sarak could not help the snort of amusement that escaped him. His friend was a simple man with simple tastes. When he was not on guard duty or maneuvers or border patrol, Mizor liked to spend his time tumbling women or downing tankard after tankard of vetch. Preferably both. He was a jovial, good-natured companion unless he drank too much of the lethal Jiboan ale. Sarak had never known a man with a harder head, as evidenced by the countless stools that had been cracked over it to little or no effect. Thank the eternal sun he usually passed out before he could use his prodigious strength to really harm someone.

"What are you getting so worked up about, eh,

Sarak? You are the one who said we should make contact with the Kargans."

"Yes, but I meant sending a scouting party, not embracing them like long-lost brothers."

"Hey, it is the dawning of a new era in peace and prosperity."

"So the town criers and all the posted notices would have us believe. Does it not strike you as strange that only a month ago the Kargans were our hated enemies and now we are about to trade with them? Why should we trust them all of a sudden?"

"Why not?" Mizor shrugged, unconcerned. He dropped the book onto the blanket and leaned back, his arms behind his neck, his hands cradling his head.

"Because we know what manner of people they are from the ancient histories."

"That was a thousand orbits ago. Things change."

"Perhaps. Perhaps not." Sarak's mouth flattened skeptically. "In spite of our patrols, they have managed to continuously pilfer from our food stores, and yet no one has ever gotten close enough to look one of the bastards in the eye."

"Maybe they are too hideous to show their faces."

"The Jiboans have somehow managed to survive contact with them. Of course those desert vermin would deal with a cornered clawcat if they could make money doing it, which does not make them the most discerning intermediaries."

"They say Queen Riga approves," Mizor pointed out with a sly little half-grin.

Sarak knew his features softened, but he could not help himself. Besides, Mizor knew of his special oath of loyalty to their beautiful young sovereign. Queen Riga embodied every feminine virtue, from the top of her elegant head to the tips of her dainty, sandal-clad feet. She was shrewd yet kind, wise yet humble, powerful yet ever eager to disperse that power to her council and to the people for the welfare of all Mesara.

He could not imagine that she had not carefully considered every possible outcome of this prospective contact with the Kargans. And yet there was always the possibility that she had been swayed by the king, her one weakness as far as Sarak could tell. Pavonis was the kind of highly intelligent, rational male that women seemed to love. Sarak thought the king's mind was too easily governed by whatever prevailing theory the megaversity was investigating that cycle. Still, who was he to question his intellectual superiors? He was just a thickheaded dominator whose usefulness to the community depended on keeping his physical body as honed and polished as the blade of his dagger.

After bidding his friend farewell, Sarak traversed the winding stone corridors of the underground barracks, working his way up to the top level and the glaring world outside. He stayed in the small antechamber for several moments so his eyes could adjust to the light before stepping from the cool, almost dank air inside the barracks into the wall of heat and humidity that was the hallmark of this northernmost area of Elithra.

He moved quickly along the exposed path until he reached the shade of the jungle canopy and the track that led to the main buildings of the town. The warriors' barracks were on the edge of Mesara, partly because of the space needed for their outdoor training grounds but also so that the women of town would not be confronted with their massive bodies and rude ways. The queen was the only woman he knew who did not recoil from the sight of a well-oiled dominator's body, but she was the exception and had probably schooled herself not to do so after years of royal training.

Sarak grimaced as he ran a hand through his shoulder-length dark brown hair. He had been shocked during the last feast to discover himself pretending that the scrawny desert woman straddling his hips, panting and squealing as he pumped her up and down on his rigid shaft, was the queen. As if the refined Riga would ever allow such rough handling or stoop to such wanton and abandoned behavior. She was a lady, a queen. He knew he imagined himself half in love with her, although no warrior could ever truly understand the ways of love.

His guilt had not allowed him to take another Jiboan woman since, although his loins still ached when he lay on his pallet in the privacy of his quarters. He had even tried self-pleasuring, a common and often necessary technique sanctioned by all the training guides. But that had only caused him to feel more guilt. It was his shameful secret, and he would take it with him to the crypt.

A noise in the thick vegetation made him reach automatically for his dagger. A pair of yellow eyes peered out at him from behind the green-and-white striated leaves of a rango bush. His fingers unclenched from the hilt of his weapon—it was only a clawcat. Although the big animals were ferocious hunters they rarely attacked people unless provoked.

Sarak breathed easier when the town finally came into view. Only the tops of the buildings were visible—everything else had been built underground, where it was naturally cooler. The blue-white sun was relentless as it journeyed across the sky, accompanied by its ever-present companion, the blue moon. According to the ancient legends, their ancestors had traveled from a place somewhere beyond the distant stars; a land where the sun hid itself for a large portion of its cycle to allow for rest, unlike Elithra, where the sun only dipped below the horizon but never far enough so that it became completely dark.

In the unenlightened ages of the past, the Elithrans had danced and chanted to coax the orb to remain longer at its rest. Now they did so for the sheer beauty and pleasure of it. Sarak could hear the stringpluckers and blowpipers warming up as he approached the massive golden-hued pillars that guarded the entrance to the large public square and the feasting area. Throngs of people were heading in the same direction, dressed in their best tunics, the women especially lovely with their long hair swept up in various elaborate designs, their slender arms and shoulders bared by the delicate straps holding up the ankle-length material that swirled around their legs.

Sarak tried to ignore the stares he received as he moved among them in his brief leather loincloth, his massive chest naked and freshly oiled so that it gleamed and rippled in the light of the torches that now lined the passageway. The dagger hanging at his waist was strictly regulation issue and worn for show, but still everyone moved aside to allow him room to pass, as though he were some scrofulous alms taker. Dalcor had issued strict orders that no warrior was to carry a sword to the feast tonight. Even though Sarak knew he had instead posted armed guards at the outside gates, the situation still made him uneasy. Everything about this new trade route with the Kargans made him uneasy.

The stone floor beneath his feet leveled out as he entered the square. Light still filtered in from the outside, but down here it was assisted by torches burning brightly along the back and side walls. The tables and benches that had been set up in long rows were already half-filled with peo-

ple, some chattering excitedly, others tapping
their fingers or moving their heads to the cheerful
throbbing of the music. It seemed everyone was
in the mood for a feast except him.

He made his way toward the platform where the
king and queen would soon be seated along with
the 13 members of the council. The sooner this
evening was over, Sarak thought grimly, the happier he would be.

"Look at that one, Phada! What a brute, do you
not agree?"

Phada glanced at the dominator Chelis had indicated and grimaced before quickly averting her
gaze. For some reason her younger sister was fascinated by the half-naked warriors who protected
the borders of Mesara.

"I did not come here to ogle some thickheaded
warrior, Chelis," she said, trying not to sound like
a prim big sister but failing miserably. Of course
they were all thankful that the dominators handled all the nasty, warlike tasks that came their
way, but that did not mean people had to admire
them for it.

"I am not ogling him; I am simply curious,"
Chelis said with a giggle. "Do you not ever wonder
what they think about?"

"The question is, do they think at all?" Phada
shot back, then bit her lip at her impulsive words.
A Keeper, even a Keeper's apprentice such as herself, would never belittle a warrior, knowing they
were a necessary evil in this less than perfect
world.

Luckily Chelis ignored her outburst, her attention now roving around the crowded feasting hall
with its massive stone walls and wooden-beamed
ceilings. "Rumor says that they can mate through
an entire sleep cycle without tiring."

"As if anyone would want to," Phada said with a delicate shudder.

"I suppose." Chelis slanted her a cheeky grin. "Jobus has promised me he will keep that side of himself under the strictest control after we are declared officially bonded. He says we will only mate when I wish it."

"Which is as it should be." Phada nodded in approval. "Only a dominator gets enjoyment out of inflicting his crude physical desires on a woman."

"Phada, please. This is a celebration, not a lesson chamber. Everyone knows that Keepers and dominators are on opposite sides of the solar spectrum. I do not need a lecture about it, thank you very much."

"Sorry," Phada quickly apologized. She did not know why she reacted so strongly to the subject. She would have to meditate on it during her next visit to the hot springs. "Jobus is a good man."

It was a peace offering of sorts, and Chelis, never one to hold a grudge, smiled as she accepted it. "He says I help him to relax his mind after spending all day poring over his books."

"You will be a good mate for him, Chelis. You would be a good mate for any man lucky enough to win you."

It was true, Phada realized as her sister turned to speak to their mother, who was seated on her other side. Although Chelis was certainly no scholar, while Jobus was an intellectual with a growing reputation, the bonds of their affection were strong. Such opposites often seemed to attract, Phada thought, the way the opposite poles of a magnet pulled inexorably toward each other. Of course if the theory truly applied to the workings of men and women, then dominators and Keepers would be mating like treerats, since the only thing they had in common was that both groups were forbidden by law to permanently bond.

Phada herself had no desire to experience any sort of intercourse with a male, be it intellectual or physical. It was one of the reasons she had asked to train as a Keeper, although her sister often insisted it was because Phada preferred to be a spectator rather than a participant in the web of life. Keepers were forbidden to bond permanently after they officially took their vows, but by the time they did, many of them had mated at least once, sometimes out of curiosity, sometimes with the desire to get a taste of what other women experienced in order to be better guides for the good of Mesara. Often at this stage a woman discovered she was not meant to live the single, solitary, and studious life of a wise woman and Keeper of Knowledge of the Ancient Ways.

The din of countless conversations filled the thick, smoky air around her until Phada could barely hear herself think. The Mesarans were a gregarious people who loved to talk. Phada had never truly fit in. She was too serious and quiet and much too guarded with her thoughts and emotions to feel comfortable holding her own in the kind of raucous debates that inevitably occurred whenever two or more Mesarans came together.

And so she did what she usually did at a such a large gathering—she watched and listened, trying to observe what was happening around her without being critical or judgmental. According to her mentor, Helenina, a good Keeper needed to be in touch with the pulse of the people. She needed to be able to put herself in the sandals of anyone from the simplest kitchen runner to the most scholarly philosopher, and even including a mindless, totally physical warrior. Only in that way could she use all her faculties to render a judg-

ment, and not just her intellect. Sometimes Phada
was not sure her faculties were up to the challenge.

As if to spotlight her particular blind spot, her
eyes briefly met those of the dominator on the
platform behind the queen. She was not surprised
when he glanced away first. She knew his name
was Sarak because he had been the one to conduct
the tour of the barracks Helenina had insisted on
subjecting her to only last mooncycle. The warrior
had avoided her gaze then as well, almost as
though he had been discomfited by the rude comments the men whispered just loudly enough for
her to hear as she hurried by. Of course that was
just an illusion. No doubt afterward they had all
shared a good laugh at her obvious embarrassment.

This time Phada forced herself to keep her gaze
upon him, taking in the gleam of his oiled torso,
the intensity of his gaze as he stared out over the
heads of the crowd. No matter how much he disturbed her he was still a part of the web of life of
Mesara, Phada lectured herself. He had as much
of a right to be here as she did. So why did she
still find it so difficult to confront his presence in
the feasting hall?

She forced herself to observe him objectively.
Actually he was not all that bad-looking, she supposed, in spite of the heavily muscled body that
spoke of the hours of grueling training he endured. Phada tried to visualize what his life might
be like, his innermost wishes and desires, but
thanks to Chelis, the only image that popped into
her mind showed him mating ferociously on his
sleeping pallet with one of the Jiboan women she
knew were imported on a regular basis to slake
the dominators' physical needs. She felt her
cheeks grow warm with embarrassment.

Thank the wisdom of the Ancient Ones that the

dominators were under control and basically segregated from the rest of society. Phada shivered
as her gaze took in the two warriors stationed near
the passageway. All that slick, naked skin . . . they
actually seemed proud of it. She glanced at the
king, a tall, lean town dweller whose wide forehead made him appear highly discerning and intelligent. Now there was a male. Pavonis knew all
the philosophers and could quote many of them
by heart. He had studied mathematics and astronomy, history and rhetoric, not to mention his well-
known proclivity for writing romantic verse
extolling the beauty and virtue of his queen.

Now he rose gracefully to his feet, clapping his
hands for attention. The music immediately
stopped.

"Good people of Mesara," he shouted, holding
up one arm. The gold-trimmed sleeve of his tunic
glimmered in the wavering torchlight. He waited
a moment while a hush settled over the crowd. "As
you all know, Queen Riga and I, along with the
members of the council, hope to establish trade
with the Kargans."

Loud hisses greeted this pronouncement, but
the king only laughed in that boyish way of his
that had charmed the hearts of so many of his
female subjects. Even Phada was not immune.

"Yes, I understand that you may be wary of such
a move. I assure you, so were we until we realized
some important things. We have not had an actual
war with the Kargans for almost a thousand orbits. Is it not time we tried to carve a pathway to
lasting peace that will benefit the entire planet of
Elithra?"

A smattering of halfhearted cheers rose from
the packed feasting area along with a louder chorus of nays.

"They are too cowardly to start a war with us,"

shouted one of the males who was seated at Pha-da's table.

"That is right," called out another from the back of the hall. "They would rather steal such small amounts that it is not worth our while to send an army across the Calabian Desert to retrieve it."

"I say let us wring their nasty hides inside out and trade them to the Jiboans—they will buy any-thing."

Pavonis raised his hand for silence. "That is ex-actly why I think this proposed plan is a good one. We can stop the raids and ensure the safety of our borders at the same time. The Jiboans have agreed to act as intermediaries in this undertaking, and since they know the route so well, they will make the scheduled treks across the desert to the Kar-gan stronghold of Gorod." Here Pavonis grinned wryly. "For a share of the profits, of course."

A babble of commentary and discussion was in-evitable after this, and Pavonis did not try to fight it. Instead he leaned down to confer with Riga. She nodded at him and he assisted her to her feet before reseating himself.

The queen waved her arms for silence and was granted it more quickly than Pavonis had been. "There is more, my friends," she assured them with a smile. Her lovely face, framed by coils of golden blond hair, beamed at them with soft goodwill and love as she gestured gracefully with slender fingers. "Yes, there is more. The Kargans are offering us a spice called faral in exchange for our surplus grains and fruit. I have been assured that once we get a taste of this unique seasoning, we will be in favor of the trade. That is why I ar-ranged this feast, so we can all be the judges. What do you say? Shall we sample this delicacy from the other side of Elithra?"

A loud cheer went up, more for Queen Riga than for what she had to say. Still, if the queen was willing to taste the spice, how could any Mesaran do less? Good-natured jibes of disbelief continued to fly from table to table, along with various comments about the acknowledged indelicacy of the Kargans, who were thought to be cruder and ruder than even the swarthiest dominator. Phada found herself laughing at the impromptu ode to faral composed by Jobus, who had come to join Chelis at their table. What rational person would not have trouble believing that any delicacy could come from the far side of the antipodes where the Kargans lived?

Jobus poured both Chelis and Phada a glass of vinasi, the mild Mesaran wine usually preferred with meals, then filled his own glass. Thank goodness for Chelis's sake that Jobus had not taken up the disgusting habit of drinking vetch, the highly intoxicating Jiboan ale favored by the dominators. In her capacity as a Keeper's apprentice Phada had gone out with Helenina on more than one occasion to tend to a Mesaran with an aching head who had spent the night emptying his stomach under some rango bush. Phada could not understand the lure of the nasty brew, but then she had never claimed to be an expert on the behavior of males.

A contingent of kitchen runners hurried through the feasting hall, balancing platters of food on their shoulders. The smell of roasted fowl and tuber roots filled the air along with another, more subtle but distinctly appealing scent that came from the wooden sapok shakers of faral that had been placed every few feet along the tables. Phada's mouth actually began to water in anticipation of the meal.

"Let the feasting begin," Pavonis cried out. He picked up the shaker and sprinkled some faral on a portion of the juicy meat. Everyone waited breathlessly as he took the first bite. His eyes widened in amazement and his handsome face broke into a smile.

"Incredible," he shouted, waving the dripping leg in the air. He took another bite and another before he came to himself. Quickly poking through the contents of the platter, he picked out a wing, more delicate fare suitable for his queen, and prepared it with the spice. Riga slipped her hands around his as he held it out to her. Together they steadied the meat as she took a taste. Seeing the tenderness between them, Phada could almost understand why so many women preferred to bond permanently with a male.

"What a unique and delicious flavor," Riga said into the hush which had suddenly claimed the hall. "I have never tasted anything like it." She quickly helped herself to more. "Please, everyone, try it."

With a great shout, the crowd complied. Murmurs of approval arose from every table as the scent of the fragrant spice mixed with the tantalizing aroma of the fowl and vegetables. People ate with enthusiasm, their heads nodding in surprise and approval. All along the trestle tables, shakers were passed from hand to hand as the drone of conversation grew to more deafening proportions.

Phada took the shaker from Chelis and sprinkled a small amount on a section of tuber root. Perhaps the opening of this trade route with the Kargans would be the beginning of permanent peace between the two enemies after all, she thought as she took a careful bite. She could not believe the pleasurable burst of taste sensations that exploded in her mouth. It had some of the properties of the salt they harvested along the shore of the great uncharted sea. Then again it contained a sweetly delicate aftertaste of herbs that lingered delightfully on the palate. Phada shook her head as she finished off the root. It was no use trying to explain the swirl of flavors, but there was no denying that it was the tastiest thing she had ever placed in her mouth.

"This is so delicious," Chelis said in amazement as she licked the tips of her fingers in a ladylike fashion. "It is sweet but not exactly sweet."

"Sweet!" Jobus hooted in disbelief. "It is definitely tart with the same flavor as meat cured in the smoke pit. Do you not think so, Phada?"

"It tastes more like herbs to me," she said.

Phada heard similar contradictory comments all around her. It seemed no one could agree on the flavor conferred by the faral. How very odd, she thought. She was about to pick up a wing for a comparison taste when she felt a squeezing sensation in her stomach, followed by another and another until her insides twisted into knots. Should she try to ride it out? Better not, she decided as another spasm wrenched a low groan from her. She clutched her middle as she excused herself from the table and headed for the passage. Maybe some fresh air would clear her head and ease the pain. Trying not to make a spectacle of herself, she managed to sidle past the last table and gratefully headed up the stone walkway.

The dominator stationed near the outside pillar stared her up and down in a totally unacceptable manner, his eyes lingering on her bare shoulders and then moving down to her breasts. Her mouth opened on a curt remark to put him in his place, but something stopped her from voicing it. Dalcor usually kept his warriors under tight control, but perhaps the festive nature of the evening had loosened this one's sworn code of moral behavior.

"Where are you going?" he asked. His eyes gleamed in the semidarkness of the Mesaran night.

He had not addressed her with the proper deference. He certainly had no right to question her, but she was not about to challenge him on it, not with her stomach churning like a kettle of boiling water. Better to let it pass until she felt more herself, and then she would see to it that the man never got assigned town duty again. Besides, direct confrontation, especially if it was unpleasant, had never been her style.

"I am going to get some fresh air," she replied evenly. "It is very smoky inside."

He eyed her thoughtfully. "Have you eaten?"

"What?"

"Have you tasted the spice?"

"Yes. It . . . it is very good." Something about the triumphant expression on his face made her uneasy. Her stomach continued to twist and clench and she knew she had to get away from him before she disgraced herself. "Excuse me, please." She hurried away toward the main trail, her heart pounding nervously as his bold laughter followed her into the jungle.

# *Chapter Two*

"Stop!" Sarak hissed roughly, gripping Zegon's wrist. "Wait until you are off duty."

His friend only grinned, his dark brown eyes as guileless as those of a newborn wood fawn. "Come on, Sarak, shake the blueflies out of your ears." He pulled his arm free, the shaker of faral he had snatched from a nearby tray still clutched in his hand. "Did you not hear the queen? She invited everyone to try this stuff."

"She was not referring to the posted-on-duty warriors."

Zegon groaned and made a face. "Do not be such a mudhog's ass. No one can see us."

Sarak slanted him a disgusted look. That was not exactly true. The two warriors were standing just inside one of the corridors that led to the palace kitchen. A steady stream of frazzled runners scurried past them, trying to keep up with the incessant demand for more food and faral coming from the feasting hall. It was an impossible task.

"Besides, this is a celebration, in case you did not notice. What is the difference between sneaking a sample now and waiting until later when we get back to the barracks?" Zegon wiggled the sapok wood enticingly, just out of Sarak's reach. "It would not be the first time we bent the rules."

"I am not worried about the sun-cursed rules," Sarak muttered. "There is something about this entire setup that rubs my skin the wrong way. Can you not feel it?"

"No. But while you try to figure it out, I am going to steal a bite."

Sarak watched helplessly as Zegon scooped up an antelope haunch from a nearby tray and sprinkled it with a substantial coating of the dark, fragrant spice. He bit into it, ripping off more meat than he could possibly stuff in his mouth at one time, grabbing at the excess with his fingers.

"Mmmm. Delicious," he mumbled around the food as he chewed. "I never thought I would see the day when I would be praising something that came from the Kargans."

Sarak shook his head in disgust. People were acting like sun-blind fools over a simple seasoning and it was making him more than a little uneasy. Even Queen Riga had been hard-pressed to remember her usually impeccable table manners after she had tasted the spice. Maybe Zegon was right; maybe he should try it now, see what all the fuss was about.

He had just picked up a loose slice of roasted rockhen when he caught sight of Dalcor standing near the passageway that led to the queen's private chambers. He was talking to two of his favorite warriors, members of his handpicked elite Desert Corps. They conferred for a few moments, and then Dalcor waved one of the men back into the feasting hall while he motioned the other to follow him down the strictly off-limits corridor.

Sarak tossed the untouched piece of meat back onto the platter and hurried to follow them.

Phada rested her forehead against the cool, rough bark of a hivea tree and wearily closed her eyes. Thank goodness she had wrapped her arms around the slender trunk—it was the only thing keeping her on her feet. That last bout of nausea had left her stomach raw and empty, and she shivered in spite of the warmth of the night and the balmy air which pressed against her flushed skin and sweat-dampened tunic.

The moon rode low on the horizon, casting its faintly blue-tinged light along the path just behind her. The sun had dipped out of sight hours ago, but its light still glowed in the western sky so that visibility in the jungle was good. On nights when the moon was not out, it became almost dark in Mesara. Phada stepped out from among the trees and made her way to a nearby stone bench. She needed a little more time to recover before she went back into the feasting hall, but she also did not want to linger too long or else her mother and Chelis might begin to worry about her.

So much for Kargan faral, she thought, trying to muster up the strength to appreciate the irony. What a shame. It was the most delicious thing she had ever tasted and now she would not be able to use it on her food. She quickly covered her mouth with her hand. Even now, just the thought of it was enough to turn her stomach. Here was one more thing to convince her that she belonged to the esoteric world of the Keepers rather than in the stream of everyday life.

She was not sure how long she sat there, breathing in the lush scent of the jungle vegetation and recovering from her ordeal. The mournful cry of a clawcat rallied her and she decided it was time to go back inside. She moved quickly along the pathway that led to the palace gates, her moonshadow hovering just in front of her footsteps.

The dominator who had leered so insultingly at her was gone. In fact, there was no one watching the entrance to the feasting hall. Phada frowned at this breach in security, then shrugged. Perhaps he had also answered a call of nature. She was not about to complain about not being subjected to his unwanted and discourteous scrutiny.

She followed the slanting path down to the hall. No music was playing—the pipers were probably taking a break. There was not much noise coming from the feasters either, which was odd. Usually she could hear the drone of a myriad of conversations from this vantage point, or at least a raised voice or two. If she did not know better, she would think everyone had gone home. Phada frowned as she quickened her steps.

She was almost running by the time she rounded the huge gilded pillar and entered the main hall. She halted abruptly, the hair on the back of her neck rising like a hound's hackles at the sight that greeted her.

No one had gone home. In fact everyone was sitting pretty much the way she remembered them, she realized as her gaze took in the filled benches—except for the king and queen, whose places at the platform table were now empty. Here and there people were talking, but not many of them, and they were speaking in a desultory manner, as if they were stupefied by drink, although someone affected by vetch or vinasi usually became louder and more gregarious, not more subdued. Phada had never seen so many Mesarans sitting in one place so quietly.

Some of the faces she gazed into simply returned her gesture with a blissful smile. Many sat staring into space while others played with their food or shifted the sapok shakers of faral around in random, senseless patterns. One male, a member of the council, was humming a tune under his breath, sounding uncannily like a swarm of battleflies at twilight. He smiled and gave a half-hearted wave as she passed by.

Phada hurried between the tables to where her mother and Chelis sat. Jobus grinned at her, a silly little smirk that made her wince because it was so unlike him. His chin rested on his hand as if he could not hold his head up otherwise. Chelis was leaning against his arm, a beatific smile on her face.

"What has happened to you; what is wrong?" she demanded, grabbing her sister's arm and shaking her.

"Go away, Phada," Chelis murmured with a giggle. "You are being much too loud." She reached for the shaker of faral, sprinkled some on her finger, and licked it off.

"Stop it," Phada hissed, knocking the shaker away. "You have had enough of that stuff."

Chelis just looked at her with glassy eyes and laughed. "Phada, dear sister, it is too delicious for me to stop now. It is too delicious for anyone to stop."

"Can you not see you have been given something to make you like this? You have all been drugged by that cursed Kargan spice," she shouted, glaring around at the crowd of subdued Mesarans. "Please, you must fight it. Get up and walk around; try to clear your heads."

The undertone of murmurs grew louder, but that was the only reaction her impassioned words evinced.

What should she do? Her mind raced with possibilities, and none of them were good. Was this some scheme of the Kargans? Had they finally come to take over Mesara through the treachery of a spice that had turned out to be more than a simple, tasty seasoning? Even now they might be massing outside the gates in the deep twilight of night, ready to march in and take over without even a struggle.

"No," she said aloud. They had to resist or die trying. The males of Mesara must be roused to action. They could not count on the warriors to defend them. Every able-bodied town dweller was supposed to know how to handle a sword—it was time to call them to arms before it was too late.

"Jobus, get up," she ordered in a pleading voice. She pushed and prodded at his shoulder but he did not budge. Sweet Mother, how quickly did this stuff wear off? She gave him one last shove, watching in dismay as he slumped forward onto the table, his cheek pillowed on his hand. It did not look as if it would be anytime soon.

She decided to try Chelis again. "Where are the king and queen, Chelis? And the warriors, where are Dalcor and his warriors? Have they slipped away to summon help?"

"They are gone," her sister answered with a dreamy smile. "They have all gone away."

Phada bit her lip. She was the only one capable of acting and she had not a clue what to do. Were Pavonis and Riga in their chamber? Should she seek them out? And what about the warriors? Had they already been overthrown by Kargans? Even the rude dominator who had insulted her was beginning to look like the best friend she had ever had, if only he would defend her from whatever was happening here.

The sound of loud voices coming from the corridor leading to the queen's chambers caused Phada's head to jerk around in alarm. She stared wildly at the passage, totally panicked, her heart pounding like a ceremonial drum. There was no place to hide, even if she had the time to do so.

The owners of those voices would be upon them in mere millimarks. Besides, what good would it do to run away? She was the only person in the entire hall lucid enough to discern what was going on. Once she discovered who was at the bottom of this, she might still be able to dash across to the barracks and rouse the dominators to action.

She threw herself down next to Chelis and rested her head in the crook of her arms. The closeness of male voices announced the intruders had just entered the feasting hall. She heard a loud crash, as if someone had knocked over one of the tables. She had to school herself not to jump in alarm. No one around her even twitched at the sound.

"Leave him there," a low male voice ordered. "He is out cold."

Phada peered through her lashes in the direction of the platform. Thank the Creatrix, the speaker was Dalcor, high commander of the warriors. Several other dominators were at his side. Everything must be all right, she thought, tears of relief springing to her eyes.

She sat up, opening her mouth to call out, when she noticed what had caused the crash. Lying next to an overturned bench near the queen's throne lay the warrior Sarak, his hands tied behind his back with a thick leather strap. His face was covered with the grayish brown dirt that always settled on the tunnel floors, and blood was running down his cheek from a deep scratch above his left eye, which had swollen shut. The rest of him was not in much better shape. The oil on his body had collected enough dirt to turn into a muddy paste mixed in places with more blood from various cuts and abrasions.

Phada remained where she was.

"People of Mesara," Dalcor cried out. His voice was loud and tinged with an air of sneering aggression Phada had never heard in a warrior before. "I want every last peace-loving, faral-licking Mesaran to listen up. I have something important to say."

Phada's eyes widened in alarm. She was not sure what kind of reaction he expected to get, but no Mesaran worth his seasalt would ever stoop to taking orders from a warrior. Warriors were brought up to serve with their bodies; they were taught to do the bidding of the people through the offices of the queen and king and the council, not the other way around. Their status might not be as high as the rest of the population, but their contributions were needed and appreciated by the community.

It had always been a fine line to walk, this training of dominators, but the Mesarans believed they had reached a satisfactory compromise by allowing these males to be as strong and aggressive as they needed to be in order to be able to hold off any Kargan attack while insuring that they comprised only a small portion of the population lest they revert totally to their dominator natures and send Mesara sliding back into the hellish nightmare of warrior rule.

Phada drew a nervous breath. As his words began to sink in, she heard grumblings and protests from the crowd, but Dalcor ignored them. He continued to wait for a few moments before repeating the order. He was wearing his sword as well as a dagger, as were the other warriors on the platform. More dominators had slipped in from outside and now lined the walls, blocking every exit. Was Mesara under attack? If so, why was Dalcor just standing there doing nothing? And why had Sarak been taken prisoner?

"Listen up," he roared again. To her utter shock and surprise, people slowly began sitting straighter on the benches, their eyes turning expectantly toward Dalcor like those of little children in a lesson chamber. Phada saw several of the town males around her, including Jobus, reach for their daggers before realizing they were weaponless because everyone had voluntarily disarmed at the door to the feasting hall. One bold Mesaran jumped up brandishing a table knife, but was immediately relieved of it by a burly warrior who leapt across two tables to reach him. He backhanded the protestor sharply across the face before snatching the makeshift weapon away as easily as taking a sweetbar from a child. No one else moved after that.

Dalcor grinned. "That is more like it. Something terrible has occurred. This desert-crawling vermin you see before you attempted to rape the queen." He kicked the motionless form at his feet. Sarak groaned but otherwise did not stir. "Thanks to my quick actions, he did not succeed."

Phada could not restrain her gasp of horror at this shocking news. Rape in Mesara was unheard of, a capital offense of the highest magnitude. The axis of her previously safe and stable world shifted painfully and her mind went numb. She glanced at Sarak's still form, trying to recall what she knew about him, but all she could comprehend was the fact that this warrior had tried to force himself on the queen, using his greater physical strength in the most reprehensible manner, hoping to violate Riga's person and her dignity, even her very soul. The thought of it made Phada's blood run cold.

"The punishment for this crime is banishment for life on the Uninhabited Island in the Sea of Stingfish. I will see to it personally that this sentence is carried out. In the meantime, Mesara will be placed under emergency rule until the queen recovers."

Emergency rule? Phada had never heard of such a thing. And what had happened to a trial for

Sarak and final judgment from the Keepers? Where was the king? Pavonis should be the one imparting this information to his subjects. Or if he was too upset at the near violation of the queen, then one of the council members should step into the breach. Whoever heard of a warrior taking such a responsibility upon himself?

Obviously that was all Dalcor had to say. He abruptly turned, conferring for a moment with the small group on the platform and then making his way toward the queen's chambers with what Phada could only describe as an eager stride. She wished she could stop him but she dared not show her hand, not if she hoped to do anything to stop this.

Another warrior stepped forward, this one short and swarthy with a thick neck like a bulloxen and ears that lay flat against his head. "Go home, everyone. The feast is over," he announced. "Go home and tomorrow attend to your usual business."

Phada imitated the slow movements of everyone around her and carefully got to her feet. At least one of her problems was solved, she realized as she shuffled toward the exit. She could not let anyone know that her body had rejected the faral until the rest of Mesara came to their senses and they could work together to get things back in order. She could not imagine any drug lasting past the morning. In the meantime she would have to think how she could help them prepare.

Her eyes strayed again to Sarak, who had awakened and was now struggling to free himself. Someone had put a gag in his mouth, but she could hear him trying to make himself heard in spite of it, the sounds coming out garbled but no less angry for being muffled. She had to wonder if what Dalcor had said about him was true, if he had attempted to rape the queen. If he had done such an awful thing he deserved banishment and more. She studied his massive body straining against his bonds—he was so strong and untamed, like a wild clawcat. She felt a funny twitching in the pit of her stomach—revulsion, she supposed.

And then their eyes met. She felt the shock of his intense gaze right down the entire length of her body from her head to her toes. Her breath caught in her lungs, but she could not tear her attention away. In fact she found herself studying him so closely she knew the exact instant he realized she was not dazed with faral like everyone else in the hall.

He struggled to his feet, knocking a table over in the process. He was rewarded with a swift kick in the ribs by one of his captors. Phada felt the sickening thud in her own tender middle as she continued to shuffle along with the crowd that was now forced to divert into two flows around the table. Phada found herself moving very closely past Sarak. She schooled herself not to glance down at him, but as she came closer he kicked at her ankle.

Her body jerked in alarm and she could not stop herself from staring at him. Immediately his eyes pleaded with her in the most eloquent fashion. What did he expect her to do? she wondered, her heart pounding. He jerked his chin downward, toward his bound wrists. Was he asking her to untie him, a warrior accused of the worst kind of domination, a possible rapist? Had he gone as crazy as everyone else in Mesara this night?

Even if she wanted to release him there was no way she could do so under the watchful eyes of the two warriors who were standing guard over him. One of them held his hand over the hilt of his sword. Phada could see the recently healed scar that snaked across his upper arm. The other guard was surveying the perimeter of the crowded room, a smirk of disdain on his thick-featured face. Either of them appeared all too capable of killing a person as casually as he might slaughter a bushhog for the dinner table. And then she realized Sarak was indicating a table knife that had fallen to the floor in the scuffle. He wanted her to kick the knife closer to him so he could cut himself free.

Her gaze flew back to his face in alarmed denial. She shook her head. There was no way she was going to attempt something that risky. He was an accused rapist, for heaven's sake. Besides, Dalcor and his men outnumbered him ten to one; even if he did manage to get free, he would not stand a chance. The furious look he gave her sent a shiver of alarm down her spine.

Phada tore her gaze away from the platform, determined not to look at Sarak again as she forced herself to move slowly in the line of subdued Mesarans moving toward the exit. But either his will or her curiosity was too strong, because she shifted her line of vision until she could again take in his sweating, straining form, although she dared not move her gaze beyond his collarbone. The highly developed muscles of his chest rippled beneath the surface of his smoothly tanned skin as he continued to fight against the leather thongs that held him prisoner, almost as if he could snap them in two. Phada was frankly surprised when he did not accomplish the feat.

Then he tried to move toward the knife. One of the guards noticed his movements and snarled something as he placed a booted foot against his shoulder, shoving him down until he was lying flat on the floor, his cheek smashed against the wooden table leg.

Phada closed her eyes against Sarak's pain and frustration. When she opened them again she found herself once again staring straight into the depths of his tormented soul. Blood from the cut on his temple had slowed to a trickle, probably because the wound was clotted with dirt. This time he shook his head at her and motioned toward the door. Whether he was telling her to look out for herself or to seek help, she was not sure, but she certainly intended to try the latter as soon as she had the opportunity. She nodded at him and again felt that strange reaction in her stomach as his gaze softened for a moment. The next thing she knew, Dalcor ordered his men to stand him on his feet and they half-dragged, half-marched him away down the corridor.

She could not believe everyone was leaving so peaceably, but there was not much she could do about it. Now that Dalcor was gone she shoved her way to the head of the line and quickly slipped into the passageway. Several warriors were stationed along the walls, directing the people toward the exit and their homes. Phada immediately slowed down, although her mind continued racing. If she took the shortcut through the jungle, the one the warriors used rather than the main trail, she might have a chance of getting to the barracks without anyone noticing her. She was not sure how much time remained until sunrise, but she knew she had to hurry. Even the twilight of a Mesaran night provided little cover.

Since she did not know what to expect, she had no idea if she was too late to stop it. She could only hope that the warriors who had remained in their barracks were aware that something was going on and had armed themselves. No one else appeared the least bit upset when Dalcor had announced the emergency rule, but then everyone was out of it, addled by whatever had been put in the faral.

Which brought up the question of who had

drugged the spice in the first place. Were the Kargans behind this? She was beginning to have her doubts about that. The only other likely candidate that she could see was Dalcor. Had he gone totally insane, reverting to his dominator nature? Was he the one who had tampered with the spice? As far as she could tell, he now had complete control over Mesara.

Perhaps Sarak was not guilty as charged. What other reason could Dalcor have for not following proper procedure and allowing the Keepers to give him a trial? Sarak might have been gagged so he could not protest his innocence. It made her head hurt to contemplate all this political upheaval. She was basically a shy, retiring person, a scholar, someone who intended to spend her life in the Keeper's sanctuary, studying the books of the wise women from the past that filled the library there, perhaps even becoming a first-rank wise woman herself. She certainly had no desire to go sneaking around the perimeters of Mesara on her way to the warriors' barracks.

Sarak awoke with a start. He was lying on his side, his wrists still tied behind him, the wretched gag still in his mouth. He tried to flex his fingers, but his arms had gone numb from being bound so tightly. He closed his eyes as he felt the wooden floor beneath him move. Not a floor, he remembered, but a boat headed for the Uninhabited Island. Curse Dalcor. And curse his own foolish caution. He had known something was amiss, but he had allowed a bragging lowlife like Dalcor to blindside him, first with reassurances and then with flat-out orders that he should have disobeyed but had not.

He heard the bow crunch against the shore. Three warriors appeared, grabbing him by the arms and dragging him to his feet. They took him to the gangplank and shoved him down its length toward the sandy beach. Sarak almost stumbled along the way but quickly recovered. Stingfish usually liked deeper seas, but he was not taking the chance of allowing even his toe into the dangerous waters. One bite and he could be paralyzed for life, not to mention killed.

One of the warriors knocked him onto the sand with a blow from the flat side of his sword. Sarak grunted against the gag as he landed on his numb arms. The searing pain that shot up through his shoulders was almost unbearable, but he managed to get past it before dragging himself to his knees. He was not about to lie there like a stuck hog when they killed him, which was what he assumed they intended, although why they had to cart him all the way to the Uninhabited Island to do it he was not sure. They probably wanted no witnesses.

Sarak saw Murk stride down the gangplank. He was not surprised that Dalcor would send his favorite underling to do his dirty work. It had been no secret that he had wanted Murk as his second-in-command rather than Sarak. Of course, the queen had the final say.

"My, my, if it is not Riga's devoted little lapdog," Murk said with a sneer. Sarak struggled against his bonds, bucking and kicking and wishing he could wipe that smug grin from Murk's face. "We have a treat in store for you."

He reached into his pouch and took out a small vial of what appeared to be a golden brown liquid, waving it in the air. "You have not tried any of the delicious faral we have begun importing, have you? You would not be struggling so hard if you had. Do not worry, soon you will get the opportunity to taste it, and then you will not have a care in the world—except for getting your hands on more of the stuff." He laughed. "And Dalcor intends to keep you well supplied."

He walked closer to Sarak, hunkering down on his haunches to study him. "Let me tell you all about the spice so you know just what to expect. It is made from mushrooms, nice dark slimy Kargan mushrooms grown in some Goddess-forsaken part of Gorod. Once a man gets a taste of it, he will do anything to get more." He paused for dramatic effect. "Anything. The rest of the time he is as docile as a castrated bullox. No, maybe I should not say that. The urge to mate remains very strong. Which means that very soon the only sword you will be practicing with is the one between your legs, mighty warrior."

He roared with laughter. The three other warriors contented themselves with smirking. Sarak stared at him in dawning horror. This was much worse than anything he had imagined.

"As you can see, this is the liquid version. Much more potent than the dried powder, I assure you. Hold him down," he commanded.

Sarak struggled but to no avail. *Kill me*, he wanted to cry out. He had seen the poor people in the feasting hall, slack-jawed and weak, with no will to fight back. Sarak managed a kick to the nearest dominator's ribs, which quickly earned him a blinding blow to his head. Oddly enough when his vision cleared he thought of the female in the feasting hall. Somehow she was still lucid but probably not for long. There was no hope for her, no hope for any of them.

Another warrior grabbed his legs and it was all over. Murk poured the liquid faral onto the gag from where it dripped into his mouth. In spite of his efforts not to swallow, Sarak could feel it soaking his tongue and pouring down his throat. The burst of flavor which filled his mouth was the most delicious thing he had ever tasted, but he tried not to think about that. Instead he concentrated on gathering the liquid under his tongue so he could somehow spit it out. But Murk was ready for such a maneuver. "Keep him on his back," he told the warriors. They obliged, holding him prone until the last of the spice had crept down his throat. Then they tossed him aside.

Sarak barely heard them striding up the gang-plank or the sound of the oars as they rowed away. He could feel the sweet warmth spreading through his veins, sapping his strength and his willpower. How easy it would be to just let go. He wanted to, so desperately. And why should he not? he thought. He was the only one left to fight them, him and some wide-eyed little Keeper's apprentice who had probably been caught and drugged by now.

Suddenly he could not hold out against it any longer. He lay on the sand and closed his eyes.

# *Chapter Three*

Phada often came home from the Keepers' Sanctuary on the pretense of spending time with her family, but it also afforded her the chance to listen to the town gossip and discover what was happening at the palace. She still had no idea what she could do to change the situation, but she knew she had to keep trying. She could still remember the shock of slipping into the warriors' barracks to discover them slumped across various tables and chairs, stupefied with faral like everyone else in Mesara except for Dalcor and his followers. Although she sometimes still wished it were possible, she knew she could not take her usual path and hide her head in the pages of a book. Maybe some kind of idea, no matter how reckless or futile, would come to her if she kept thinking about it long enough.

It was painful to be home, to see how much her mother and Chelis had changed. She carried a jug of water into the house, passing her mother, who sat beneath the stone overhang of the porch, rinsing off the vegetables for their supper. The older woman did not even glance up but continued to hum softly to herself, a tuneless song that gave Phada the chills. She had been singing ever since Dalcor had taken over Mesara half a mooncycle ago.

Chelis would soon be home from the orchards. Everyone now worked planting and growing and harvesting—it was the only way they could get more of the highly addictive faral. Dalcor had set it up very craftily—he traded the goods harvested by the Mesarans for more of the spice and governed the kingdom along with his warriors. Phada could not understand why he would want to sit as ruler over a group of spice-addled citizens who had not the strength to foment a rebellion even if they had possessed the wits and willpower.

During the days after the immediate takeover, a small group of warriors had come to each house, making sure everyone had partaken of the faral. Phada had dutifully eaten her share, but as soon as they left had run outside to empty her stomach in the tall grass. For some reason, the spice was like poison to her system, although as far as she could tell she was the only one it affected that way.

Being the only one whose wits were intact, she had not found it difficult to wander surreptitiously around the town, slipping inside the stone bastions of the public buildings and hovering outside in the fields searching for someone like herself whose body could not tolerate the spice. She had not found a single clear-eyed person. She had to be careful not to appear too alert.

The council had been disbanded, although the Keepers had been allowed to stay in their sanctuary. Gossip had begun circulating that the queen had become Dalcor's pallet partner. Soon after, the rumors were confirmed when Dalcor paraded her through the town, a leather collar around her neck like those worn by slaves many cycles ago when Mesara had been a more barbaric place. In spite of the dulling effects of the spice, Riga refused to look any of her subjects in the eye. Phada's heart had ached for her.

This was what happened when a town let warriors gain control. This was why they had provided so many safeguards against dominators in their laws. And look where it had gotten them, Phada thought in disgust. She hated the sight of the warriors' broad, muscled bodies as they strutted along the pathways, lording it over the citizens of Mesara. At night they feasted in the great public square, drinking vetch until they were barely coherent, roaring with laughter as the single females from the palace, from lowly kitchen runner to highborn lady, were herded in for their inspection. Each warrior would then choose a pallet partner for the evening, forcing the woman to stand beside his chair and serve him while he fondled her for the duration of the meal before dragging her off to his chamber. Phada knew it would not be long before they grew tired of their sport and began setting their sights on the other women in town, including the Keepers. She swore she would kill anyone who tried to touch her, even knowing her own punishment would swiftly follow.

Except for Riga, the dominators had not violated a bonded woman—so far. No one knew what had happened to King Pavonis. The warriors who had refused to side with Dalcor were being held in the palace. They had been fed faral along with everyone else but were still considered dangerous enough to keep in holding cells. The rest of the town males grumbled and complained and made halfhearted plans to overthrow Dalcor, but no one seemed to be able to muster up enough energy and coordination to carry it through.

In the meantime, warriors patrolled the streets, swords at their sides. Even under ideal conditions, not many males in Mesara could best a warrior in hand-to-hand combat. Now that their brains and reflexes were befuddled by the faral, no one dared go up against a clearheaded dominator.

Once a week, shamefaced Mesarans lined up to obtain their allotted portion of the spice from the laughing, condescending warriors. Once looked down upon, they had gotten their vengeance in abundance. In fact, one afternoon a group of warriors had chosen a man and a woman at random from the crowd and denied them the spice just for sport. The bewildered couple had set up such a howling of pleas begging for faral that Phada had covered her ears in shame. They had all been reduced to the level of animals.

Phada sometimes found herself wishing she could hide her head in the sand as dobbies were reputed to do when in danger. The Jiboans used the birds to carry their belongings across the desert. Phada had often seen the awkward-looking creatures with their thick, sturdy clawed feet, their heavy legs and long necks, as they were being driven into Mesara loaded with trade goods. Sometimes she wondered if she were any better than a brainless packbird. She knew she should do something, but what could one person alone do against a regiment of warriors? She was only a Keeper's apprentice; she was not equipped to handle this sort of thing.

She had not yet told anybody about her reaction to the faral, including her mentor Helenina. Not even her own mother and sister suspected. The dominators had no compunctions about withholding the spice in order to obtain information, and the danger that someone might betray her, albeit unwillingly, was ever-present in her mind. Sometimes she almost wished she were as spice-addled as everyone else—the responsibility of her position was daunting.

If only she possessed the strength and untrammeled fighting spirit of that warrior Sarak, the one who had resisted his captors so fiercely. Phada now doubted the charges that he had raped Queen Riga were true—especially since Dalcor was doing the same thing on a daily basis, with no hint of shame or remorse. Nay, he even seemed proud of the fact that he could dominate the helpless queen with his prodigious strength. That did not make him much of a male in Phada's eyes, not that the brute cared about her opinion.

Accusing Sarak of such a despicable crime had probably been an excuse to get rid of a possible rallying point for resistance. As Mesara's second-in-command, Sarak could presumably gather enough resources to make trouble for the usurper. He would certainly try to rescue the queen— everyone knew how devoted to her he had been.

Phada paused thoughtfully in the doorway, wondering what had happened to the warrior. As far as she knew he had been shipped to the Uninhabited Island, banished for the rest of his life. There was no escape from that blighted place, surrounded as it was by stingfish-filled waters. Even had he tried to build a raft, it would still need to be coated with resin from the hivea tree to ensure a safe passage. To do otherwise was to court certain death. Still, as determined as he had been to escape, she would not put it past Sarak to try the raft without the sap, rather than live his life fruitlessly as a captive. It was part of some warrior code that she knew little about.

And yet he had obviously fought hard against Dalcor. She even supposed she could consider him an ally. What if she tried to contact him? Her heart started pounding as the idea flashed along the far reaches of her mind to settle dead front and center in the conscious thinking portion. It would mean crossing over to the island, but she could probably manage that if she left after evenfall. The question was, what could he do to help? They were outnumbered in an impossible situation. He would probably end up getting himself killed and her along with him.

No, it was a bad idea.

She leaned over the hearth to stir the stew that bubbled in the heavy iron pot her mother always used. The smell of faral was deliciously tempting even though she knew it was deadly to her body. How much harder must it be to resist when your very being craved it like the hivea flower craved the sun? She tried to squash the idea of finding Sarak, even though she thought she had already banished the subject from her mind. *It would be nice not to be carrying this burden alone,* one part of her whispered insidiously. If she could get him off that island it would then be his responsibility to do something about Dalcor and she could go back to her books and her life of quiet introspection.

*Do you really believe you can go back to meditating when the rest of Mesara is being held captive by a renegade dominator?* another part of her answered in disgust. *Think about Helenina, who has been trying so hard to fight her craving for the spice and who has failed at every turn.* Helenina, known for her iron will, was now as helpless as a babe before the seductive power of the faral. *And what about your cheerful sister, who cries for no apparent reason, and your mother, who cannot seem to stop her inane humming? And do not forget Jobus, whose brilliant mind has gone into dormancy and who works as a common physical laborer in the fruit orchards.*

Phada sighed wearily. No, life would never be the same for any of them. And she could not remain the cautious Keeper's apprentice whose ruling passion was to honor Mother Elithra and maintain Mesaran society as a model of cooperation and peace. What little hope there was of returning her beloved city to its former glory rested in her—if she could bring herself to meet the challenge.

"Have you added the faral, daughter?" her mother asked in a soft, querulous voice, her brow furrowed in that anxious look that Phada was beginning to dread.

"Yes," Phada snapped more tartly than she intended. She had always possessed a mild temperament, but it was becoming increasingly difficult to keep her impatience in check these days. All anyone concerned themselves with anymore was the sun-cursed spice.

"It does not smell very strong," Ariel persisted. "Are you sure you put in enough?"

"Yes, Mother. I added exactly the amount that you instructed."

Phada's mouth flattened in resignation. During the first week, when everything was still in confusion after Dalcor's takeover, she had stayed with her mother and sister rather than at the Keepers' Sanctuary. During that time she had tried to gradually decrease the amount of the spice in her family's food, but to no avail. Her mother and sister had simply used the faral shaker on the table to make up the difference. Thank the Mother neither of them had taken it to the level of craving of their nearest neighbor, Phineas, who had collapsed outside his front door one day after consuming an entire rockhen coated with faral. His heart had simply stopped, according to the Keepers who had attended him.

"Let us not wait for Chelis. Let us eat now."

"As you wish, Mother."

Phada waited until her mother had filled her

bowl and seated herself at the simple wooden dining table before she reached behind the oven and grabbed the portion of spiceless stew she had saved for herself. Even the simple act of eating had become another complication.

"I suppose you are returning to the sanctuary again," Ariel said in a conversational tone. Now that she had satisfied the initial fever of her craving, she was more like her old sociable self, although her once clear eyes were dull and her hair only halfcombed, when before she had spent such time and care on her personal grooming. "Helenina must be expecting you this evenfall."

Phada's eyes widened as she realized that if she ever intended slipping away, this was the perfect opportunity for her to accomplish it. "Yes, she is expecting me," she answered carefully. "In fact, I think I will stay there for a few weeks. There is a manuscript I have been wanting to study and one of the other Keepers just finished with it, so it is a perfect opportunity."

Actually Helenina thought she was going to spend the next weeks with her family, and now she had convinced her mother that she would be spending that time with the Keepers. No one at either location would miss her if she suddenly disappeared. Sweet Mother, was she ready to take such a drastic step?

She tried not to think about any of it as she chewed her food. Chelis arrived home just as she was finishing her meal. Her sister looked tired and vaguely unhealthy, like everyone else these days. There were circles under her usually bright eyes, and her hair was limp. In fact, it looked as dull and lifeless as the rest of her. Chelis had inherited their father's curly blondness, while Phada's hair was straight and thick and more of a light brown with golden highlights. She usually kept it braided out of her way but sometimes she allowed it to flow freely down her back. At those times she felt like another creature entirely, a jungle wingbird perhaps, the kind that dipped and soared over the canopy of the trees only to dive recklessly into the branches in search of insects.

Phada washed up the few dishes—no one else seemed to have the energy to accomplish even that simple task. She was afraid that after she left, few of the household chores would get done, but she could not help that. She had a more important task ahead of her than washing dishes and baking bread.

The three of them sat in the tastefully decorated living quarters afterward, sipping herbal tea. The conversation was desultory at first and then ceased altogether as Ariel and Chelis drifted into that horrible, faral-induced state where they seemed to hover somewhere between waking and sleeping.

Phada came and knelt before her mother, taking her hands and gazing into her face. "I am going now, Mother. They are expecting me back at the sanctuary."

"Yes, Phada, you must hurry before the sun goes down." Ariel squeezed her hands with limp fingers before releasing them. "You know, in the long run, I think nothing in Mesara has really changed," she added dreamily.

"Nothing has really changed?" Phada could not believe her ears. Did the effects of the faral include self-deception now? "Our queen is being held captive. The council has been disbanded. No one knows where Pavonis is. A crude dominator is in charge, and you can sit there and say nothing has changed? This spice has turned Mesara upside down."

"Come, Phada." Chelis roused herself to defend their new way of life. "It is not as if you are so noble you refuse to use it. You eat your share; I have seen you. And it tastes too good to stop, does it not? What harm is there in a spice, Phada? You always were so self-righteous about things, so unbending. Maybe Mesara needed to be shaken up."

Phada bit her lip against any further retort. There was no purpose in it. May the Great Mother forgive you, she thought to herself. You cannot help it, I know that, but it is so hard to deal with you when you are like this, my sister. I have no right to criticize you when the only reason I am not just like you is because my body rejects the spice.

Phada bid farewell to her mother and sister, holding them tightly because she realized she might never see them again. As they waved to her from beneath the stone overhang she could only see the outline of their faces, not the drugged features. It was like an illusion of better days, a good omen perhaps. She promised herself she would remember them as they had always been, holding that image in her mind to give her the courage to carry through with her self-assigned task.

The sun was a fierce blue-white ball on the horizon, its rays still strong and hot as they filtered down through the jungle canopy. Soon it would be evenfall. Phada could not imagine that anyone would be wandering about at night, not if they were like Ariel and Chelis, who took to their beds and slept deeply throughout the sleep cycle. She might run into a warrior patrol, but even they would not be expecting anyone to be prowling around except the odd clawcat, not when they knew they held Mesara under their total domination.

She had not been able to pack more than a change of clothes and some food and supplies. With the leather pouch over her shoulder she walked along the pathway at a slow, considered pace, the way she had noticed that people moved these days. When she was sure no one was about, she slipped around the trunk of a huge, flowering rango bush and ducked into the jungle.

She crouched there for the longest time, her heart pounding so loudly in her ears she feared she would not be able to hear if anyone came after her. No angry shouts of alarm followed her actions. No one had noticed her. She quickly cut across the trail and headed for the ocean, her sandal-clad feet sinking heavily into the spongy ground. The moon was rising by the time she reached the edge of the sea.

Small waves lapped the shore and the smell of brine and seaweed was strong in her nostrils. Phada took a deep, refreshing breath as though she could clear the smell of faral from her senses and her memory. There was no one in sight—why would there be? This was the edge of the boundary of Mesara. There were only stingfish beyond this point, stingfish and the Uninhabited Island that she hoped still sheltered Sarak. What if they had not left him there after all? What if they had killed him? Phada clenched her jaw. She wouldn't think about that now, she chastised herself—too many what-ifs could drive a person to madness.

She moved quietly to where a couple of boats were pulled up on the sand, secured to a koalnut palm tree. The rope was thick and damp with condensation, but she managed to untie the smaller of the two boats and drag it to the water, being careful to step inside without putting her feet into the sea. Stingfish reportedly did not come this close to shore, but she was not taking any chances.

She paddled as quietly as she could. The light of the blue moon reflected on the surface of the water like a glittering jewel in the firelight, although the heated orange of hearthflames was a decided contrast to the cool, blue color given off by the moon. Such a low-riding moon was called a warrior moon, Phada remembered with a start, because it hid as much in its long, distorted shadows as it revealed, perfect circumstances for a warrior attack.

Her arms felt as if they were going to fall off by the time she spied the shimmering outline of the island in the distance. She adjusted her course and paddled with renewed vigor now that her target was in sight. And yet her heart had begun to pound with trepidation. Suppose the dominator had already spotted her? Suppose he was waiting to pounce on her as soon as she stepped ashore? She could still visualize his intense eyes, a vivid shade of brown that had matched his tanned features and dark hair. She also remembered his teeth gritted around the gag as he had glared at her. He was so powerful; he had tried to coerce her to do his bidding with only the energy of his will. He was a force to be reckoned with, and yet although she had felt frightened then, her fear had been mixed with a sense of compassion for the defeated warrior. She had never thought to feel sympathy for any dominator.

The prow of the boat touched land. She quickly stepped onto the shore, her sandals sinking into the soft sand. What in the name of the great Mother was she doing here? She must be crazy, she thought yet again. Now she was sorry it was night. A little harsh daylight would go a long way toward soothing her nerves. Every long, foreboding shadow cast by the light of the blue warrior moon seemed to move, ready to leap out at her if she so much as twitched a muscle. Everything was unnaturally still. Even the kwara birds were silent. Phada gritted her teeth and forced her body to walk toward the trees. If Sarak was asleep somewhere, it certainly would not be on the beach.

As she drew closer to the line of trees she realized there was a path leading to the interior of the island. With only the slightest hesitation she began following it. Up ahead, just beyond a clump of nut trees, she saw light spilling out from a doorway. Sarak must live there and he must still be awake. She pulled in a deep, hissing breath and pressed on.

A faint noise in the bushes to her right was her only warning before a massive body launched itself from its hiding place by the side of the path and knocked her to the ground, tumbling her over until she was lying on her back and pinned in place. Sarak's warrior body was large and heavy, and she had to fight hard not to scream or struggle.

"Sarak," she said in a quavering voice.

"Sweet Mother, a woman." He grunted. His body lay like deadweight on top of her, and she was finding it difficult to breathe between her fright and his overwhelming presence. He moved his hand until it pressed heavily against her throat. Oddly enough his head rested on the ground next to hers in the most intimate fashion. "Who are you?" he growled in her ear.

She had to swallow before she could answer. "My name is Phada," she whispered, trying not to let panic overtake her. "I saw you in the feasting hall, the night Dalcor seized power."

Everywhere their bodies touched she could feel only his bare skin. Did the man have nothing on? And if so, was their compromising position inciting his lust? Just because he had not raped the queen did not mean he was not capable of such a heinous deed. Every warrior was.

"What do you want?"

"I . . . I need to talk to you."

"Did Dalcor send you?" he demanded.

Dear Goddess, he believed she was some kind

of spy, Phada thought, drawing in a breath to protest. "No one sent me."

He lifted his head and Phada immediately shut her eyes. She could feel him studying her face, but she was not about to return his stare in these close circumstances. The hard ground beneath her back and thighs was faintly cool against her heated body; she could feel small pebbles pressing into her shoulders, the sandy dirt sticking to her perspiration-moist skin.

"Dalcor sent you to taunt me, did he not?" Sarak said in a harsh, bitter tone of voice that made her cringe. "May the sun scorch his already blackened heart. Does he think to test my willpower? He should know I have none left. Does he expect me to remain noble in this sun-cursed hellhole? I have no reason to do anything but please myself."

"I came of my own free will," she insisted softly.

He ignored her statement. "I cannot believe that rutting son of a Kargan wants me to have the pleasure of your soft woman's body," he continued in a deceptively flat-toned voice that made the hair on the back of her neck stand up. "But I accept his gift and damn the consequences."

"I tell you, no one sent me. I came to see you of my own free will."

"So much the better," he murmured.

"Please, Sarak." She felt very bold, using his name in such a pleading fashion but she was desperate to make him listen to her. "We must talk about Mesara," she insisted. "I need your help. . . ."

"Hush, sweet lady." He moved his hand until it covered her breast. "You are welcome to everything I have to give."

Goddess help her, he had totally misunderstood her reason for being here. Phada sucked in her breath but otherwise forced herself to remain motionless as he began to move his body against hers.

She had heard that some dominators liked their
women to struggle and she was afraid any resistance on her part might set him off. She had to
remain calm, to reason with him. Was he drunk
on vetch? She could not smell it on his breath, but
maybe he had consumed it earlier in the evening.

His fingers were surprisingly gentle as they caressed her. "Stop it," she ordered as evenly and
calmly as she could. Even so there was a catch in
her voice because of the riot of surprising and dis-
tressing sensations he was evoking with his hand.
Mostly she was ashamed because it was not at all
as repulsive as she had imagined a warrior's touch
should be. "Stop it, please. I am not one of your
Jiboan desert women asking to be manhandled by
a dominator."

"Yes, I noticed." His weight was angled across
her, and his lower body flexed then pressed
against her hip in the most alarming manner.
Phada's eyes flew open wider as she struggled to
push him off. He did not budge. Instead, his head
moved closer so he could nuzzle her neck. She
could feel his breath warming her skin and it finally galvanized her into more decisive action.

"Stop, Sarak," she shouted into his ear. He
flinched, so she kept her voice raised. "You do not
understand. I am a Keeper; it is forbidden for you
to touch me. Quit acting like a spice-addled fool
and let me up."

"What did you say?"

Phada swallowed hard but did not back down.
"I said let me up."

"You called me a spice-addled fool." His voice
was barely above a whisper.

"I said you were acting like a spice-addled fool,"
she pointed out. "There is a difference."

"There is a difference all right. Look at me," he
snarled. Phada cried out in protest as he dragged
her closer, pulling them both into the light spilling

out from the doorway of the stone hut. He turned her so she was forced to look straight into his face. The faintly blue rays of the moonlight illuminated the horrible reality. Phada gasped in shock and horror, for there, written on every one of his features, was the truth—he was as spice-addled as any male or female in Mesara.

# Chapter Four

"Oh no," Phada whispered, although there was no one to hear her anguish except the spice-enslaved warrior who still held her body pinned with his legs.

"Oh, yes," Sarak spat out, rolling away from her. He sprawled by her side, breathing heavily, his forearm across his eyes. "Did you expect Dalcor would leave me here, untainted by that cursed Kargan concoction?"

"I did not think." Phada bit her lip. She had been so worried about Sarak being killed that she had not considered the possibility that he had been drugged along with everyone else. She was ashamed of her naivete in thinking Dalcor would leave him to his own devices.

"Dalcor sends a warrior over twice a mooncycle with a fresh supply." The bitterness and self-loathing in his voice were palpable. "I tried to overcome my craving for it but its lure is far stronger than my puny willpower."

Phada could tell he hated to admit such a weakness. Not that he was different from any of the people of Mesara, warrior or otherwise. No one could resist the power of the faral once it got into their bodies. Dear Goddess, the Mesarans were truly lost now.

"Why is it you are not enslaved?" he asked, his eyes narrowed suspiciously. She could see he was working hard to keep his mind on track. The spice tended to diffuse a person's rational facilities. "I remember you now. You are that Keeper's apprentice, the one who refused to help me back in the feasting hall."

"You would only have gotten yourself killed."

"Of course. And this"—he gestured toward himself in disgust—"is better?"

She had no answer to that and so remained mute.

"Why did you come here? Wait, I think I know. I am sure you have already seen the power faral has over normal mating urges. I would wager even the righteous town dwellers back on the mainland have been reduced to doing anything for a quick tumble in the rango bushes. Or a slow, leisurely one, for that matter. Is that what you have come to find? Your own personal warrior slave? I have heard the tales of town women who secretly long to tumble a barbarian dominator, but I never thought I would be so sun-blessed as to meet one of them."

"Dear Goddess, no!" she whispered under her breath. She scooted away from him, but one big hand grabbed her by the leg before she could scramble completely clear.

He started to caress her leg, his palm rough against her tender flesh. She had visions of him wielding a sword countless times to achieve such callused skin. "No need to act so shocked," he said in a low, soothing tone of voice, as if he were try-

ing to gentle a recalcitrant bushhog before moving
in for the kill. "There is no one to see, no one to
impress with your disdain."

"Please stop. You are mistaken in your deductions," she said. She hoped she sounded like a dig-
nified Keeper, wise with years of experience and
not the frightened female she really was.

He ignored her as he continued to stroke her
leg. He moved to touch her thigh. Phada tried not
to gasp in shock in case it incited him. "It is a good
plan, well thought out," he continued, nodding.
He acted as though the horrible act he contemplated were no more serious than interpreting a
poetry performance. "You can secure your pleasure and return to Mesara before anyone knows
you were gone."

Phada stared at him in horror, her body frozen
with shock. She had no idea what to do, since she
had never fallen into a situation like this. It had
been a mistake to come here, a terrible error in
judgment. And yet she could not just lie here like
a tethered dobby. She gathered her legs beneath
her, ready to spring up when the opportunity presented itself. Could she outrun him? He was
drugged with faral but that did not mean he could
not catch her if he turned his mind—and his
powerful body—to that purpose. She had already
felt the strength in him.

"What is your name?"

"I . . . Phada. I am called Phada."

"I know you despise me, Phada, but I do not
care anymore. I will take what I so desperately
need and give what pleasure I can." Suddenly his
eyes gleamed. "I will also finally learn how a town
woman compares to a Jiboan desert wench."

He reached for the ties of his breechcloth.

"No, stop it," she cried. She reached out to grasp
his wrist, bold in her desperation. He might be on
faral but even using all her strength, she had no

more effect on him than a bluefly landing on his arm. He undid the cloth and his member sprang free, huge and menacing in its alien maleness. Phada quickly averted her eyes. She recalled what her sister had said about dominators mating for an entire sleep cycle. Looking at Sarak, seeing his muscled chest slick with sweat rising and falling like the mighty bellows at the iron forge, hearing his excited breathing, she could well believe it.

"Come ride me, Phada, and we will fly like the wind."

"You are disgusting," she hissed, slapping at the hands that reached for her. "First you raped Queen Riga and now you want to rape me."

She was surprised it was her words that finally brought him up short. He stared into her face, reading the disgust there. "I did not rape the queen," he said in such a fervent voice that she found herself believing him. He rolled away from her for the second time that night, wrapping his arms around his knees and pulling them up to his chest. He buried his head against them with a half-stifled groan.

Phada hesitated. She knew she should just leave, climb into the boat and row herself as quickly back to Mesara as she possibly could. For some reason she could not seem to move. Sarak was still naked but she could only see the side of his thigh and leg and his muscled buttock pressed into the ground. She swallowed hard. She had never seen a naked male before, not a live one anyway. Illustrations in a scroll did not come close to the reality, especially when the male in question was also aroused. She felt a prickle at the back of her neck and turned her head to find Sarak watching her, his eyes hooded but showing the proper deference any town woman expected from a mere barbarian.

"I beg your pardon, Phada," he said looking her

full in the face. There was a lot of time before cycle-rise but she could clearly see the dark red flush of color along his cheekbones. "I thought I was a fool before, but now I have gone beyond all reason. If you had wanted a rutting bullox, you would have made that clear right from the start."

She shuddered again and knew he had seen her instinctive reaction to his coarse words. "I came here to ask your help. I thought together we could do something to save Mesara. It was a foolish idea."

"Yes. I am useless to you or anyone else in Mesara."

He reached for the rumpled scrap of cloth that had covered him. Phada immediately jerked her face away, although she could still see his movements out of the corner of her eye as he unfolded his legs and wrapped the okapi leather garment around his waist with a practiced flip of his wrist. He hauled himself to his feet and waited respectfully until she stood up. No warrior touched a Mesaran female unless she specifically requested assistance.

"What will you do now?" he asked.

"I do not know."

"You are welcome to take refreshment in my hut before you return. It is not as fancy as your villa, or the Keepers' Sanctuary for that matter, but the sun is fast climbing toward the treetops."

"Thank you." She did not want anything to eat or drink but she was still reluctant to leave. What did she have to go back to; how would she live with herself and with the others, spice-addled as they all were? It was a bleak life that awaited her and she was in no hurry to return to it.

Sarak gestured her to precede him into the small, cool interior of the hut. It had been hewn out of the natural stone on the side of a small hill. Phada entered and gazed around, allowing her eyes to adjust to the dim interior. An old, ramshackle sleeping pallet stood in one corner. Hanging suspended from a hook over the hearth was a big iron stewpot, the cooking fire beneath it dormant, the ashes cold. She could not imagine a warrior like Sarak preparing his own meals. A rough table made of plankwood took up most of the rest of the small area. Pouches of sun-dried meat and vegetables scattered across the surface of another, smaller table before the hearth gave evidence of Sarak's diet.

He motioned her to one of the single chairs, wiping the seat and gesturing for her to sit down. "I have manganberry juice," he offered.

"That is fine." She nodded, feeling a hysterical urge to laugh. He was acting like a polite guest at a Keepers' afternoon tea.

He reached for a jug next to her chair, pulling out the cork and setting it on the table. Grabbing the sole cup sitting on a shelf, he poured her a much too generous portion. She did not protest when he set the cup in front of her.

Phada took the opportunity to study him. She had never been in such close contact with a dominator for such a length of time and had no idea how to act. There were no rules laid out for social interchange with a warrior, since they never mixed with the people of the town. Each class kept to itself. As far as she knew, warriors stayed busy tending to their sword practice and their patrols around the perimeter of Mesara. She supposed they socialized with their own kind, but what could they converse about except military matters?

And yet she could not ignore him. His presence was compelling in a way she had never experienced. She supposed it was because his big, highly trained warrior's body took up so much space and seemed to use so much of the air around them.

Even after cycles at inactivity, his muscles still looked as sleek and powerful as any predatory clawcat's. They certainly had not lost all their strength, as she had already discovered.

Everyone had long ago accepted the practice of exposing almost all of a warrior's body for public view and commentary—the loincloth that dominators wore was solely for the sensibilities of the women. Their scant attire had been designed partly to highlight their closer connection to the animal side of the spectrum and partly to allow for needed discipline. A warrior's sole purpose was as a fighting machine, a means of protection for the entire population of Mesara when necessary. Dominators were not allowed to grow fat and lazy. If they did, any Mesaran could point out his deficiency and he would be ordered back to training camp to be brought up to fighting standards.

Phada wondered how it would feel to live in such a manner, to reside in a barracks, to have no privacy of body or mind. Still, they did not seem to care. In fact, most warriors showed no sense of shame at parading around half naked in front of everyone, including the queen. They obviously did not possess the sensitivity and cultured personalities for which Mesaran men were so renowned.

Sarak spoke, startling Phada out of her musings. "How is it that you are not controlled by the spice?" he asked, his voice still faintly laced with suspicion at her possible motives. "They forced me to take it—against my will." The thought obviously still rankled his fierce warrior's pride.

"I . . . they forced the rest of us as well. Groups of dominators came to each dwelling to make sure everyone had consumed the spice and was under its control. It tasted wonderful but for some reason my body rejected it. My stomach refuses to keep it down."

He moved restlessly, albeit sluggishly, around the hut's cramped interior. The catlike grace she had noticed in him at the feasting hall was gone, a victim of the faral. "How have you managed to hide your condition from Dalcor and his men?"

She took a sip of her juice. "It has not been difficult. They are so busy taunting everybody, and the people are so concerned with trying to ensure they have faral to put in their cooking pots, that so far no one has noticed."

Sarak grunted. "But soon someone will. And when they find out they cannot control you, they will kill you."

"You are sun-blinded. That could never happen to a citizen of Mesara."

"You think not? I know Dalcor. He was ruthless before he overthrew Queen Riga, but now that he has absolute power, he will let nothing stop him from total domination. The only reason he allows me to live is because it amuses him. As soon as it no longer does, he will get rid of me as easily as another man might wring a rockhen's neck for the supper pot."

"Then I will remain at the Keepers' Sanctuary."

Sarak laughed mirthlessly. "Where your days will still be numbered."

"What do you mean?"

"Dalcor's men have taken the women of the palace, have they not?"

Phada blushed at his blunt manner of speaking. "Yes," she replied, avoiding his gaze. "That is what I have heard."

"And Dalcor himself has shamed our beloved queen." He spat the words out, his features taut with helpless fury and pain.

"Yes. He parades her through the high street on market day," Phada informed him softly.

"The better to humiliate her." Sarak gritted his teeth. "So tell me, Keeper's apprentice: What happens when they grow tired of their conquered playthings and want more sport?"

"Sweet Mother, no," Phada gasped.

"No one can stop them from doing anything they want. And so they will move on to other town women, even bonded women. And then they will commit the highest sacrilege of all—they will mate with the Keepers."

"That will never happen," she cried indignantly. "It is just your depraved mind that is conjuring up this horrible fantasy."

He stopped directly in front of her, his hands clenched into fists. "Is it, Phada? Dalcor has long had an aversion to the High Keeper since the day she chastised him in the feasting hall in front of everyone. He has never forgiven her. Now that he has Mesara in the palm of his hand, he will have his revenge."

"Then we must do something. Anything."

"If I were a whole warrior, perhaps." He turned away from her. "The odds would be against me, but I would die trying. And I would make sure to take Dalcor with me, curse his sun-blackened heart."

"It is obvious what we must do."

"What?"

"You have to free yourself from the power of the spice."

Sarak laughed, the sound filled with bitterness. "Do you think I have not tried? It is an impossible task."

"You must. I can do nothing by myself."

"What can two of us do?" he asked scornfully.

"I do not know. I will think of that later. But for now we must find a way to wean you from the spice."

"I am not part of a litter of squealing bushhog young to be weaned from his mother." Sarak threw himself down on his sleeping pallet. "Go away, Phada," he growled. "Go back to the Keepers' Sanctuary and bury your head in your books while you can."

He lay on his side, his face turned to the wall. Obviously he expected her to take the hint and walk out the door of the hut, to leave him there. She hesitated for long moments, unsure exactly what she should do, but knowing she could not depart, not when the very course of the future was at stake. Her life, the life of every individual in Mesara was meaningless now. Sarak had shown her that with his harsh assessment of what they had become.

Only the Goddess knew why she had been spared, but she could not believe it had been for nothing, a simple trick of fate. She had to try; there was nowhere for her to go otherwise. She was as good as dead anyway, as Sarak had already pointed out. If a mere dominator could face the situation head-on with that kind of unflinching courage, a Keeper's apprentice could do no less. It was time to take responsibility for the fate of Mesara. Whether she liked it or not, it had come to rest in her hands.

She crept across the room to hover anxiously by Sarak's sleeping pallet, feeling both bold and nervous at the same time. He looked large and intimidating, even lying down. The faint smell of his body mixed with the bedclothes was not unpleasant.

"Sarak?"

She knew he was not asleep; she could feel the aura of watchfulness that surrounded him, in spite of his drugged condition. Still, he refused to give any indication that he had heard her.

Phada moistened her dry lips. She thought of her mentor Helenina. In spite of her forthright dealings with everyone, the older Keeper was skilled in softening the blow with soothing, well-chosen words. Phada hoped she could emulate her now.

She tried again, speaking louder this time. "Sarak, you are correct. I cannot return to Mesara. But you cannot hide here any longer either. You took an oath to protect Mesara and its citizens and now it is time to fulfill that oath. For my part, I vowed to interpret and uphold her laws and I promise you I will not shirk my duty."

Still no response.

What else could she say, how could she rouse him? The only thing she knew for certain was that he wished her gone. A small smile parted her lips as she said the next words. "It seems I must remain here indefinitely with you."

"You cannot! Dalcor or one of his men will be here in less than a mooncycle with food and another healthy dose of faral for me. They must not find you here—for both our sakes."

She ignored him. "I suppose I had better hide the boat," she continued, feeling more cheerful by the minute. It felt good to have something to do besides worry. It was also wonderful to have someone to talk to, someone she did not have to guard her tongue against. "Let us hope when they come they do not notice it is missing."

"Did you not hear me, Keeper's apprentice?" he exclaimed in exasperation. He pulled himself into a sitting position on the pallet, using the wall to help prop him up. "You are worse than a bothersome battlefly."

"That is because I need your help. . . . "

"And as persistent," he added darkly.

"The boat is too heavy for me to lift out of the water by myself." She walked toward the door, praying he would follow. She could order him directly; as a warrior he was sworn to obey her. But she found she did not want to do that, at least not just yet. For one thing she had never ordered a dominator in her entire life. For another, she did not want to antagonize him until it was absolutely necessary. She had a feeling that time would come soon enough.

As she stood in the doorway, waiting for him to move his massive frame into a more upright position, she could feel the heat of the cycle beating against her back and the coolness of the air in the hut's interior brushing the skin of her face. She felt an odd sense of freedom. There were no books to be copied here, no grinding daily chores of the apprentice, no afternoon classes in the ways of the Ancient Ones. She might as well enjoy that aspect of her enforced exile from town. Of course there were no plays, no music, and no visits to the hot springs either.

Sarak glowered at her as he dragged on his sandals. "I suppose you can stay for a couple of days," he offered grudgingly. "Until you decide what to do. There is another hut just beyond the rise."

"I am sure it will do just fine."

He grunted as he rose to his feet. "Let us go then, before it gets too hot to venture outside."

Phada turned on her heel and walked out the door with Sarak right behind her. He stayed in that position, at first because the path was too narrow for the two of them to walk abreast, and then because a warrior always kept his distance from a lady. It was not conducive to conversation, not that Phada had anything to say to the dominator or imagined he had anything to say to her.

They reached the shore. The stark white rays of the sun with their faintly blue cast streaked across the water, making it painful to look directly at the brilliant aquamarine sea. Phada moved to the bow of the shagbark boat, prepared to do her share by lifting one end, but Sarak waved her away. He easily dragged the vessel completely onto the pale, greenish-hued sand before bending down to hoist it onto his shoulder.

Phada followed him into the thickly wooded area to their left. She could hear his heavy breathing and saw that a sheen of perspiration already covered his body. She imagined that without the faral running through his system, lifting a boat would be child's play for him.

His next words confirmed it. "Goddess curse it. I am as weak as a puny treerat," he said in disgust.

Together they covered the boat with branches, although Phada surreptitiously did more than her share of the work to spare what was left of Sarak's strength. If the warrior noticed her behavior, he was too exhausted to protest. Phada was worried about him. The skin around his mouth was pinched and had an unhealthy blue cast that had nothing to do with the sun.

They began the trek back to the hut. Again Sarak remained in the rear, although this time it was because his steps lagged alarmingly. His breathing grew ragged and harsh. Phada immediately slowed her pace to match his.

The gesture was not appreciated.

"I would ask you to cease your condescending actions," he said, tight-lipped. He managed to sound curt in spite of his breathless condition. "Move along to the hut, Phada. I am not a nursling; I do not need your aid."

Phada had been feeling sorry for him but now she huffed and then flounced ahead, going much faster than she normally would have because of her anger. Let the thickheaded bullox have his way. She did not need or particularly want his company. She was doing this for the good of Mesara, not that anyone appreciated her efforts.

Finally, she too began gasping for breath and slowed her pace once again. The thick canopy of trees blocked out the most penetrating of the sun's harsh rays and it was almost cool beneath its shelter. The raucous chorus of uncounted numbers of insects reminded her how alive the jungle was. The scuffling noises of small animals scurrying under cover of the brush sent a small shiver up her spine. Most of them were shy and hid from people. It was the pretty ones, the ones who did not bother to disguise themselves, that were the most deadly.

Phada reached the edge of the jungle and paused. The hut lay across an open tract of land about 50 measures away. She assumed the second hut was on the other side of a small rise just behind it.

The sandy path already looked hot enough to burn the soles of her feet. Of course she had her sandals on, but she had neglected to bring her head covering. It would not harm her to be exposed for such a short time, but she must remember not to venture outside without it again. What if Dalcor appeared unexpectedly and she had to cross open patches of land in order to hide? She could not guarantee that the usurper or his henchmen would stay away the usual semimooncycle.

She decided to make a dash for Sarak's hut first. From there she could make a second foray to the empty dwelling. She heard Sarak drawing closer. She had no desire to watch him bake in the sun as he made his slow, painful way across the unprotected stretch of land. Of course his skin was tanned and much tougher than her pale complexion, but Elithra's sun could do damage to even the most hardened veteran of its rays in a very short amount of time. She shuddered as she recalled studying the early history of the planet. What little they knew about it, they had learned from what was left of the ancient accounts. Phada remembered reading about how men had once been punished by being staked out beneath the blistering sun. She could not imagine a more agonizing way to die.

Thank goodness they had come so far from those barbaric times—or at least most of the population had. Everyone knew the dominators were throwbacks to those earlier cycles and retained more than a little of the brutish qualities they had all worked so hard to eradicate. The warriors had served their purpose of protecting Mesara these many sun orbits, but now Phada could see that it had only been a matter of time until one of their number revealed his true antecedents by reverting to warrior rule and sending them hurtling down the wrong side of the spectrum.

Phada jogged quickly along the rutted trail, reaching the cool interior of the hut in a matter of millimarks. Sarak's dwelling might be primitive but it still provided protection, and any Mesaran could appreciate that. Of course, it had no antechamber to ease the transition from the light outside to the dim interior, but she had not expected such niceties.

She drew in a deep breath as she waited for Sarak and considered her situation. She was placing all her faith in a dominator who was just as likely as Dalcor to turn barbarian on her. Had that not been Queen Riga's mistake? Phada had no way of knowing Sarak's true character. He had seemed obedient and well trained in his duties as second-in-command, but then again so had Dalcor.

Phada picked up her unfinished cup of manganberry juice. Why had Sarak not joined Dalcor in his successful bid for power? She knew there were rival factions in the palace guard, with Sarak being the queen's favorite, although Dalcor was first-in-command. Was Sarak hoping to be rewarded for his loyalty if Riga returned to the throne? Or had he simply been biding his time and discovered too late that Dalcor had made the first move? It was obvious there was no love lost between the two dominators.

The room darkened appreciably as Sarak appeared in the doorway. He clutched at the rough stone portal, holding himself upright by wedging his hands and feet into the corners.

"You need sleep," she said in a practical tone of voice that revealed none of her lingering suspicions. "We both do. We can decide what to do when we are more rested. Where is the other hut?"

"Follow the trail around the side of the hill. It is but twenty measures to the doorstep."

"Fine."

"I . . . it is very crude. The sleeping pallet has no covering. There is no fresh water with which to wash." He drew himself up, his bearing straight and proud. Phada could see that the effort was costing him. "I will go there instead. You remain here."

"No!" Phada shocked herself with the vehemence of her protest. The very idea of lying in the pallet where a warrior had slept made her heart thud painfully beneath her rib cage. She rushed into further explanation before he could guess the true reason for her reaction. "No, it is better if you stay here. I know you do not like to hear such statements, but you are exhausted. I am a Keeper's apprentice; we are not used to palace luxury. I will wash later, after I sleep. Goddess grant you peaceful rest, Sarak."

She brushed past him before he could return her politely formal declaration of parting. She almost forgot her pack, snatching it from the floor by the door at the last moment and making good her escape into the blinding light. She stumbled along the rock-strewn trail, arms groping around her in extended arcs so she wouldn't land headfirst in a rango bush. She shaded her eyes by using the pack, squinting until she saw the hut outlined in the harsh glare. She pitched forward through the doorway into its blessed dimness.

Compared to outside, it was like being in utter darkness. It took several long moments for her eyes to adjust, and then she glanced around. The interior was identical to Sarak's meager dwelling. There was no bedcovering, as Sarak had said.

She crawled onto the sleeping pallet. It had been a long night and an even longer cycle-rise. She felt as exhausted as Sarak looked, she decided, not even bothering to stifle a yawn. Tucking her pack beneath her head, she closed her eyes. She felt gritty with dirt, rumpled, and out of sorts, but it was too much effort to do anything about her condition now. Perhaps when she woke up her entire outlook on this abysmal situation would improve, but somehow she doubted it.

Sarak rolled onto his back and stared at the unfinished stones in the ceiling of the sun-baked hovel he had been calling home for almost an entire mooncycle. He could not hide from the fact that he was pitifully exhausted after their excursion to hide the boat. Shame flooded through his body as he remembered how Phada had slowed her steps to accommodate his weakened condition, as if he were a stumbling babe trying out shaky legs for the first time.

He grimaced, also recalling how quickly the little Keeper's apprentice had quitted his presence at the first opportunity. Not that he blamed her. He had never been the kind of warrior who felt at ease in formal social situations, not that he would label the unexpected appearance of Phada on his doorstep a social occasion. Still, a dominator was supposed to be on his best behavior in the presence of a Mesaran lady. If he could not say anything to the point, he should say nothing at all.

Sarak knew he had been surly, even rude. The sun-cursed faral had wreaked havoc with his good sense as well as his physical condition.

He folded his arms behind his head, studying the patterns in the rock above. He knew the lines and indentations by heart but he always managed to find a new shape. This time he saw that the sharp edge in the corner looked like the snout of a mudhog, although if he considered that discolored blot as the rest of the animal's body, the poor beast had no legs or tail.

Phada had insisted he needed rest. Sarak snorted in self-derision. He had been sleeping for what seemed like endless cycles since coming here. He did not like to admit that despair had overtaken him on more than one occasion. No warrior gave up in the face of adversity. It was an integral part of the dominator's code of ethics. Then again, no warrior had ever been forced to deal with a situation such as the one in which he now found himself.

He could not imagine what Phada thought they could possibly accomplish, a broken-down warrior and an inexperienced Keeper's apprentice. She would probably have as much effect as a wingbird against a clawcat. In fact, she reminded him of one of the graceful, swooping birds whose daring headlong dives and last-minute saving swerves made them the acrobats of the jungle. Her movements were as quick and sure as the brightly colored blue and red avians, although the utilitarian apprentice tunic she wore was more subdued in tone.

Actually, the tan color of the garment matched her hair, he decided. He found himself wondering about the body she hid beneath the fine material. It still shocked him to realize he had already touched the lush roundness of her breast and smelled the sweet scent of her skin and hair. He quickly squelched such thoughts. They would only lead to an urge to relieve the insufferable pressure in his loins. Somehow he could not do such a thing with Phada only measures away.

He breathed deeply as his eyes drifted shut. She was not pretty in the aggressively lavish way of many of the town women, but her skin was smooth and pale and her profile delicate and pleasing to the senses. She was certainly not as beautiful as the queen. He had never touched any part of the queen's royal person besides her soft white hand—except, of course, in his dreams.

His body quickened in spite of his stern effort to control it. He had always been above himself with his forbidden fantasies of mating with the queen. Recalling his audacity never ceased to make him flush with shame. By the blue moon, he hated the spice and its almighty power over his pleasure pathways. He had no idea what he was capable of under its influence. He had never tested its limits and he intended to make sure he never did. It was imperative that he get Phada off the island as soon as he possibly could, not only for his sake but for hers. She was placing herself in deadly peril by staying here, and not only from Dalcor.

"Sarak?"

His head jerked up at the sound of his name. He pushed himself to a sitting position on the sleeping pallet, which groaned in protest under his weight. He had kept his loincloth on, in the event Phada returned before he roused himself, so he was decent, although some town women thought no dominator was decent in their scanty attire and averted their eyes whenever a warrior passed near.

Phada had not been able to look at his rude physique either. She still avoided gazing anywhere but at his face. However, he had no other garment

with which to cover himself except a threadbare
lana-wool blanket, and he would be sun-blinded
before he wrapped himself up in it like some
swaddling babe.

"Enter," he called.

She stepped over the threshold, only her general
outline immediately discernible. And then she
came further into the room, blinking against the
abrupt change in lighting, and Sarak could see her
in detail.

"Did the Goddess give you rest?" he inquired politely. In spite of what she might think, he was not
a total barbarian and knew his manners. After all,
he had once reported directly to the queen. And
been unable to warn her or help her in her time
of greatest need, he reminded himself bitterly.

"Yes, I thank you for your concern," she replied,
equally polite and formal.

He could see that she had gone to the effort to
draw water from the primitive well outside and
had combed and rebraided her long, wheaten-
colored hair. She looked as fresh as a rata flower
after a rain, her skin glowing with good health,
her eyes bright and clear. They were an unusual
shade, neither gray nor blue but a combination of
the two colors that reminded him of a rare stormy
day when clouds covered the sun and the land was
blessedly cool for a change.

She set her fine leather pack on the table and
sat down beside it. "I know what our first action
must be in our plan to save Mesara. I called upon
the wisdom of my Keeper's training, little though
it may be, and I remembered the first principle."

Sarak hid the smile that threatened to take over
his expression as he stared at her. Although the
comparison was ludicrous, she sounded like a war
leader, mapping out a campaign. "And that is?"

"In order to do your best, you must be healthy,
well rested, and as free as possible from the crav-

ings of mortal life that might divert you from your duty."

"What in the blessed blue moon does that mean?"

"It means that I am going to help you free yourself from the clutches of the spice."

# *Chapter Five*

The grin faded from Sarak's face at Phada's words.
"I told you, I've already tried to stop using the
spice. It was impossible."

"Yes, but you tried it by yourself. Maybe with
someone to help you it would be different."

"It would not be different." Sarak stared at her
in alarm. By the Goddess, she meant it. He would
rather die than to parade the groveling weakness
of his dependence in front of anyone, but most
especially a town woman. He would rather be
staked out in the hostile desert for a week than to
go through that.

"What method did you use?" she asked.

"Method? There was no method."

"I mean, did you try to get off it gradually or did
you just stop seasoning your meals completely?"

"I tried everything I could think of," he muttered
darkly.

He had no desire to go into the various tactics
he had come up with to break his enslavement.

One time he had even gone so far as to bury his last pouch of the stuff deep in the jungle. He had managed to make it through an entire cycle and part of a night until the longing for just a taste of the sun-cursed condiment had driven him back into the jungle, where he had sweated and searched for hours before finding his hiding place. His hands had been shaking so hard he had managed to spill the contents of the pouch all over the ground. Thank the Goddess no one had been there to witness him licking granules of faral from the ground like a greedy bushhog.

"I think the only way is to simply quit using the stuff," Phada continued blithely, tapping her slender fingers on the table. "When I was home last time, I tried secretly to wean my mother and sister off the spice. I was not successful. Whatever amount I neglected to add to the supper pot, they made up for at the dining table with the faral shaker."

Sarak paced over to the sleeping pallet, his hands clenched at his sides as he tried to control his breathing. Just the thought of doing without the spice made his knees shake. A fine sheen of sweat broke out over his body. Could she not see that this plan of hers was useless and give it up? He had thought she resembled a wingbird but he had been grievously mistaken. She was more like a stubborn woodhammer, pecking incessantly at the bark of a tree, determined to reach the softer sublayer where a hard-earned dinner of insects awaited.

Speaking of food, it was time for the morning meal. His mouth began watering at the thought of how easily the faral would transform his utilitarian meal of cooked cereal, enhancing its flavor until it became as succulent as a spit-roasted rockhen, dripping with its own juices. He needed the spice now. No untried Keeper's apprentice was going to stop him.

He dropped his arms to his sides and turned to face her. Maybe she could not stop him but he found himself reluctant to reveal how badly he needed another dose. She would be gone soon and he did not want to be remembered as the weak-willed failure of a warrior that he actually was.

"We should eat," he said in a nonchalant tone of voice. "I offer you my hospitality. I must warn you that I am not much of a cook."

"Thank you. Sarak, you have not given me an answer. Will you try to break free of the spice? I realize I have no notion of how it is to be dependent on it, but maybe that is not such a bad thing. I will be able to remain strong."

"You are right. You know nothing of the gut-wrenching craving the spice produces. I cannot do this thing."

"Even for the sake of Mesara?"

"I wish I could. But I know that it will only lead to failure and disappointment for you."

"For me? And what about you? With an attitude like that, of course you will never succeed."

He glared at her. "My attitude, as you call it, is based on reality, while yours is based on wishful dreaming."

She met his gaze, her stormy slate blue eyes filled with determination. She had not given up yet. Oh no, she still hoped to convince him, to make it work. "I have heard that any warrior worth his seasalt is not afraid to take on the most daunting opponent—even if it means his own death."

"Faral is not an opponent; it is a curse," he retorted.

His heart began racing at the pull of emotions that flooded his senses. She was trying to shame him into agreeing and, sweet Mother, it was almost working. He felt a strong urge to prove to her that he was just the kind of fearless warrior she described, as indeed he had once been. No, it was an impossible undertaking. He had to keep his head connected to his shoulders for both their sakes.

She had no notion of what might happen should they try her foolish plan, and he had no desire to explain the finer details of the kinds of behavior she could expect from him. He could not begin to predict what he might do while in the throes of faral-induced craving. He had already almost gone mad. What if he really tried to rape her? He might harm her, even kill her to get at the spice— its seductive powers were that enslaving. All knowledge of proper conduct, all sense of pride were eradicated, leaving only shame and degradation in their wake.

He could not stand there a millimark longer. He had to move. He walked over to the hearth where the kindling was already laid for the morning fire. Using a flint, he lit the small pile of twigs at the bottom, grunting in satisfaction as it caught nicely and began to burn. Then he swung the cookpot directly over the flames.

"You could pretend that the spice was a Kargan opponent," she pointed out. "In a way, I suppose it is true, since they are the ones who manufacture it." She paused thoughtfully. "I wonder if they produced it especially for us. They could not be addicted as well or they would never be able to carry out the raids they have subjected us to these many orbits."

Sarak felt her gaze on him, but he remained busy, setting the table with the crude pottery plates that were the extent of the hut's meager furnishings, placing the sapok wood shaker on the end of the table farthest from Phada. He knew he should be concerned with what she was saying, but he could only think about the spice and how good it would feel to be free from its craving for that short space of time between eating and the half-stupor that inevitably followed every meal as his body assimilated the toxin. He was approaching what he had labeled the time of anxiety, when the body and the mind both began to insist on another dose of faral but had not worked themselves up to full-blown desperation. He knew every stage on the way up to blissful oblivion and on the way down to the abyss of despair.

"According to the historical texts, the Kargans live in a poor land and are able to grow only the barest necessities," Phada continued. She sounded a bit like one of his instructors in the warrior training school, although her voice held none of the condescension of the Mesaran intellectuals who taught the dominators as part of their civic duty. "I guess they grew too impatient to be satisfied with the small amount of goods they were able to steal from us and decided to take everything. I wonder why they worked through Dalcor instead of coming to attack us themselves."

"Why should they attack us when the faral has done the job for them?" Sarak pointed out bitterly. He gave the pot of bubbling cereal a last stir before he began dishing it up. He set Phada's plate before her, then took his own over to the sleeping pallet. If he had not been so concerned with getting more of the spice into his stomach, he would have felt the awkwardness of having to break the night's fast with someone like Phada, a lady and a Keeper, someone who looked down on barbaric warriors until she needed their aid.

He returned for the shaker. To his surprise, Phada grasped his wrist. "Please, Sarak. You must try to stop. I know you can do it."

He looked down at her hand on his arm. Phada's skin was so pale and tender compared to his tanned flesh. He was not too far gone to absorb the gentle touch of her fingers. He knew he could knock her hand away, even in his weakened condition, but he was in no hurry to break the contact. He made the mistake of gazing into her eyes. They were filled with a pleading softness that would move any male to carry out her bidding and feel honored to do so.

When she added what she must have known was her most persuasive argument, he knew he was defeated. "If Queen Riga were able to journey here herself, she would ask the same service of you."

Sarak groaned, lowering his head to cradle it in his free hand. Phada released his arm and he actually felt a loss. He must really be a sun-blind fool to think that Riga, not to mention the little Keeper's apprentice who sat across the table, would ever look at him as a male worthy to be her savior and not as a crude dominator. If he were somehow successful in conquering the spice's hold over his body, he knew he would be rewarded with position and riches. But it was the futile, foolish hope that Riga would smile on him with genuine appreciation and affection, the way she often looked at Pavonis, that finally pushed him over the precipice and caused him to agree.

"All right, Phada. I do not promise anything, but I will try."

Phada clapped her hands together, squeezing them tightly as she held them in front of her, almost as if she were praying to Mother Elithra at the harvest ceremony. He hated to inform her, but he was going to need a lot more than prayer to get him through the upcoming ordeal. He wondered if he would even last a cycle.

"If you will let me add my willpower to yours, I know we can succeed, Sarak," she insisted.

She was so adamant that he found himself

yearning to believe her. And yet he found he could not silence the cynical, disillusioned side of his personality that had been born the morning he had been sentenced to train as a warrior, the morning his parents had publicly disowned him because he had besmirched the family name.

"And after I am free from craving the spice? What happens then?"

"I do not know," she replied thoughtfully. "When you are clearheaded again, I am sure you will think of a plan. After all, restoring the physical integrity of Mesara from usurpers and traitors is your sworn duty."

She stood up, reaching for the shaker. Sarak swallowed hard, his gut twisting painfully. By the blue moon, what had he let himself in for?

"Where is the rest?"

He pressed his lips together to hold back the flood of negative words that crowded his mind, then pointed grimly at a small basket. He would wait and let her see for herself how enslaving the faral was. Maybe then she would leave him to his misery. Phada lost no time in seizing the leather pouch that contained every last grain of faral on the entire island.

"What are you going to do with it?" he managed to ask in spite of his dry throat.

"I thought to hide it."

"No!"

"What?" She stared at him, surprised at his vehemence, her brows raised in that kind of feminine, aristocratic disapproval he had often seen cross Riga's delicate features. It was a look that made him feel lower than a greenback ground snake.

"You must toss it into the sea and you must do it now."

"But what if you lose your reason and I . . . I cannot handle the consequences?" Phada averted her gaze. He knew what she was thinking. She was afraid she might have to touch his body, to subdue him, an impossible task given her small frame, especially while he was under the influence of the cursed faral. "I saw people in the town when they needed the spice. They acted out of control, like . . ."

"Like wild animals? Is that not what you were going to say? It is a label often applied to dominators."

She had the grace to remain silent, although her cheeks turned pink.

"No," he insisted. "If I am going to do this, I want no access to the faral or I might weaken." He gritted his teeth, amazed that he was making such a mad statement. He would regret it later, he knew, but the surprised look of approval in Phada's eyes, mixed with something that resembled admiration, drove him on.

"As you wish," she said. "I will do it now, as you ask."

"Fine." His voice came out in a strained croak. He watched her move toward the doorway, clutching the table in a death grip to keep himself from springing after her. A splinter dug into the thumb of his right hand but he only squeezed harder, relishing the pain. As she disappeared out the door, he opened his mouth to call her back, but what was left of his pride would not allow it. Maybe this ordeal would kill him but it was better to die this way than to go on living as Dalcor's unwilling playtoy.

Let Phada believe he was doing this for Mesara. He supposed in some ways he was, but another part of him had a different motivation. So far he had not broken down and begged for his portion of faral from the warriors Dalcor sent from the mainland. But it was only a matter of time. Only last week his former commander had revealed his newest strategy. He planned to drag Sarak back to Mesara, where the warriors would be allowed to have their sport with him in the feasting hall. Sarak knew he could deal with that. It would be a simple matter to charge at one of the dominators, forcing him to pull his dagger and end Sarak's miserable existence by cutting his throat.

But Dalcor would not be satisfied with humiliating him in front of the warriors who had once served under his command. The newly installed leader of Mesara had also promised that the evening's entertainment would include something very special—a seat of honor for Sarak at Riga's royal bedside, where he could watch while Dalcor mated with her. And when the new leader was satisfied that he had been pleasured beyond a dominator's wildest dreams by the queen's acquiescent, soft female body, something he promised his former second-in-command would likely need endless marks of time to achieve, he swore that Sarak would die screaming for the spice with Riga looking on.

Sarak's mind cringed from the horrible vision of the delicate queen sitting atop Dalcor's pumping body, his hands all over her, fondling her breasts and the sacred place between her thighs. His hands clenched into fists and his heart pounded until he thought it would burst. He cursed the Kargans and their sun-blackened hearts; he damned Dalcor and his ambitions to the eternal abyss. He knew he could never withstand witnessing such an act being committed against his beloved queen, not without losing what was left of his mind. Even before Phada had appeared on his doorstep, he had decided that since he possessed no knife or weapon of any kind, when Dalcor came for him, he would throw himself into the sea and let the stingfish have his useless carcass.

Maybe Phada's plan would save him the trouble.

Phada sat at the crudely fashioned table in Sarak's hut, picking through the dried beans she had just placed in the cooking pot and waiting for Sarak to return from his expedition into the jungle to gather some of the wild vegetables that grew there. Even with the thick jungle canopy, the cycle could be unbearably hot when the sun was at its zenith. Now that the orb had begun its descent toward the horizon, it was safer to move about outside. In fact, this was the time of day most Mesarans began emerging from their homes to chat with neighbors. Phada felt a pang of homesickness, which she quickly pushed away.

They had decided that even though she outranked him in every way, Phada would handle the cooking and other chores, not that there were very many things to do in this hovel, chores or otherwise, she decided wryly. Knowing how her mother and sister often behaved under the influence of the faral, Phada did not expect much help from Sarak. Soon he would have enough to do to handle his withdrawal from the clutches of the spice. She prayed he would be strong enough and that she would be able to handle any emergency that arose.

She had tried to keep her eyes off him, but she could not help perusing his face at intervals that had grown increasingly frequent. She realized she half-expected him to turn into a ravaging beast before her very eyes, although he had been quiet, if somewhat sullen, during the part of the cycle they had so far spent together. The only sign of discomfort she had noticed was a sheen of perspiration that slicked his muscled body. Of course it was hard to miss such a thing when naked flesh was just about all there was to see of him.

She had not heard him approach but suddenly the room darkened as he stepped inside the threshold, filling the doorway with his massive frame. The brilliant sunlight outlined his body like a halo, accentuating his thick muscles and intimidating strength, even if it was subdued beneath the weakening power of the spice. She would never be able to control him if he became violent.

He paced over to where she sat, dumping a pile of vegetables on the table in front of her that contained tuber roots, calla greens, and sweet onion. She noticed that his skin was sallow and his nostrils pinched with the effort of breathing. He might be somewhat breathless after his trek into the jungle, but she was afraid he was also beginning to feel the effects of his long marks of time without the faral, as her mother and Chelis always did before a meal.

She was afraid that this supper and its aftermath were only the beginning of their troubles. One step at a time, she reminded herself. It was the only way to get through this.

Sarak stalked over to his sleeping pallet and threw himself down with a motion so violent the wooden frame crashed against the stone wall of the hut. He grunted in what sounded like satisfaction at the loud noise that resulted. Phada wisely made no comment, instead reaching into her bag for a knife to use in cutting up the vegetables. The big warrior was obviously not in the best of moods and she had no desire to provoke his ire. It would probably end up turned in her direction soon enough.

Actually they had not had much to say to each other the entire cycle. That was because they had nothing in common, Phada reminded herself. They were complete opposites, like a giant jungle tuskboar who cared only for the basics of dominance and survival and a wingbird whose only de-

sire was to soar into the highest reaches of the sky.
Then again, she added to herself in the name of
fairness, although many of the warriors were like
the tuskboar, even resembling that creature in
their beastliness and thick-necked, flattened features, the result of numerous broken noses in
combat practice, Sarak reminded her more of a
graceful clawcat. He was still concerned with the
basics of survival, but there was a kind of ruthless
beauty to his method of attaining it.

She had often wondered what a dominator did
all day, and now she had her answer—he slept if
he was not on patrol or practicing with his
weapon. Of course Sarak had no weapon here, she
realized, watching uneasily as he stared at the
knife in her hand. She wondered what he was
thinking. Probably that he would dearly desire to
thrust the well-honed blade right between Dalcor's ribs.

She shuddered at the animal barbarity of committing such a deed, then quickly realized that
Sarak was used to such acts, maybe even on a
daily basis. She had no idea exactly how the dominators protected the town and she did not want
to know. That was why they lived in separate barracks on the edge of Mesara, where their brute
ways would not spill over into the more refined
daily life of the rest of the population.

Her thoughts and her revulsion must have been
evident on her face because when she surreptitiously moved her gaze, it was to find Sarak staring back at her from his propped-up position on
the pallet, his mouth twisted in a sneer. As he
started speaking, she realized his disgust was directed not at her, but at himself.

"I find I still have too much pride to use a common paring knife to kill myself with," he said, nodding at the blade. He snorted mirthlessly. "I will
also admit to much curiosity as to how you will

handle the cycles to come."

"In the usual way," she replied with a wry grin and more confidence than she felt. "One at a time."

"You seem to be able to see the light at the end of this long, dark passageway, but I cannot."

Her mouth tilted up on one side in a half smile, half grimace. "I only wish that were true."

He made no reply, so she continued with her supper preparations, cutting up the vegetables and tossing them into the cooking pot, adding more beans and water. She swung the arm of the tripod to move the heavy metal container back over the flames. By the time she observed Sarak, she discovered his back was turned toward her. By the evenness of his breathing she assumed he was sleeping.

She wished she could return to her own hut. Although it contained even fewer of the comforts of town living, at least there she could be alone with her thoughts. But she dared not leave Sarak to his own devices. She had no idea what kind of crazy ideas might creep into his mind while his body fought its dependence on the spice. For all she knew, he might go crazy enough to steal her boat in order to return to Mesara.

The thought set her heart racing. She had not considered that possibility but realized she should have. She had seen the cunning of people in their quest to obtain more faral. The warriors kept everyone on short supply, more for their own entertainment than because they did not want people to have access to the spice.

She had to safeguard their one means of getting off this island. She could not have Sarak abandoning her on the Uninhabited Island—it would mean both their deaths. As quietly as she could, she gathered up her pack and crept to the door. When she saw that Sarak made no move, she slipped into the glaring light of the postzenith sun.

It did not take her long to reach the spot where they had hidden the boat. Moving it to another location was a much harder task. She thought her heart would burst from the exertion of dragging it far enough away so that Sarak would not be able to easily discern its new location. Then she had to retrace her steps and gather up and scatter all the branches they had used to cover it.

By the time she returned, the sun had moved several degrees in the sky. She stood just outside the threshold, her hand covering her eyes so she would not be caught sun-blinded when she first entered the hut. The appetizing aroma of the bean and vegetable stew filtered out from the small chamber, urging her to hurry inside, which she did.

Sarak had shifted position. He was now lying on his back, his head turned toward her, one arm thrown wide across the sleeping pallet while the other rested on his chest. The utter openness and vulnerability of his position, along with the sound of his deep, even breathing, which she could hear above the chattering of the kwara birds outside the door, told her he was fast asleep.

She stepped into the room. Her presence did not alter the rhythm of his breathing. Laying the pack on the table, she lowered herself into the ugly wooden chair. The worn straw seat creaked beneath her weight, but still Sarak did not stir.

She took the opportunity to study him. Not his body—she had already seen more of that than she cared to—but his face. He did not seem so alien in sleep, although there was no denying the powerful masculine contours of his highly trained physique, almost a caricature of the leaner, slighter build of most of the Mesaran men she knew. She had heard that the warriors hefted leather bags filled with stones to build their strength and, judging from Sarak's muscles, she could well believe it.

His face in repose had regular, even features, not all that different from Jobus's, although everything about Sarak was bigger and more . . . more aggressive, she supposed was the proper word to describe it. The shadow of his beard was visible across his cheeks and along his jaw. It looked rough, especially compared to the smooth, tanned skin of his throat.

He sighed and stirred. Phada's face flamed with embarrassment. Suppose he awoke to find her scrutinizing him so intently? She assured herself that she held only a scholar's curiosity about his physical exterior, but she doubted he would believe her. She jumped up from her chair and crossed the stone floor to the hearth, where she busied herself checking the stew. As she added more water and stirred the mixture, she realized she had not eaten since early this morning when Sarak had given her the cereal.

The skin at the nape of her neck and along her scalp tingled warningly. She knew Sarak had awakened and was now watching her. She turned to face him. "Supper is ready."

He looked sullen. "I am not hungry."

"Try to eat something."

"Did you throw away all the faral?"

What game was he playing at now to ask her such a question? She frowned as she answered. "You know I did."

"You kept none in reserve—in case?"

"In case of what? You told me to toss it all into the sea and I did."

She was not sure what she would do if he refused to eat, but he rose from the pallet and came to sit at the table. Phada scooped the stew into the mismatched pair of pottery bowls she had discovered. Then she moved one of the bowls and a spoon in front of him before taking her own seat as far away as she could without being too obvious.

It was more than awkward as they began eating together—a Keeper and a dominator. Phada kept her gaze averted, hoping to spare Sarak the embarrassment of her witnessing his crude table manners. She was not even sure that a dominator used eating utensils, although she supposed all those wild tales about some of the things the warriors did within the confines of their barracks were just that—unsubstantiated stories.

Unlike his earlier, sometimes unfocused attention, Sarak's dark brown eyes now missed nothing as they scanned the chamber. In fact his senses appeared sharper and as cunning as a weasula. He nodded at her with a sarcastic, irreverent grin before picking up his spoon. Phada decided her best course of action was to ignore him. She concentrated on taking her first bite of the steaming stew.

She thought they had finished with the topic of Kargan faral but she was mistaken. "You threw it all away?" Sarak grumbled. "Since when does a lady obey the words of a dominator?"

"Since we made an agreement," she replied in a carefully uninflected voice.

Phada could see that he was spoiling for an argument. The skin around his eyes was drawn tight with tension, and his lips were flattened against his teeth as he toyed with his food. Already he was showing the effects of his withdrawal from the spice. It could only get worse, Phada knew. She had to remain rational and steady and get them through the rest of the cycle or at least until evenfall when she could safely escape to her own hut. She knew not what else to do for the moment, except answer his accusations and ignore his wild mood swings; she had already learned that rational argument had no bearing on a spice-controlled individual. She was beginning to suspect she might have taken on more than any mortal being could handle.

"I am sorry, Phada," he said, suddenly contrite. He pushed his bowl away. "But I tell you, I am not hungry."

"You need to eat—to keep up your strength."

"How can I eat when this flat-flavored food tastes like mudhog droppings without seasonings?"

"I have some herbs I can add. And there is seasalt as well." She got up to fetch the shaker of seasalt that sat on an overturned basket near the hearth.

"I do not want seasalt!" he roared, rising from his chair like one of Mother Elithra's chosen avengers. Before she knew what he was up to, he hurled his supper bowl against the far wall. The already battered pottery crashed to the ground in pieces. The bulk of the dripping mass of stew remained glued to the wall for a brief moment, then dropped to the dirty stone floor below. The remainder slid in a more leisurely fashion, leaving behind a trail of beans, vegetables, and shiny juices.

Sarak slumped back into his seat. He looked so stricken at what he had done that Phada said nothing. She went to fetch a rag and began cleaning up the mess.

He groaned as he watched her. He wished she would say something, anything. He deserved the strongest rebuke for his unpardonable breach of conduct in her presence. And yet she continued without comment, methodically scooping up the sad remains of the meal she had prepared for him. Her calm actions hit him like a thrusting dagger to the gut.

"You shame me," he said, so low he wondered if she had heard him.

He knew she had when she replied in that soft, cultured voice of hers, "Sarak, you cannot help it."

"I am a warrior. I should be able to help it." He turned to stare into her eyes. He saw Phada swallow hard at the intensity of his gaze. "There are ropes in the chest. You must make use of them tonight."

# *Chapter Six*

"Ropes?" Phada was aghast, her stormy blue eyes horrified.

"You must tie me to the bed," Sarak told her. "It is the only way."

"I cannot tie you up like some animal."

He snorted mirthlessly. "I am no better than an animal in the eyes of most Mesarans. Or had you forgotten?"

"That is not true. All Mesarans value the sacrifice the dominators make to protect us."

"Save your polite, learned responses for display before other town dwellers," he retorted, unable to keep the bitterness from his voice. "You may be a Keeper's apprentice, you may have studied the Ancient Texts, but you know nothing about the basic truths of a warrior's existence."

"You are correct, Sarak."

She bowed her head, her eyes downcast so he could no longer see their expression. Was she laughing at him for being a thickheaded fool?

How could she help laughing when he was acting like a temperamental child who wanted a sweet-bar and had not yet learned to temper his reactions when the treat was denied? It was so unlike him.

"I will do as you wish." She spoke the surprising words quietly.

Her soft reply knocked the remaining breath from his body. He stared at the top of her head, willing her to look at him. She must have sensed his desire, for she raised her face. She met his gaze warily and he could see the fear she tried to keep hidden. He had sworn to protect, not induce fear, in gentle ladies. Even loathing was acceptable, but not fear.

"You must do it now," he said. *While I am still docile enough to handle,* he added to himself. He did not need to frighten her any more than she already was. He also discovered he could not admit to her that he no longer recognized himself in some of the things he had done and said since her arrival.

"As you wish," she replied.

He stalked over to the wooden coffer that held the few items this sun-cursed hut contained. Pulling out a long, coiled rope, he set it on the table before closing the lid. His body was screaming at him to do something, anything, to relieve the agony. Only a healthy dose of faral could soothe his torment, and there was now none to be had until one of Dalcor's warriors returned. He was sure he could not endure that long. He would be glad to die except the thought of leaving Phada all alone on this island twitched at his conscience.

"Where is your knife?" he asked.

She said nothing but brought it to him.

He beckoned her to follow him to the sleeping pallet. Sitting on the edge, he cut the rope into four equal lengths and handed them to her along with the knife. She accepted them with obvious reluctance.

"You must bind each of my limbs to the corners of the frame. It will divide what strength the spice has not already sapped out of me."

She indicated her agreement by briefly lowering her eyes and nodding.

"Do you know how to tie a hitchknot?"

She nodded again, more slowly this time.

"Then use it."

She seemed about to protest, but no words came. She must have realized that her own safety depended on carrying out his wishes. They both knew what the result of such a knot would be. If Sarak tugged or pulled against it, it would tighten in equal measure. It would also be virtually impossible to undo under these circumstances and so was the safest course.

Sarak crossed the room to stand in the doorway. It was just coming onto evenfall, one of his favorite times of the cycle. The planet's surface began to cool off at evenfall. It occurred around the ninth mark on the sunclock and signified the time when Mesarans retired to their sleeping pallets, although the sun had not yet dipped below the horizon in true nightfall.

He would probably not survive to see another.

He stared at the sunlit world before him for several long moments. Then without a word or a gesture to betray his feelings he turned on his heel and strode over to the pallet. Phada hovered nervously beside him. As he pushed aside the worn lana-wool blanket and lay down on the pallet's meager, cloth-covered mattress, he avoided looking toward the door, afraid he might change his mind and make a dash for the illusory freedom of the jungle.

Instead he briefly closed his eyes then raised his arms above his head to the corners of the pallet.

Phada hesitated, biting her lip. She seemed to gather herself under control and began to tie him. The rope, made of woven vines and coconut husks, felt cool against the flesh of his wrist.

He tried to concentrate on something pleasant, but his mind refused to provide such an image. In spite of what he had told Phada, his stomach twisted and churned with hunger. And yet the smell of the spiceless food had instantly killed his appetite.

The bed sat in the corner, two of its sides against the wall, so she had to lean across him to tie his other wrist. Sarak caught a whiff of her female scent, clean and sweet as any rata flower. In spite of his condition he was horrified to feel his loins stir with the beginnings of desire. With her pale, soft skin and gentle ladylike ways she reminded him of Riga; he supposed that explained his unwanted reaction, that and the lust-inducing aftereffects of the spice. He refused to acknowledge that perhaps some of those effects had worn away after more than half a suncycle of abstinence.

She made quicker work of his ankles. Soon he was as trussed and helpless as any rockhen on its way to market. He jerked his arms and legs, grunting in an uncomfortable combination of uneasiness and satisfaction as the ropes grew tighter. The little Keeper's apprentice had done a thorough job.

He had never allowed himself to be at the mercy of anything if he could help it, whether a person or a situation. And now he was giving himself over to the care of a virtual stranger, a woman who had vowed never to mate with a male in order to pursue her quest to become a Keeper of the Ancient Ways.

He must be out of his mind.

He closed his eyes in despair. How long would it take before he began begging her for the spice?

He knew it was only a matter of time. No matter that she had none to give him, his body would scream for a dose while his mind joined in the chorus. Then she would regard him with disgust, as a creature lower than a soldier beetle on the jungle floor, fit only to be crushed underfoot. She would be right to do so. That brief glimpse of admiration he had caught on her face would be wiped away forever and she would remember him as a pathetic example of a warrior.

He heard a scraping noise. Opening his eyes he saw that Phada had dragged one of the chairs into position next to the sleeping pallet. She sat down beside him, holding a fresh bowl of the stew in her hands along with a spoon. Holy Mother, she meant to hand-feed him as if he were a mewling babe.

"No!" he shouted, glaring at her. He bucked his body off the mattress, pulling at the ropes, which tightened painfully against his wrists and ankles. What in the name of Mother Elithra had he done by putting himself into Phada's hands? he wondered frantically.

"You have to eat something," she insisted in that cool voice he was beginning to dread because it meant she could not be swayed from her purpose. She refused to meet his gaze, which only made him angrier.

"Go away and leave me."

"I cannot. That was not part of our agreement."

"Feeding me like a helpless newborn was not part of our agreement either."

"How else did you expect to eat if not with my help?" she asked, then added dryly, "If you had eaten earlier, when you had the chance, you would not be in this situation."

He groaned. She was right but that did not mean he had to like it. He watched in resignation as she dipped the spoon into the stew and brought the utensil to his lips. His stomach turned over at the smell of the spiceless stew but he opened his mouth for her, feeling worse than he had as a young warrior in training when his weapons instructor had shamed him in front of the entire class.

She fed him another bite. "There is no one here to see you but me and I promise I will never tell a living soul."

Sweet Goddess, did she think those were words of comfort, that he did not mind if she saw him in this state? After carefully scrutinizing her averted profile, he decided that she had no idea of his feelings.

"I am responsible for you until you are free from the spice," she added softly.

Sarak's mouth was full, so he could not reply even had he wanted to. When he had begged her to bind him to the sleeping pallet he had only been thinking of her safety, not of his own humiliation. He had the feeling things were going to get a lot worse before they got better.

He managed to eat a couple more spoonfuls before he called a halt. Surprisingly, Phada did not argue. She must have sensed his dark mood but it did not stop her from moving the chair back to the table and sitting down, obviously prepared to watch over him. Was he to have no peace in his final agony?

He turned his head to the wall, trying to lose himself in the jagged pitting of the stone. Every particle of that section of his rock prison was familiar to him from the many cycles he had spent staring at the cracks since Dalcor had dumped him on the beach. He only hoped he would lose consciousness soon. He did not want to live in this helpless condition anymore. Without the spice he knew he would surely die.

The sooner the better, as far as he was concerned.

Phada stood in the doorway, watching as evenfall ended and deep night approached. Of course it never truly became dark in this part of Elithra because the sun only hovered just beneath the horizon, but the semidarkness was soothing to her eyes all the same, the coolness a balm to her battered spirits.

Sarak had spent most of the evenfall groaning and twisting as far as his restraints would allow. After the passing of several endless marks of the sunclock, he was sleeping at last. Phada glanced over her shoulder at his unconscious form as he lay in an awkward and uncomfortable-looking position on the pallet. The glow from the stub of candle she had found and lit earlier showed that his body glistened with sweat. His face looked drawn and tense, even in slumber, and the sides of his mouth were pulled down in a frown. She could not imagine he was getting much rest.

She crossed the room to stand over him. The muscles of his massive frame trembled intermittently as if he were deathly cold, although she knew he was not because she had checked him earlier. She still remembered how she had gently laid her hand along his cheek, how he had bucked as though her fingers were a burning brand. She had not touched him like that since.

She knew she needed to get some rest herself now that Sarak was finally quiet. She might not have many opportunities. She tried not to think of what might happen next with the big dominator, what he might do. As horrified as she had been at his suggestion to bind him, she was now glad of it. She felt as safe as she could under the circumstances.

Taking the blanket, she curled up on the floor

close to the door where she could feel the cool air.
It stirred the loose tendrils of hair around her face.
She closed her eyes and in her exhaustion fell in-
stantly asleep.

It might have been mere moments or several
marks later when a horrible cry from Sarak awakened her. Phada jumped to her feet before she really knew what was happening, all her attention
riveted on the form in the corner of the room. Sarak's eyes were closed and he appeared to be sleeping.

She held her hand over her chest as though that
gesture would calm her hammering heart. Drawing in a deep breath she slowly inspected the
room. Everything seemed quiet. The light was a
brilliant, blue-hued half-circle on the floor as it
filtered through the small brace of trees just outside the entrance and streamed onto the floor.

Phada sighed as she walked over to peer outside. The sun was cresting the treetops. Both sunrise and cycle-rise had already come and gone.
She and Sarak had both been sleeping longer than
she had originally thought.

She focused again on the dominator. No sign of
movement. She decided she would prepare the
first meal of the cycle even though zenith was already approaching. But first she had to make a
quick trip outside since the crude little hut provided none of the amenities of town life.

It did not take her very long after she returned
to measure out the grain and get the porridge simmering over the rekindled hearth. Her empty
stomach rumbled with pangs of hunger. She wondered if Sarak would again give her a difficult
time. She wished she could untie him and allow
him to feed himself, but now that he was bound,
she realized she had no desire to free him.

"Behind you, Mizor! Use your dagger," he suddenly shouted, yanking with his arms at the ropes

until Phada feared he would harm himself. "Zegon, move the left flank to the trees. That way we can head them off."

She stared at him, horrified. He was obviously delirious and thought himself in the midst of some past skirmish.

"You bloody Kargan rabble. Come out here where we can see you."

He bucked and turned and twisted while the sleeping pallet groaned and creaked alarmingly beneath his weight. The top end was bolted into the stone wall, but she feared Sarak's frenzied thrashing might jerk it free. His face was distorted with various emotions that flickered across it in the heat of his imagined battle—rage and anger at his foe, shrewdness and determination to overcome his hated enemy.

"You cowardly, beady-eyed treerats! May your hides shrivel and blacken in the sun for all eternity," he yelled, clenching his fists and trying to strike out. His voice was hoarse, his eyes wild with the kind of blood lust she had only previously read about in the ancient texts that often spoke about war. Even knowing she should be a student of every aspect of human nature, from the highest qualities of character to the lowest depths, she had never wished to experience this kind of savage emotion firsthand.

The Mesarans were a civilized people. The dominators were the repository of their former barbaric ways, the last vestige of their inglorious past. No wonder they were forced to keep to themselves, Phada thought with a shiver. She stared down into his face from her safe position across the room, although safety was relative in this situation. His lips were curled back from his teeth in a snarl as untamed as any clawcat's—and more vicious, because there was human hate behind it.

Everything about this side of Sarak filled her with disgust.

She hovered near the doorway, every nerve ending in her body urging her to run outside, the only action that would enable her to escape the raw emotion trapped within the small parameters of the hut. She did not care about her agreement with Sarak. She wanted only to get away from this room, away from the brutish warrior. One part of her mind shrieked at her to hurry back to Mesara as fast as she possibly could. She was only a Keeper's apprentice; she was not equipped to deal with this. She simply could not handle him. No one would expect her to. Even Mother Elithra, the Great Goddess who provided for all her children's needs with the rich abundance of her plants and animals, would not hold it against her that she had to leave Sarak to his fate. She had to protect her own sanity.

She whirled on her heel, about to bolt out the door, when she heard Sarak moan as if in mortal pain. She stopped in her tracks, her eyes squeezed closed.

"Borkar, can you hear me? Borkar! Dear Goddess, no!" Something that sounded suspiciously like a sob issued from his mouth, although it was quickly muffled. Actually, it was more as if the cry came from the depths of his very being. She could only think that this Borkar was a close companion of Sarak's and that he had been killed in the battle.

A scream tore out of his throat, causing the hair to rise on the nape of her neck. Her arms and legs quivered with gooseflesh. "Aaaaaiiiii! They are not Kargans." He raised himself up from the pallet as though shouting after someone. "Filthy Jiboan scum," he roared, his voice breaking with emotion on the last word.

She did not think the knots she had tied would hold under the beating they were taking. Neither could Sarak's wrists and ankles, which she now saw were slippery with blood from his frenzied movements. He continued to jerk and pull in his delirium, oblivious to the consequences. At this rate he would do serious injury to himself.

She found she could not walk away. After all, she was the one who had coerced him into trying to break the faral's hold over his senses. She had a duty to him now, no matter that he was only a warrior. Had he not insisted that she tie him? Where would she be now if he had not?

*Goddess protect me.* She moved her lips as she fervently prayed, creeping over to the pallet, fearful that he would rear up at any moment, breaking his bonds as easily as if they were strands of stretch candy, reaching out to grab her around the throat. She remained a good half-measure from the edge of the pallet.

"Sarak," she whispered. Her mouth was so dry the words were barely audible. She tried again. "Sarak. You must cease this useless ranting. You are only hurting yourself."

His entire body went still. It was not the stillness of concession, but that of the predator on the hunt. Phada swallowed hard, her gaze never leaving his face. Suddenly his eyes flashed open. For the briefest moment of time, no more than a single beat of a fleafly's wings, he appeared disoriented and confused. Then his dark brown eyes focused on her with the intensity of ten hot blue suns.

Phada could not stop the gasp that came from her throat at the look she saw in their depths. She was not sure who he thought she was, but from the murderous expression that distorted his face into a mask of rage, he wanted very badly to kill her. She took an involuntary step backward.

She could not believe how helpless she felt, watching as Sarak thrashed around like a wounded tuskboar in the jungle underbrush, crazed with pain and unheeding of danger as it was driven toward the net. She had to do something to stop him. She knew nothing about potions for sleeping; she had no training as a healer because the Keepers had quickly ascertained that she had no talent in that direction.

She had to gain Sarak's attention, break through his delusions until he realized where he was and what he was doing to himself. One of the few things she knew about the dominator before she came to this island was that he was devoted to the queen. The mere mention of her name had stopped him before. Pray Goddess it would do so again.

"Queen Riga commands that you quiet yourself," she told him, injecting every ounce of authority into her voice that she could summon, as if she were reading a royal decree. "Your queen appreciates all your service in the past and desires that you do not incapacitate your abilities, so that you may serve her in the future."

His arms and legs fretted against the ropes but Phada took courage from the fact that he had ceased his awful thrashing.

"Renegade Jiboans have killed Borkar," he announced as though giving a report to a superior. His voice and his expression overflowed with deference, a decided contrast to his wild behavior just moments earlier. Had she succeeded in calming him?

"I will have revenge," he shouted. He raised his shoulders as far as the ropes would allow, his stomach clenched so tightly it looked like flesh over a ridged washing board rather than a part of an individual.

Phada reacted instinctively. Otherwise she would never have reached out to grasp his shoulders, using them as a lever to push him down into the mattress, holding him there. Oddly enough he did not fight her. She soon realized why.

"Do not touch me, Lady Queen. Have you forgotten that I am an unworthy dominator?"

"I am not the queen, Sarak. I am Phada."

He ignored her. "My lady Riga," he said, bowing his head. "You should know by now that I am always at your service, no matter how difficult the task."

She was about to open her mouth to correct his error until she realized that perhaps she could use it to her advantage. Goddess help her, she needed all the assistance she could get. Let him think she was the queen if it would quiet him. He would realize his error as soon as he regained his wits, but in the meantime she needed to tend to his wounds before they festered. She hoped he would not hold her deception against her—if she was lucky, he would not even remember what she had done.

"You must let me bandage your wrists and ankles," she said.

"No, my lady, that is not a task for you to perform. I will seek out the palace healer."

"The palace healer is otherwise occupied," Phada replied. "Therefore I will do what is necessary. I cannot have my second-in-command unable to fulfill his duties for lack of proper attention."

Thankfully, her answer seemed to satisfy him, at least for the moment. Phada had learned enough of the rudiments of healing to know what to do, and all Keepers carried a special salve in their packs as a matter of course. As she gathered her supplies, the face of Rudela, the palace healer, floated into her mind. A wave of sadness swept over her. Rudela was the latest in a long line of palace healers stretching back to the dark ages of warrior domination. It was a special lifetime position, filled from the healing class of Keepers who served queen and community on a more intimate basis than those who spent most of their time in the sanctuary, as had Phada.

Now the poor woman was a prisoner of a renegade pack of dominators. Phada hoped Dalcor was astute enough to realize he needed the services of a healer, but she had her doubts that the brutish usurper would allow the Keeper to carry out her appointed mission undisturbed. It was more likely that Rudela had been forced to mate with one of his bestial dominators like the other palace women. Phada did not know the higher-ranked Keeper well, but it was not a fate she would wish on her worst enemy.

Sarak remained quiet as she carefully untied one leg and applied the salve to his ripped flesh. She bandaged it with one of the torn strips of cloth from her pack and retied it as gently as she could. She winced at the thought of the coarse ropes moving against his injuries, especially if he again became agitated. If only he would remain calm. She repeated her actions with his other leg and then his wrists, always one at a time. He seemed not to know that any part of him was free, even during the brief moments she tended to them, but kept his head averted from whichever side she happened to be working on and his eyes closed.

Phada was exhausted by the time she sat down at the table. The smell of the porridge caused her stomach to growl with hunger, but she was too tired to make the effort to dish it out. In a while she would eat and then she would worry about getting more nourishment into Sarak.

She allowed her gaze to return to the beleaguered warrior. He seemed to have drifted into sleep, although from the restless little movements and mutterings he made, it was not a very restful slumber. The skin of his face remained pale and sickly, except for two spots of color burning high along his cheekbones. His wan, drawn expression provided a stark contrast to the rest of his robust frame. He had no pillow, so his shoulder-length brown hair fell limply against the mattress except for the parts closest to his head, which were soaked with perspiration and plastered to his scalp.

Phada had no idea how many marks passed as she continued to care for Sarak. The sun's zenith came and went and the long Elithran cycle drifted toward evenfall. He became feverish, his body burning hot beneath her hand. She filled an empty jug with water and placed cool cloths on his forehead and over his chest. Every time she touched him, he pulled away, although not as violently as he had in the beginning. He was probably not used to being handled in such a fashion, Phada decided. There was certainly no healer assigned to the dominators' barracks, so she had no idea what happened if one of them got sick. It seemed a cold, lonely way to live, but of course she was not a warrior and had no idea how they thought or felt. They probably liked it just fine.

Not long after evenfall she managed to get some broth into him. He stared at her with lifeless, confused eyes as he ate. It was a shock when she recalled him as he had been that night in the feasting hall, striding around like the healthy young male animal he was. His eyes had been cool yet alert, his instincts razorsharp in the service of the queen.

Phada shook herself to clear her mind of such mad thoughts. He was a crude dominator, not a town dweller. He had been chosen for such a life based on his behavior and his tendency toward aggression just as she had been chosen to study to become a Keeper based on the abilities of her mind. She had no cause to feel sorry for him. She certainly should not be admiring his courage and stamina in the face of this grueling ordeal.

"Phada."

She jumped at the sound of her name, uttered in a hoarse whisper. She hurried to Sarak's side. "Yes."

"I must relieve myself. Untie me so I can go outside."

She blushed at his blunt speaking. She hesitated, hating the thought of his being completely mobile, yet knowing it was necessary.

"I am too weak to cause you any trouble."

She nodded, then reached for the binding at his wrist. "How do you feel?"

"Like the crossroads after an army has marched through. Every part of my body aches."

His speech was lucid, if slightly slurred from tiredness. His eyes still appeared dazed, but he was certainly no longer delirious. The worst must be over, she thought exultantly. It had not been as difficult as they had both imagined.

Sarak held up his bandaged wrist. "I see I have not been docile in my bondage." He sounded almost satisfied at that.

"I think you were fighting Kargans in your sleep."

"Ah, yes." He sat up slowly, groaning as he pulled himself to the edge of the pallet and placed his feet on the floor. "I remember a torrent of dreams and nightmares. My head was filled with so many images I could not keep track of them. Did I . . . did I do anything, say anything . . . ?"

"You did not give away any deep, dark warrior secrets, if that is what worries you."

He breathed deeply. "I dreamed that you touched me, that you bathed my body with cool water."

"It was no dream. You were feverish. I had to cool you down."

"I am sorry to put you through this."

She forgot her awkwardness and her embarrassment as she stared at him in amazement. "I am the one who is putting you through this. You are the one who is going through it. I only watch and witness as a Keeper."

"Which is as it should be," he intoned in a polite voice, reminding her that he was fully aware of their disparate ranks. His tone considerably eased her reservations about freeing him.

He dragged himself to his feet, stretching his muscles as he stood. Phada swore parts of his body actually creaked in protest. She watched him disappear out the door. Embarrassing as the thought was, a part of her wanted to go with him, to make sure he did not run off into the jungle or try to steal the boat. She waited for what seemed a reasonable length of time before she moved to the door.

"Sarak?"

There was no answer.

"Sarak, are you there?"

Nothing. She strained her ears, listening for any noise above the usual sounds of the jungle that would indicate his whereabouts. Insects buzzed and screamer monkeys howled their blood-curdling cries into the semidarkness of the Elithran night, but there was no sign of Sarak.

She hesitated in the doorway, squinting her eyes, searching for any movement. Surely someone as large as Sarak would be impossible to miss. Should she search for him? Suppose she came upon him before he had finished what he had gone out there to do in the first place? The thought of such an embarrassing encounter gave her pause. Better to give him a quartermark more, just in case. She bit her lip anxiously.

Suddenly he appeared to her left, making her gasp at the way he materialized out of the shadows. He must have been lurking behind the rango bush at the side of the hut. Tonight the moon rode high in the sky, adding to the brightness outside. Beneath its blue light, his eyes gleamed in what she could only describe as a predatory way, and his skin appeared pale. There was a stillness about him that chilled her flesh in spite of the warmth of the balmy night air. She wished she could run but there was nowhere to go.

As soon as he began speaking, she realized why her instincts had urged her to flee.

"Did Mizor pay for you?" he asked, his voice low and caressing. "He is a good friend to want me to have the pleasure of a warm and willing pallet partner for the rest of the sleep cycle." He held out his hand. "Come, wench, show me what you can do."

# *Chapter Seven*

Dear Goddess, Phada thought as she stared at Sarak. He believed she was some common Jiboan desert female, paid to warm his pallet. Every muscle in her body tensed at the sight of the big warrior standing before her, his legs spread in a wide dominator's stance that sent waves of terror crashing through her. What was she supposed to do now? There was no one to whom she could cry for help, no way to get off the island quickly. If only she could escape from him she might be able to hide until he regained his senses. Right now it seemed unlikely, because he blocked her path to the world outside the hut and its semblance of safety.

She had to try to bring him back to reality. Somehow she did not think pretending to be Queen Riga would assure her of victory this time.

"Sarak. I have prepared the evening meal. Come inside and let us eat."

"Did Mizor pay you to cook as well?"

"Mizor did not pay me at all."

"You do not have to pretend that you are doing this out of the goodness of your heart," he said with a self-deprecating grimace. "I am most willing and have neither the need nor the desire to be flattered or coaxed. Indeed, I find I am most eager to mate with you."

The look he gave her after that startling statement could have roasted a rockhen at 20 measures. Phada's pulse jumped from its already heightened pace into a pounding discomfort impossible to ignore. She feared her heart might beat its way out of her chest. "It is me, Phada. Do you not remember that I crossed the sea to seek your help? You gave me your word as a warrior that you would help me to free Mesara." That was not exactly true but it was close enough.

"Phada," he said, tasting the name on his tongue and ignoring the rest of her statement. "It does not sound like other Jiboan names I have heard, but it is very pretty. Come here, Phada."

"Stop it, Sarak. Stop it right now. We have too much to do to play games."

"I like games as well as the next warrior," he replied softly. "Which one shall we play?"

His eyes glowed with what she could only describe as lust. The one other time she had experienced such a distasteful emotion was when she had first arrived on the Uninhabited Island and Sarak had ambushed her, knocking her to the ground and covering her with his considerable weight, making it difficult for her to breathe.

She was having just as much difficulty breathing now. His burning expression as he scrutinized her body, his gaze lingering at her breasts and hips, made it seem as if he wanted to devour her. She knew it was the wrong thing to do, but she panicked and tried to sprint past him into the welcome shadows of the night. He caught her before she had gone three steps, swinging her up in his powerful arms, holding her dangling in the air above him so she was forced to brace her legs against his thighs for balance. He pulled her closer until they were nose to nose, then lowered her slowly to the ground, using his chest and hips as a guidepost for her to slide down. Her heart stopped when she felt his erection pressing against her stomach.

Her toes finally touched the ground, not that it did her any good when he was holding her so tightly. He buried his face in her hair, breathing in her scent as if he were a hound in the hunting-dog compound and she a female brought to him so they could breed a litter of pups. It was un-nerving. And yet his big hands were gentle and coaxing as they pressed into her back. She wondered how it would feel to be protected by such strength, to be able to trust him and depend on him. His arms reminded her of the haven of her father's embrace when she was a child. She shook her head, unable to believe she was entertaining such a ridiculous notion. Her father and this war-rior had absolutely nothing in common. She did not need the illusion of Sarak's protection; she needed to be protected from him.

"You do not smell the same as other desert women," he said in a crooning, husky voice near her ear. It sent shivers up her spine. "Your hair is an unusual color, too, for one of that tribe." He stroked his palm along the length of her braid. "Unbind it for me."

She pressed her hands against his chest and ten-tatively pushed. He was as unyielding as the rock walls of the hut. When she made no move to com-ply with his request, he pulled her braid forward and untied the leather thong that held it. Groan-ing, he combed his fingers through the thick mass, spreading it across her back, spilling it forward over her shoulders.

"Ah yes, Phada, you please me well. Come."

He did not seem to notice that he had to half-drag, half-carry her toward the pallet. His grip on her wrist was inexorable, and yet he was careful not to hurt her. What in the name of Mother Elithra was she going to do? Her mind could come up with no way to stop him. She supposed she could scream, but she knew it was useless, and besides, her pride simply would not allow her to stoop to such a cowardly action.

The one thing she realized she should not do was fight him. Everyone knew a panicked reaction would only incite the aggressiveness of a dominator even more. Perhaps if she remained unresisting it would go easier on her. Perhaps he would even stop. Or if she seemed cooperative, he might lower his guard long enough so she could escape into the jungle. What she would do afterward, she had no idea. She would worry about that later.

And if worse came to worst, and he did manage to mate with her, she supposed it could be no worse than that time with Taltos. She had been a mere 16 suncycles, and had already decided that she wanted to become a Keeper. Feeling that she should experience all aspects of the human condition, she had chosen Taltos to mate with for her first time—her only time, she had assumed. He had been clumsy and rough, and his weight pinning her to the ground had crushed her until she could not breathe. Everything about the encounter had been sordid and shameful, especially Taltos's labored panting. She had changed her mind as he had begun to push himself inside her and she had shoved him away. Being a town dweller and a scholar, he had not insisted, although Phada could see the anger and annoyance in his eyes.

Now Sarak sat on the edge of the sleeping pallet,

drawing her closer to stand between his thighs. He raised her hand to his mouth, kissing her fingers one by one before moving to her wrist to press his hot lips to the frantic pulse beating there. He ran his other hand down her arm and along her hip, his eyes closing as he pulled in a slow, unsteady breath. Color burned along his cheekbones.

And then to her shocked surprise, he lay down, still keeping a tight hold on her wrist. "Come, Phada," he said, tugging on her arm. His voice was husky and deep and oddly compelling, considering that she had no desire to be his pallet partner. "I am your steed until cycle-rise. Come ride me and together we will fly through the night like the wind."

Dear Goddess, of course, she thought, as her mind flooded with the realization of what he actually meant. She remembered he had used these words before, when he had first caught her outside his hut. She had not given it a thought at that time because she had been too terrified, but now the words of the ancient law came back to her.

A dominator could not mate as other Mesarans did. They were thought too volatile and excitable. No, a warrior was only allowed to be pleasured by a female while in the prone position, with the woman on top and in control. To do otherwise was to court severe punishment. It explained why the crime of rape was so quickly followed with the sentence of banishment from the rest of society. A dominator who covered an unwilling woman violated the law of stationary mating as well as multiple laws against warrior aggression toward any town woman.

She gazed at him as he lay on the pallet before her like some profane offering to the Goddess. It was almost as if he were at her mercy instead of the other way around. His eyes were tightly closed; his lower body moved restlessly against the mattress. She knew in principle how mating worked in the normal fashion but she was not so certain how it could be accomplished this way. Not that she had any intention of climbing onto Sarak's lap to find out, especially now that she knew how to stop him. Sarak might be a disgusting dominator but she had learned in the short space of time she had spent with him that he had a sense of honor. He would not force her—had he so desired he could have taken her long before now, even weakened and faral-addled as he was.

Instead he had agreed to put himself through torment to release himself from the hold of the spice over his mind and body, simply because she had asked him. He had demonstrated the kind of courage and determination any Mesaran could be proud of. Just because he was delirious now did not mean the core of his character had changed. He might desire to mate, but that was only because he thought she was a Jiboan female, ready for the taking. He would never break the law by wishing to couple with a Keeper. It was forbidden.

His eyes flashed open, focusing on her face to the exclusion of everything else in the room. His gaze was so intense she felt he could see right through to her soul. Thank the Goddess that was impossible, because he might realize that she was not as repulsed as she should be by his big body, his oddly gentle touch. It was probably because she had cared for him in his helpless condition, although that was no excuse. She would rather die than admit her sudden and unseemly fascination with this lowly warrior.

"Why do you hesitate? Do you think I am not ready?" He let go of her arm to reach for the ties to his breechcloth. "Let me show you how ready I am for you to mount me."

Now was her chance to run away. But she could

not move a muscle. Waves of shock radiated through the center of her body at the sight of his member springing free from the confinement of the breechcloth. By the blue sun above, no wonder warriors were made to yield control to any female brave enough to take them on. They were brutes and animals, just as everyone said.

"Leave me alone, dominator," she spat as he again reached for her. He stared at her in confusion as she backed away from the pallet. He pushed himself up on his elbows but otherwise made no move to follow her. "I would not lower myself to mate with a warrior even to save Mesara!"

"Phada?"

She was more than halfway to the door but something in the tone of his voice caused her to turn around. She could see the surprise in his now lucid brown eyes as he looked down at his aroused body and then back at her, his brow furrowed. His gaze took in the unbound mass of her disheveled tawny hair as it fell around her shoulders, the flush on her cheeks. He made no move to pull the scant piece of material over his nakedness. In fact, he did not even appear embarrassed, which was more than could be said for her.

"You wished to mate with me?"

Phada's face burned with humiliation at the question. "No!" she replied in quick denial, too deeply engrossed in her own confused emotions to notice the faint traces of undisguised hope that threaded through his voice.

"I see," he said flatly. "Then what is going on here?"

Her throat tightened and she could not seem to find the words to explain.

"Phada, please answer me," he persisted. "Why is your hair unbound? Why am I naked and aroused? Why would you untie me if you did not wish to mate with me?" He gazed around in bewilderment for a moment, and then his expression cleared. "You need have no fear I will reveal what goes on here between us. You have my word as a warrior. I will tell no one that you were curious to experience the act with a warrior. No one wants to believe that such tales about town women are true, even though others have done it before you."

"I do not wish to mate with you," she shouted. "I am in training to become a Keeper!" She was incensed at his misreading of the situation, even more so because of her momentary lapse in not fleeing while she had the chance. "You needed to go outside to relieve yourself. So I untied you. But you became delirious while you were gone. You thought I was . . ." She choked over the word then calmed herself. "You thought I was Jiboan."

He closed his eyes in dismay, then opened them to meet her angry regard. "I am sorry, Phada," he said.

He sat up, his jerky movements further proof that he was now thoroughly aware of her discomfort at his state of undress. He quickly covered himself, fastening the ties to his meager dominator's garb. He was still erect and it pressed at the material in a most obvious way, but she supposed there was little he could do about it.

"I cannot promise I would not have forced you," he continued in tones laced with self-disgust. "I know not what I am capable of in the grip of this cursed faral. It is obvious I am not free of it yet." His gaze probed her face as his voice gentled. "Did I hurt you?"

"I . . . No, you did not hurt me."

"Then come, bind me again quickly. And next time, before you release me to go outside, you must get your knife and keep it close by for protection."

"Oh no. Are you saying you want me to . . . Sarak, I cannot plunge a knife into you."

"You can and you will. I am surprised you have not done so already. If you are not prepared to defend yourself against my unwanted attentions, then this ordeal is over right now. Mesara can rot like a piece of fruit on the jungle floor for all I care."

Phada wanted to cry, although she was not sure exactly why. Nothing was going the way she had planned. But the longer she remained here on the Uninhabited Island with the dominator, the more she realized she had no choice but to press on, no matter what the consequences.

She found she could only nod in agreement as she moved toward the sleeping pallet she had fled only moments before. Sarak had lain down again, his face averted from her as he stared at the wall. Her heart turned over at the poignancy of watching him bend so compliantly to her will when both of them knew he could crush her with one hand if he so desired. He raised his arms over his head and spread his legs so she could more easily tie them to each corner, an act of bravery beyond any she had ever witnessed. Only the Goddess knew how much more agony awaited him as the price of his withdrawal from the spice, and yet he calmly waited for her to render him completely helpless and at her mercy.

She reached for the rough strand of coconut-husk rope and began the painful process of binding his limbs. Just as she finished with his wrists and was about to move to his ankles, he bucked completely off the pallet, smothering a low-pitched groan. His eyes rolled up into his head as he closed them with a grimace, and a greenish pallor spread over the skin of his now sharply etched features.

"You are in pain," she said, biting her lip, her

expression filled with anguish. "What can I do to ease it?"

"There is nothing you can do."

She gazed at him in distress, watching his stomach muscles clenching against what had to be horrible pain. He refused to utter another sound, instead pressing his lips together until the skin around them turned white. Had she thought him helpless in his bondage? She was just as helpless in her own way, for she could do nothing to ease his terrible suffering.

"Who would have thought a spice could tear a body apart like this?" he commented grimly. His hands gripped the ropes to alleviate their pull against his flesh, but Phada could see that his wrists were once again bleeding beneath the bandages. "I am beginning to think I would rather be gutted by a newly sharpened Jiboan dagger. It is . . . a quicker way to die."

"You are not going to die." As she tied the last hitchknot, a tear slipped down her cheek. Another soon followed. "You cannot."

"Do not cry, Phada," he whispered. "I have the feeling this will soon be over, one way or another. Can you not see that I have no wish to exist in this condition? Nor do I desire to be dragged back to Mesara to provide Dalcor's amusement."

Phada's eyes widened at this statement. She should have guessed that Dalcor had further plans for his former second-in-command. She had seen the hatred in the older male's eyes as he had declared Sarak's fate in the feasting hall. She could not blame Sarak for wanting to avoid that final humiliation.

"You might yet succeed in weaning me from the faral," he continued, although Phada could see that he did not really believe it possible. "But if you do not, I still thank you for ending my miserable existence. You have no cause to feel shame.

You did everything you could."

She could not believe what she was hearing. He seemed more concerned about her feelings than he was about dying a horrible, agonizing death. How could he speak so casually of his own demise? Or of her carrying on without his help? No, by the blue sun of Elithra, she was not going to let him die. Too many people were depending on them. Goddess help her, at this stage she was almost willing to mate with him if that was what their success depended on.

His next words took her completely by surprise.

"I know you are a noble town woman from a good family and I am but a crude dominator. But I would have been gentle with you, little wingbird, had you come to me. I would have done everything in my power to give you what pleasure I could, even at the expense of my own. I know you do not believe me about this and I cannot blame you for that. But, Phada, not all warriors take without trying to give something in return."

The next two days passed in a blur for Phada as she cared for the now ranting, out-of-control warrior. Sarak thrashed around on the sleeping pallet until she was sure he would snap the ropes or kill himself trying. During the times he was calm, she rubbed the perspiring skin of his torso with cool cloths and gently bathed his face. She had completely lost her embarrassment at seeing him clothed only in the minimal breechcloth that did little to hide his masculine assets. After all, why should that bother her when she had seen him completely naked and lived to tell the tale? If she were honest with herself, every muscle and sinew of his form had become as familiar to her as her own flesh.

She grabbed snatches of sleep whenever she could. One time she even awoke to discover she

had fallen into an exhausted slumber while caring
for Sarak, so that she was half lying on the bed,
her head next to his. Luckily he was passed out
cold when it happened.

She did not mind the times he raved about Dalcor or the Jiboans or the Kargans. Being a witness to snatches of conversations and pieces of
already-fought battles did not seem too personal.
But when Sarak called out for the queen, Phada
felt distinctly uncomfortable having to witness the
love, devotion, and yes, even desire for Riga evident on his softened features. She still found it
difficult to associate such gentle emotions with a
warrior chosen for his brute strength and aggressive tendencies, a dominator trained to serve, even
to the point of killing. But the proof was before
her eyes.

She grew so tired that all her defenses dropped
and she could no longer fool herself about the
qualities Sarak had demonstrated since she had
arrived. Although he had frightened her when he
had tried to coerce her into mating with him, he
had never actually carried his purpose through,
but had stopped when it became apparent that she
was not interested. He had even shown concern
about her feelings. Were these the actions of a
brute warrior bent on domination?

No, Sarak was different from any warrior she
had ever met or heard about. She admired his unparalleled courage and determination. She
flushed when she recalled how he had promised
to be gentle with her. Was that possible? Of
course, he would not be able to crush her because
he would be the one lying on the bottom. She felt
her pulse begin to throb at the idea of sitting
astride Sarak, her lower body pressed against his
erect male flesh as the big dominator held her
hips.

Was the woman able to retain all control in such

a position? She could not imagine Sarak simply lying back and doing nothing. She shook her head in denial at her horribly wayward thoughts. The entire image was too intimate to be tolerated, and she quickly thrust it from her mind.

Even her sister had been curious about the intimate details of the lives of the warriors. At the thought of Chelis, Phada felt her throat tighten. Her sister's sparkling personality had been subdued by the faral, as had her mother's sweet nature and Jobus's fine mind. Phada vowed again that she would do whatever she could to save Mesara.

On the morning of the sixth cycle, Phada checked on Sarak to find him breathing quietly in restful sleep. His color appeared normal and his face did not have that haunted, tense expression that tugged at her heart. She had not thought she possessed an abundance of nurturing instincts, but somehow Sarak had called them forth.

She gazed down to find he had awakened. His brown eyes, when he turned them in her direction, appeared clear and bright. He looked healthy and fit, his mind and body returned to him in full measure. Soon he would not need her anymore, and the thought caused a surprising pang of sadness. For a while a strong dominator had been under her control and it was like having tamed the mythical wild Elithran desert horse who was said to have once roamed the far reaches of the Calabian Desert. Sarak would never allow himself to be broken to anyone's hand, but the illusion of having him at her bidding was tantalizing nonetheless.

"How many cycles have passed since you came here?" he asked, his voice urgent.

"Six."

"Then we must hurry. Dalcor or one of his warriors could show up anytime. They must not find you here."

She sighed. Already he was taking command, as any warrior was taught to do in a crisis situation. The intimacy of their previous relationship was over. She did not regret its passing, but she liked the sense of being in command. Now, although she was his social superior, he was the one with the kind of tactical knowledge they needed and she would have to bow to his superior ability, something she was not often required to do.

"How do you feel?" she asked. "Can you eat something?"

"I am not hungry." He lifted his head from the mattress with a grimace, avoiding looking at her. "But if you will untie me, I will try."

"Are you sure you are ready?"

"Untie me, Phada. I have shirked my obligations to you and to Mesara long enough."

She hurried over to the sleeping pallet. He must be anxious to be released from the infernal ropes. She could not blame him. She untied one hand but she had to sit on the edge of the mattress in order to undo the knots at his far wrist.

"Do not come too close," he cautioned her quickly. At her surprised look, he explained, "I need a good scrubbing before I am fit company."

You have had one from me, she thought with a wry grimace of her own. I have bathed and handled your body for six cycles; there is little I do not know about you, Sarak. She wanted to laugh aloud at his sudden reticence. It was proper behavior with any Mesaran female, and yet it seemed so ridiculous after all they had gone through. She felt a stab of hurt that he felt the need to revert so quickly and so completely to their designated roles. She was surprised at herself; she had always been such a stickler for the codes. She should be glad that Sarak was doing what had been decreed lawful conduct for over a thousand orbits.

He nodded at her to move aside, then bent forward to take care of his ankles himself. She supposed he was glad to be free again.

"I must stand guard," he said as he swung his legs around and set his feet on the floor. He stood up gingerly, testing his strength. "Curse it, I am as weak as a newborn woodfawn."

"All the more reason you should eat," Phada told him primly.

She served him from the pot of stew she had made earlier before sitting across the table from him. "When will Dalcor come?"

"If he follows the pattern he has established, someone should be here tomorrow." He made a face at his bowl as he swallowed another mouthful. "I wonder if I will ever enjoy food again. It is not your cooking," he hastened to assure her. "The lack is in the seasoning. I have grown too used to that cursed spice."

"I am sure that will change in time," she said as casually as she could, her mind shocked that he still craved the faral.

He shrugged, neither accepting nor denying her statement, and she wondered why she sought to reassure him when she knew so little about what they were trying to do. No one had any idea of the consequences of the spice—except perhaps the Kargans.

"That is it, Sarak!" she cried out excitedly. "If the Kargans do more than simply ship the faral to Mesara they might know how to . . ."

Her voice trailed off as she got a good look at the suddenly silent warrior. Sarak's jaw was clenched tight and his hands pressed against his stomach as though to squeeze his body into compliance with his will. Phada had seen him like this before. His beautiful brown eyes were again cloudy with pain. Surely he was finished with these bouts of delirium; surely he had overcome any last vestiges of his hallucinations. How long could the spice continue to affect him before his system was free of its cursed hold?

And then she realized what had triggered the attack. It was the stew. She thought back and realized that every time he ate, especially solid food, he became like this. Somehow, his body expected to have faral along with any nourishment. Phada cursed herself for forcing him to eat.

"You must lie down, Sarak," she said in a loud, clear voice. He did not become as violent as he had during the first few cycles, but he was still a force to be reckoned with and she did not want to have to handle him without the aid of the restraints. She had to get him to the sleeping pallet now, before he became completely uncontrollable.

Thank the Goddess, he cooperated readily enough. She supposed some part of his mind registered the fact that he had done this before and come to no harm. She quickly tied the ropes to his wrists and ankles. He began thrashing and muttering almost immediately. Phada dipped a cloth into the bucket of water that stood by the bed and wiped his face before laying it across his forehead. It seemed to soothe him as it always did and he turned his face toward her as if seeking something more. She indulged herself as she had not before, stroking his whisker-stubbled cheek with gentle fingers. He murmured something and stilled.

The postzenith passed slowly, with Sarak alternating between a drugged sort of sleep and that restless tossing and straining at his bonds that twisted her insides with anguish. She waited until he grew quiet again before hurrying outside. She had to escape from her guilt at not realizing the connection sooner and thus sparing Sarak this latest round of torment. She had to get away for a small space of time.

The blue-tinted sun had crossed its zenith long ago. Although its searing presence still rode a good distance above the horizon, it would soon be evenfall. The air had lost some of its heat. She decided to take a walk through the jungle where she could check on the boat and then along the beach. Perhaps the sight of the brilliant aqua water would soothe her battered spirits.

The gloom of the jungle engulfed her as soon as she stepped beneath its thick, lush canopy of greenery and vines. A screech primate scrambled to put distance between them, but the insects carried on with their busy humming and buzzing. Phada breathed deeply of the humid air, thick with the scent of rata flowers and jasa blooms. It was familiar and beloved but she could not seem to enjoy it.

After assuring herself that the boat remained well hidden, she headed back toward the hut. She had been gone long enough; it was time to check on Sarak. She pushed aside the last hanging vine, although she remained in the shadow of the trees so her eyes could adjust to the sunlight. Some movement, a bird perhaps, caught her eye and she gazed out to sea.

"Oh no," she breathed aloud in despair.

It was a boat. Although still a good distance away, Phada could see the small cabin on its deck and the movement of the oars.

"Please, Lady Goddess, no," she prayed, knowing it was useless. She wished she were she were only viewing the effects of a sea mirage, but she was afraid it was all too real.

Dalcor had arrived a cycle early.

# *Chapter Eight*

Sarak groaned as he awakened from the nightmarish dream. In it he had been running, pursued by a band of fierce Kargans who chased him through the jungle. Each time he thought he had eluded them, they reappeared, the sound of their pounding feet echoing in his head. He tried every jungle trick he knew and still they edged closer until Sarak had dared to glance over his shoulder, only to discover that they threatened him with shakers of faral instead of weapons.

He shook his head, trying to clear it of the tantalizing image of the spice. Curse every black-hearted, sun-scorched son of a Kargan, but his mouth still watered when he thought of sprinkling the vile, enslaving substance on his food. The power of a simple condiment to control his every waking moment still shocked and dismayed him. Mesara's mortal enemy had conquered them without ever picking up a sword—or even showing up for the battle.

He tried to stretch his stiff shoulders, then realized he was still tied to the cursed sleeping pallet. His wrists and ankles ached abominably and his stomach continued to roil as it had for what seemed like endless cycles. He could not remember how it was to feel healthy and whole. He could barely remember yestercycle. Why could he not just die and be at peace?

He gazed around the empty hut. Where was the Keeper's apprentice? He needed to relieve himself and soon. "Phada?" His voice came out in a croak. He licked his lips and tried again, more loudly this time. "Phada, where are you?"

No answer. Maybe she had finally had a bellyful of his groveling, faral-craving ways and returned to Mesara. He would not blame her for choosing such a course, although she could have at least untied him before she left.

He snorted in disgust at his conjecture. Of course she had not departed. She had the mad notion that she should save Mesara, and she was as tenacious as a swarm of hungry battleflies once she got an idea into her pretty little head. Too bad he was the one she had chosen to assist her on her self-appointed mission. True, she had been given no choice, but she would have been better off staying in the sanctuary and taking her chances acting the part of a faral-dependent slave of Dalcor and his warrior band rather than spending her days being forced to come into contact with his crude, disgusting dominator's body.

By the blue moon, he was in a foul mood. He knew he should not take out his frustration at his own weakness and ineptitude on the Keeper's apprentice, but she was the only one within range. He hoped she stayed away until he got himself under proper control.

He pulled again on the ropes, grunting as the rough coconut husk rubbed against his blood-soaked bandages. The sound of Phada's voice penetrated the haze that now cloaked his once-sharp mind. She sounded breathless, as if she were running. How long had she been calling him?

"Sarak," she gasped, bursting through the doorway. "Thank the heavens and all the stars above you are awake. Quickly, you must get up." She staggered across the room, almost falling on top of him as she lunged for his ropes.

He smiled at her urgency as she freed his hands. What wild idea had she conjured up now? "Calm yourself, Phada," he said in a soothing voice. He was surprised to discover that his ugly mood had vanished with her bright presence. "I am feeling somewhat recovered, but I do not think we can rescue Mesara in the next few moments."

"This is no time to jest." She fumbled with the recalcitrant knot at his left ankle, hissing in annoyance from between her clenched teeth when it did not instantly yield. "I just spotted a boat on the horizon."

"Dalcor," he breathed, reaching down to brush aside her hands and taking care of his other leg himself. "It is just our cursed luck he is early."

"I ran all the way back, so I do not think he has gotten far. We still have some time."

"Not much," he muttered. "I want you out of here now. I am taking no chances that he might spot you." He gathered up the ropes and shoved them into her arms. "Take these and your pack and hide yourself in the jungle. I want you to go as far as you can, beyond where the pathway ends. I do not want you near this place, do you understand?"

"What about the other hut?"

"I will check to make sure there is no evidence of your presence. Now go!"

She did not even question the way he was barking orders at her. It was obvious she was frightened and looked to him to keep a cool head, something he had once had a reputation for doing. She was a scholar, not a battle tactician, and this was the first skirmish in their private little war with Dalcor.

She paused in the doorway. "Sarak?" she said in a small voice. "How many will there be?"

"Most likely two."

"Will they give you more spice?"

"That is what they are here for."

"Will they then leave?"

He wanted to lie to her, but somehow he could not. "I do not know, Phada," he finally replied.

"Suppose they want to take you back to Mesara?"

He shrugged at the obvious answer to that. There was nothing he could do if that was their intention. Even if he tried to fight, they would knock him over the head with the flat edge of a sword and haul him onto the boat.

She nervously fingered her pack, her eyes on the floor. "They will not make you eat it while they watch, will they? I saw warriors do that often in Mesara, on days when they were feeling particularly spiteful."

"It depends if they are in a hurry. Do not worry; I have a plan in case they do."

"What plan?"

"Never mind, we do not have time to discuss it. You must trust me."

"I do trust you," she said with a simplicity that touched a dark corner of his heart that had not seen light since he was a boy. He wanted to kneel at her feet in gratitude, as he had once done with the queen.

"Good," he said. They walked together into the bright sunlight, both of them blinking at its harsh glare. "Now go quickly. As soon as they are gone, I will come fetch you. You are not to return by yourself. It is too dangerous."

She looked as if she wanted to say more, but she turned on her heel and fled along the rocky path that led to the jungle. He watched her go, wondering if it would be the last time he would ever see her. She might be worried about his willpower, but he could not believe the fear he felt for her. The thought of Dalcor or one of his minions finding Phada, laying their rough hands on her as they dragged her back to Mesara, made him physically ill. She was untarnished by the spice, pure and innocent, in spite of the hours she had spent perusing the ancient texts in the Keepers' Sanctuary that told about the dark ages of their past. If any warrior dared to inflict his lust on her, Sarak knew he would kill the brute with his bare hands.

He quickly checked the other hut but there was no sign that Phada had been there. Why should there be when she had spent all her time with him, trying to sever him from his dependence on the faral? He retraced his steps to his own hut, slipping inside and gazing around one last time to make sure there was nothing to give away Phada's presence. All was clear.

He headed for the beach to await his visitors. Even if he had the time, he would not have told Phada the humiliating details of what he planned to do. He knew if he begged for the faral the warriors would most likely laugh at his enslaved condition, toss him the bag of spice, and leave. The hard part would come later, when he had his hands on the spice and before he went to fetch Phada. He prayed he would be able to resist its temptation. For her sake he had to, no matter what the cost. He did not think he could face her otherwise. He would rather die than witness her disappointment should he fail her.

The boat was only a hundred measures offshore

now. He closed his eyes in relief when he saw that neither of the warriors was Dalcor. It looked like Murk and one of the new recruits he had never had the opportunity to meet before Dalcor had seized Mesara.

He stepped into their view, walking slowly, carefully watching each of his steps, the way he might do had he drunk too much vetch. The spice did not addle one's wits the way the potent Jiboan ale did, but the loss of control of the leg muscles was similar, as was the urge to pretend to a normality the individual obviously did not possess. Out of the corner of his eye he saw the two warriors jump to shore.

He stumbled to a halt 20 measures away.

"How the mighty have fallen, eh, Halgos?" Murk said to his companion with a knowing smirk. He made sure he spoke loudly enough for Sarak to hear.

Sarak wished he could plant his fist in the other warrior's ugly face. Instead he summoned forth his best ingratiating smile. "Did you bring my supplies?" he called as if he had not heard a word.

The two warriors closed the distance between them with long strides, unhampered by faral-induced weakness. The one called Halgos dumped the sack of provisions he carried on the sand, then placed one ready hand atop his sword.

"Hold, Halgos." Murk laughed. "I do not think you will be needing that. Look"—he gestured contemptuously at Sarak. "The spice has finally broken him as it has everyone else in Mesara. See how he rushes to greet us. He cannot wait to get his hands on more faral."

Sarak had to bite his tongue to keep from retorting. Every muscle and sinew in his body urged him to rush the two warriors. Murk might have the clarity of mind not to draw his weapon, knowing that Dalcor had given orders to keep him alive, but Sarak judged that the younger dominator could be prodded into reacting before thinking. For his own part, Sarak did not care if he got himself killed, but he knew it would distress Phada, especially since she had gone to all that trouble to straighten him out. She was counting on him and he knew he could not disappoint her.

Murk gestured toward the sack of supplies. "Maybe we should stay and make you perform for your supper the way the queen's lapdog used to beg at the table. You remember that, do you not, Sarak?"

Sarak glared at the other warrior, not bothering to hide his hatred.

"Times have changed for the better," Murk continued. "Now the queen is the one who begs—she begs Dalcor for admittance to his sleeping chamber so she can impale herself upon his mighty lance."

The two warriors roared with laughter at this sally.

"Shut your foul, lying mouth, Murk," Sarak hissed between clenched teeth, barely able to control his fury at this reminder of Queen Riga's debased condition. "Dalcor may have subjugated her body but he can never conquer her spirit."

"He can and he has," Halgos interjected with a nasty grin. "He has also done something far better. He has repealed the law of stationary mating. Now he can crush her beneath his body and ride her to his heart's content."

Sarak launched himself at Halgos with a roar of protest. He did not care about anything except getting his hands on the other warrior and grinding him into dust. His fingers closed around the younger dominator's throat and he began to tighten his grip. He had never felt anything more satisfying. He ignored the weakness in his limbs, fighting past it. The blood pounded in his brain until he thought his skull would explode, and still he squeezed. Suddenly the world went black as something cracked against the back of his head. His entire body lifted as he was knocked to the sand.

Murk leaned over his prone form, his sword now drawn, the tip of the blade pressing against Sarak's throat until he could feel a warm trickle of blood running down his neck. Halgos held his arms.

"Hear me well, you pitiful excuse for a warrior," Murk snarled, his face twisted with anger. "Dalcor takes the queen to his pallet every night, without fail. He wanted especially for you to know he does it in your memory."

He shoved Sarak's head into the sand with the sole of his leather boot.

Sarak was barely conscious. The pain was almost unbearable and the back of his skull felt as if it had been cracked open with a mallet. He lay there for what seemed a small eternity, although when he finally dragged himself up on one elbow, the sun was still hovering a good distance above the horizon.

Their boat was nowhere to be seen. He realized Murk and Halgos had departed without making him beg as they had threatened. They must have realized they did not need to stoop to such torments, for they had done more damage to him with their cruel words than any actions meant to further humiliate his tattered pride.

He managed to get up on his knees, moaning as he did. The pouch of faral lay to his right in the sand. He reached for it, clutching it in his hand in a death grip. He gazed down at the leather strips that were threaded through the neck of the pouch to hold it closed. Dear Goddess, what was the use? Why not seek the oblivion the faral could give? He could not even help himself, let alone anyone else.

The thought of Mesara's beautiful sovereign being held under Dalcor's domination, forced to submit to his lust, sent him spinning downward into the darkest depths of despair. Knowing his former commander, Sarak imagined that his use of Riga was neither gentle nor discreet. He could not banish the image of Dalcor covering the delicate queen with his body, pumping his seed into her.

Sarak had never dared dream of such an act, even with a common Jiboan wench, never mind the queen. It was forbidden for a warrior to mate that way, although of course, all of them had secretly wondered how it might feel to cover a woman's body the way the male partner of a bonded couple was allowed to do.

Sarak knew that several of the dominators took the Jiboan women that way, in spite of the laws. It cost extra and it was a dangerous and deadly game that could end up in banishment, so he had never tried it. He had never felt more than a mild affection for the females with whom he had mated and so had no desire to experience something akin to the sacred act of bonding with them, especially since it could never be permanent. He had assured himself it was better that way, that the Ancients who had devised the laws knew what they were doing when they prescribed such boundaries of conduct for the warrior class, even if those laws had been set forth in a different time and under different circumstances.

Sarak closed his eyes in hopeless dismay. He had no energy to get up. He wished he could just die right here on the sand. He could not bear to think of Phada, nor did he want to have to face her, knowing he would never be the warrior he had once been. He wondered if he would ever again feel pride in his duty to protect Mesara, a privilege he had once taken for granted.

He slumped forward, feeling the heat of the sun on his back and especially on the sore portions of his neck and head. Amid the jumble of confused thoughts racing around in his mind, he realized that he was jealous of his former commander's newfound freedom. Of course, Dalcor had taken it to extremes unworthy of a warrior, but the idea of being able to seek pleasure the same as other town dwellers was as tantalizing as it had always been forbidden. It was a traitorous notion and he quickly squelched it, but the images it conjured up were not so easy to dispel.

He had no idea how long he sat there, his head bowed, his eyes closed. The ever-present sun continued to beat down on him, hot and insistent, its rays prickling beneath the top layer of his skin until he knew he would eventually burn, but he did not move. His fingers flexed and he realized he still held the pouch of faral.

Why not? he decided, gazing down at it. He did not need to take the time or the effort to prepare a meal, even though his stomach rumbled. He could partake of the spice now. The thought of its sweetly tempting flavor, along with the sense of oblivion it so easily produced in his body and mind, urged him on. He would hardly even notice his cracked skull after a healthy pinch of faral.

I am sorry, Phada, he thought with sincere regret as he fumbled with the leather ties. You picked the wrong warrior for your avenger. Believe me, it is better this way. The image of her face, filled with concern over his suffering, suddenly flooded his mind. She had not simply cared for him as a healer; she had gone beyond that when she had handled his body, bathing him and cooling his feverish brow with wet cloths.

His loins quickened. Dear Goddess, he realized that at some point during those times she had touched him, he had begun lusting after her. What

was it with him and the type of woman he could
never have? Why did he have to torment himself
with thoughts of something that was forbidden,
especially when he knew it was disgusting to her
modest sensibilities?

Truly, she was better off without him, no matter
what she believed. He could not help her. He only
hoped he could face the disappointment he knew
he would see in her pale, delicate features.

"Sarak!"

The sound of Phada's voice coming from so
close startled him into dropping the grains of
spice onto the ground. He looked up to see her
coming along the beach toward him, her steps as
hurried as she could make them considering the
soft, shifting sand. Even from this distance he noticed that her brow was drawn into a worried
frown. Her entire posture showed her anxiety.

"Sarak, what are you doing? Why did you not
come fetch me? I have been worried sick wondering what happened. Finally I could wait no
longer."

She rushed to his side, dropping on her knees
next to him. "Ah, you have the faral. Good." She
snatched it from his unresisting fingers. "You . . .
you did not use any, did you?" she asked, her voice
soft and tentative. She tipped her head back, as if
to study his eyes, but she immediately straightened. "Forgive me, Sarak. Of course you did not
taste the spice. Why would you after all you have
been through?"

His gaze snapped to meet hers, shame coursing
through him. The only reason he was not already
light-headed on faral was that she had not stayed
put as he had ordered. "Listen, Phada," he began.

She waved a dismissing hand at him. "You do
not have to say another word," she assured him.
And then she smiled at him. It was as brilliant as
the sun at its zenith, the brightness of that smile.

"I knew you could do it. Did I not tell you?"

He grimaced wryly. "Yes, you told me," he agreed.

"Now we can begin to make the rest of our plans." She rose to her feet, still clutching the pouch in one hand. "First I had better get rid of this."

He watched her march away from him toward the water. He did not utter a sound to stop her, even when she arched her arm back and hurled the faral as far as she could into the sea. How could he tell her after that stunning testimonial of her implicit faith in him? She had trusted him and believed in him, more than anyone ever had, including the queen. She deserved whatever help he could give her. She would learn all too soon that it was little enough. But until then, he swore he would savor the admiration he had seen in her eyes for the wonderful gift it was. And, he promised himself, he would keep his newly discovered lust for her under control. She deserved so much more than to be subjected to that.

She returned to his side, breathless from her sprint back from the water's edge. She plopped down in the sand next to him before reaching for the woven satchel. "I see they left you other supplies." She rifled through the contents. "Good, there is dried meat here. Now I can make us something more filling to eat."

Sarak could not help smiling as he listened to her bright chatter and watched her quick, graceful movements as she repacked the satchel and rose to her feet. Little wingbird, he thought. Her cheerfulness was infectious. She sounded more lighthearted than he had ever heard her. She had every right to be proud of herself. It was her will that had gotten them this far, after all. He was not out of the jungle yet, but even so he was still amazed that the first step in her plan had met with any success at all.

"Come, it is almost evenfall," she said. She started to walk away.

He struggled to his feet, swaying unsteadily as he tried to secure his balance, suppressing a groan at the sharp pain in his head.

Phada heard him. "Dear Lady in Heaven, what happened?" she cried, dropping the sack and running back to him. "Are you hurt?" It did not take her long to discover the lump of clotted blood at the base of his skull. The look of pained sympathy on her face was almost enough in itself to chase away the dull, aching throb that had begun in his neck and was now moving to encompass every nerve in his body.

"Cursed bluefly spawn," she muttered in a low voice. "Disgusting dominator brutes."

Sarak flinched at her uncensored words. Although she seemed to treat him as an equal, he must never forget that he, too, was a disgusting dominator brute. Before he could stop her, she slipped a slender arm around his back, using her surprising strength to support him as she helped him walk toward the hut. He did not push her away because he needed her assistance.

It was incredibly arousing to feel the soft curves of her body pressed against him. He had never been this close to a woman like Phada before. Even when he had been tied to the pallet she had not been touching him in so many places at once. He could smell the flowery scent of her hair. It brought back vague yet insistent memories of that first night, when he had ambushed her on the path to the hut. She had been soft and sweet-smelling then as she lay beneath him, trapped in a position no town woman should find herself in with a dominator. He was amazed now that he had remained on top of her like that as long as he had. Of course he had been too spice-addled to move immediately away, although that was no excuse.

Sarak felt himself beginning to perspire as he fought against the waves of dizziness that threatened to engulf him, as well as the intoxicating pleasure at Phada's nearness. The going became easier when they stepped off the sand onto firmer ground.

"I can walk alone now," he informed her gruffly, although he was not sure that was exactly true.

"Of course." Phada blushed as she stepped with alacrity away from him. Obviously supporting his body had been just as much of an ordeal for her, although not in the same way. She must be tired of being forced into unwanted intimacy with him, taking care of him, and tending to his wounds. She must think him a poor example of a warrior. Dominators were trained for strength and agility and here he was, as clumsy as a day-old hound pup.

He crossed the threshold of the hut, grateful for its coolness. He managed to make it across the room to one of the chairs, sinking down gratefully onto its rough surface. Phada gathered a bowl of water and a cloth. He took them from her and set them on the table.

"I can clean the wound," he said.

"Do not be a stubborn mudhog," she scolded him, snatching away the cloth. "Of course you cannot clean it. Unless you have eyes in the back of your head so you can see what you are doing." She dipped the cloth into the water and pressed the cool material against his aching neck. It felt as if an entire swarm of stinging sweetbees were attacking his scalp, but he made no sound. "What did they do to you?"

"It is nothing, a small injury only."

One corner of her mouth crooked up in a smile. "Of course. I had forgotten that it is part of the warrior code not to complain of any kind of bodily discomfort, even a mortal wound."

"This is not a mortal wound."

"I realize that." She chuckled as she applied some of her Keeper's healing salve. Her touch was as light as any wingbird's, her fingers gentle against his sore flesh. "I have to admit that if I had a lump the size of a gull's egg at the back of my head and my hair was matted with blood, I would not be sitting here so calmly."

"I am not so sure about that," he replied.

She lowered her eyes at the implied compliment, then backed away from him with a shrug. "There," she said, gesturing at his head. "That is about all I can do."

"It is more than enough. Thank you, Phada."

She moved toward the hearth, pulling out the heavy pot on its swinging arm so she could fill it. Sarak watched as she began the preparations for their meal, feeling oddly content in spite of his aches. Even the thought of another supper without faral to spice his food did not seem to bother him at the moment.

"I have been doing some thinking these past cycles while you have been waging your battle against the faral," Phada announced.

"And?"

"I think the Kargans may hold the answer to our problems."

He nodded in agreement. "Since they are the ones who produce the faral, that is an obvious conclusion to draw."

"Dalcor has everyone in Mesara working to harvest extra crops, which he then trades to the Kargans for the spice."

Sarak's mouth flattened with anger. "Yes, he has set up a nice arrangement for himself."

"Do you think the Kargans are addicted to the

spice as well? Is that why they did not come to do the job themselves?"

"I think the Kargans were happy to get their hands on our goods with so little effort expended on their part. They may yet be planning to overthrow Dalcor at some future time."

"Or they may be perfectly happy with the arrangement as it stands."

"If Dalcor had not betrayed his honor and the honor of every warrior, they would not have found it so easy to conquer us," he said, his voice laced with bitterness as well as disgust.

"In any case, the Kargans are the ones who produce the spice," she pointed out eagerly. "Which means they must know all about it."

"I suppose they do." He shot her a wary frown. "What are you getting at, Phada?"

"We must find out what they know."

"There is no way to do that."

"There is if we travel to their stronghold in Gorod."

# *Chapter Nine*

"Are you mad?" Sarak exclaimed. "We cannot go to Gorod. Gorod lies beyond the Calabian Desert. It is an impossible journey."

Phada frowned at him. She did not think her suggestion was illogical enough to produce such an incredulous reaction. "The Jiboans do it all the time."

"The Jiboans are desert rodents. They are born knowing how to survive in that wretched inferno."

"We could get a Jiboan guide."

Sarak snorted. "A brilliant idea. And which tribe do you suggest we put our trust in—the one who betrayed Mesara to the Kargans?"

She bit her lip thoughtfully. "You are right, of course. We can trust no one but ourselves. However I still believe it is possible to cross the desert."

Sarak lowered his face into his hands. It was several long moments before he finally lifted his head to gaze directly into her eyes, his expression grim. "I am flattered that you think I can do this.

I am sorry to disappoint you, but no warrior alone in the desert can last the ten sun cycles it will take to reach Gorod."

"You will not be alone. Did you not hear what I said? I am coming, too."

Sarak slammed his arms against the table in a gesture of pure, unsuppressed astonishment. "Now I know you have truly gone sun-blind mad. You would not last until the first sun's zenith, never mind ten cycles."

Her hands flew to her hips as she glared at him from her position near the hearth. Why was he being such a stubborn mudhog over this? Could he not understand the desperate necessity behind her plan? "Do you have another idea?"

"Not at the moment," he admitted grudgingly. "I have not been able to give it a lot of thought."

"Well, I have. And believe me, this is the only way. Perhaps the Kargans have some kind of antidote for the spice or know of some other way to free people from its enslavement. Once we know the secret, we can return to release the warriors who opposed Dalcor. With you to lead them, they could retake Mesara and restore the queen—and Pavonis, if he is still alive," she added darkly. "No one has seen the king since the takeover."

"And no one will ever see us again if we attempt to cross the desert."

"We did not know if you could free yourself from the spice until you tried, and yet you achieved that."

His expression softened and Phada felt a rush of warmth flooding her senses. "No, *we* achieved that. Although I am not sure I am out of the battle zone yet when it comes to craving the faral."

"I hate to point out the obvious, but there is no faral here to crave," she replied.

"And I am sure a grueling trek through the desert will continue to keep me on a straight and narrow pathway, is that it?" he asked with a rueful grin.

"That is just one of the benefits," she said, warming to her argument. "Surely you can see it is the next logical step. We need help to overthrow the renegade dominators, and the only ones you can trust for that task are your fellow warriors, the ones who resisted Dalcor and were given faral for their pains. Do you not want revenge for their treatment—and yours?"

"More than you know."

Phada smothered a smile. She reached over to casually stir the pot containing their supper, turning her back to him so he would not see the expression of triumph on her face. She had him now, she thought. The urge for revenge was known to be a strong dominator trait. They were ruthless when injured and could not let an insult pass without retribution. "So we will journey to the Kargans' stronghold?"

"No. I will go there alone," he decided.

She let out a surreptitious sigh. He would not defeat her plans so easily. She figured she was already halfway to getting what she wanted. He had agreed to go to Gorod. Now all she had to do was convince him that she should accompany him. "And what am I supposed to do in the meantime? Where am I supposed to go? Dalcor may already have learned of my absence."

"You can hide here."

She shot him a look brimming with disgust. "What happens when the warriors return and do not find you? Do you not think they will turn this island upside down to search you out? And when they do, they will discover me instead."

Sarak groaned. "I cannot take you with me, Phada. There are too many dangers. Not only do we have to cross the great Calabian Desert—twice—but we have to spy on the Kargans about whom we know nothing and escape unnoticed with the secret of the faral. And even if we somehow managed to accomplish all that, we would probably end up dead, or worse yet captured, while trying to sneak into the barracks to free the warriors."

She crossed the room to stand beside him. "Please, Sarak." She touched his arm lightly, then quickly jerked her fingers back, shocked at herself for her boldness. Sarak must also have been surprised, for he flinched beneath her hand.

She took a deep breath before continuing. "It is our only hope. We have already proven that we can be strong if we work together. I may not be much help on the journey to Gorod, but I promise you I will not be a hindrance. Besides, once we get there I might prove useful."

"I do not doubt it," Sarak murmured.

Phada shrugged aside his wryly spoken words. "You will realize soon enough that I am not as brave or as noble as a Keeper should be. But I am willing to do my utmost on this quest. I am sure you have already discerned for yourself how frightened I am of crossing the desert. But I am even more fearful of staying behind alone."

She could not tell him the other reason she refused to stay, that she would worry about him, wondering every mark of every cycle where he was and what he was doing. And what if he never returned? He might be a dominator but she had been forced by circumstances to put all her faith and trust in him, and now that she had, she found herself unwilling to take it back. She had committed herself totally. He was stuck with her whether he wished it or not.

She kept her gaze averted so he could not tell what she was thinking. Of course that meant she could not read his thoughts either, not that she ever managed to achieve that, even in the best of circumstances. Sarak and every other warrior she had ever come into contact with kept their expressions stoic. In fact, she had never seen a dominator actually break into a smile the way Sarak had done with her.

"All right," he agreed. "I do not have much choice, do I?"

"No, I do not suppose you do. Neither of us has had much say in these matters since Mesara was overthrown. We can only hope the Goddess is on our side."

"She dare not be otherwise, not with you mapping out strategy as ably as any war leader." This time Sarak actually grinned. It made him look younger, almost boyish. She wondered what he might have become had he not been chosen to train as a warrior.

"We will need the proper clothing, supplies, packbirds," he continued, ticking the items off on his fingers. "Since we have no coin with which to purchase such necessities, and nothing of value to barter, we will have to steal them." His brown eyes glinted with anticipation. "It will give me great pleasure to turn the tables on those sun-cursed desert vermin for once."

Phada grimaced in concern. "Will they not chase us to get their things back?"

"Not if they have no idea who robbed them. I can make it seem as if Jiboans from another tribe are the culprits."

"When shall we leave?"

"We will rest until evenfall, then eat the meal you have prepared. After that we can cross over to the outskirts of Mesara. With luck, we will find a suitable Jiboan camp by nightfall. I will need deep shadow for cover. If all goes well, we will be measures into the desert and our tracks obliterated before the Jiboans have time to sound the alarm."

Phada swallowed hard. Dear Goddess, they were really going to go through with this. She was more than fearful; she was terrified of the task that lay before them. And yet somehow, knowing Sarak would be by her side made everything a lot easier to bear. Who would ever have expected that a dominator's presence could provide such comfort?

Phada tugged on the hood of the loose, flowing robe called a kenta that she wore, pulling it closer around her face to protect her delicate skin. Even though the sun was not yet halfway to its zenith, the day was already blistering. She could feel the searing heat of the sand as it sifted through the leather sandals she wore. At least in Mesara, she could seek the protection of the jungle canopy that provided pleasant shade and shelter. Here in the desert there was not even a single cloud to shield the ground from the blazing rays of the sun.

She had to squint in order to make out Sarak as he walked ahead of her, the lead rein of his dobby trailing loosely over his shoulder. She could not see his face or much of his form—something she had grown rather used to viewing in her short time with the warrior—because he wore the corresponding robe and headdress of the male Jiboan called a kanzu. These head coverings, long flowing robes, and layers of light-colored material provided insulation from the extreme desert temperatures as well as protection from the hot sun.

She glanced behind at her own packbird. They were not known for their great intelligence. This particular bird, a female, plodded docilely along in her wake, its throat vibrating to emit a weird, high-pitched noise that Sarak said helped keep them cool. It seemed they had no sweat glands, lucky creatures.

The bird noticed that she was gazing in its direction and chirped cheerfully before returning to its throaty whining. Phada could not help chuckling. Why should she pity the bright-eyed desert dweller when it seemed perfectly content with its fate as a beast of burden? The bird was fitted with a leather-and-wood saddle decorated with red tassels and blue pom-poms, white beads and strings of complicated knots that swayed with its graceless, heavy-footed movements. Phada had no idea what they might symbolize, if anything, but the overall effect was pretty and colorful in the midst of the vast monochrome reaches of the desert.

They had already crossed measure after measure of the pale Calabian sand, overlaid with a hint of green because of the blue rays of the sun. Phada knew they had measures more to cross before they reached even the halfway point. According to the Jiboans, a great oasis lay somewhere out there called the Kali Oasis, a paradise in the midst of the desert inferno, where water gushed to the surface from deep layers of rock, and koalnut palm trees provided blessed shade. Sarak had not actually said so, but Phada believed that unless they found this oasis or another stopping point where they could refill the water bags, they might not be able to make it to Gorod.

"We will make camp here," Sarak called back to her.

Phada nodded before gazing around in dismay. She realized that they would make better time if they moved long after the sun had reached its peak and throughout the hours of the short Elithran evenfall and night, but the thought of setting up a shelter in the middle of this sea of sand dunes at high zenith was not at all inviting.

She held the dobbies while Sarak made quick work of staking out their tent. He unloaded and unsaddled the birds and then settled them against the wall of the tent, which would soon provide at least a modicum of welcome shade as the sun began its afternoon descent toward the western horizon.

At a gesture from Sarak, Phada scrambled inside their makeshift shelter. It was smaller than the hut. Even after he opened one of the side walls to catch any breeze that might be blowing, it still seemed much too crowded for the two of them to coexist comfortably together.

He handed her a graincake and some dried meat. "Not as good as your stew, but it will have to do," he told her cheerfully.

Phada bit into the graincake first. She was not very hungry and it had a flat, unexciting taste that did little to perk her appetite. She glanced at Sarak, who was gnawing at his meat with strong, white teeth. Ever since he had successfully raided that Jiboan camp, he had seemed in good spirits. He was in his element, she supposed, facing danger and the unknown with a warrior's undisputed courage.

She felt very uncomfortable in such close quarters with him, especially now that he was restored to full dominator strength. He had had no further aftereffects from the faral, even when he ate solid food. His brown eyes sparkled with animation and his tanned skin glowed with rude good health. She felt ashamed of her thoughts, ashamed that she still feared he would take her against her will, against every Mesaran law.

She had been told that warriors could go no more than a couple of suncycles without mating. Just because Sarak was tramping through the desert on his way to Gorod for the good of Mesara did not mean he would not eventually seek his own pleasure. Why else were dominators kept separate from the rest of the population? Knowing Sarak as she now did, she believed he would fight the urge as long as he could. But in the end he would not be able to control his deep-seated, lustful warrior instincts.

She had already seen an example of his determination and prodigious strength of will as he battled his addiction to faral. She was counting on him being able to fight his desires longer and harder than any other two warriors combined. For her part, she simply had to take care not to place herself in any more jeopardy than she already was in.

She had not taken this cursed tent into account. She reached for the water bag, brushing against Sarak's arm in spite of her best efforts to avoid it. "How do you know we are going in the right direction?" she asked, more to divert him than because she really wanted the information.

"I do not know for sure. I only know that according to Hotek, we must use the sun's position to keep heading south-southwest."

"Oh. And what about that oasis? Do you think it really exists?"

"If it does, the Kali lies closer to Gorod than to Mesara. According to my calculations, we should reach it in about five more suncycles."

She did not bother to ask what would happen if they missed it or if there turned out to be no such place. It was better not to dwell on one more thing among the many that could go wrong. They had been very fortunate so far, thank the Goddess, and Phada only hoped their luck would continue to hold.

After their brief meal and separate trips outside to relieve themselves, they settled down to rest until late afternoon on the sleep mats Sarak had stolen. Like the tent, they were made from goat hair, which had been dyed in bright colors and densely woven into the intricate patterns the Jiboans seemed to favor. Although she had only spent one entire suncycle in the desert, Phada could appreciate their craving for color and texture.

"We should rest now," Sarak said. As was proper, it was not an order but a suggestion, uttered in a tone of complete respect for her rank. He kept his gaze mostly averted and yet he did not need to look at her to make her feel uneasy. "I know I do not need to remind you that we should conserve our strength whenever we can. The less time we have to spend in the desert, the better."

"Yes, of course," she replied.

Phada was surprised to find that his deferential tone rankled. She did not want him to be so completely subservient, not when it was obvious he was the one with the knowledge they needed to survive. She would be the first to admit she was completely out of her element, tramping through the Calabian Desert with a warrior and a pair of packbirds. The solid realm of the physical was not a place in which she felt comfortable. Books and scrolls, scholarly pursuits, those were the endeavors at which she excelled. All she could do was try to take Helenina's sage advice to heart and hold herself open to these new experiences, gather all the knowledge she could, even about dominators, so that her judgment would be sound and true when the time came for her to make decisions for her beloved Mesara. If that time ever came.

She sighed as she laid her head down on her pack. It was not very comfortable, since she was still wrapped in the voluminous folds of the kenta. She considered removing it but the thought of disrobing in front of Sarak, even though she wore her own tunic underneath, was too embarrassing and perhaps even too dangerous to contemplate.

Sarak had no such compunctions. Even though her back was turned to him, she knew the exact moment when he removed his kanzu. She closed her eyes against the vision of his nearly naked body clad in the warrior's breechcloth, but the image stubbornly persisted. Her discomfort and shame caused the blood to pound through her veins, making her even hotter beneath her robes.

Sarak stared at Phada's back. She was curled into such a tight little ball, he could not imagine she was comfortable, let alone able to sleep. She must not wish him to look upon her with his disgusting dominator gaze. He had tried to keep his avid interest in her cloaked beneath the proper code of conduct, but she was much too intelligent not to be able to sense the way his loins stirred and his body quickened the few times she had touched him.

Did she think he would ravish her on the spot? He had no coin to offer as enticement, not that Phada would ever consider such an exchange. She was not a Jiboan barracks wench with pierced ears and blue tattoos on her forehead. Phada's skin was smooth and unmarked and as soft as the petal of a jasa flower. Even though Mesaran women avoided the sun, her hair had still managed to pick up golden streaks that threaded through its thick length and highlighted its tawny color.

Sarak dragged his mind away from Phada's personal assets but it did him little good. All he could think about was how long it had been since he had tasted a warrior's night pleasure with a bought woman, the only kind of female someone like him was permitted to have. His wild fantasies about Phada had to stop before he disgraced himself. This town woman was a Keeper's apprentice who had come to seek his help. She did not want his lustful and forbidden desires.

If truth be told, neither did the Jiboan females. From what he knew of them, most Jiboan males were greedy for profit. They used their oldest daughters to cement alliances through permanent bonding with males from other tribes; any other female children they had, they brought to the warrior barracks to sell to the highest bidder. These young females accepted the system, for they were eager for the promised chance to buy their way to freedom and their own households after a large enough sum had been earned.

Sarak settled himself on his mat, stretching out his legs but careful not to come too close to Phada's huddled form. By the blue sun and moon, she would not be able to sleep in such a position, especially all bundled up in her robes. She had to rest. They had just begun their trek. Conditions would only get worse.

He knew she was still awake. "Phada?" he called softly.

"Yes."

"You must remove the kenta."

"What?" She scooted the last tiny measure of distance away from him, although she did not turn around.

"It is too warm in this tent to sleep, covered with all that cloth."

He said nothing more. Instead he watched her, his posture stiff and unyielding as he allowed her plenty of time to voice a protest against what amounted to a virtual order on his part. She must have been too shocked at his boldness or too dismayed at his blatant suggestion to speak. Perhaps even both.

Just when he thought he could bear her silence no longer, she finally spoke. "Thank you for your concern but it is not necessary. I am fine as I am."

"Are you?" He reached over to grasp her cloth-covered shoulder, turning her onto her back so he could see her face. As he suspected, her skin was covered with a fine sheen of perspiration and her cheeks were flushed. She lowered her eyes as even more color flooded her face. "You do not look fine," he pointed out in a scathing voice.

"I . . ."

Suddenly he was furious at her cringing attitude. He knew he was not being fair to her, knew she had every right to be wary of him after the way he had attacked her the night she had arrived on the island, but he could not help it. He had thought after these cycles together she would have come to realize that simply because he was a dominator did not mean he had to act like a rampaging tuskboar.

"Do not worry, Keeper's apprentice. I know my place and it is not in your sleeping pallet," he told her.

She gasped at his bluntness, her hands flying to her face, her eyes widening with trepidation. "Sarak, I did not mean . . . that is . . ."

"This situation is no different than it was back at the hut."

She raised her eyebrows, eloquently conveying her disagreement without uttering a word. She was probably still speechless with dread, although he swore he noticed a glint of wry humor lurking in the depths of her blue eyes. Although he did not wish it, he could feel some of his anger dissipating.

"All right, so it is not quite the same," he admitted. "Then you needed to control me with ropes because of the faral. Now I have regained control over myself."

That did not seem to reassure her the way he expected. Curse the reputation all warriors were burdened with in Mesara. According to most Mesarans, no dominator could be trusted to control anything except his weapon. His anger bubbled back to the surface. The word of a warrior was as good as any town dweller's, not that anyone believed it.

"You will be safe enough with me, I swear it on my honor as a warrior," he said, deliberately sar-

castic. He turned on his side away from her, pil-
lowing his head on one bended arm and closing
his eyes, although sleep was the farthest idea from
his thoughts. "Do as you will; it matters not to
me."

He lay there beside her, so close and yet as distant in outlook as the farthest antipodes, controlling his breathing to subdue his runaway
emotions the way he had been taught at the Warrior Academy. He wished he were back there now.
If he were, he would grab a sword and hack one
of the practice targets to pieces. Imagining the
deed did not offer him much satisfaction. It certainly did not soothe the savage beast inside him.
Phada was right. He was an animal to feel the stirrings of desire for a woman not of his own kind,
a woman forbidden to him in every way.

He heard her shifting on the mat, followed by
another, softer whisper of sound that could only
mean one thing. His entire body froze as he listened, unable to believe what his ears were telling
him. Phada was removing the kenta.

He could not control the heavy pounding of his
quickened heartbeat. He feared she might be able
to detect the sound right through the sand beneath them, so loud and powerful did its thudding
seem to him. He heard her settle back on the goatskin rug with a breathless, almost inaudible sigh.

He wanted to leap to his feet, to shout out his
gratitude for this small, but significant, sign of
trust from her. He managed to contain his roiling
emotions, instead contenting himself with a grin.

He vowed she would not live to regret it.

Phada awoke feeling tired and out of sorts. Even
in her sleep she had been aware of the necessity
of staying on her side of the tent, of making certain her tunic did not ride up her thighs. The effort
to ensure those things had used up a good portion

of her precious rest. Besides, sleeping through the
long postzenith was a jarring and unsettling experience in itself, disrupting her usual cycle of activity. She lay still, using her senses to discover
what Sarak was up to. He did not seem to be in
the tent. Maybe he had gone outside to check on
the dobbies.

She pulled herself to a sitting position and
gazed around the interior of the Jiboan shelter. It
was still warm. She could sense the hot sun beating down on the roof. Sometime during the postzenith, Sarak had lowered the wall flap. She could
see by the shadows around the edges of the tent
that a good deal of sand had shifted or blown
against the sides while they slept. She wondered
with a horrified shudder if one of these times
when they made camp they would end up completely buried.

The thought propelled her off her sleeping mat
and onto her feet. She reached for the water bag.
She felt sticky and hot, but they did not have
enough water to indulge in anything more than a
small splash on her face and hands and several
swallows of the tepid contents. She retied the neck
of the bag, then gazed at its strange, rounded
shape. According to Sarak, it was made of goat
intestines, not a very appetizing thought. In Mesara they used fired clay pots and jugs to hold liq-
uids. No wonder the water tasted strange.

She felt more like herself after she combed and
rebraided her hair. After slipping on her sandals,
she ducked under the folded-back tent flap that
was the door and stepped outside into the blinding desert sun.

It was a mistake. The heat and glare that greeted
her almost brought her to her knees. The air in
the desert was dry and hard to breathe, unlike the
humid atmosphere of Mesara. It burned her lungs
and scorched the inside of her nose and mouth at

the same time the direct sunlight seared the unprotected skin of her arms and legs.

Sarak came around the side of the tent. "Where is your kenta?" were the first words out of his mouth as he planted himself in front of her, the folds of his kanzu swirling around him.

She could not help grinning at his exasperated tone. "I left it inside," she admitted as she squinted up at him. She could not make out much of his face because of the concealing Jiboan costume, but she was surprised at the way her spirits lifted at the mere sight of him, in spite of his scolding.

"You will burn your skin," he said.

Phada's heart began to pound at the concern evident in his soft comment. His hand moved slightly, as if he wanted to reach out and touch her, but of course that was a ridiculous notion. Still, she had to admit it felt good to know he worried about her well-being. No one had ever done that in quite the same way before.

"I will go put it on now."

"What is it with you and that cursed piece of clothing?" he grumbled, shaking his head in exasperation. "You insist on wearing it when you should remove it and refuse to wear it when you should."

She paused in the doorway to glance back at him. The urge to wipe that serious expression from his face, to soften it into something less formal, was impossible to resist. She assured herself that she was simply feeling benevolent because Sarak had stayed on his side of the tent while they slept. "You are not being fair," she told him with a smile.

"What?"

"I said you are not being fair to me. I took the kenta off when you pointed out the obvious advantages of such an action, did I not?"

He looked startled. "Well, yes, but . . ."

"And now I am putting it back on, again at your eminently sensible request."

"I . . . yes, I thank you, Phada. I am sorry if I offended you, but it is for your own good."

His gaze locked with hers for the briefest moment, his expression unreadable, before he pivoted on his heel and disappeared around the side of the tent. Phada sighed. She had meant to tease him a little, perhaps even thank him for his care of her, and instead it seemed she had insulted him.

She ducked into the tent and grabbed the kenta. Shaking it out, she pulled the simple garment over her head. The warrior took things so literally—and so seriously. He was supposed to be formal and polite with her, but under these circumstances could they not circumvent the rules just a little? She found she desired to know him better, not the warrior but the real individual behind his social role. Was that such a terrible thing?

Yes, she supposed it was. After all, the rules had been carefully formulated to protect the people of Mesara, especially the women, from the aggression and lust of the warriors, instead channeling their natural qualities of strength and dominance into a way of life that had proved its usefulness for everyone. If she let down her guard, there was no telling what the warrior might do, how he might take advantage of her. She could not afford to take that chance.

And yet Sarak seemed different from any other dominator she had ever come into contact with. He had restrained himself with her, even when he had been in the thrall of the spice, even after he had removed his breechcloth and she had seen the force of his desire. He made sure she was comfortable and took care of her. He had even allowed himself to be coerced into following her plan, half-formulated as it was, simply because she had asked him. She could not imagine Dalcor doing such a thing.

No, Sarak was correct to keep a formal distance between them. They could never become friends because they came from opposite sides of the spectrum. She had best leave matters alone and concentrate on the difficult, perhaps even impossible, task ahead, that of getting to Gorod alive and in one piece.

She frowned as she began packing up their meager supplies and possessions. Suddenly the evenfall and night of walking that awaited her seemed the longest and most tedious task she could imagine.

# *Chapter Ten*

Sarak glanced over his shoulder, checking Phada's progress for the hundredth time that evenfall. The sun had dipped below the horizon more than a mark ago, which meant they still had another couple of marks before it would reappear and perhaps another five marks before they would have to stop to rest.

Phada had not complained of anything since they had set foot in the Calabian Desert, not the heat or the pace he was setting or the unappetizing food or the lack of amenities. She had been as brave and stalwart as any warrior under the same circumstances, braver perhaps, since she had never undergone the rigorous training needed to teach her body to submit to her will in spite of hunger, thirst, or pain. He was sure she had never before suffered such hardship and privation.

To his amazement, she had even managed to tease him about it. At least, now that he looked back on the incident, he thought she had been teasing him about the kenta and his instructions regarding her use of it. He had been too thick-headed to realize it at the time and had thought she was complaining about his forward behavior in telling her what to do. The thought of the smile she had bestowed upon him lightened his heart, helping to alleviate his gloomy thoughts regarding the chances of the success of this mission.

She had not been so informal with him since that time. He wondered what he should do, how he should act to merit such treatment at her hands again. He could not tell her how to wear the kenta, for she had quickly taken it off the last two times they had stopped to rest and she had never again gone outside the tent without first cloaking herself within its protective folds. In any case, this time he would be ready if she made another overture. No matter if she joked with him or smiled at him, he would not lose his presence of mind or behave as if his head were filled with rocks.

The sound of Phada talking to her dobby drifted on the soft desert wind to reach his ears. He chuckled to himself. He knew if he turned around now he would see the creature walking with its head just above Phada's shoulder, its beady eyes alert as if hanging on her every word. Sometimes Phada stroked the thick skin of its knobby, featherless skull. The bird seemed to have formed a bond with the Keeper's apprentice, following her around even after they made camp.

He did not doubt that Phada had a kind heart. He imagined that was why she had taken pity on him and treated him the way she did, not like all the other town women who scorned him or cringed from contact with him. He wondered suddenly if Phada would flinch were he to touch her now. He had been very careful to avoid such an occurrence, especially inside the tent where he could see how wary she was of his presence, no matter how she tried to hide it.

Just because she had handled his body during his time of faral enslavement did not mean she had changed her views about dominators. She had touched him out of necessity. It obviously had not stirred her senses the way it had his, nor had it fired her imagination to the point where she had trouble falling asleep the way he did. If his friend Zegon were here he would be quick to point out that Sarak was behaving like a mudhog's ass.

Enough, he sternly ordered himself. He brought his mind back to the task before him, shading his eyes with his hand as he scanned the horizon. So far they had been lucky that they had not been sighted by any of the Jiboan tribes that roamed the desert. He had tried to pick a route away from the main concentration of Jiboan travel, but there were many smaller, related tribes who inhabited the Calabian. It was up to him to ensure they did not accidently stumble upon one of them.

One thing he knew for certain—he was heartily sick of the sight of the endless measures of pale green sand and shifting desert dunes that stretched out before him. He was not sure he could bear to listen much longer to the constant whining of the dobbies as they vibrated their throats in unison. No one knew exactly how they were able to go for such long stretches of time without food or water but it was suspected it had something to do with that irritating habit.

He realized the whining had ceased when the musical chirping of Phada's dobby broke into his musings. He slowed his pace, waiting for her to catch up. He noticed she did not even carry the lead rein anymore; she did not need to, since the packbird followed her most willingly. He could not fault the loyal creature, not when he felt his own gaze rivet onto what he could see of her face beneath the hood of the kenta.

"What are you saying to that annoying bird?" he asked, truly curious. "Or maybe I should ask what it is saying to you."

"She is not annoying," Phada retorted, laughing up at him. Sarak felt his heart turn over at the sound. "Her name is Gisba and I was telling her what a good job she is doing to carry her load so cheerfully. You should try such sweet encouragement with yours."

I would like to try it on you instead, Sarak thought. He knew he would willingly walk into flames if Phada whispered such encouragement in his ear. "I do not think she likes me," he replied instead.

Phada chuckled. "That is because you do not appreciate her. Did your father not tell you that women like to be appreciated?"

"My father disowned me before witnesses in the town square when I was ten."

"Oh." She hesitated, unsure of what to say.

Sarak braced himself for some careless, cutting remark. Town dwellers were remarkably insensitive to the realities of a warrior's life. True, his father had taken the usual behavior to extremes by publicly disowning him. But it was not uncommon for families to ostracize a male child after he had been ordered to the Warrior Academy, nor for the rest of their neighbors to follow suit. Most warriors never saw their parents again until many sun orbits later when they were posted to duty in the town, but by then the connection had been severed, both emotionally and physically. It was never acknowledged by either of the parties.

"That was a harsh thing for him to do."

"No harsher than what the other fathers did. At least mine dealt me a clean, quick blow. I did not have to sit and wait every mooncycle for the visits that never came."

"I did not realize a family could visit a warrior son. Actually, I do not know of any families whose sons became warriors."

"That does not surprise me. I warrant you have never heard of one single family who ever spawned a dominator."

She wrinkled her brow as she trudged along in the sand beside him, considering his statement. "You are right; I have not."

He snorted. "Do you not find that odd?" he asked, unable to keep the bitterness from coloring his voice, even after all these orbits. "Does no one ever wonder where all the warriors come from?"

"We all know where they come from," she answered piously. "And we are grateful to the boys who sacrifice themselves for the sake of Mesara and choose that as their life path."

"Choose!" He jerked to a halt so quickly his dobby nearly collided into his back. The bird backed off, blinking in confusion as Sarak raged. "You think young boys voluntarily choose such a life for themselves, ostracized from the community, scorned, and reviled? Is that what that lying pack of Keepers with their colorless tunics and sanctimonious faces taught you?"

"Oh!" Phada's mouth dropped open in outrage. She closed it with a snap, glaring at him. "Now I understand what my teachers meant when they warned me about warriors. They said that dominators were crude and ill-tempered, that they were not fit company for anyone except their own kind, which is why they are kept away from the rest of us in barracks. Obviously they were not mistaken in their conclusions."

Sarak found himself speechless. It was bad enough knowing the town dwellers thought, and sometimes spoke aloud, such sentiments about the warriors. But hearing Phada utter them with such vehement belief was the most horrible experience he could remember since his miserable early days at the Warrior Academy.

She tossed her head scornfully as she resumed walking. "Come along, Gisba," she said to the attentive dobby. "We have many more measures to cover before this wretched night is over."

Keeper's apprentice and packbird marched blithely away. Silly Mesaran female, she did not realize she had somehow turned herself around and was now headed in the wrong direction. He glanced up at the sun and then swept his gaze across the horizon. With a sigh, he tightened his grip on the reins of his dobby and started across the sand at a sharp angle from Phada's course.

"Gorod is this way," he announced curtly.

She did not say a word in reply, but after a short while he noticed that she was once again following him, although at a greater distance than she had kept between them previously and off more to the side. Obviously she did not want his rude, barbarian presence to contaminate her line of vision.

Out of sight, out of mind did not work so easily for him. The night dragged on as they walked what seemed like endless measures, slogging through the heavy sand that did its best to impede their progress. The air grew uncomfortably cool as the sun kept its vigil just below the horizon for far longer than it did in Mesara. Even watching the moon rise after a seven-cycle absence did nothing to lift his spirits. Although Phada was also bathed in its soft blue light, he realized they were poles apart in their training and outlook.

Which was as it should be, he supposed. He was the one who had foolishly believed he glimpsed something more in Phada. Once again, in his ignorance—or perhaps his pride—he had reached beyond himself only to be shot down.

This time he vowed to learn from his mistakes

instead of repeating them. No matter what happened on this trek, no matter what the Goddess had in store for him, he was a warrior and would always remain one. The urge in him to protect was strong; if he had to exercise it at the expense of some of the other qualities he possessed and endure the derision of the very people he had sworn to protect, then so be it.

"It is time to set up camp," Sarak announced briskly.

He did not look at Phada and she did not even raise her eyes to glance at him as he began to stake out the tent. As she waited on the searing sand, she took a swig of water, then offered some to Gisba.

"When you have no water left, after wasting it on that brainless packbird who is better used to doing without it than you are, do not come begging for some of mine."

You would like that, would you not, mighty dominator, she thought angrily. Her jaw tightened but she hid it, instead casually retying the thong that closed the neck of the water bag. "I ask nothing of you save that you carry out the mission we agreed upon."

"I gave you my word on that."

She was so tense she almost laughed out loud as he stomped off to unload his still nameless dobby. And then she wanted to cry. Phada knew it was foolish to give her water to the bird, but somehow Gisba had become a companion on this journey. Phada had actually grown fond of her funny face and beady eyes, her tall, awkward body and heavy, clawed feet. Without the packbirds, they would never be able to reach Gorod alive and she, for one, was grateful for their contribution.

Sarak disappeared into the tent without another word. She had no desire to crawl in there with him, but she had no choice. She needed her rest and she could not stay out here in the blazing sun. She settled Gisba next to her companion by the side of the tent and then slipped inside.

"If it were possible, I would offer to sleep outside to save you from my unwanted presence," Sarak announced as soon as she had settled herself on her sleeping pallet.

Phada experienced a guilty start as she glanced at his stiffly held body and unyielding profile. If she did not know better, she might almost believe she had hurt his feelings. No, that could not be. Warriors were reputed to have thick skins. None of the insults she had ever heard tossed in their direction seemed to have any effect on them, so why should her puny disapproval bother Sarak?

She had gone over in her mind what he had said this afternoon and she was beginning to feel guilty. After she had managed to get past his insult to the Keepers, she realized he had stated emphatically that he had not chosen to become a dominator. According to him, no one willingly picked that path. Then how had he become a warrior? Now that she thought about it, the entire process was all very hushed up. Of course, being a girl, she had attended First Training with other girls and so had no idea what the boys did or what they learned. She had assumed that they made the decision then, as she had to become a Keeper.

She got angry all over again when she recalled how Sarak had accused the Keepers of lying. The Keepers had always held a position of high honor in Mesara, since the early days after the downfall of warrior rule. They were respected for their devotion to truth and justice. They would never lie. Perhaps some young warriors-in-training regretted their decision after arriving at the Warrior Academy and so pointed their fingers at others for what they considered their misfortune. Dominators were not always known for having the best characters.

And yet Sarak had demonstrated through his actions that he was as honorable as any Mesaran male. She could not imagine him blaming someone else for something he had done.

She removed her kenta without a word. It was very hot inside the tent; the air pressed against her like a smothering blanket. No sooner had the thought crossed her mind than Sarak crawled over to one side and lifted the flap to allow the breeze to enter. The air was too hot for it to make much difference, but still he made the gesture.

"Here. Have something to eat," he said, holding out the inevitable graincake and chunk of dried meat. She took them from his hand, feeling ashamed. Even now, even knowing she was angry and refused to speak to him, he still offered her food and worried about her comfort. Perhaps she was being too hard on him, especially since she needed his help. Of course it was his duty to protect Mesara, so she should not even have to ask, but she still felt beholden to him for agreeing to what many would consider an impossible scheme.

She did not know how to break the silence or the tension between them, so she lay down instead. She realized she had neglected to tend to her needs outside, but it did not seem pressing. The dry desert had absorbed all the moisture from her system. Sleep was what she needed now. Things would look different after she slept.

Her restless body and busy mind decreed otherwise. She tossed and turned throughout the morning and into the postzenith. The air inside the tent grew hotter and hotter until she wished she could remove her tunic as well, a scandalous thought indeed. Sarak lay quietly beside her, his breathing deep and even. The sleep of the guiltless, she thought sourly, while she kept running their conversation over and over in her head.

She must have finally drifted into slumber because she found herself awaking with a start sometime later, her heart pounding, her throat dry and raspy. The water she had consumed just before going to sleep had cycled through her system and she needed to go outside.

She glanced over to find that Sarak was not on his pallet. Instead, he was crouched in the corner farthest from the tent flap which led outside, his back to her and his head to the ground. What in the name of Elithra was he doing? she wondered with a puzzled frown. When she returned she would ask him, she decided as she stumbled to her feet. She did not have the strength or the willpower to remain angry at him. He was her only companion besides a packbird. He was not talkative by any means, but she missed the conversations they had.

"Do not go out there," Sarak hissed.

Phada stared at him, shocked at his harsh tone. She had thought he was not sulking, but she had been wrong. She ignored him, moving quickly toward the exit. She could not believe it when he made a diving grab for her legs. With a small yelp, she managed to escape him as she tumbled outside into the late postzenith light.

Of all the brazen actions, she thought, scrambling to her feet, then bending from the waist to brush the sand from her calves and the hem of her tunic. Sarak was a beast, a brute, and she should never forget that fact. She should not have let down her guard as much as she had.

She straightened her spine, still facing the tent. Suddenly she felt the back of her neck prickle as if someone were staring at her. Gisba, she thought, smiling. She spun around only to find a menacing group of Jiboan males surrounding the tent.

"What have we here?" It was the tallest figure, the one directly across from her, who had spoken. He seemed to be their leader, since he was the only one who sported a fancy ceremonial dagger, encased in a colorful, highly decorated leather sheath that dangled around his neck on a length of golden chain. The others had daggers at their waists, but they also carried bows slung across their shoulders. She could see only his dark eyes, but they stared at her assessingly. Did he truly expect her to answer? Where was Sarak anyway? She backed up until the wall of the tent stopped her.

"She is Mesaran. A Keeper by the look of her tunic," another pointed out.

"Why was she wearing the kenta of the Tuargas then?" a third questioned in a suspicious voice. "Mayhap she is spying for them."

"I am no spy," Phada quickly denied. She had no idea who these Tuargas were, but they were obviously not thought of very highly by this particular band of Jiboans.

"Where is your companion?" the leader asked.

Before she could answer, the sound of a scuffle coming from somewhere behind the tent reached her ears. The leader jerked his head and four of the group disappeared around the sides of the tent. Phada closed her eyes against the grunts and the sound of fists against flesh. Sarak was strong, but he could not hold out against such numbers.

She opened her eyes just in time to see four of the Jiboans dragging Sarak before the leader. They forced him to his knees with the assistance of their sharp, shiny daggers. Phada had never seen such weapons. Their viciously curved blades came to a point more lethal than the tusk of a giant jungle boar. Dear Goddess, one of those points barely rested against the back of Sarak's neck and yet it had sliced his skin.

"It is him, Wodabi," one of the Jiboans yelped with barely restrained excitement. It was hard to tell who was speaking, since their headdresses covered their mouths and chins.

"You speak true, Babua." That was the leader again. Phada would recognize his harsh, rasping tones anywhere. She did not know if his name was Wodabi or if that was his title, but she wished she had never lain eyes on him.

She glanced at Sarak, clad only in his breech-cloth. His expression was stoic, in spite of the lump she could see rising above his temple and the blood running between his shoulders. He did not meet her gaze but she expected he had other things on his mind than worrying about her.

Each Jiboan had on a nearly identical kanzu of red and yellow, although the basic diamond pattern was different for each. There were thirteen males, none of them as tall or muscular as Sarak, but they were overwhelming in their numbers. Off to one side, she noticed that the women and children were approaching, burdened down with tents and water bags and other supplies. They stopped a good distance from the males, although they did not relinquish their loads.

"Sarak!" Wodabi barked out the name.

Sarak did not move, but she could not help gasping in surprise. She wanted to kick herself for giving his identity away. Wodabi grinned; she could tell by the way his eyes crinkled at the corners. Forgive me, Sarak, she thought, although of course it did little good because he could not hear her.

"We have been told of the warrior who escaped from the Uninhabited Island. I am sure Dalcor will pay well to have you returned." He pivoted toward Phada, his eyes gleaming with greed. "And you, little Keeper. I have heard that the warriors of Mesara have developed a taste for town women along with our comely Jiboan females. Is it really true that all Keepers are virgins? If so, we can collect a tidy sum selling such forbidden fruit to the highest bidder."

Phada shuddered. The thought of being sold to a rutting warrior turned her stomach. Of course Wodabi had his facts wrong. Keepers remained celibate after they took their vows but that did not necessarily mean they were virgins. She did not bother to correct his error.

He gestured toward the group of women. "We pitch camp here," he announced, and then turned back to Sarak. " 'Tis a rare pity you wore the distinctive robes of our hereditary enemies, the Tuargas. We have been following you for two suncycles, thinking you were one of them. Now we have garnered a much greater prize."

"No warrior will mate with a Keeper," Sarak said. "Let her go."

"I think we will let the marketplace decide that, eh, brothers?"

The other Jiboans laughed, a horrible wheezing sound that made Phada want to clap her hands over her ears.

"Our coffers have been empty for too long, thanks to our conniving Tuarga kinsmen," he continued in a less jovial tone. "It is only fitting that someone using their robes as a poor disguise against capture should help us to fill our purses with coin."

"What shall we do with them?" the one called Babua asked.

"Put the woman in the tent. We must pamper her fair skin in order to make the best deal. Leave the warrior outside. Mayhap the heat of our desert sun will burn some of that stubborn defiance from him."

He strode away across the pale green sand, accompanied by eight of his followers. The four

holding Sarak pushed him to the ground while another grabbed Phada and shoved her inside the
tent. She waited until her breathing had slowed
before daring to push aside the tent flap and peer
out. She saw that the Jiboans stood in a semicircle
around Sarak, effectively trapping him against the
front of the tent.

She dropped to her knees just inside the door.
"Sarak. Are you all right?" she hissed.

He merely grunted. She supposed it was not the
most brilliant of questions under the circumstances.

"I am sorry I went outside when you warned me
not to. I did not know they were waiting for us."

"It matters not. I do not believe it would have
made much difference. There were too many of
them."

"What are we going to do?"

Before he could answer, one of the Jiboans
paced over and smashed his fist against Sarak's
head. Phada gasped, horrified. The blow was so
hard it knocked him to the ground. She knew she
should move away from the tent entrance but she
was rooted to the spot. Tears filled her eyes at her
helplessness—and his.

"I have no plans right now, Phada," he replied
in defiance of his captors' obvious wish that they
not converse with each other. His rebellious statement earned him a backhanded slap across the
cheek.

Phada had to exert all her willpower to keep
from running outside and screaming at them to
stop abusing him. She knew it would do no good.
She forced herself to sit down, determined to
think through their options. It was better if they
could seem to cooperate, at least until they came
up with some plan of escape. What on Elithra that
might be, she had no idea.

Mark after sun clock mark passed and still they

left Sarak in the scorching sun with no protection.
Phada periodically prowled the confines of the
small tent, wringing her hands in frustration. She
even dared to lift the flap and peek out at Sarak a
couple of times. He sat on the sand, his back
hunched over and his arms around his knees to
protect as much of his body from the sun's blistering rays as he could. She noticed that the skin
of his back had a pink tinge beneath his tan. Later,
she knew, it would turn a more painful shade of
red. She wondered if he were cursing her and
wishing she had never come to his island.

Finally she grew too exhausted to pace and
slumped down in a dejected heap on her sleeping
mat. She might as well face it: they were doomed
to be returned to Mesara. Sarak would end up
back in Dalcor's hands. She knew the usurper
would have no mercy on his former second-in-
command. As for her, she would be forced to become a pallet partner to an endless array of brute
dominators, to mate against her will, against all
that Mesara held sacred. Right now, death seemed
a blessing.

She raised her head when she heard a commo-
tion outside. Before she could compose herself or
even sit up properly, the flap of the tent was flung
open and two Jiboans ducked inside. They gestured for her to rise. One of the robed figures ex-
ited the shelter while the other motioned her to
follow. As soon as she cleared the door, the first
Jiboan grabbed her arm and began to escort her
in the direction of the largest tent.

The desert dwellers had wasted no time in setting up their camp. Goat-hair tents of various
sizes, their sloping silhouettes similar to the one
Sarak had stolen, dotted the area, all in that same
combination of red and yellow. It gave an overall
orange effect that was quite colorful, like flames

against the pale green of the desert sand and the blue sky.

After blinking to adjust her eyesight to the still potent blue-white sun that was slowly sinking toward the western horizon, she noticed that Sarak was being dragged in the same direction, just a few measures ahead of her. A Jiboan on either side held him by the arms, helping to keep him upright in the soft, shifting sand because his hands had been tied behind his back with leather thongs.

This must be Wodabi's tent, she decided, as her gaze took in the elaborate decorations that graced the entrance. A pair of what looked like some kind of desert antelope had been embroidered on either side of the door, while large, fringed bags covered with blue beads and obviously containing supplies, hung from poles. The ceremonial knife that she had noted before dangled directly over the portal. Rows of pots and dishes inlaid with precious stones proclaimed the wealth of the owner for all to see. Gaily colored woven rugs jutted out from the interior of the tent, covering the sand and marking the path inside.

If this was a poor tribe, she wondered which ones were considered rich. She hesitated on the threshold, beneath the canopy that provided a buffer between the glare outside and the noticeably cooler interior. The men at her side prodded her to move forward, so she had no choice but to enter. She did not have to duck her head to come inside Wodabi's dwelling.

They marched her down a narrow corridor formed by woven curtains on either side that swayed with the motion of their passing. And then they shoved her onto the rug-covered main area of the tent.

# Chapter Eleven

A loud, raucous cry went up from the assembled Jiboans as Phada stumbled into their midst. She stared through the smoke-filled air of the shelter, trying to focus on the vague shapes that surrounded her. As her vision cleared, she gasped in shock, realizing with a start that she was standing in the middle of a circle of Jiboan males who gazed at her leeringly. They had removed their disguising headdresses and now she could see that the skin on their faces was tattooed with blue markings that traced exotic patterns along their foreheads, snaking down across their cheeks. It appeared savage to her, like something from a nightmare. She tried not to show how badly it unnerved her.

The females and children were seated behind the males, forming an outer circle, the shadowy outlines of their bodies blending into the dark corners of the spacious interior. They, too, had taken off their veils and headdresses and Phada could see their black hair shining beneath the light of the lamps. Many of the women had pierced ears from which dangled shiny circlets of silver and gold that caught the light. They seemed to have a single blue line marking their foreheads—it curved to an elaborate peak at the center before dipping down to undulate just above either eyebrow and ending in a decorative swirl at their temples.

Some of the members of the tribe sipped a beverage from a sieved metal straw out of what looked like the pod of a koalnut tree. Everyone had platters of strange-looking food before them. The smell of fresh-cooked meat drifted through the air. Phada was surprised to feel her stomach rumble. She had forgotten all about food. Her last meal had been consumed many marks ago, just before she and Sarak had settled down to rest.

Sarak was already there, standing to her right. Except for his raw, sunburned skin, he appeared to be all right. He glanced at her once, his dark eyes eloquent with meaning. She immediately made a move to close the distance between them, but he shook his head ever so slightly. She stayed where she was, puzzled by his action. The Jiboans already knew they were traveling together; they were both in a sea of trouble, why could they not stand together against their captors?

Her heartbeat accelerated. Maybe he had a plan. She gazed around at the blue-tattooed faces, realizing how very outnumbered they were. More likely, knowing Sarak, he probably hoped to draw attention away from her, although in their present predicament, located at the center of every gaze, that seemed impossible. Still, if he wished her to stay put, she would not defy him.

"Sit. Make yourselves comfortable."

This inane comment came from Wodabi himself and brought another ringing chorus of laugh-

ter. Phada had not noticed him at first because he
was seated behind her, closer to the door than to
the center of the room, and he was surrounded by
his inner circle of males. He looked strong and
fierce, with a head of curly black hair and startling
white teeth that flashed when he laughed. His skin
was more swarthy than some of the others', and
the blue tattoos on his face were not as noticeable.
His eyes were the same as she remembered from
earlier though, intense and shrewd and so dark in
color Phada thought they might actually be black.
He did not look like someone she wanted to pass
within a thousand measures of, never mind share
table talk with in these close quarters.

Sarak jerked his head at her. She frowned. If he
wanted her to sit, she would sit. She had no idea
of the customs of these people, but she did not
think their offer was one of hospitality. She lowered herself to the rug, feeling behind her with her
hands as she bent her legs to one side. She did not
take her eyes off Sarak in case he wanted her to
do something. Sarak managed to sit more gracefully, in spite of his bound hands.

No one bothered to offer them food or drink,
although Phada noticed several of the women
staring in her direction, their expressions filled
with pity. Whatever was in store, she did not think
she was going to enjoy it. She glanced at Sarak
from time to time, but it was obvious he was not
going to acknowledge her, so she focused her attention on the pattern in the rug beneath her. In
fact she scrutinized it so long and so hard she
should be able to weave an exact replica of the
quivering lines and diamond shapes—if she ever
managed to get out of here.

Her eyes watered from all the smoke in the
room. As if the crude lamps which gave off a grayish haze along with their light were not enough,
many of the men puffed on pipes filled with some

horrible plant or herb. Whatever it was, the stench was awful, sharp and bitter, and it made her eyes smart and her lungs wheeze.

Suddenly a hush fell over the assembly. Phada waited nervously. To her surprise, the sound of music filled the tent. She turned her head to find that several of the males had picked up the Jiboan version of a stringfiddle, filling the air with their mournful notes. They started out with a slow, deep rhythm. People clapped along, but then the pace picked up, faster and faster until Phada found her heart beating more quickly in anticipation, although she did not know what to expect.

Loud, feminine screams erupted from the entranceway, followed by the screamers themselves, four Jiboan females in filmy garments that flowed around their lithe bodies, along with their waist-length black hair as they leapt into the inner circle and began dancing. They swirled and dipped, waving their arms in graceful arcs and flinging their hair around as they circled closer to Sarak. The men shouted ribald comments which only seemed to incite them to wilder movements.

Sarak did not move. Instead he stared straight ahead, seemingly unheeding of the tangle of graceful female bodies that ebbed and flowed around him. Phada returned her attention to Wodabi. She noticed the malicious hostility glinting in his eyes and realized that this performance was for Sarak's benefit, although what the Jiboans hoped to achieve with it was beyond her.

Wodabi held up his hand and the music instantly stopped. "I see that our guest is trying to appear uninterested in the pageant before him, when we all know Mesaran warriors have a definite taste for Jiboan female flesh." Several of the males guffawed while some hooted in derision. "I do not wonder at this, for Dalcor has told us of your reduced male powers. Did he make you a eunuch that you do not react to what is displayed before you?"

A muscle twitched in Sarak's cheek but otherwise Phada could detect no other movement. He must be made of stone, she thought as she shifted to relieve the discomfort of sitting in a position to which she was not accustomed. One of the dancers moved closer to Sarak, leaning down with exaggerated motions to lift his breechcloth and peer beneath it. Phada blushed at her boldness but the woman seemed to have no such compunctions as she rose to her feet and grinned, shaking her head in denial of the charge.

"He has all the right parts," she announced. The group roared in reply.

"No matter," Wodabi continued with an evil smile. "However Dalcor achieved it, we know that your strength has been drained away at the same time that your desires have become heightened. It will be amusing to watch you respond to the wiles of Mahina and the others, although I am sorry to tell you that you will not be allowed to find relief."

Phada jumped to her feet, unable to restrain herself another millimark. "You are the worst brutes I have ever known," she screamed at the startled leader. "Is this what you call entertainment, thirty of you goading a single warrior who is tied? How brave! How heroic! I would think you could find something better to do. I do not wonder that the Goddess has cursed your people to roam the desert for all eternity."

"Phada, do not distress yourself," Sarak said, his gaze suddenly riveted on her face where before he would not even look at her. "I can deal with this."

"Deal with it? These people are barbarians," she cried. "You are worth more than all of them put together."

Something flashed in his dark eyes, but before she could think about what it meant, two wiry Jiboans grabbed her arms and dragged her over to the low table in front of Wodabi.

"Sit here, little firespitter," he said, grinning. "I admire your loyalty to a warrior we both know is beneath you in every way."

She made no reply to that, not trusting herself to answer civilly, which she knew she must do unless she wanted to get herself into more trouble.

"I like your spirit," the tattooed leader continued. "I promise you have nothing to worry about until we get to Mesara. Come, ease your mind. I will make you the same offer we give our excess daughters and allow you to keep a percentage of the money you earn coupling with the warriors."

"Why in the name of Mother Elithra would I want to do that?"

He laughed at her ignorance. "Because in time you will be able to buy your freedom."

He looked so pleased at what he considered his own generosity that Phada yearned to spit in his blue-tattooed face. She managed to restrain herself. Carrying on like a wild clawcat was not going to get her anywhere, she reminded herself. She had to learn everything she could about these people in the hope that it would eventually be useful.

"How much of a percentage do you give them?"

"Two. Sometimes five if they are really eager."

"You mean you keep ninety-eight percent of the profits for yourself?" she yelped. She could not even begin to inject enough scorn into her voice to reflect the disgust she felt at such unfairness, especially when the daughters were doing all the work.

"Of course." He offered her a portion of the meat he was eating. She refused, hungry though she was, because he had already gnawed off one corner. "Only the eldest daughter can be given in bonding, so this allows the others a way to buy their own tent and their freedom. And it fills the tribe's coffers. Everybody gets something."

Phada rolled her eyes, but the leader did not notice. He clapped his hands and the music recommenced. The dancers closed in on Sarak, reaching out to fondle his body, touch his skin, caress his chest. Did he long to mate with one of those women? she wondered. All of them? She had heard that a dominator possessed a large appetite when it came to the pleasures of the flesh, although Sarak had easily been able to resist her. She closed her eyes, unable to bear watching any longer.

And yet the images continued to haunt her. Sarak, sitting with his legs crossed and his back straight. His poor burned back. He did not even flinch from their caresses as the hands of the women slid all over his reddened flesh. Did that mean he was enjoying their touch? Was he as aroused as he had been at the hut when he thought her a Jiboan female?

In spite of her command not to think about it, she found herself wondering about the mating act itself. A warrior was only allowed to mate if his pallet partner had complete control by straddling him. Since that aborted attempt to mate with Taltos, she had never really considered how it would feel to have that part of a man inside her, but she found herself dwelling on it now, much to her discomfort. The thought of sitting atop Sarak caused a funny, melting sensation deep within her. Probably from the shock of pondering such forbidden things, she quickly assured herself, things a dedicated Keeper had no time for because she had other priorities.

Phada squirmed a bit on the rug, then opened her eyes. No one seemed to be paying her any attention, thank the Goddess. She tried not to look in Sarak's direction but she could not help herself. He was still sitting there, legs crossed, with that stoic expression drawing the skin of his face taut. If he were flushed no one could tell, since his flesh was already reddened. The Jiboan women continued to laugh and dance and touch him.

Another image flashed into her suddenly ungovernable mind. What would happen if Sarak were ever allowed to unleash his full strength and desire by lying on top of the woman, pressing himself down on her smaller, more delicate body, the way Mesaran males were allowed to mate? Of course Mesaran males eventually pledged their lives to a female and bonded with her and so could be trusted to be tender and gentle. Sarak would be intense no matter how he mated. She wondered how it would feel to be the focus of such a proud warrior's attention, to have complete access to his body in the mating dance. Somehow she could not imagine any woman wielding control over Sarak's mind or his muscled body. He would always be the one to remain in command.

Even though he was not looking in her direction, Sarak could see Phada's form out of the corner of his eye. He knew he could bear anything they did to him. He did not mind for himself but he was shamed that Phada was there to watch. He could not look directly at her, he tried not even to think about her. He clenched his teeth together even harder as one of the dancers stroked his chest, forcing his mind to concentrate on the pain of her long nails raking across his tender, sunburned flesh.

He did not feel anything for these Jiboan wenches, even though they touched him the way they had been trained, caresses meant to arouse and tantalize rather than to give pleasure for its own sake. Their skin was smooth but it was tanned, not pale. Their eyes, dark and lined with black, did not tempt him as did the stormy blue-gray color of Phada's, free of enhancement, direct and open and without wiles.

In spite of his will, his mind drifted into further thoughts of the Keeper's apprentice, with her tan hair and beautiful pale skin. He recalled the courage and determination she had shown in the face of odds that would beat down the most ferocious warrior. He remembered how she had cared for him while he was in the throes of faral dependence. Even tonight, his heart had warmed with pride when she had leapt to her feet to defend him. *You are worth more than all of them put together*, she had said in front of the entire gathering. No matter what happened after this, he would never forget that moment. Of course she had called the Jiboans brutes and barbarians, terms she had tossed in his direction on more than one occasion. These were obviously the worst insults she could conjure up, but that did not lessen what she had done.

He assured himself that her actions were the result of her loyal character and did not mean that she harbored any special feelings for him, other than as a necessary partner in her quest to save Mesara. It certainly did not mean she wanted him to place his brute hands upon her. He doubted the thought had ever crossed her mind the way it seemed to do with him so regularly. He was an opportunistic animal to think of using her in that way.

He closed his eyes, a big mistake, for suddenly the hands that caressed his body with such knowledge became Phada's hands, the sounds of rustling cloth became Phada's kenta when she removed it in the tent before settling down to rest. Much to his alarm, he felt himself harden. He quickly wiped all thought of her from his mind, instead forcing himself to concentrate on a particularly difficult sword-thrusting drill he had of-

ten practiced with Mizor behind the warriors'
barracks.

When they finally realized they would get no response from him, the dancers moved off to find
more cooperative partners. Sarak breathed a sigh
of relief as he watched them bend and sway over
the low tables where a cluster of Jiboan males
were seated.

Over in another corner, several Jiboans roared
with appreciation at some sally from one of the
dancers. The women behind them in the circle
covered their mouths with their hands in giggling
embarrassment. These more sedately dressed females were the honored mated partners and
mothers of the tribe's children and so were kept
more sheltered than the "excess" daughters whose
favors were sold in the barracks and to the males
of other cultures. Sarak knew that even after these
other daughters achieved their freedom and
maintained their own tents, many of them continued to sell their services, finding it a continuing
source of income that could be put away for their
old age.

Wodabi made a curt motion with his hand and
the women immediately began clearing the dishes
from the tables. In a matter of moments, they had
removed all evidence of the meal. Wodabi bowed
his head respectfully to one of the women. She
seemed to be the oldest female there, the matri-
arch of the tribe, perhaps. She returned his gesture, obviously one of dismissal, since the entire
group of women filed out of the tent, each one
bowing formally as she took her leave.

Now only the males and the five dancers remained. And Phada, who still sat in front of the
head male's table. At another signal from Wodabi,
several of the males rose to their feet and crossed
the room to one corner, where piles of their supplies had been unloaded and stacked. They ig-

nored the sacks and wooden crates on the ground, instead reaching for several large goatskin bags that dangled from hooks attached to the tent poles.

Sarak suspected they did not contain water. He was right. Soon the Jiboans were passing the skin from table to table, pouring the contents into their cups. Even if the unmistakably tangy smell of vetch had not soon filled the air, he would have guessed the contents from the suddenly increased noise level inside the tent.

A loud, piercing female giggle turned all heads in that direction. The Jiboan called Babua had pulled the lead dancer into his lap and was fondling her breast. He lifted his gaze until it met Sarak's from across the room and the warrior's stomach clenched at the intention he saw in the other male's eyes. They were not done with him yet. Now that they had dismissed the women and begun getting drunk on vetch, he was fair game.

"Listen well, my brothers, and let me tell you the truth about this mighty Mesaran warrior." Babua gestured contemptuously at Sarak before raising his cup and pointing around the circle of eager, laughing faces turned toward him. He took a long swallow of his drink, then grinned. His white teeth gleamed against the dark skin of his face. "We all fear them, do we not?"

Shouts of protest greeted this comment, followed by more raucous laughter. The dancer in Babua's lap, a sultry creature with long, curling black hair, rearranged her body until she was able to reach his neck, which she began kissing with passionate abandon. Sarak knew better than to look away from the spectacle—it would only make matters worse.

"Tell us, Jilanda," the Jiboan continued. "How does it feel to mate with a mighty dominator, the pride of Mesara?"

"It is as nothing. We feel nothing when we go to their pallets," she answered, her sloe-eyed gazed fixed on Babua's face, her full lips parted in a smile that promised much. She flicked her fingers in Sarak's direction as if he were no more than a pesky fleafly.

"Warriors think they know how to pleasure a female but it is a lie," Babua said, scooping the voluptuous Jilanda into his arms and rising to his feet. She twined around his body like a treesnake. "They do not kiss the female's mouth. They do not caress her skin to ready her for the act. They do not even mate as true males but take the woman's position beneath. Then, a few thrusts"—he demonstrated what he meant by graphically pumping his hips—"and it is over."

He finished his diatribe with an obscene gesture toward his loins before dropping back into his seat, his mouth open wide as his mirth spilled out. Sarak was so ashamed that Phada was a witness to his crudeness, he could feel the color rising to his cheeks. Even the tips of his ears felt red. He ventured a quick glance in her direction. Her eyes were downcast, her hands clasped in her lap. She looked uncomfortable, as if she would rather be anywhere else on Elithra. He could not blame her.

And yet, in spite of his embarrassment, he could not help the direction of his puzzled thoughts. Was it true, he wondered? Was there more to mating than the simple act of thrust and climax? As a warrior he had never been taught how to please a female. It was a skill thought unnecessary, since a dominator could never bond and had no need of the tactics of wooing. They paid for their pleasure and therefore took it.

He had never considered it before, but now it seemed obvious that the Jiboan wenches who came to the barracks had been told to simulate the sounds of pleasure. Satisfied customers meant repeat business. It also meant that the act lasted a shorter amount of time and they could collect their payment more quickly. After all, they were only doing it as a means to an end, in order to purchase their freedom, not for their own pleasure.

Sarak remained stoic through the taunts that the Jiboans continued to hurl his way. His bound arms ached, his legs had become cramped from sitting in one position for so long, but he dared not move and call further attention to himself. The celebration seemed to be winding down. Already several Jiboan males had slipped away, one of them obviously a man of some wealth because he proudly displayed a dancer on each arm as he ducked through the shelter's opening.

Phada's head drooped with fatigue. She had to be as exhausted as he was. Wodabi rose to his feet, raising his arms in dismissal, the folds of his red and yellow robe billowing gracefully around him. The interminable evening was finally over.

"We must separate the captives," he announced. "Escort the woman back to her tent. Babua, set up one of your spare dwellings and take this mighty warrior there."

"It is not possible. I plan to sell that tent when we reach Yalala."

"You, Sanu. I know you have an extra shelter. Put the warrior in it."

"But, Wodabi, I have been promised a purse of coins for it from Dalebba who wishes to buy it for her daughter who has just become betrothed."

Wodabi snorted in disgust. "Never mind. I am sure all your shelters are worth coins on the market and you are all too shrewd to forgo the profit."

He stalked around the table to where Phada sat, her elbows propped on her knees to hold up her weary body. When he reached her, he grabbed her arm and jerked her to her feet. "Tell me, Keeper, are you eager to face your task of mating with the Mesaran warriors?"

She came to life at the question. "I would rather die," she spat, her face distorted with revulsion. Sarak felt as though he had sustained a mortal blow.

"Do you see, my brothers? We can place them in the same tent after all. She will not touch him and he cannot touch her. Babua, take two men and post a guard at all times. We head for Mesara at cycle-rise."

As they hustled him out, Sarak noticed a pile of familiar-looking brown woven sacks. Faral, he thought in amazement. Yes, it was the spice; he could smell its sweet fragrance as he passed by. Did these Jiboans trade it? It was obvious that they did not use it. They seemed to have no idea of its properties or they would have already fed him some. He chuckled mirthlessly to himself. It was more likely they were too greedy to try any for themselves, not when it was worth a purse of coins.

The sun was barely hovering over the western horizon when they reached the tent. The two Jiboans who held him captive shoved him inside. He stumbled before losing his balance completely, landing in a heap not far from where Phada sat huddled, her knees gathered to her chest and her arms wrapped around them.

"Sarak," she cried. She crawled over to him, her eyes brimming with concern. Her expression soothed away a small portion of his hurt and anger, although it did not touch the core. "Are you all right? These Jiboans are a vile and disgusting people. I am at a loss for words to convey the depths of my loathing for their crude ways."

"I think you have made a good start," Sarak replied blandly. He pulled himself into a sitting position, using his bound arms for leverage. At least some of his strength was returning now that he had been off the spice these cycles. He realized with a start that he no longer craved its taste after smelling it in the Jiboan main tent. Looking at their present predicament it was not much to crow about, but it was something.

"Sarak." Phada's voice called him back to the present. "What do we do now?"

He turned in a half-circle until his back was to her, then held out his wrists. "See if you can untie me."

Phada nodded. "Yes, of course."

She scooted closer, reaching for the leather thongs, careful not to touch him anywhere else because of his raw, reddened skin. His sunburn looked much worse than it had earlier. Some of his flesh had already begun to blister, especially along the tops of his shoulders.

"Wait," she said, looking around for her pack. "Let me put some salve on that burn."

"We do not have time for that." He impatiently thrust his hands toward her. "Besides, I did not completely unload the dobbies. Your pack is outside."

She felt like wailing aloud at this further demonstration of their horrible reversal of fortune, then decided it could wait until after they escaped—if they ever managed to pull off that difficult feat. Even if she did get him untied, what then? There were three guards prowling around their tent and only one Sarak, and he had not recovered his full strength from his ordeal with the faral, never mind the stress of a postzenith spent in the broiling sun. Still, he was correct; their most important task was getting out of here.

She worked at the knots, struggling and huffing as her fingers plucked and pulled at the thongs. Whoever had tied him had done a masterful job, winding length after length around Sarak's wrists and knotting the cord at various intervals until Phada had no idea which knot to loosen to get the most benefit. No matter what she tried, his bonds seemed to grow tighter rather than looser until the leather scored the already ripped skin of his wrists.

After trying everything she could think of, Phada sat back on her heels and blew out her breath. She knew her efforts were hurting him and she could not bear it another moment. "No," she moaned, her hands clasped together in dismay. "I am only making it worse."

"It does not matter. Try again."

"It is no use, Sarak," she cried. "No matter what I do, they only tighten."

"Jiboan slipshank knots," he muttered in disgust. He turned to gaze at her over his shoulder, his eyes softening at her obvious distress. "Leave them alone for now. You can try again later."

He drew himself up on his knees and moved toward the back of the tent. Jerking his head at Phada, he motioned for her to lift the material so he could peer out. No sooner had she done so than a sword swooped down toward the sand, barely missing cutting off Sarak's nose.

"Consider that a warning. Next time you pull a trick like that, I promise I will be more accurate." Babua's voice came out of the half-darkness.

Phada dropped the side of the shelter, her hands shaking with terror at the close call. Sarak did not look at all disturbed and she wanted to shriek at him to stop taking so many chances with his life. Did he truly value it so little when she was coming to count upon him so much? She drew in a deep, steadying breath. Women's tears would not get either of them very far. She must follow Sarak's example and keep her head.

"They are too alert for us to do anything," he said. "Come, let us rest for a while."

Phada did not protest. She was drained, both emotionally and physically. Maybe after a couple marks of sleep she would find herself less filled with despair. Just the thought of blocking out the reality of their plight seemed a Goddess-sent opportunity.

She searched the area for her kenta to use to cushion her head. Obviously the Jiboans had taken it and Sarak's as well. The only things inside the shelter were their sleeping mats. Well, no matter, it was always hot inside the tent and she was too tired to miss a pillow.

She drifted into immediate sleep only to wake up shivering a short time later. She discovered she had already curled up in a tight ball against the chill. She remembered the nights they had trudged through the desert, taking advantage of the lowered temperatures that descended across the Calabian after the sun dipped below the horizon. She realized now that it had grown cooler then, but their exertions as well as their enfolding robes had kept them warm.

Now they were farther into the desert than ever before, much farther south than Mesara, which lay at the northern pole of the planet. The sun hid its face longer beneath the horizon at this location, so of course the nights would grow increasingly colder. Still, she could not ever remember feeling this bone-wrenching cold in her entire life.

If she were this chilled, what about poor Sarak? Between his sun-reddened skin and the scant warrior garb that barely provided cover, let alone warmth, he must be freezing to death. She rolled over so she could face him. He lay a short distance away, his back to her, his body shaking in a futile effort to warm itself. She could hear his teeth chattering.

As Phada crawled closer to him, she could feel that he was generating body heat all right, the bulk of it dissipating directly into the cold night air, doing little to aid his dilemma. Before she could stop herself, before she could think about what she was about to do, she slithered the rest of the way onto his sleeping mat and wrapped her arms as far around his chest as she could.

The startling sensation of a warm, definitely female body pressed against his back shocked Sarak from half-sleep into instant awareness. His breathing stopped, and his entire body froze when he realized that it was Phada who held him in her arms, Phada whose thighs pushed against the backs of his, sending flames of fire darting along the surface of his skin.

He closed his eyes against the sheer pleasure of it. What in the name of the merciful Goddess was she trying to do to him? His loins tightened and his heart began to pound like the waves of the sea against the beach. He glanced down at her hands where they gripped each other, their smooth skin pale against the deeper color of his more weathered flesh. She had threaded one of her arms through the space between his neck and the ground while the other snaked around his bound upper bicep to meet it. Her slender fingers were interlaced as she held on tightly.

She was trying to warm him, his dazed mind finally realized. Her hands gently rubbed along his arms and chest, causing licks of blue-hot heat to move along with the now coursing blood in his veins. He knew he should say something to stop her but he could not utter a sound. The ties at his wrists had cut off his circulation for marks and yet he swore he could feel the tender muscles of her stomach where his cold, numb hands rested. He was certainly aware of the searing imprint of her breasts against his shoulder blades, even through her tunic. She made no attempt to retain any sort of distance between them, so intent was she on her task.

It took him a moment to gather his wits together to speak, so affected was he by her sacrifice. "Phada," he finally said, turning his head so his whispered words would carry over his shoulder. He did not want one of their guards poking his head in to check on them now. "I am more grateful than I can say for your kind concern, but it is not seemly for you to do this."

She continued her gentle kneading of his chilled flesh as she replied, "You are half dead with the cold."

"It matters not. You must stop."

"Oh!" Her hands stilled. "Am I hurting you?"

He wanted to say yes, she was piercing him to his very soul. But he could not. "No, you are not hurting me."

Sarak's breath hissed out as he closed his eyes. He was painfully aroused, although Phada seemed to be unaware of his condition. If he turned around she would notice soon enough. The breechcloth provided nothing in the way of concealment. He must remember that she had chosen the intellectual path and so was still an innocent in the ways of the flesh. She did not realize what she was doing to him.

"Does it not help make you warm?"

"It makes me too warm," he muttered in embarrassment.

"I see," she answered in a small voice. "So you are still thinking of those Jiboan dancers."

Sarak did not hesitate but quickly grasped at the reason she had, in her innocence, handed to him. He consoled himself that it was not a flat-out lie—now that she had brought the subject of the dancers into their discussion, he was certainly thinking about them—they were simply not the cause of his distress. "Yes."

"They are . . . very skilled."

"It is their trade. They are trained in its ways."

He felt the wisp of her sigh against the sensitized skin of his back. "They must be if they can make you desire them even when you are no longer in their presence."

Sarak knew he had to change the subject before he lost the last remaining vestiges of his sanity. "I am warm enough to sleep now. Believe me, Phada, there is nothing else we can do until cyclerise, when we break camp. Even then our only hope is that one of your Jiboan captors drops his guard long enough for you to escape."

"I am not leaving without you!"

"If you get the chance, you must," he told her fiercely.

She had no time to frame another protest, for suddenly they heard a faint noise at the entrance. Someone was coming into the tent. Phada did not care if the Jiboans saw her pressed so intimately to the warrior's body. What did it matter anymore? She had no desire to quit Sarak's warmth, nor could she bear the thought of leaving him to shiver. Let them do to her what they wanted; her life had been over since Dalcor's plot to rule Mesara had succeeded.

They waited breathlessly as the flap covering the doorway quivered and jerked up and down. What was going on? It looked as if someone were punching the side of the tent. Had Babua or one of the other guards decided they needed more entertainment?

To their utter amazement, Gisba poked her head inside. Her bright, beady eyes fastened immediately on Phada, and with a throaty chirp she scrambled the rest of the way into the shelter.

# *Chapter Twelve*

"Gisba!" Phada gasped. The bird dropped to its knees next to her mistress, chirping and warbling and poking her hard beak against Phada's face. "Yes, Gisba, I am glad to see you, too, but no more, please," she said breathlessly, shoving the eager dobby back. She looked up to find Sarak staring at them, shaking his head.

"Now I have seen everything," he muttered. "You two make a fine pair."

"I would hold my tongue if I were you," she replied with a smug smile. "I do not see your dobby in here trying to rescue us."

"Is that what she is doing?" He rolled over, struggling with his bound hands until he managed to right himself into a sitting position.

"Of course. Are you not, Gisba?" She fondled the big bird's knobby head affectionately in the way she knew the creature liked. Gisba warbled blissfully. "The Jiboans did not bother to unload her

204

saddle. See, she has brought us my pack. My healing salve is in there."

"Fine. I am glad to know my sunburn will be eased before I die."

Phada slanted him a triumphant look. "My vegetable knife is also in there."

His eyes widened as the knowledge hit home. He watched as Phada rifled through the contents of the pack, finally producing the knife. She frowned as she stared at its small, unimpressive blade, which jiggled back and forth because of a loose connection to the worn wooden handle. After the honed, ornate daggers the Jiboans carried at their sides, this looked about as threatening as a sharpened stick.

Sarak, however, grunted in satisfaction. "Your fierce little vegetable knife. I well remember the first time I saw you wielding that thing."

"Never mind reminiscing now." She hurried to kneel beside him. "Let me cut you free."

It was easier said than done. Phada struggled to saw through the leather thongs that were wrapped so tightly around Sarak's wrists. The task was made more difficult because she did not want to cut him in the process, although the blade was so dull it was probably not something she needed to worry about.

"What are you doing back there?" Sarak asked impatiently. He wiggled his fingers.

"They tied you well."

He chuckled. "Perhaps you should let your devoted pet packbird bite me free."

"Do not make fun of Gisba."

"I promise you, Phada, if we get out of here alive, I will never make fun of Gisba again."

She laughed. "I will hold you to that."

"Good. Now hurry. We do not know when our friend Babua might decide to pay us a friendly visit."

She froze as a thought struck her. "What if someone saw Gisba come in here?"

"I think we would have known by now had that been the case."

"Perhaps. Or perhaps they are waiting outside the tent for you to make your move."

"Now there is a cheerful thought."

She managed to sever another of the many thongs that crisscrossed between his wrists. A few more and Sarak would be free. "Do you think we can get away?"

"Finish cutting me free and I will tell you."

"I am working as fast as I can."

She realized their chances of escaping from their captors were slim, but just knowing that Sarak would soon be untied lifted her spirits immeasurably, perhaps more than such an action warranted. Only a couple more strands to go, she thought. Sarak, however, had come to the end of his patience and began jerking his hands apart. One final, mighty tug and his bindings released him.

He groaned as he eased his arms to his sides, flexing his stiff fingers at the same time. He had been in that unnatural position for most of an entire suncycle, Phada realized. Just the fact that Sarak even allowed that little moan to escape his whitened lips told her that the pain must be excruciating. Add to it the agony his sun-reddened flesh must be causing him and Phada could not stop herself from wincing in sympathy. She wanted to rub her healing salve all over him, especially along the tops of his shoulders where the sun had beat down the hardest, but she knew he would never allow that, not when time was of the essence.

"What now?" she asked.

"Now we figure out where those three guards are stationed. And we hope that the other two consumed more vetch than Babua did." He moved silently to the back of the shelter, dropped to his stomach in the sand, and lifted the hem of the tent the barest fraction of a measure. Phada remained absolutely still as he peered out. "Curse it, it will soon be sunrise. We have very little time if we hope to slip away unnoticed."

He got to his feet, stamping them softly against the ground, shaking his arms and flexing his muscles. Phada felt her stomach drop to her knees as the danger of what he was about to attempt became more apparent. In spite of the Jiboans' desire to keep their captive alive, they might still end up killing him in the melee that would ensue should one of the guards manage to call out for assistance. She would be all alone then, without Sarak's bracing presence, without anything to hope for—not for herself and not for Mesara. She almost wanted to cry out to forget it, but of course that was impossible. They had to take the chance.

She took a deep breath, hoping it might restore her courage. It did not help very much. But then she looked at Sarak, at the determination etched on the features of his handsome face. She realized with a jolt of intense emotion that he had grown handsome in her sight. She had been mistaken when she had considered him too big and too much the dominator to be as attractive as the leaner, less muscular Mesaran males.

If anyone could get them out of here, it was Sarak. She was surprised to discover she believed that with every fiber of her being. Whatever assistance he asked of her, she swore she would give to him without question.

"I need you to provide a distraction," he said.

"What should I do?"

"You must call out to Babua at the front of the tent while I take care of the other two at the rear."

"The other two!"

"From what I could see, it looks as if they are

sleeping off the effects of too much vetch. That should make them easy enough to handle."

She made a face. "As long as one of them does not notice you before you are able to dispatch his brother," she commented wryly.

"It is our only hope. And we must act quickly. Go now," he said, jerking his head toward the flap of the tent. "I am ready whenever you are."

Phada stepped toward the entrance, her heart pounding, not at all sure what she intended to do. She glanced back to find that Sarak had once again dropped to the ground, prepared to slip beneath the side of the tent as soon as she made her move. He clutched the vegetable knife in one large hand, where it looked even less threatening than it had before.

She bit her lip. Babua had been close to the entrance when he had narrowly missed them with his sword earlier, but he must have moved away from that position since then. How else had Gisba managed to get inside without raising a cry of protest? She could not imagine that the Jiboans would ignore a gangly packbird, not when she still had all their possessions attached to her saddle.

Still, she had no intention of sticking her head beyond the flap without ample warning. "Guard," she called out boldly. "Guard, I wish to speak to you."

She knew her timing was critical. She wanted to assure that the Jiboan approached the entrance, and yet she did not want him to actually come inside before Sarak could escape out the back.

Gisba crowded her from behind, pushing against the middle of Phada's shoulder blades, thinking her mistress was going to exit the shelter. She was not about to be left behind. The devoted creature warbled and clicked her eager approval into Phada's ear. "Stop it," she hissed at the dobby.

And then the bird solved Phada's problem with a mighty push, thrusting her right out through the tent flap and onto the sand at Babua's feet.

The Jiboan already had his dagger drawn. He thrust it with menacing intent toward Phada's chest, using it to gesture her back inside. From this close distance, she could see the whirling pattern of blue lines that covered his face and emphasized the whiteness of his teeth as he leered at her.

"There is a problem," she said. She pointed at the bird. "See. This packbird is disturbing my sleep."

She almost burst out laughing when she heard how inane the statement actually sounded when spoken aloud. Babua did not even crack a smile. He motioned her to step aside, then sheathed the dagger before reaching for the dobby's reins. Gisba squeaked and ducked away, jerking the leather from his grip, then ran to plant herself behind Phada, her throat fluttering anxiously. Phada understood the bird's reluctance—she had no desire to place herself into Babua's hands either. She wished she could comfort the loyal bird but she dared not.

"Move aside," he ordered her.

She did, but the bird moved right along with her. Phada wanted to giggle at the sight they must be making, as if they were partners in a stately, ritual dance.

"She has become attached to me," Phada explained. She reached back to lay a reassuring hand against Gisba's chest.

"Stand aside. I will take her now." Babua looked determined. "Packbirds do not have enough brains to differentiate one master from another."

I beg to differ, Phada thought as the Jiboan again lunged for Gisba's reins and again came up empty-handed. The bird squawked and scrambled a safe distance off to Phada's right. Where was Sarak? she wondered, shifting her eyes to glance around the area without turning her head and making it too obvious she was searching for someone. Had he managed to overcome the two guards? She gazed back at Babua, who now circled a wary Gisba. Everyone thought dobbies were stupid, brainless creatures meant by the Goddess to be used as beasts of burden, but the crafty look in Gisba's eyes belied that notion.

A hint of movement behind Babua caught her attention. It had to be Sarak. "Please," Phada said, placing herself between the angry Jiboan and the bird. "Let her be. I am sorry I disturbed you. I think she should stay with me after all."

Sarak lunged, knocking Babua to the ground. A quick, lethal blow and the Jiboan lay motionless in the sand.

"I think she should stay with you also," he said, rising to his feet with a grin.

Phada decided she had never seen a more welcome sight in her entire life. She wanted to hug the big dominator, but she restrained herself. Time enough for her gratitude later, when they were truly clear of the Jiboan camp and on their way to Gorod once more.

He tossed her a kanzu. "Here, put this on."

She quickly donned the Jiboan male garb. It was much too long and the hem dragged in the sand. Also the wider cut of the neck caused the material to slip off her shoulders. Still, it would provide protection against the hot sun. They were going to have to travel during the hottest part of the cycle—they needed to put as much distance as they could between themselves and the Jiboans.

Sarak had donned another kanzu, presumably from one of the other guards. His was too short, only reaching halfway past his knees. Thank the

Goddess for the loose folds of the cloth that allowed some room for his broad shoulders. The garment looked small but not entirely uncomfortable.

Sarak ducked inside the tent and immediately returned, holding a length of the leather thong that had bound him. He handed it to her. "Here, use this as a belt."

As she tied the leather around her waist, he disappeared around the side of the tent, only to reappear leading their other packbird.

"I think she was coming to see where her companion had disappeared to," Sarak commented with a crooked grin. "Grab Gisba and let us get out of here."

Since their tent was located on the outskirts of the encampment, it was not difficult to slip away into the open desert. They moved quickly, quietly, along the length of one particularly large sand dune before Sarak decided it was safe enough to traverse it. Phada was breathless by the time they reached the other side. At least they were now out of sight of the camp. That did not mean they were safe, not by any means, but Phada felt much better anyway.

They did not talk. Sarak set a grueling pace and Phada found she had no breath left with which to speak. The sun crested the horizon not long after their escape, which meant they were still highly visible should they be pursued, especially wearing the distinctive red-and-yellow-patterned kanzus of the Jiboan tribe.

Marks later, sometime after cycle-rise, Sarak called a brief halt. "We will rest only long enough to unpack our food and water," he told her. "Once we do, we must get moving again. We can eat as we walk."

Phada nodded in reply. Talking was superfluous until after she could catch her breath. The thought of a long cool swallow of water practically revived her on the spot. She watched Sarak rifle through the various compartments on Gisba's saddle. He handed her a portion of graincake. Phada frowned, knowing she had not the heart even to attempt the dry, chewy food until she had a drink of water. She held it clutched in her hand.

"Do you think they will come after us?" she asked.

"I am hoping they drank too much vetch to rise very early this cycle. There is nothing worse than heat and bright sunlight after a night of downing cups of that potent brew."

Phada smiled. "You sound as if you know what you are talking about."

"I have drunk my share."

Phada noticed he avoided her gaze, as if ashamed of this fact, not that it was any kind of shocking revelation to her. Everyone knew the dominators favored vetch over vinasi. Knowing some of the things she now did about Sarak's life, she realized that drowning his reality in a barrel of Jiboan ale was not the worst crime she could imagine.

In fact, she found she could not fault him for anything this cycle. He had gotten them out of the Jiboan camp against all odds and with a little help from a dobby. "I hope you thanked Gisba for her timely assistance."

He chuckled. "I never thought I would be grateful to a packbird."

While Sarak moved to search the other dobby's saddle, Phada laid an affectionate arm around their rescuer's neck, giving her a squeeze. Gisba raised her head, uncoiling her long neck with a movement not unlike that of a greenback ground snake as she crooned out her appreciation. As awkward and odd-looking as they were, packbirds were also loving, loyal creatures. Phada thought their qualities had been grossly underestimated.

"Curse them," Sarak muttered. "Curse their sun-blackened, tattooed hides."

Phada was still smiling over the antics of the bird, but Sarak's tone caused her to frown. "What is it?" she asked.

"They did not touch our packs—except to remove the water."

"We have no water?"

"Not a drop." He shoved the flap of the saddle down with an angry gesture.

"Are you saying that they removed only the water on purpose, that they wanted us to escape?"

He shook his head. "I do not believe they wanted it, but they were well prepared for it in case we did."

"No water?" Phada's mouth had been dry before, but now she found she could barely swallow. Her tongue reached out to touch her parched lips. "What are we going to do?"

"They know we have no choice but to go back."

"No!" She whirled in alarm to face him. The thought of such utter defeat made her throat ache. She wanted to cry, but her thirsty body had no tears to spare. "Oh, no, Sarak, we cannot go back there."

"In case you have forgotten, we had to leave our tent behind as well. We have no shelter and no water."

Phada's suddenly shaky legs gave out and she slumped down to the sand, a puddle of red and yellow material at Gisba's huge, clawed feet. The promise of water to moisten the sticky insides of her mouth and throat was the only thing that had kept her placing one sandal in front of the other all this time. Now she did not think she could go any farther. And yet she refused to return to that Goddess-forsaken Jiboan camp, knowing the fate that awaited them.

"We cannot go back. They will bring you to Dalcor and he will kill you."

"Yes, but there is a chance I can help you escape, especially once we reach the jungle paths on the outskirts of Mesara."

She glared at him. It only made it worse, knowing his stubbornness was solely on her behalf. She could not imagine him giving himself up otherwise. "We have been through all this before. There is nowhere for me to go."

"Phada, I cannot drag you deeper into the desert only to watch you die."

"What about that oasis?"

"The Kali Oasis is at least another cycle from here. That is if we are lucky enough to stumble across it. We might pass it by completely."

"We have to try."

"No. It is out of the question."

"Going back is out of the question," she countered in exasperation. "If what you are saying is correct, the Jiboans will not follow us. They will sit in their tents and fondle women and drink vetch while they wait for us to come crawling back. Have you not noticed how quick they are to take advantage of any source of profit that may tumble into their laps as long as it does not take any real effort?"

He continued to stubbornly shake his head.

"I can make it through another cycle without water if you can," she goaded him softly.

He did not fall into her little trap. "It is not a question of who can last the longest. I have found that the desert is supremely indifferent when it comes to matters of survival."

"Exactly. That means we will have an even chance, just like any other creature beneath the blue sun."

"We are not desert dwellers; we do not know all the secrets of the great Calabian." He gazed at her, his eyes soft with an emotion she had never seen there before. "Ah, Phada," he said gently, reaching out his hand to touch her cheek with one long finger, then quickly dropping it to his side. "Do you think I have not come to realize you can do anything you set your mind to?"

"I only wish that were true," she replied with a crooked smile and a shake of her head. "If it were, we would already be continuing this journey to Gorod instead of standing here debating the issue." Her mouth widened into a genuine grin as she scanned his obdurate expression. "I think you must have gotten too much sun yestercycle, Sarak. Perhaps it addled your brain into concocting this good opinion of me, although I do not deny that I am flattered."

"I do not need to concoct anything when it comes to you, Keeper's apprentice, including my opinion," he grumbled. He sounded as fierce as he always did, but Phada knew he was not truly angry. "You are like a waterfall, able to wear down the hardest stone if given enough time."

"Does that mean I have worn you down, mighty warrior?" She cocked her head and placed her hands on her hips, unable to believe that she was actually teasing a dominator. How could she possibly feel so lighthearted in the midst of their terrible troubles? And yet she did.

"To a tiny pebble."

She chuckled softly at the image his reply conjured in her mind. "Good. Then let us keep moving. Please, Sarak, we have come all this way and endured so much. We cannot give up now."

"No, we cannot give up now," he agreed. "But you must ride one of the dobbies for a while to conserve your strength." She looked stricken so he added, "They are strong, surefooted desert birds, Phada. Your weight will not burden them. I know Gisba will be glad to carry you. I will shift some of the contents from her saddle to that of the other bird."

Phada nodded. He reached down to haul her to her feet, using one arm to steady her in the shifting sand until she recovered her balance. Sarak noted she did not flinch away from his unrequested gesture of assistance. Instead she gripped his forearm without a second thought, her fingers warm and firm upon his skin. He imagined the shock her sister Keepers would exhibit should they view Phada now, consorting with a dominator, touching his body as casually as if he were her bonded mate instead of her social inferior.

She allowed him to help her onto Gisba. The packbird turned her head to see who was climbing onto her back, then chirped loudly before returning to the throat vibrations that kept her cool. Sarak grabbed both sets of reins and they set off, heading south while the blazing blue-white sun approached its zenith high overhead. They would eventually have to stop and rest. There was no way they could continue to walk in the intense desert heat of the postzenith cycle. He was sure he could construct some sort of shelter using their kanzus and the dobbies.

He glanced back at Phada. She had pulled her hood down over most of her face so that all he could see was a portion of her mouth and nose. Her hands gripped the horn of the saddle beneath the covering of the too-long sleeves of her borrowed robes, and her legs dangled over one side amid the pom-poms and tassels. The jerky motions of the dobby might be uncomfortable, but at least she did not have to walk.

He rolled his head from side to side, stifling a small groan at the tightness of his burned skin. Even though he was protected from the direct rays of the sun, he could still feel its heat piercing through the layers of cloth. His mouth quirked up at one corner as he recalled Phada's comment about wearing him down. Did she but know it, she did not need to resort to such tactics with him. He had been conquered since the moment he had allowed her to tie him to the sleeping pallet.

He realized better than she did that they were more than likely marching to meet their deaths. As a warrior it was what he had always expected, but he did not wish such an end for Phada. And yet she was correct: what else was there for her back in Mesara? They had made their decision—it was in Mother Elithra's hands now.

Still, there was something to be said for being all alone in the desert with Phada. He could not find it in his heart to regret any of it.

Sarak looked at the makeshift shelter he had rigged with a silent groan of dismay. It was barely large enough for him, let alone the two of them. He had stretched their kanzus from the backs of the two sitting dobbies over to the side of a steep sand dune, where he had anchored the material with their saddles. The thought of crawling inside with the Keeper's apprentice made him swallow hard against the excitement and desire he felt stirring to life deep within his body. He was exhausted and knew Phada must be also—they had to rest.

He nodded to Phada. "Come," he said gruffly.

She crawled beneath the shelter. Their sleeping mats remained behind along with their tent, so they had to lie directly on the sand. As long as they did not move around too much, he supposed it should not be too bad. He took a deep breath and followed her inside.

She flashed him a somewhat subdued smile. "I remember what I felt when I entered our tent that first night in the desert. I was indignant because I did not think it was comfortable or luxurious enough for a Keeper's apprentice. Certainly not for a town woman of Mesara. I admit I did not think it was worth the trouble you took to steal it." She sighed. "What I would not give for that tent and those sleeping mats now."

He chuckled. "I suppose everything is relative."

"It is a lesson I have learned well these past cycles."

Sarak had placed her pack inside the shelter. She reached for it and removed the small jar that contained her healing salve. "Come, I must apply some of this to your burned skin."

"That is not necessary," he quickly assured her. He did not need the torment of Phada's hands all over his body along with everything else.

She frowned. "Not necessary? Do not be absurd. The sooner I rub this on, the sooner you will heal."

"I do not need your salve."

She eyed him uneasily. "Why not? Is it because you think we have no chance of reaching the Kali Oasis?"

That was another good reason, but he could not bring himself to say it aloud and dash her hopes. There would be time enough for that later. "No, of course not. I thought to save your salve for something more urgent than sun-reddened skin."

"If you could see your back you would think it urgent enough. Does it not pain you?"

He shrugged. "Not overly much."

"Of course, I had forgotten," she said with a grin as she got to her knees and gestured for him to roll over onto his stomach. "A warrior is trained to handle pain and deprivation." He heard her draw in a hissing breath at the sight of his back. He did not think it was as bad as all that, but Phada had a tender heart. "I will be as gentle as I can."

He closed his eyes at the first touch of her cool, soothing hands against his skin. It was heaven to

lie here and have Phada tend to him, a fantasy
come to life. She was more than gentle as she
smoothed the salve across his shoulders and down
his back. He could smell the pungent odor of the
mentholated alaba leaves it contained. The sticky
substance burned as she applied it, but the
strength of its healing properties soon spread a
layer of cool relief across his heated flesh.

She moved down to his lower back, spreading
the unguent on a little at a time so as not to stretch
his skin too much. He realized he was rhythmi-
cally pressing his loins into the sand, unconsciously trying to ease the ache that had suddenly
appeared. He felt her hesitate and was sure she
was going to pull away, appalled at his animalistic
reaction when she was only trying to heal him, not
arouse him. He sensed her hands hovering over
his back. Knowing Phada, she was probably trying
to find a tactful way of saying how much he disgusted her.

"What is it?" he asked. No sense prolonging the
tongue-lashing he knew he deserved. She was finished touching him in any case.

"I . . . I am sorry. I am being rude."

"What?" He flipped over so he could see her
face. Her cheeks were flushed with color. "I think
I am the one who should apologize."

"Why should you apologize when it is I who
have been caught staring instead of tending to
your injuries?" She ducked her chin even further
into her chest in an effort to avoid his gaze. "I
know it is unseemly, but I found myself curious
about your scars."

"My scars?" He was astonished. He had not expected that she was examining his body as she
rubbed the medicine into it. Then he realized the
further source of her embarrassment. The scars
she was talking about were mostly hidden beneath
his breechcloth. Only the trailing edges were vis-

ible as they snaked onto the small of his back and only if his garment slipped down as it must have when he rolled onto his stomach.

He quickly tugged the leather cloth to cover the damning evidence. It had been so many orbits ago he had almost forgotten how he had been punished during his early days in the Warrior Academy, beaten on his bare buttocks with a long, whiplike piece of coconut husk favored by the trainers because of the many rough strands it contained.

"I am sorry. It is none of my concern," she said softly.

"I was husked," he blurted out.

"What?"

"It is a form of punishment using a coconut-husk vine. I was beaten for insubordination."

"No, I do not believe it."

He grimaced. Her faith in him was touching, if misplaced. "It happened when I was eleven years old. I tried to run away from the Warrior Academy. They caught me just beyond the mangan-berry patch outside of town and dragged me back."

"That is abominable."

He shrugged, trying to appear indifferent, although he was far from it. "You are right. I disobeyed orders and I deserved it."

"You deserved it?" she exclaimed. "You were an eleven-year-old boy beaten hard enough to give you scars like that and you deserved it?"

Sarak's eyes widened. She was in a rage but it was not directed at him. He felt a weight lift from his shoulders that he had not even realized was there.

"Why did you run away?"

"I did not want to become a dominator."

"If that is truly the way we recruit our dominators, it does not seem fair."

"Most things in life are not. What matters is that I learned the lesson my trainer sought to teach me."

"What lesson is that?"

"That I was born to be a dominator. That I could not escape my destiny."

Phada looked at him then, really looked at him. He could not help but stare back into the depths of stormy blue-gray eyes that had become soft and gentle with emotion. He did not want her pity but he realized it was not pity he saw there. Still, whatever it was, he was not yet ready to accept it.

"Are you finished with that vile-smelling stuff?" he asked.

She smiled. "Not quite."

She dipped her fingers into the pot of salve, then reached toward his face. He grabbed her hand to stop the movement before she could make contact. What he really wanted to do was pull her on top of him so her knees were straddling his hips and her lower body was pressed against his.

"I can handle my face," he said.

They stared into each other's eyes for a small eternity out of time. Sarak knew he was beginning to breathe hard enough for her to notice. Sweet Mother, why could he not control himself with this female? He was as bad as the rutting bulloxen she had once compared him to.

Her next words stunned him out of his self-preoccupation.

"Is it very painful, this need warriors have to frequently mate?"

He shook his head, convinced he must be hallucinating. "Is that what you think is happening here? That I need to mate and that you are the only female this side of the Calabian?"

She shrugged, suddenly intent on returning the glob of salve covering the ends of her fingers back to its container. "You do not need to flatter me,

Sarak. I know I am not as alluring to you as those Jiboan women."

"Are you mad? They are but poor substitutes for the kind of female I really want."

"You mean someone like the queen?"

"I mean you."

"You would wish to mate with me were it allowed?"

He turned his head away from her astonished scrutiny, staring instead at the endless pale green sand outside the shelter. It did not cool his ardor. Curse it, she might as well know the truth. She must surely have guessed it by now from his behavior.

"I wish it more than anything I have ever wanted in my life," he admitted, then quickly added, "Do not worry, Phada. I will not rape you."

"As you did not rape the queen," she murmured softly. "I know I am safe with you."

Sarak closed his eyes against the wonderful agony of this trust she kept insisting on placing in his integrity. Pray Goddess he could continue to maintain it.

"I suppose you can tell I have never mated with a male," she added diffidently.

His eyes widened. "I thought all Keepers did so before they took their vows of service."

"Most of them do. I tried one time but it was an abysmal failure. I guess I do not possess the intense emotions of other women. I have been told my even-tempered nature will contribute toward making me a good Keeper."

"If they thought you even-tempered, they did not know you very well," he said teasingly. He could not help it; he felt as lighthearted as a young wingbird must feel on its first solo flight from the nest. All he knew was that it was sheer ecstasy to be able to act in such a free and easy manner with Phada, the way he had sometimes been able to do with Mizor or Zegon. And yet with Phada it was even more glorious, more enticing. He had never expected to experience anything like it in the daily monotony of his warrior's life.

"Are all dominators like you?"

"Most have not had the blind good fortune to cross paths with a certain Keeper's apprentice."

"Blind good fortune, indeed." She snorted in amusement. "Now I know you are jesting. I am sure you considered yourself most fortunate you crossed paths with me when I forced you to give up the pleasures of faral, never mind the way I have dragged you halfway across the planet on a dangerous if not impossible quest."

"Impossible quests seem to be my destiny, Phada." He smiled. "I would not have missed it for anything."

# *Chapter Thirteen*

Phada smiled as she dreamed about a ferocious storm that poured out rain from its ominous-looking clouds. Usually she hated the rain. She opened her eyes. They felt scratchy, as if filled with particles of dust. Her entire body felt dry and desiccated. The air around her was hot and stifling, painful to breathe into her burning lungs. She tried to swallow before she remembered why she could not—they had no water. They had not had any liquid in almost a cycle and they would not have any until they reached the Kali Oasis.

She stretched her sore body and then stiffened when she felt something solid pressed against her. She realized it was Sarak, his chest tight against her back and his face buried against the hair at the nape of her neck. She could feel his even breathing against her skin and it sent shivers of awareness down her spine and deep into the core of her body.

Of course the shelter was small, which explained

why Sarak had rolled toward her sometime during the postzenith. And yet he had never touched her in the similarly cramped confines of their tent. She supposed they were getting used to each other, if one could ever be said to grow comfortable with a warrior.

With a start, she realized she had done just that. Sarak no longer frightened her or disgusted her. Far from it. Much to her amazement, she had done practically everything but mate with the dominator. She had come to admire his courage and determination, his droll sense of humor, his care of her every need. She appreciated his unique way of looking at the world. He had taught her things she had never suspected about herself and even more about the Mesaran way of life.

She did not like to admit that she had also come to appreciate his muscled body, an instrument of strength and undeniable beauty. How had she ever thought otherwise? She could think of no one she would rather be with on this journey. Certainly not King Pavonis or Jobus or any other Mesaran male. Their highly trained minds, filled as they were with philosophy and poetry and rhetoric, would not be of much use in surviving the desert. Besides, she already knew most of what they did; she had no knowledge of the things Sarak took for granted.

She touched her hand to her cheek as the words Sarak had spoken to her before they went to sleep came flooding back. He had told her he wished to mate with her. He must admire her, she thought, feeling somewhat embarrassed and chagrined, yet secretly delighted. He must find her attractive as a female, even after experiencing all those sultry, knowledgeable Jiboan women. She had always considered herself a cool, calm, unemotional person, not particularly subject to the desires of the flesh about which so many Mesaran women loved to rhapsodize. And yet here she was, wondering what it might be like to mate, not with a Mesaran male, but with a dominator.

She cautiously stretched her body, taking care not to jostle the sleeping warrior. She could feel the coarse hairs that covered the flesh of his legs, but it was not unpleasant. He responded to her movement instantly, shifting his thighs so that they continued to cushion hers. That simple, unconscious action, something he would never do while awake, assured her that he was still deeply unconscious.

Another notion suddenly struck her. Suppose that Sarak was thinking of Queen Riga? Suppose that he believed mating with Phada was the closest he could come to joining with his adored sovereign? He had called out Riga's name in his faral-induced delirium, his face filled with tenderness and what she now recognized as desire. She did not look at all like the queen, but they were both town dwellers and they were both forbidden. Was that the lure that explained his desire for her?

She discovered that at the moment she did not care. She only wished that he would hold her and comfort her, reassure her that everything was going to be all right. She did not know how much longer she could last under these harsh conditions. She suspected that without her he could cover much more distance in the same amount of time. She did not want to be more of a burden to him than she already was.

Her alert senses knew the instant that Sarak awoke. She quickly closed her eyes and deepened her breathing, embarrassed in case he should learn that she had been awake and had not moved her body away from his. She felt him slowly slide his legs until they no longer touched hers. As soon as he shifted away, she became uncomfortably aware of the light sheen of perspiration that had formed from their intimate contact. She shivered as her moist skin cooled in the sultry air.

He touched her arm. "Come, Phada. We must get moving. If the Goddess sees fit to bless us, we should arrive at the oasis, perhaps by evenfall."

She rolled onto her back, turning her head to gaze at him. He looked as weary as she felt, despite their rest. The skin around his eyes was drawn taut and his mouth was flattened. His entire posture declared that he thought their chances of reaching the Kali were slim to none. "You do not sound as if you believe we will find it."

"I am trying to be realistic."

"Sometimes it is better to allow yourself to hope."

His gaze riveted on hers. "Is it?" he asked softly, his voice alive with hidden meaning.

For once she did not turn away. "Yes."

Suddenly he smiled and her heart turned over. "Then so be it."

It did not take long to dismantle the camp. They donned their kanzus and loaded up the dobbies. Gisba looked as cheerful as always, while her companion stood docilely beside her. Their reins had become tangled because the two comrades insisted on entwining their necks, chirping and warbling to each other in secret bird language.

Phada decided to walk for a while. Her bottom was sore from the saddle and she did not think she could feel any worse than she already did. Although the sun was slowly making its downward journey toward the horizon, its heat was still blistering. Phada was surprised the hems of their kanzus did not ignite like dry kindling beneath the intense, scorching rays. They could only hope that evenfall would arrive to relieve them. The nights were longer here in the desert, now that they were so far away from the pole of the planet. They were also colder. But feeling the sun penetrating through the material of her kanzu, Phada could not help but wish for the swift return of darkness, in spite of the drawbacks.

The postzenith dragged on endlessly. Phada continued to place one foot in front of the other, but she knew she would not be able to carry on for much longer without taking a rest. And yet she knew that stopping only provided the illusion of surcease. She was so thirsty that neither walking nor resting gave her any relief from the torment of her parched throat and cracked lips, her thickened tongue and strained, burning eyes.

They hardly said a word to each other. There was nothing to talk about and besides, she did not have the energy to speak and walk at the same time. Sarak seemed to be having no such difficulty, but she knew he had inner reserves she did not possess. Sometimes she focused her gaze on his broad form, clad in the colorful kanzu. With his trained warrior's body, he was able to keep up a steady pace, although he went slowly enough so that she would not fall behind.

She closed her eyes to ease their burning—only for a moment, or so she thought, until she found herself slumped on the ground. She felt Sarak kneeling beside her, propping her up with one arm around her shoulders and allowing her to rest against his thigh. When she realized his hand was softly brushing strands of hair away from her cheek, she finally opened her eyes to find him staring down at her with an expression on his face that took her breath away.

"Sarak." Her voice came out the barest croak of sound.

"Hush, Phada. Do not try to talk. We will rest here a while until the sun goes down. It will be cooler if we wait to walk after evenfall."

"No. If we stop now, I will never get up. It is best that we keep going."

"Curse this hellish place to perdition. I am sorry I ever let you talk me into continuing this journey."

"Oh no, Sarak," she said, stricken. "Do not say that. I thought you had no regrets."

"I did not—at least, not until this moment. It is just that I cannot bear to see you suffer like this." His mouth tightened and he gazed around as if the answer to all their problems were to be found in the pale desert dunes.

"Help me up," she said.

He assisted her to her feet. Then, before she knew what he was about, he hoisted her onto Gisba's saddle. There was plenty of room; their possessions had dwindled alarmingly since their encounter with the Jiboans.

Phada slumped over Gisba's neck as the bird resumed walking. The dobby's surefooted stride that caused her back to sway in jerky movements was no easier to endure than it had been previously, but Phada was too tired to try to compensate. Her bottom was numb, the backs of her legs raw from rubbing against the leather of the saddle. She tried to distract herself with the unusual elliptical motion of the swaying pom-poms, but it was no use.

She realized Sarak was speaking. She could see that his lips were moving but his voice sounded as if it came from very far away, even though he was pacing right alongside Gisba's outstretched neck. They were only a measure apart.

"What?" she asked, dazed.

"I think we should slaughter one of the birds for its lifeblood." He held up one hand. "Not Gisba, of course, but the other one."

"You cannot kill Ral!"

He stared at her darkly. She wanted to laugh at

his scowling expression but she did not have the strength. "Do not tell me you have named that one, too."

"I had a lot of time to think while we were walking." She tried to smile, her mouth parting just the tiniest fraction, but it caused one corner of her cracked lips to begin bleeding. "She deserves a name for her good service, even if she is not as personable as Gisba."

He shook his head. "Now I have heard everything. Do you not understand that it could mean the difference between life and death?"

"Please, Sarak." She dropped forward, her arms encircling the base of Gisba's skinny neck. She simply could not sit upright any longer. She buried her fingers beneath the warm feathers of the bird's chest and let her body slump awkwardly across the saddle. It was more uncomfortable than anything she could imagine with the saddle horn pressing into her stomach and her neck twisted at a horrible angle, but she no longer cared about anything except going to sleep and never waking up again. Pray Goddess, it would happen soon.

The next time she opened her eyes it was evenfall. The cooler air must have revived her. She groaned softly, her lungs jerking in air as she tried to straighten her spine from the cramped position she had been in for who knew how many marks. Sarak moved immediately to her side.

"Come, let me help you down."

He lifted her from Gisba's back, and she immediately crumpled to the sand in an agonized heap. The pain was excruciating, especially in her back and along her inner thighs. She must be permanently crippled, she thought, her eyes prickling as though she might cry, although no tears actually came to relieve their dryness. "Leave me,

Sarak. I cannot go any farther. I cannot even straighten my legs."

"You are cramped from remaining in one position for too long. It is my fault; I should have stopped long ago. But you seemed to be sleeping and I hoped to cover as much distance as I could before you awakened."

"What you should have done was stake me out for the carrion eaters. It is all I am fit for, food for birds."

He actually had the audacity to produce a small snort of laughter, in spite of his cracked and bleeding lips.

"I am glad I am such a source of amusement to you," she pouted, glaring at him with as much indignation as she could muster.

"You have become a source of many things to me, Phada," he said, his voice roughened by the lack of water, his brown eyes crinkled at the corners and gleaming softly in the half-light of the blue moon, which was barely peeking over the horizon. "I am not laughing at you; I am merely awed at your courage in spite of everything you have gone through."

"Hmph." She could not decide if she should allow his response to placate her. And then he began massaging her legs, his strong fingers pressing the soreness from her tight muscles, and she no longer cared. The sudden realization hit her that only a half mooncycle ago she would have died of shame and humiliation before allowing a warrior to touch her as freely as Sarak was now doing.

He kept up his ministrations for at least a quartermark before Phada felt ready to test her legs. At her nod, Sarak helped her to her feet. At first she hobbled back and forth like an old woman, but finally each movement contributed toward easing the stiffness from her abused muscles. If only they could solve the water problem as easily.

"How much further, do you think?"

He looked worried. "I do not know."

"We should have reached it already, should we not? We have missed it."

"I do not know." He took off his kanzu, spreading it on the sand and gesturing for her to sit. "Stay here with the dobbies. We had to detour around a towering sand dune about half a mark ago. I am going to return there and climb it. Perhaps I can spot something from the peak, especially now that the moon is rising."

She did not have a better plan so she nodded, suddenly uncomfortably conscious of the contours of his bared body, of the way his dark hair brushed against his shoulders, of his strongly etched profile. She thought she had grown used to seeing him thus, but she discovered that she was more aware of him than she had ever been. Her reaction did not make any sense to her. She should be growing ever more familiar and comfortable with his near nudity, not more reserved and awkward. Why was it she never reacted to circumstances the way others did?

She watched Sarak's form until it disappeared into the semidarkness of the desert night, her head pillowed on her hand. The sun was not in the sky, but rays of light continued to filter along the horizon even as the moon added luminescence from the opposite side. Phada slipped into a completely prone position and was soon fast asleep.

She awakened sometime later, disoriented and frightened. Her tongue was swollen and stuck to the roof of her mouth; she had to patiently work it free; otherwise it might begin bleeding. She tried not to think about how thirsty she was, instead staring into the surrounding darkness of the night that now closed in on her like a living presence, darkness such as she had never experienced. There was no sign of the sun now, and the moon rode higher in the sky than she had ever known it to do. Its blue light provided illumination but it was eerie and filled with shadows. The most astonishing sight, however, was the number of stars scattered across the dome of the sky. Phada had never seen so many, some twinkling brightly, others dim specks of white.

She was truly far from home, she realized, her heart slowing to a more even pace as she became more alert. She had left her beloved Mesara far behind and not just in physical distance. Her ideas and attitudes had undergone a change as well now that she was no longer among her own kind. She wondered how she was ever going to resume her normal mode of thinking and behavior when she finally did return.

She sighed, wondering how Sarak was faring on his quest to locate the Kali Oasis. How much time had passed since he had departed? Had he retraced his steps back to the dune already or was he even now on his way to her? She hoped he had been able to retain his sense of direction on this dark night.

She lay back down against the folds of the kanzu, which she now realized still smelled faintly of Sarak's skin and hair. Her stomach fluttered nervously at the thought of how he had worn the garment these past couple of cycles, since their timely escape from the Jiboans. She pulled the material of her kanzu closer against the chilly air before glancing over to check on the dobbies. The larger Gisba had wrapped her neck around Ral, who lay snuggled close, her beak buried beneath Gisba's wing.

It felt wonderful not to be walking or riding. Phada's gaze kept drifting back to the sky with its panorama of stars like tiny lighted paths through the vast reaches of the heavens. She knew she would never forget this sight for as long as she lived—no matter how long that might be.

She wanted to keep watch for Sarak's return but she was not even sure anymore which direction was north and which was south. The endless horizons of the desert at night were deceiving. She thought about the Goddess and her favorite consort, Taisom, about how they celebrated their love by traveling through the sky in a chariot of radiant light, passing right through the sun. Only the Goddess could endure the brightness of that orb at such close range; her lover had to hide his face in the folds of her tunic until they were well clear of its blue-hot rays.

Phada squinted her eyes at the stars, trying to imagine not being scorched by the sun at that close distance. A faint glow on the horizon caught her eye, causing her to sit up. But when she stared at the spot, it disappeared. Only when she approached it obliquely by glancing in the general direction from the corner of her eye could she keep the pale semicircle of light continually within the range of her vision.

What could it possibly be? It was too faint and too small in diameter to herald the coming of sunrise. Was it possibly another Jiboan camp? She clasped her hands together in excitement. Perhaps the Jiboans were stopped at the oasis. Even if they were not, Sarak might be able to steal some water from one of the tents while they lay sleeping. It was a dangerous idea, but they could not go on much longer without water.

The birds began stirring, causing her to scramble to her knees in a posture of self-defense.

"Phada."

She let out the breath she had been holding. She could barely discern the outline of his form. "Over here, Sarak."

He moved quickly to her side, dropping to the sand in a crouch, just beyond the edges of the spread kanzu. "Are you all right?"

"Yes, of course. Never mind that. What did you find out?"

His head drooped. He looked defeated. "Nothing," he said, his voice thick with disappointment and raspy from the lack of water. "I have never known such an all-encompassing darkness. I could see for a fairly good distance, or at least I think I could. But everything looked the same—endless, undulating sand dunes."

"I think I may have spotted something," she said, pointing eagerly. "There is a faint circle of light on the horizon."

He frowned. "I do not see anything."

"Wait. It is better if you do not look at it directly, but from more of an angle."

He did as she suggested. "Yes, yes, I see it now. A very faint light toward the southeast. Perhaps it is a Jiboan caravan returning from Gorod."

"Sarak, they might be camped at the oasis."

"Yes." He nodded. "They will have water in any case. And we are going to help ourselves."

Phada grabbed Gisba's reins with more enthusiasm than she had felt in what seemed a small eternity. The bird sensed her changed attitude and cheeped encouragingly. "How far away do you think it is?"

"It is difficult to tell, but I think we should be able to make it in a couple of marks at most."

"A couple of marks." She sighed as she fell into step beside him. "I can almost taste that cool, delicious water already. I think I would even drink vetch if someone would be so kind as to give me a cup."

Sarak chuckled. "That is my Phada, ever ready to take on a new challenge."

Phada felt warmed to the soles of her feet at Sarak's words, in spite of the still cooling temperature. She knew she possessed the mildest, most

uncurious of personalities, but somehow, on this
journey, she had become a brave explorer—of
herself and her world and most especially of the
warrior who trudged by her side. She had Sarak
to thank for all of it. He had not allowed her to
cower in fear but had forced her to act and react
at every turn. She knew she would be a better
Keeper because of her experiences both on the
Uninhabited Island and in the Calabian, and she
was grateful for it.

Helenina had tried to tell her she should not
shrink from experiencing life in all its manifestations. Now she knew how right her mentor had
been. If only I could tell her that, Phada thought
sadly. In fact, there are so many things I would
like to say. She pulled her thoughts away from
that unproductive pathway, filled as it was with
regret, and set her sights on the horizon, where
blessed water awaited them.

The moon had traversed a good portion of the
night sky and still they had not reached the source
of the light. Oddly enough, it had not grown
brighter as they approached it, instead remaining
the same pale, luminescent glow on the horizon,
barely visible unless looked at indirectly.

"Do you know of anything like this?" she asked.
She glanced over at him as he walked alongside
her, her mouth twitching into a smile at the sight
of Ral's large head hovering companionably just
above his shoulder as she plodded behind him. It
seemed the bird was developing an affection for
her master, although Phada decided she would let
Sarak figure that out for himself.

"Yes."

The rest of his answer was long in coming and
Phada felt a sense of disquiet wash over her. "Tell
me," she urged.

"I have heard tales of disappearing lights and
other desert mirages while on maneuvers in the

Calabian. Supposedly the consort of the Goddess sets various traps, hoping to lure the unwary deeper into the empty heart of the desert and away from the places sacred to Her, such as the Kali Oasis. We were always told to treat such reports as just another tactic to mislead us."

Phada's eyes widened in alarm. "You do not sound very sure about it."

"That is because I am not. There are many things we cannot explain."

"What should we do?"

"We have come this far. We might as well continue, at least until sunrise."

At the thought of the return of the hot sun and no water, Phada felt her hopes sliding away. Were they simply marching toward the nothingness of more sand? Was it some sort of trick to pull them away from the Kali instead of toward it? All her aches and pains returned full force and her mouth felt drier than burnt ashes.

They trudged onward. Suddenly the wind began to pick up, whipping her kanzu around her body with surprising force. The intermittent blasts of air came from behind and yet they still managed to swirl around her so that the sand pelted her face, creeping into her mouth and hair and stinging her vulnerable eyes. Phada pulled the garment closer but it did not help much.

Sarak pointed in the direction from which they had just come. She glanced over her shoulder to see a bank of clouds at their backs. In Mesara, clouds always heralded a storm, which promptly dropped its quota of rain on the town and then disappeared as the sun dried up the puddles and again heated the air to sultriness.

Did it rain in the desert? she wondered. These low-lying clouds looked more than a little ominous because there was nothing out here to halt their progress and no protection should they con-

tinue to unleash torrents of wind with no precip-
itation. It had been known to happen from time
to time. If they would only disperse rain or any
kind of moisture on their heads, Phada knew she
would be eternally grateful.

"Perhaps we should stop," she yelled to Sarak.
The wind whipped her words away and she had
to repeat them two more times before Sarak understood her.

"Not without a tent. A sandstorm like this will
bury us."

She nodded her understanding. So much for the
hope of rain. She soon found herself bending
backward to compensate for the force of the driving wind. She could barely see in front of her.
Gisba hovered even closer than usual. She probably knew more about such storms than her mistress did, Phada thought with a grimace. If only
the dobby could talk.

As suddenly as it had come up, the wind disappeared. Clouds still covered the moon, however,
and it was very dark.

"Look." Sarak pointed.

Phada stopped beside him. "Holy Mother Elithra," she gasped.

They could see the glow on the horizon much
more clearly without the rays of the moon to mask
it. If appearances were not deceiving, whatever
was causing the luminescent light was not very far
away, perhaps just over the next sand dune. Phada
rubbed some of the grit from her eyes and blinked
to clear her vision before she looked again. She
had not been mistaken. The mysterious semicircle
of light gleamed an impossibly pale, delicate
shade of pink, not the purplish color often noted
at sunrise but more like the phosphorescent hue
seen on the inside of a seashell. It made her distinctly uneasy.

"What is it?" she asked, moving closer to Sarak.

"I do not know." He laid a reassuring hand on her shoulder. "But at least we can be sure it is not a Jiboan camp."

"No, it is much too pretty for that."

"Let us go." When Phada did not immediately move, Sarak tugged on the sleeve of her robe. "Phada, we cannot turn back now."

"Why not?"

"Because whatever is out there is our destiny. Can you not feel it?"

"No, I cannot," she retorted flatly. "How can you be so sure about this? Maybe this is one of the sacred places of the Goddess. Maybe we are supposed to show how very clever and respectful we are of Her feelings and turn away from it. The Goddess works in inexplicable ways. Even in the jungle such eye-catching beauty is a warning. The prettiest, most colorful animals and plants are always the deadliest."

Sarak grasped her arms, turning her until she was forced to face him. "Believe me, Phada, we have no choice. The sun will soon be up. We cannot survive even part of another cycle without water." She opened her mouth to speak but he placed a gentle finger against her lips to forestall her. "I believe the Goddess has entrusted you to my care."

She glared at him. "Perhaps the Goddess has entrusted you to my care," she replied curtly. "If I gave you an order to detour around the strange light, you would have to obey."

"Are you not the least bit curious?" he wheedled, ignoring the direct challenge she had issued.

"Oh yes—the way a treerat is curious about a hissing ground viper. You give me no choice but to command you . . . oomph!" All the breath whooshed from her lungs as Phada found herself being swung completely off her feet and hefted over Sarak's shoulder as easily as he might sling a saddle over a dobby's back. "Put me down!" she yelped. "That is an order."

"You may not believe this, especially considering some of our close calls, but I have done everything within my power to keep you from harm."

"You are not . . . doing . . . a very good . . . job," she sputtered, the words jerked unevenly from her lungs with each jarring contact of his shoulder into her tender stomach, not to mention the fact that she was dangling upside down facing his broad back. She tried to push herself away from his body using her hands for leverage, but the ride was too bumpy and the strain on her arm muscles too much to maintain the position with any sort of dignity. She gritted her teeth and held on, vowing all kinds of revenge when he did eventually set her down.

She held her tongue for as long as she could, but the jostling motion of his walking on the uneven sand became unendurable. She swore she was going to become even sicker than she had those few times she had taken faral. "Sarak. If you do not put me down . . ."

Before she could finish he stopped abruptly. She tried to move her body so she could peer around his left arm but suddenly he was swinging her down to the blessed relief of solid ground and her own two feet. She held one hand pressed against her sore stomach, prepared to give him a blistering lecture on his duties, when she saw what he was staring at.

They were standing at the edge of a ring of phosphorescent pink sand. At its inner border, a brace of koalnut palm trees rose tall and stately, their fronds dipping gently in the barely discernible night breeze. Beyond the ring of trees she could see thicker ground vegetation straddling either side of a narrow path that led to the interior. The entire ground glowed, including an outcropping of rocks that was also composed of the strange, phosphorescent material. Just the smell of the moist soil in which the green plant life flourished, so reminiscent of Mesara, was enough to make her close her eyes in bliss.

"You were correct," she admitted in a small voice.

"It matters not."

"Yes, it does." She stepped closer to him and laid her hand on his arm. She raised her face until she was staring directly into the depths of his dark brown eyes, her gaze neither shy nor condescending. The Keepers taught that everyone was equal in the eyes of the Goddess, although many seemed inclined to forget that fact, including herself. "I am sorry, Sarak. I may know many important and wondrous things, but I do not have the practical knowledge of a warrior—or his instincts."

He looked inordinately pleased at her statement, although he proceeded to brush it aside in his usual self-deprecating way. "Most Mesarans look down on both."

"I know." She pressed her dry lips together. "But they are wrong to do so. I was wrong."

"No, you are perfect."

She snorted in disbelief. "I am hardly perfect. Did you not just hear me admit what an ignorant mudhog I am?"

"Yes, but you are willing to see things as they are and change your mind accordingly, which is more than I can say for any other Mesaran town dweller I have ever known."

"Including the queen?"

He covered her hand where it still lay against his warm flesh, squeezing her fingers. "Yes, even including our esteemed sovereign."

Phada knew she was flushing with pleasure, so she quickly pulled her hand free. She crouched down to scoop up some of the glowing sand, allowing it to trickle in a small, steady stream back to the ground. It was cool to the touch and felt no different from the rest of the Calabian sand.

She turned her head in his direction. "What is this place?"

"I believe we have reached the Kali Oasis."

# *Chapter Fourteen*

Sarak boldly scooped her up into his arms and began carrying her along the path toward the sound of what could only be running water, the packbirds close behind him. She did not protest, but allowed her body to relax against his without recoil or reservation. The cool, moist scent of fresh water clung to every particle of the air around them, causing his mouth to pucker in anticipation.

After a winding journey they finally stumbled into a clearing. Sarak tightened his grip across Phada's back and beneath her legs. Just ahead lay an iridescent pool, fed by a small, steady stream of water from the pink rocks above. More rocks glowed from the bottom, lighting the shadowy forms of fish swimming lazily beneath the surface, their scales sparkling.

The dobbies made a dash for the pool and soon had their beaks in the water, their long necks stretched, their eyes closed in bliss while they drank. Sarak lowered Phada to the sand on the shore, pushing the kanzu from her shoulders and using his hand to splash water on her face and upper body. It was enough to revive her, for she was soon dipping her hand into the cool liquid, scooping handfuls into her mouth and groaning with pleasure.

Sarak had no time for such restraint. He dunked his entire head into the pool, shocking his body with the cool wetness. He could not remember anything feeling so good, not even the time he had returned from the Carpon, the Mesaran outpost located where the Calabian met the sea. He had spent two mooncycles there with only a sword and a cupful of brackish water for company.

"I am going for a swim," he said, pulling the kanzu over his head and tossing it to the ground, leaving only the warrior's breechcloth to cover him. He could tell sunrise was not far off because the air had already lost its nighttime chill. "I recommend that you join me. Your body needs moisture in every way it can obtain it, both inside and out."

She looked dubious. "Do you think it is safe? I see fish swimming around in there. Perhaps there is something bigger or more dangerous lurking in the depths."

"Then I will go first. If we stay near the shore I am certain we will be safe enough. After all, this is an oasis and all such places are under the special protection of the Goddess."

He dove into the water, his extended body cleanly slicing the surface so that there was barely a ripple. When he finally came up for air, he shook his long hair from his eyes, gasping and laughing at the sight of Phada, still hovering cautiously on the shore.

"Come in," he urged her. "You will not be sorry."

He floated on his back, shooting a stream of water from his mouth into the air like a blowfish. He kept one eye on Phada, wondering if she would dare come into the water with him. Warriors did everything separately from the rest of Mesara, including bathing and swimming, as if town dwellers would be contaminated by such contact. Phada had shown that she did not care for many of those rules, but even Mesaran males and females did not bathe together.

She took off her kanzu and came to stand uncertainly by the edge of the water. He did not know what, if anything, a Keeper wore beneath her tunic, so he did not dare ask her to remove it. He did not want her to become disgusted with him or frightened that he might attack her as she had so often in their early time together. She seemed to have gotten over that, he mused, remembering with a jolt of sensation how she had pressed the warmth of her body against his back when he had been bound and shivering with the cold.

His body reacted to that image and he quickly shut it from his mind, agilely maneuvering onto his stomach and swimming in the opposite direction, away from Phada. The sight and smell of the water must be causing him to lose what little sense he had left when it came to the Keeper's apprentice. She needed him to stay alive and she had forced herself to perform forbidden acts in order to ensure he stayed that way. That was all it was and all it ever could be.

Small splashing sounds informed him she had entered the water. She moved far enough away from the shore so that the water reached her shoulders. "I do not know how to swim," she explained with a small shrug.

Swimming was another physical activity performed by the dominators to build stamina and strength. No town dweller wished to swim in the river that flowed along the outskirts of Mesara because it was unprotected from the scorching rays of the sun. It also contained various snakes and other creatures. Although they tended to avoid people whenever possible, it was not unknown for one of them to attack. A warrior was always prepared for such an event.

Sarak dove beneath the cool surface of the water. It did not matter that he was underwater; he could not stop himself from smiling. The cool liquid pressed against his teeth and soothed his blistered lips. He could not remember such joy, not since he was a small boy, before he was taken to the Warrior Academy. He felt a sense of freedom as hints of the infinite possibility of life washed over him. Perhaps the water was imbued with the spirit of the Goddess. Whatever it was, he wanted to share it with Phada.

He burst to the surface, then kicked his feet and dove again. He swam underwater, using his powerful legs to propel him across the pool toward Phada. He surfaced beside her, causing her to gasp in alarm before she glared at him.

"Very amusing," she muttered. "I did not know you were part fish." She stood stiffly, unsure of herself in this new setting. His earlier question was answered in any case. He could see by the pale straps at her shoulders that she wore some kind of undertunic.

"Come, I will show you how to float on your back," he offered.

She shrugged casually but he could see the light of excitement shining in her eyes. "I do not suppose I will ever need to use such a skill, but I must admit I am curious about how it is done."

He grinned. "Lie back," he instructed, placing his arm beneath her shoulders. "Good. Now bring your legs up to the surface. Slowly now."

Phada was a good student. She was soon floating around like an expert, kicking her legs to propel herself and laughing at her success. She looked like a goddess with her wet hair flowing down her back. Her braid had come undone, swirling around her body like waterweeds in the early morning rays of the sun, which had just begun to show its colors along the eastern horizon. The strands appeared darker because they were wet, yet her skin was still pale and smooth despite their trek across the desert. Thank the Goddess the Jiboans were known to be solicitous of their females' looks, if not their overall well-being. They had not forced her to spend marks beneath the burning sun without protection the way he had. Her skin would never have survived the ordeal.

The water was having a definitely liberating effect on both of them, Sarak decided moments later when Phada kicked water into his face. He used the flat of his arm to answer her challenge and soon they were in the midst of a splashing battle. Phada got so enthusiastic in her efforts to deliver the definitive splash that she spun around in a circle. He used her momentary confusion to dive beneath the water, grabbing her around the waist and legs and lifting her up to toss her into the water.

She came up sputtering and laughing. "You win; I yield," she said, her voice breathless.

The other possible meaning behind her words seemed to hit them both at once and they stared at each other. Phada appeared alarmed at the inadvertent statement of surrender she had uttered. Sarak tried not to let it go to his head but he could not help himself. The thought of leading her gently from the water, lying down on the grassy vegetation at the edge of the pool, then pulling her down on top of him to straddle his hips, drove everything else from his mind.

"It was a hard-fought battle and you acquitted yourself well," he finally said. Best to keep their interchange light, he told himself. But it was easier said than accomplished in deed. His insides roiled with so many emotions he barely managed to keep them in check. He pressed his lips together, his mouth taut with determination. Somehow this female had become more important to him than his own life, and he was at a loss how to deal with his feelings. One thing he felt certain of was that she would not want to hear the details of his improper reaction.

It did not surprise him that she played along. "That is high praise indeed from a warrior."

She nodded formally to him before wading to the shore, where she grabbed her kanzu and used it to dry her face and arms. Sarak stood with water dripping from his hair and down his chest, his gaze riveted on her every action. He had to restrain himself from going to her, so strong was his longing to hold her close, to meld their bodies together in the way of male and female.

He had never experienced anything like it. Even when he had lusted for a woman, it had never been for one female in particular. Now he had no desire for anyone but Phada, whom he could never have. It was suicidal and self-defeating. He must purge these feelings from his mind and heart and body, where they had taken up residence. He did not know if he could, certainly not while he was forced to gaze upon her every millimark of every cycle.

She snatched up her pack and disappeared around the other side of the rocks that bordered one edge of the pool. Sarak slowly waded out of the water, his joy at their reversal of fortune fled, along with Phada's stimulating presence. She soon returned however, wearing a dry tunic in the bland tan of the Keeper's uniform and wringing out her long hair. Sarak could not help but wonder what she might look like in blue to match her eyes or royal purple to match her spirit. He realized she appeared beautiful to him no matter what she wore. He must have fallen further into the depths of his impossible fantasy than he thought.

"We had best eat something and then get some rest," he said, hoping he did not sound too gruff. "After sunrise we will gather what supplies we can for the final segment of the journey to Gorod."

"Is it much farther?"

"No, I do not believe so. Perhaps another couple of cycles."

She began spreading out her kanzu a short distance away from the pool when he stopped her. "We should not stay near the water. It is the center of all activity in this place—and the first destination of anyone else who might arrive here."

"Yes, of course."

He gestured for her to wait while he scouted out a safer location to spend what was left of the cyclerise. Together they moved their supplies and the dobbies to a sheltered area beneath a circle of koalnut palms surrounded on one side by thick vegetation. Sarak gathered figs and dates from the nearby trees to add to their staples of dried meat and graincakes. They ate silently. Sarak knew she was correct in her wish not to speak to him, but it hurt all the same.

The cycle was already warm by the time they finished their meal. Phada smoothed out her kanzu, then placed her pack where she intended to lay her head. Sarak made sure he was an appropriate distance away before he shook out the voluminous folds of his own garment and settled it down on the grass.

"I have never seen pink sand before," she announced suddenly, breaking the long silence between them. "Or pink rocks. It is all so beautiful. Do you think it will be the same in Gorod?"

He made a face. "Somehow I am not able to

associate pink sand with the Kargans." He continued rolling the blade of grass he had plucked between his fingers, releasing its sharp, tangy scent. Anything to keep from gazing at Phada and remembering what he must not want, what he could never have. By the blue moon, what was wrong with him that he could not control his own body after all the training he had been given for just such a purpose?

"I have been wondering about our fate once we reach Gorod," she continued. She lay propped up on one elbow, gazing past him into the trees.

"We have made it this far," he pointed out.

"Sarak, what I said to you before—I meant it."

His heart started hammering against his rib cage. She could not mean what he thought she did. "What are you talking about?"

"I am talking about what I said at the pool." Her voice was the barest whisper, her face flushed as she lowered her head to look down at the kanzu beneath her.

He sat up abruptly, almost leaping the rest of the way to his feet to rush to her side. He could not find the words or the daring to question her any further.

"Do not make it any harder for me than it already is," she pleaded softly. "I have thought about this a lot. We do not know if we will ever make it out of Gorod, much less back to Mesara. And I have never experienced the act of mating."

Dear Goddess in heaven, he thought, closing his eyes and clenching his fists against the rush of yearning and desire that washed over his body like a windswept storm cloud. His loins tightened almost painfully. "What are you saying?" he finally managed to whisper.

"I am saying I wish . . . that is, I want you to . . ." She slapped her hands against the kanzu in frustration at her inability to make her meaning clear.

"You told me once that you would like to mate with me. Did you not mean it?"

"I meant it. But that is not the issue."

She was grateful, that was all, he hastily assured himself, thankful for his protection and care of her. Now she wanted to pay him back in the way she knew would most please him. He could not let her sacrifice herself in that way. She would never be accepted in Mesara if it was learned that she had mated with a warrior. It was forbidden, although it was the warrior who was harshly punished for the transgression rather than the town woman. Still, she would never be allowed to continue with her training to become a Keeper, something that she held dear. Knowing Phada, she would not allow herself to continue once she returned among her own kind, knowing she had broken not just one, but several sacred laws with the same act of rebellion.

"Please, Phada. I cannot do this thing with you."

"Why not?"

"You are not yourself. Things always look bleak and impossible when it comes down to matters of sheer survival. You will feel different once you return to Mesara and you will be glad I did not take you up on your offer."

"You do not wish it?"

He groaned. "Of course I wish it. That is not the point."

She finally raised her head to glare at him in exasperation. "Will you please tell me what is the point in not doing something both of us wish?"

"Because you will regret it."

"But you will not?" she asked astutely, attuned to his every nuance.

"I have always found mating to be a pleasurable experience. They say it is even more so with someone you care about. Although a dominator is not allowed to bond, I think I understand what they mean." He sighed. "I could never regret joining with you, little wingbird."

The endearment rolled off his tongue before he could stop it. Much to his surprise, his words did not deter Phada but rather seemed to galvanize her into action. She rose to her feet and crossed the distance between them, dropping to her knees on his kanzu, her hands clasped together and resting lightly on her thighs as though she were making an offering to him. Which of course she was, although she did not seem to think so.

"You could pretend I was one of those Jiboan dancers," she suggested.

"When we were in that tent I found myself pretending each one of those dancers was you."

"Oh!" She flushed with pleasure. "There is one thing, though. I do not think I can mate with you the way they do. Could we not try it in the more seemly manner of town dwellers? Since we are breaking all the other rules, we could pretend to be bonded if you like. Just for this one time. No one will ever know," she added coaxingly, as if he needed any encouragement to take what he yearned for with every fiber of his being.

His gaze on her face was as soft as a caress. He could not resist her further. He wondered why he even bothered to try. "That would surely be considered sacrilege," he whispered, reaching out his hand to touch her face. He could not hide the evidence of his shaking fingers as he stroked the soft skin of her cheek before dipping down to cup her chin. "Sweet, forbidden sacrilege." He traced the outline of her lips with his thumb. "I have only mated in the stationary position. I might disappoint you."

"You must allow me to be the judge of that," she said in that matter-of-fact way of hers he found so endearing. Then she brightened. "Besides, we can learn together and I will not feel such a novice."

A novice. He chuckled to himself at the idea. She was as daring and brave as any warrior, as astute as the most learned Keeper, as royal as any queen. What he had felt for Riga did not come close to the emotions Phada called forth in him. He realized he was too far gone past sanity to be sensible for himself, let alone for both of them.

She waited there expectantly, the blush still coloring her cheeks. He tugged on her hand until she lowered herself down beside him, where she lay as stiff as a sapok board, her arms held awkwardly by her sides, staring up at the bright desert sky. She looked extremely nervous and uncertain now that she had revealed the secret of her innermost wishes. He was not really so sure of what to do himself, but he was more than willing to give it a try.

The taunting words of the Jiboans rang in his head. Were they just trying to confuse him into performing in an inappropriate fashion? He did not think so. He considered asking Phada how she would like him to proceed but realized she knew no more about pleasing a woman than he did. His instruction on that score had been woefully inadequate.

And yet Phada trusted him to do the right thing. It was a grave responsibility and one he took seriously. He only hoped he could control himself long enough to carry it through.

He continued to lie beside her, afraid to make a move in case it was the wrong one. He found that he longed to press his mouth against hers, the way he had often seen Pavonis kiss Riga when they thought no one was looking. At times he had feared the king would devour the queen's mouth, so demanding were his actions. And yet the queen had returned them with unbridled enthusiasm and passion. Would Phada like that as well? he wondered. He supposed now was the time to find out, although he hated to do something that might cause her to reconsider.

Maybe he would wait a bit to try something so untested, he finally decided. But he had better overcome his inertia before she thought he had changed his mind completely.

"Phada," he murmured, rolling over on his side until he was facing her. He slid his arms beneath her shoulders, lifting her from the ground and gathering her closely against his body, tangling his legs with hers. It felt so good to stroke the silky skin of her thighs, the slender firmness of her waist before it blossomed into the fullness of her hips. She let out such a small, soft sigh he almost missed it, but he did not mistake the soft cushion of her breasts pressing against his chest or the way she allowed her arms to shyly encircle his neck.

Her small action inflamed him beyond belief. He suddenly realized why she felt safe enough to mate with him. There was no one to see them, no one to know the forbidden things they were about to do together deep in the heart of the Calabian. No other Mesaran need ever know. Phada had a wild streak that Sarak suspected she did not give enough credence to and perhaps did not even realize she possessed. Had she not shown it by coming to seek him out? Why should she not take it a step further and satisfy her curiosity? She might never get another chance.

He began to stroke and caress her as the Jiboans had instructed. It seemed to work wonderfully well, so well in fact that he soon forgot his own needs in his desire to give pleasure to Phada. Every touch, every gliding caress brought him closer to the brink of madness. Every time she sighed, every time her skin quivered in response, he discovered such singular pleasure that he felt a greater sense of pride in this than in anything he had ever accomplished before.

His flesh burned with heat; his mind grew dazed with desire. He had never prolonged the waiting once the female indicated she was willing, but then it had always been a business transaction, straightforward and simple. Nothing was like that with Phada. She might not want him for himself, but at least she wanted the act and he was available to perform it for her. He had to keep reminding himself that she was untutored in the ways of mating. Besides, every indication that he was giving her pleasure spurred him on to provide her with more.

He flattened one palm against her breast and she moaned. His pulse raced through his body like the hot roaring flames that turned metal into liquid at the foundry. If she hoped to encourage him, it was certainly working. Would she allow him to remove her tunic? He wanted to see all of her before he joined their bodies in the timeless mating ritual. The Jiboan females charged extra for total nakedness because it allowed the warrior complete access to a female's body so he could fondle her breasts to his heart's content or take her nipple into his mouth, something Sarak particularly loved to do. Was such an action too coarse and animalistic to inflict on a town woman like Phada?

When Sarak tried to remove his hand from her breast, Phada could not stop herself from reacting instinctively. She had never felt anything like the explosions of sensation she had experienced at his tentative exploration of her breast and she did not want it to end. She grabbed his wrist, holding him in place.

"Have I hurt you?" he asked in a strained voice.

"No, oh no. Please do not stop." She hesitated. "Unless you wish to."

"I do not know what is permitted."

She giggled. "Actually, neither do I. I guess that

means we can do whatever we want."

"Do you mean that?"

"Yes. I want you to feel as free with me as you would with a Jiboan female."

"By the blue moon, Phada, will you please, just this once, forget about the cursed Jiboans?" he grated out in exasperation. "Do you not understand that I care only about you and what you want?"

"I want you," she said simply.

And it was true, she realized as he covered her breast with one big hand, nuzzling her neck at the same time. At first she had tried to reassure her guilty conscience that she just wished to experience the mating act while she still had the chance, that Sarak happened to be the one available to carry it through. But she quickly realized she was lying to herself. It was much more than that, much more than she had ever dared to dream. And it was all because of the big, gentle dominator who now lay sprawled across her, his weight pressing her body into the ground in the most satisfying manner.

She was eager to go wherever he led her. When he tugged on her tunic, she obediently raised herself up and allowed him to remove it, along with her undertunic. Soon he was kissing her all over, everywhere, including several places that made her blush, especially when his mouth lingered for the longest time at her breasts. Lightning-bolt flashes of blue-hot heat flooded her lower body when he suckled her nipples, causing a strange wetness to develop between her thighs.

His hands were everywhere on her body, caressing and stroking until she thought she would surely fly apart into a million pieces. She wanted more, although she could not imagine what more there could be to this raging pleasure. Sarak, however, seemed to know. He was awkward at first when he rolled completely on top of her, but he soon grasped the dynamics of the matter, using his elbows to keep his weight from crushing her as he thrust himself inside her.

Phada gasped at the burning pain, but it soon dissipated to become a burning of another sort. Like a fire that needed more fuel to sustain it, Phada knew she would sputter and die without Sarak's male flesh gliding into her and pulling back, stoking the flames of pure desire that coursed through her entire body. The noises of satisfaction that issued from his mouth as he pumped himself into her body secretly thrilled her.

Suddenly she became aware of her own intense gratification as waves of pleasure radiated from the core of her being to encompass every part of her body. She cried aloud then, losing all sense of direction or location, knowing only that she and Sarak were entwined in a dance of passion and desire unlike anything she had ever known. He stiffened and then thrust harder, shouting his final release to the scented desert air.

She had no idea what to say in the aftermath of such sheer physical satiation. It did not seem much like a time for talking. All she knew was that she did not care about Gorod or Mesara or anything else. She just wanted to lie in Sarak's arms forever, basking in the afterglow of the most intense experience she had ever known.

Sarak pulled her against his chest, while one hand stroked the hair back from her face. "Goddess above, I did not know it could be like this," he said, burying his face in her hair. "I never suspected."

Phada sighed, her eyes closing in contented exhaustion. And yet she did not fall immediately asleep the way Sarak did, his breathing deep and even near her ear. Her analytically trained mind remained too active, trying to understand what had happened between them.

She realized that strength alone was nothing to fear. She had witnessed that for herself on this journey. And strength tempered by logic and good sense could be a potent combination, as Sarak had already demonstrated. Perhaps warriors did have a reason to complain about the state of affairs in Mesara. They risked their lives and were denigrated because of it. Surely they deserved more consideration than they presently received, maybe even an easing of some of the rules that kept them so strictly segregated.

Her eyes widened in horror at the wayward direction of her musings. What on Elithra was she thinking? Dominators were beasts and brutes who could not be trusted. She had to remember that Sarak was the exception rather than the rule.

He gathered her closer as he slept and she sighed at the sheer pleasure of feeling his legs tangle with hers, his soft breath against her hair. Had she lost her reason along with her virginity? Perhaps, but she could not muster up the indignation to care.

# *Chapter Fifteen*

The sun was approaching its zenith when Phada finally awoke. Oddly enough, the air was cool and fragrant with the scent of flowers and green vegetation. The koalnut palms interspersed with a slender-trunked, leafy tree she did not recognize provided ample shade. A lone bird, a lovely blue in color with white markings, warbled diligently, as though bidding them to rise and greet the already fleeing cycle.

She rolled over to find Sarak awake as well, watching her with his intense dark eyes. He was not smiling; in fact he appeared so serious she wondered if something were wrong. Was he sorry about what they had done? Was she? In spite of their indisputable transgression of the laws of Mesara, she knew she would never regret experiencing the mating act with this warrior. Besides, technically they were no longer in Mesara. They were in a world of their own making and she liked it too well to wish herself anyplace else.

She felt shy and awkward after what had passed between them, especially when she realized that they were both still naked, although Sarak must have covered them with her kanzu sometime during their sleep. She clutched the brightly woven red-and-yellow material to her chest in the face of his continued silence.

Finally she offered him a tentative smile. "Greetings, Sarak," she said.

"Phada." He closed his eyes as if in relief, his big hands balling into fists at his sides, although she could not understand his response. Did he think she was about to denounce him? There was no one to denounce him to, not that she would ever consider doing something so unfair. After all, they had mutually sinned against the accepted code of behavior. She was as guilty as he was, maybe more so since she was a Keeper's apprentice and should be able to control herself better than a dominator.

"I hope you are well and that the Goddess gave you good rest," she added formally, unable to bear the distance between them another millimark.

Sarak chuckled, his face creasing into a broad smile. "She did something much better than that," he told her softly, his hand caressing her cheek. "She let me have you."

Phada lowered her gaze, embarrassed at the intense light in his eyes as they perused her face, and yet pleased at the same time. "I feel so strange. I do not know how to act with you anymore."

"You must do as you feel."

"Oh!" She blushed. What she wanted was to mate with him again. She wondered if that would shock him. It certainly shocked the living blue sunrays out of her. She shook her head. "No, I . . . I cannot."

His expression sobered instantly at her words. He jerked his hand away. "Forgive me, Phada. I am a fool not to have realized it sooner. You are ashamed to be lying here with me like this. I understand. I will leave so you can get dressed."

He reached for his breechcloth, fumbling to put it on beneath the protection of the kanzu, presumably so he would not offend her with his naked body in broad cycle-light. This was going all wrong, she thought despairingly. She was not ashamed; she did not want him to leave. Why was he misreading the situation so badly?

And then she realized what was happening. He had been brought up believing he was not as good as the rest of the population, especially when it came to carnal matters. He had been segregated from all town dwellers and not allowed to touch a woman intimately unless he paid for it. Even then he could not mate as other males did.

She had no idea how that kind of treatment might feel over a lifetime. She was powerless to change the past, but she could do something about it now by offering herself to Sarak during their uncharted time together at the oasis. They did not know what the Goddess had in store for them, but she found she wanted Sarak to have something pleasurable to remember in the cycles to come. She could not be certain if their mating had been as special for him as it had been for her—probably not, since he had experienced such pleasures of the flesh before—but she knew he had enjoyed it and she wanted him to feel that way again.

She placed a hand on his chest. He stopped his movements, staring straight ahead. "Sarak," she whispered. "Please do not go."

She had no idea what else to say, but she was encouraged that he remained where he was. His chest began to rise and fall more rapidly. She knew because she watched her hand, which rested just below his collarbone, move up and down with it. She tried a couple of tentative strokes, enjoying the smooth feel of his tanned flesh, the ripple of muscle beneath. When she dared a glance in his direction, she saw that the skin of his face was pulled tautly back, especially around his eyes, and a hectic flush had appeared along his cheekbones.

"Do you have any idea what you are doing to me?" he grated out between clenched teeth.

"Reciprocating what you were doing to me this sunrise, I hope. I am sorry I am not as skilled as you are in such matters."

"No, stop." When she ignored his command, he grabbed her hand, holding it in place against his chest. "Phada, you do not owe me anything. What we did earlier was not meant to be part of a transaction. At least it was not for me."

"Nor for me. I just thought that since it felt so wonderful when you touched me the way you did, that you might like it as well."

"By the Goddess, I like it better than anything."

"Then hush, great warrior, and stop fighting me. You have been fighting me since the moment I met you."

He brought her hand to his mouth so he could kiss the palm. "And losing the battle every time," he added wryly.

He released her hand and lay back, offering himself to her to do with as she pleased. She experienced a surge of excitement at the thought of wielding such power over his strong warrior's body. He could crush her with one hand and yet he had surrendered all that strength to her.

She was not daunted by the task she had set for herself—to make him weak with pleasure. She had not thought to touch him before, so busy had she been simply taking in all the sensations his hands and mouth had aroused in her. But now she was more coherent and she allowed her fingers to stroke his tanned skin even as she leaned down to kiss and lick his chest the way he had done with her. His indrawn gasp assured her that it pleased him.

She grew bold enough to uncover his lower body, flipping the material of the top kanzu away. He had not quite succeeded in donning his breechcloth. She pulled at the leather strips he had managed to tie on one side before tossing the garment onto the nearby sand.

"Oh Goddess, yes, Phada, please," he moaned, half delirious with the intense feelings she was generating in every part of his body as she stroked and caressed him as he had never been touched in his life. He did not understand why she felt compelled to do this, but he was not about to ask any questions. This entire journey seemed a dream, and mating with Phada the most glorious fantasy he could ever imagine.

He wanted to touch her, too. But when he reached up to do so, she grabbed his arms and pushed them to the ground beside his head. Before he knew what she intended, she had straddled him, the hot core of her femininity burning against his loins.

"You once asked me to ride you," she said. She sounded bold, but she was blushing to the roots of her hair. "Do you still wish it?"

He was so moved that she would go to these lengths to please him and so excited by the sight of her mounted on top of him that he could barely speak. Instead he reached up and grasped her hips, lifting her just high enough so that he could slide her down onto his erection. "By all means, ride me . . . as hard as you like for as long as you like."

He did not remember much after that except for the waves of pleasure that washed over him one after the other without ceasing. He thought he might die from the sensations, but he did not care.

She continued her rhythmic pumping, never letting up until she finally cried out and collapsed, sobbing, onto his chest. That was when he allowed himself his final release, his arms around her, her hair draped across his face and its delicious, flowery scent filling his nostrils.

When Sarak came awake again, the afternoon was just beginning to slide into evenfall. Phada was still asleep, her soft breath fanning against his neck. The rest of her warm, enticing body lay curled along the length of his like a contented palace cat. He wished he did not have to get up, but there were things to do if they were going to be able to leave the oasis this night. Staying as long as they had was dangerous, since they were so near the approach to Gorod. Even now another Jiboan caravan, filled with faral, might be heading their way, and this group of desert dwellers might know better what the spice was good for besides selling to Dalcor.

He carefully slipped his arm from beneath Phada's head. She murmured in her sleep but did not awaken. Fierce little clawcat, he thought, remembering how she had wrung every last ounce of pleasure from his body. He had always been powerfully aware of her beautiful, tawny hair and her stormy blue eyes, but he never would have suspected the fierce courage and the brave heart that beat beneath the drab tunic of the Keeper's apprentice.

It did not take him long to gather what supplies they needed from the bounty the oasis had to offer. He packed fruit and dates into both saddles as the dobbies stood docilely beneath the shade of a large koalnut tree. He found himself talking to the birds, calling them by name. Phada's foolishly tenderhearted compassion for animals must be rubbing off on him.

Luckily there was a spare water bag in one of the compartments, which he filled from the pool. In the light of the sun the pink color had disappeared as if it had never been. He wondered if the relationship he had forged with Phada would also vanish once they left this place.

He realized they might still run short of water, so he also gathered a dozen koalnuts. They would be able to crack them open as needed and drink their milky liquid interiors. He also found two flat stones to help in the task, since they had no knife strong enough to do the job. He placed them in the leather sidesaddle.

They were as prepared as they would ever be. He paused next to the deep water of the pool. He had time for a swim but he was too eager to get back to Phada. Instead he splashed some water on his face and upper body before returning to the shady glen where Phada still rested. He lowered himself next to where she lay, her body mostly covered by the kanzu, but her shoulders and part of her bare back exposed to the soft oasis air.

He could not stop from pressing closer to her. She murmured a little but allowed him to gather her against him. He could not resist stroking her skin with long, languorous movements. By the time she awakened, she was as eager to mate as he was. He took her again as night fell over the Kali, his body pushing her into the folds of the kanzu. He knew it was foolish to pretend he was just like any other Mesaran male, but he could not help himself. It was a fantasy he would never know again and he wanted to cherish it.

They drifted into sleep. He estimated they had been resting for a couple of marks when he gently shook her shoulder. "Phada. Wake up."

He hated to rouse her but it was time to go. He wished they could stay there forever. But a Jiboan caravan was sure to arrive and there was no telling what kind of trouble they might get into wearing these red-and-yellow kanzus. Dalcor had already posted a bounty for his capture. He might have upped the price by now, especially if he heard the reports of their escape from that last band of Jiboans.

"It is still dark," she murmured, snuggling closer to the warmth of his body. He hugged her before moving away.

"Yes, it will be cooler walking at this time of night."

"You are right, as always," she said, sitting up and rubbing her eyes.

"I do not want to leave, but I am afraid we might run into more Jiboans once the sun rises. We cannot take such a chance. In fact, from here on out we will have to be very careful to scan the horizon so we can avoid any unwanted company."

Phada stared at him unhappily. She knew he was correct about departing immediately, but that did not mean she had to like it. She also decided she did not have to put up with his suddenly formal attitude when she still felt so emotionally and physically close to him. It was almost as if they were bonded, she thought, shocking herself into further silence with the thought. She had been taught, repeatedly, that no female could ever achieve such a state with a warrior—they were known and often praised for their loyalty, but it was believed they were incapable of love.

Maybe she should let things be; maybe Sarak was right in trying to maintain a modicum of emotional distance between them. She picked up her kanzu, shaking out the voluminous folds of the material. She could not bear to put it on quite yet. The temperature in the oasis felt perfect against her skin, although she knew once they left its protection, the desert would be much cooler, especially until the sun rose.

She realized that the telling differences in their newfound closeness with each other would be evident, even to an outsider. Only moments ago, Sarak had offered his hand to assist her to her feet. Now his gaze lingered on her as she took her place beside Gisba, although his expression remained stoic and unemotional. A single word from her could change that. She did not know if she dared utter it.

She could not stop herself from peering over her shoulder for a last look at the shaded glen where they had mated. She noticed Sarak doing the same. His dark eyes met hers for a brief, shockingly intimate moment, and then he turned away, as though putting it behind him. Would they ever experience such closeness again? Phada wondered as she began walking behind him along the narrow path.

She had heard that warriors were like animals, filled with lust and then, when it was sated, able to go about their tasks without a backward glance. That was why they were considered unsuitable material as a bonded mate. And yet Sarak had been tender this morning. He had wished to mate with her again, in spite of having done so twice before. She realized he was probably making up for all those days of celibacy while they had been hiking in the desert. And perhaps, although he might not like to admit it to her, the sight of those Jiboan woman had stirred his desires to the breaking point.

He stopped when they reached the pool. "I will wait if you want to wash. I doubt we will have another such opportunity until we return."

*If we return.* Phada could almost hear the words he had left unspoken. "Yes, that would be wonderful," she said.

She draped her kanzu over Gisba's saddle before hurrying to the water's edge, kneeling down so that her legs were covered and dashing handfuls of the cool, clear liquid on her face and arms. Sarak led the birds over for one last drink. Then he, too, knelt and washed.

When they were finished, he picked up Ral's reins and led the way out of the oasis. Phada felt even worse than she had leaving Mesara behind. They were heading into unknown territory, the land of the Kargans. They had no idea what to expect, knowing only what the Jiboan caravaners had chosen to tell them and knowing this was filled with exaggerations and perhaps even downright lies.

The wind immediately picked up once they crossed the first massive sand dune beyond the Kali. She quickly donned her kanzu. Sarak still wore only his warrior garb. She was shocked at herself and somewhat uncomfortable with the realization that she loved watching his tautly muscled physique as he paced ahead of her, his movements as graceful as the sleekest clawcat. She squelched the vague murmurings of her conscience over what she had done. There would be time enough later for repercussions. Besides, in the vast reaches of the desert, nothing seemed real.

They traveled farther and farther south. The sun had risen and the air grew hot, although nowhere near as scalding as it had been in the heart of the Calabian. The desert dunes turned flatter; the ground was littered with rocks. Phada found her sandals were not the best protection against the small pebbles that wedged between her feet and the leather and that she had to shake out at regular intervals. Every so often Sarak would stop to run his fingers over the larger stones. He explained that the rougher, more pitted surface indicated north, the side of the prevailing winds.

The landscape continued to change, becoming

even more rocky, windswept, and barren. The wind that whipped against their backs was raw and cold, the horizon composed of bleak and colorless tans and browns. Even the dobbies looked miserable as they blinked away the dirt that blew into their eyes. After the soft hues of the desert, and most especially the Kali Oasis, the scenery was depressing.

They walked the entire next cycle until the sun set. Sarak made camp beside an outcropping of rock where an overhang provided shelter against the biting wind. There was little vegetation, although more than in the deep desert. They did not dare make a fire in case someone spotted them.

"I am not sure how much farther it is to Gorod, but I suspect we will reach it sometime tomorrow," he told her as he hauled Gisba's saddle from her back, then proceeded to do the same with Ral. The birds fluffed the feathers along their entire bodies and flapped their small wings, useless appendages, since they could not fly with them. Sarak settled them a short distance away, beneath the sheltering rock.

Next he used his kanzu to form a tent of sorts to provide them with protection against the wind. She did not wait to be invited but scrambled inside while he was still fastening the far corner. Once there, she sat huddled, trying to get warm. The skin of her face felt especially raw and cold, along with her hands. Although the kanzu had protected her from the worst of it because of its tightly woven construction, the wind had still been able to swirl beneath the material at times, dissipating the warmth she had managed to generate and cooling her entire body.

She was huddled in the farthest depths of the shelter when Sarak crawled in beside her. Immediately the limited space became even smaller, but she found she did not mind the boundaries of their dwelling the way she had before. In fact she wished she had the boldness to move closer to him, but she felt too shy and unsure of what her welcome might be.

Then she realized that she could hear Sarak's teeth chattering. The poor warrior was clad only in his breechcloth now that he had donated his clothing for their mutual benefit. She forgot everything else in her haste to scoot closer to his side, pulling her kanzu over her head and using the material to wrap around his shoulders.

"What in the name of Elithra are you doing, Phada?" he asked in astonishment, shrugging the cloth away. He quickly wrapped it around her upper body, holding her immobile with his arms when she tried to struggle. "It is much too cold for you to remove your garment."

"What about you?"

"Now that I am out of the wind, I will soon be warm."

She glared at him. "You are acting like a stubborn mudhog. This thing is big enough to cover both of us."

"Leave it be. I am fine," he said. He sounded testy and ill-tempered, exactly like the mudhog she had compared him to.

He released her abruptly, moving as far away as it was possible to get within the confines of their shelter. He also avoided her gaze. She frowned, unsure exactly what was going on. He acted as if he were loath to touch her or to have her near him. Was he trying to tell her, tactfully, that he no longer desired her?

Dominators were known to grow eager to move on to greener fields once they had conquered a female. She thought she had tamed a warrior, if only for a short span of time. Perhaps she was only fooling herself. Perhaps, instead, the warrior had captured that rarest of trophies—a forbidden

Keeper as a willing and eager pallet partner. Now that the thrill of the hunt was over, he no longer wanted her.

Had it really been just a game to him? She did not want to believe that, but in the face of the evidence she was not so sure. She lowered her head, praying he would not notice the tears that suddenly filled her eyes, threatening to spill down her cheeks and complete her humiliation.

If this was what mating did to a person, she wanted no more of it. She was as weepy as a child, sensitive and unable to cope with even the mildest rejection from Sarak, a warrior she had every right to command. She was certainly not acting like a proud and noble Keeper-in-training. If she was not careful, she would soon be begging for his attention.

Sarak was obviously not suffering from the same complaint. He sat there staring at the rock wall in the most stoic fashion, although she knew he must be cold. What was he going to do tonight when it came time to sleep? He would never be able to rest comfortably in that skimpy garment with no other protection than a one-walled shelter. They had to be practical, for the sake of Mesara and what they hoped to accomplish.

He finally roused himself enough to begin handing out their supper. The hard fruit he had packed had softened after only one cycle and now seemed ready to eat. He handed some to Phada, along with dates and the last of the graincakes. He placed the goatskin water bag between them, propping it against the rock wall and loosening the neck, but not enough so that it would spill should it tip over. Phada was silent as she began eating and he followed her lead.

It was killing him not to touch her. He had thought long and hard about their situation during their endless marks of walking through the harsh southern portion of the desert. He had finally convinced himself that it was better to give her up now, while he thought he still might be able to accomplish the deed, rather than wait until they reached Gorod.

Part of him insisted that he should try to live each cycle to the maximum. But he could not do it. He was already in gut-wrenching pain at the prospect of eventually returning to their own civilization. He did not know how she would act if they ever got back to Mesara, but he hoped she would be able to part company with him without a backward glance and return to her Keeper's training, her head held high, not telling anyone of what they had done. He wanted that for her. He was the one who had coerced her into mating with him, using both her isolation from her own kind and her compassionate nature against her. If anyone asked, he would say that he had forced her. That would exonerate her. In the meantime, he could at least allow her to retain her dignity as a Keeper's apprentice while they remained together.

He could not forget that she had been a virgin, curious and scared, with no real conception of what the act entailed, when she had asked him to take her. He should have known better than to break such a sacred law. Look at the results. His peace of mind was shattered, probably forever, not to mention his ability to concentrate on the important points of their survival. All he could think about was her soft skin and her welcoming body. He deserved every bit of punishment the Goddess dealt him and more.

He needed to concentrate on the task ahead. He had no idea how he intended to slip into the Kargan stronghold unnoticed. He was sure Phada would want to accompany him, and that worried him to no end, not that he could leave her waiting somewhere along the track for him to return. What if the Kargans caught him? She would never be able to recross the desert alone, not unless she went with a Jiboan caravan, and he knew what her fate would be should that happen. He almost wanted to turn around and return across the cursed desert because he could not bear knowing it might be her fate to remain among their enemy forever.

Somehow, for Phada's sake, he must not fail.

He finished eating before she did. He waited politely until she had swallowed her last bite before turning over on his side, his face away from her, preparing to sleep. He decided it would probably be an impossible task but he was going to give it his best effort.

Suddenly he felt something covering him. Before he could react he heard Phada's soft voice. "It is better for both our sakes that we share the kanzu this night. I believe it is more than adequate in size to accommodate us. You must rest and you cannot do so if you are cold. I will stay on my side and you can stay on yours."

He grunted in agreement, knowing she would not cease until he did so. His mind supplied him with a vivid picture, complete with sensory details, of the way she had pressed her body against his when he had been tied up in the Jiboan camp. What sweet bliss that had been. He blanked the memory away and settled down to sleep.

He realized he had drifted into a dreamless rest when he awoke suddenly sometime later. He understood why when he felt Phada's warm body snuggled up against him. He had his arms wrapped tightly around her and he could feel her breasts pressing into his forearms. Sometime during the night he had rolled over so that he was facing her and she had unconsciously curled herself against him, seeking his warmth in the position they had used after mating.

She slept deeply, soundly, and he did not have the heart to wake her up by moving away. He felt his heart swell with pride that she should seek him out for any reason, especially in the depths of slumber. Her actions proved that she bore him no ill will for what he had done to her, not that Phada would ever allow herself to harbor such resentment against another living soul.

He tried to force himself to ignore her closeness but it was impossible. He could not resist smoothing the skin of her arm, little caresses that he hoped would not disturb her. Every time he moved he could feel the shape of her breasts more distinctly. His hands ached to close over them, to feel her nipples harden beneath his touch. He realized with a shock of awareness that he was now moving his lower body in a counterpoint rhythm to his stroking of her arm, pressing his aching hardness against her bottom, biting his lip to keep back a groan.

This time she sighed his name and stirred. He stopped his motions instantly, but it seemed it was too late. As he pulled back, she slid her body beneath him. Instead of moving away as he knew he should have done, he lifted himself until he was lying between her soft thighs, his weight supported by his elbows.

"Sarak," she whispered. He could see that her eyes were still closed, although she was smiling. Even in the semidarkness of night he could tell that it was a sad little smile, at odds with the increased tempo of her breathing that informed him that she was not unmoved by the way his body covered hers, their entwined limbs. "I thought you did not wish to mate with me again."

"I wish it more than life itself."

"Ah, yes, now I finally understand the force of this desire I have been told about. It does not matter what a person thinks or says in his most rational moments. When the opportunity arises, it is impossible to resist."

"Is that what you think?" he asked. "That I desire you only because I have the opportunity?"

She touched his cheek with the backs of her fingers. "It does not matter. It seems I have no willpower where you are concerned, in spite of my upbringing."

"Goddess knows I should leave you alone," he said, his hands reaching for the hem of her tunic and tugging it up past her hips so that her lower body was exposed to his avid gaze. He leaned just far enough away so that his fingers could maneuver between their bodies to slide inside the secret core of her femininity. He groaned as if in terrible pain when he felt the wetness there. "If I were any kind of a warrior, I would do so. But I find I am no match for my own desires when it comes to you."

She seemed to melt in his hands, her body pushing against his fingers, forcing them deeper inside her. He thought he would explode from the sheer beauty and wonder of her untutored response. And then she wrapped her arms around his neck and lifted her breasts so she could press them tightly against his chest. His flesh burned like jungle wildfire.

"Teach me how to kiss, Sarak," she pleaded, her mouth close to his ear. "Teach me everything you know about mating."

He did not have to be asked twice.

# Chapter Sixteen

Phada and Sarak reached the trampled crossroads long marks after the sun's zenith. The town of Gorod was nowhere in sight, but they knew they had to be close because of the way several roads merged into one main thoroughfare that continued to head south. There was little vegetation to shelter them from prying eyes, although the oddly compelling rock formations provided some cover and protection. The landscape had grown even bleaker and more windswept, and the temperature had dropped until it was uncomfortably raw. It was hard to believe, but the blue-hued rays of the sun did not provide much warmth now, especially hidden as they were behind a dark, overcast sky.

All in all, the land of the Kargans was not a very welcoming place.

"Stay here with the dobbies," Sarak instructed her. "I am going ahead to reconnoiter. Perhaps the town lies on the other side of these rocks."

Phada watched him slip away, the wind whipping his kanzu around his legs. From the back he looked like a common Jiboan merchant. Until she got closer and realized how massive he was and how much taller than any Jiboan she had ever seen.

Sarak had been most solicitous of her since they had awakened this morning. He did not seem as awkward as he had after the first time they had mated. Phada had come to the conclusion that he thought he was doing her a favor by withholding himself from her. He believed he had somehow coerced her into lying with him, that she had acted against her will, perhaps out of curiosity, perhaps because of the decidedly risky, seemingly hopeless task she had set for both of them.

She had come to realize that her actions entailed much more than that. She had thrown aside every rule set out in the law scrolls by mating with the dominator; it was not something she had done on a whim, although in the beginning she had tried to convince herself that was all it was. She had broken her own code of ethics, and yet she could not find it in her heart to regret it. Later, perhaps, but not now, not when the thought of having Sarak take her in his arms was so compelling.

She knew that if they managed to make it back to Mesara, this interlude would have to come to an end. In the meantime, she meant to live each day to the fullest, with the dominator by her side. She could see that he truly cared about her. His concern washed over her like a physical caress. She knew how to break down his defenses. She did not consider it selfish to do so, not when she needed him so much and he seemed to need her in return, and especially not when their chances of success in Gorod were so small.

Sarak appeared from behind the wall of rock.

He hurried quickly to her side and she could see that he was grinning. She wanted to reach out her hand to touch those smiling lips, but she restrained herself. There was an unspoken code between them when they were not entwined on the kanzus. They had a task to perform and they did not need the complication of their new relationship to distract them or cloud their judgment. Still, it was hard to revert to being distant and proper with him, knowing he had caressed every inch of her naked body.

"There are several Jiboan caravans breaking camp just ahead," he explained. "If we are careful, we can slip in amongst them and enter Gorod when they do."

"Have you seen it? What does a Kargan town look like?"

He smiled at her eager curiosity, his dark eyes warm with what she could only label as affection as they scanned her face. "I do not know. There is no sign of the place yet."

He gathered Ral's reins and began walking. Phada followed his lead with Gisba close behind. The birds had made known their dislike of the colder climate from the very first, but they had soon settled down into the placid acceptance that was their nature. Phada had grown quite fond of the pair of them, and the feeling was mutual.

They made their way to the edge of the rocky formation with the sound of the dobbies' claws scrabbling on the hard ground echoing all around them. Just ahead, Phada could see the colorful Jiboan tents, some of them already lying on the rocky ground, waiting to be packed. Dobbies squawked and children chased each other between the piles of equipment and goods. Thank the Goddess, none of the kanzus and kentas she could see sported a red-and-yellow design similar to theirs. They did not need to run into any kin of the Jiboans who had captured them and tried to drag them back to Mesara.

"Keep your face hidden," Sarak warned her. They carefully approached the tail end of the last caravan, whose members wore distinctive blue-and-white woven garments. "If I see the opportunity, I will try to procure a kenta, but until then, you will have to pretend to be a male."

"That will be easy," Phada said, flashing him a saucy grin. She felt more lighthearted than she could ever remember being in her entire life. It made no sense, not when they were about to march into the den of the enemy. She suspected it would not last and she wanted to enjoy it for as long as she could.

He leaned closer so he could whisper, "You seem in fine spirits. Perhaps you would tell me your secret."

She stared into his eyes for an intense, timeless moment, then dropped her head and blushed when she realized just what her secret was.

His hand came up as if to touch her face, but he stopped himself in time. "Ah, my bright little wingbird." He seemed at a loss for words for a couple of millimarks, and then he continued to speak. "I promise you, I will do everything in my power to complete the task you have asked of me. Everything," he vowed in a fervent voice.

"Yes, I know." Phada smiled shakily, her mood broken. It struck her again, more forcefully than ever, that they were heading into terrible danger. They had no idea of what lay ahead. If anything happened to Sarak, she did not know what she would do. And yet they could not return to Mesara without the secret of the spice. They had nowhere else to go, no choice but to press on.

The caravans finally began to move. Sarak kept maneuvering them closer to the head of the straggling column. Soon they were second in line, after

the Jiboan tribe dressed in green and red stripes.
There was still no sign of a town and Phada wondered how much farther they had to travel. For
the last couple of hundred measures, they had
been drawing closer to a towering rock wall.
Phada stared until her eyes hurt, but she could not
discover anything at its base. Soon they would either have to turn aside or be forced to come to a
complete halt.

The lead Jiboans did not turn aside. Sarak and
Phada exchanged puzzled glances, but they did
not speak. Were these Jiboans not going to Gorod?
And yet where else could they be headed, loaded
down with trade goods as they were? Phada had
already observed the fresh fruits and grains of
Mesara strapped to the backs of their packbirds.
She had also taken note of the cumbersome bar-
rels of what could only be vetch.

And then she saw it, an opening in the cliff face.
As they drew closer, she realized that it was large
enough to allow at least four or five dobbies to
enter side by side. Just inside the yawning entrance a couple of guards huddled next to small
huts constructed of stone and wood, where they
obviously passed the time between caravans. They
wore long red cloaks with hoods that effectively
covered their bodies and faces. They were still too
far away for her to be able to estimate their size.
She would have to wait a while longer to get her
first glimpse of an honest-to-Goddess-created
Kargan.

She was afraid the sentries would ask for some
kind of documentation, but they gestured indifferently to the train of Jiboans and dobbies to
move along. Phada felt her hopes shrinking as
they descended down a long, sloping tunnel lit by
torches. The fact that Gorod had only one entrance might mean trouble for them later on. It
was damp and cool inside, although without the

stinging bite of the wind, it seemed comparatively warmer.

Suddenly they emerged into a huge, cavernous room, twice as large as the feasting hall in Mesara. It resembled the town square back home, although the Mesaran meeting place was bright and sunny because it was located beneath the jungle canopy on the east perimeter of the town. This place was well lit and yet it still gave an overall gloomy, colorless impression. At least it was warmer than the tunnel, due to a huge, roaring fire she could see off to her right. It burned along a portion of one wall, in a fireplace carved right into the stone. They could roast an entire bulloxen in there, Phada realized with an uneasy start.

Sarak hovered by her side, but not so closely that it was noticeable. They kept the kanzus drawn over their faces, even though many of the Jiboans had already tossed theirs aside. The merchants immediately began setting up their stalls and were soon hawking their wares. But to whom, was the question. At the moment there was no one else in the large hall.

And then the Kargans emerged from another tunnel located high above the floor of the market. They descended the rocky pathway, mostly women clutching baskets and children, but there were men among them as well. The women wore long dresses with sleeves in contrasting colors. Their hair was unbound and tumbled down their backs, in the most unusual shades of blond she had ever seen, some golden and yet the majority almost silvery white. Some of them had pulled the long strands away from their faces with brightly hued strips of leather. The men had on long trousers made of some kind of leather and matching vests, and they, too, had the same flaxen hair. Several wore long-sleeved shirts beneath the vests but most did not, and it was then that she realized what else made them so different.

She could not completely stifle her gasp of startled surprise. Their skin was so pale it appeared
almost white. And their eyes—even from where
she stood, still some distance away, she could see
that their eyes were the palest of blues, so pale
they almost appeared to have no color at all. The
overall effect was eerie and disconcerting.

The women walked meekly behind the males,
whose strutting gait reminded her of rockroosters
displaying their tail feathers for the hens. Except
for their pale complexions and blond hair, these
males resembled the warriors of Mesara, with
their finely honed muscles and their bulky chests
and arms.

The next wave of Kargans appeared. Phada realized that the first group of females must be servants or slaves of some kind when she saw the rich
fabrics these women wore. The sleeves were in a
contrasting color to the bodice, which was cut so
low their breasts almost spilled over the top. They
wore veils that shielded their faces from onlook-
ers. Each of these females appeared to be attached
to a specific male, Phada decided as she watched
the group separate into pairs as they made their
way down the path toward the market. Each
woman followed behind her warrior, her head dutifully bowed.

Phada gasped when one of the males suddenly
slapped his female partner with the back of his
hand. The woman did not even raise her fingers
to her cheek but nodded as he roared at her, his
face flushed with anger. He jabbed his finger next
to her nose to emphasize the point he wanted to
make and her veil quivered noticeably. But she did
not utter a word in her defense. Phada could not
believe her eyes when no one came forward to in-
tervene. No one even seemed interested. She
watched, horrified, as the Kargan male swiveled

on his heel and stormed off, leaving the poor woman to scurry after him to keep up.

"Did you observe that Kargan male's outrageous behavior?" she demanded of Sarak, her voice filled with fury. "These Kargans are uncontrolled dominator beasts."

"Hush, someone will hear you," he cautioned. He knew he sounded testy but he could not help it, not when Phada's expression showed such disgust for the Kargan warriors. Her vehemence reminded him of the way the majority of town dwellers viewed Mesaran warriors. "Yes, I noticed. What would you have me do? If I go to her aid, it will mean the end of all our plans."

She calmed down a little at his words. "Yes, I realize that. It is just so difficult to watch these arrogant males casually displaying their violent ways. Did you note how he used his larger size and brute strength to bully and dominate? These warriors remind me of Dalcor."

Sarak's heart sank even further. He knew Phada had once had little respect for warriors, and these Kargan examples of the breed were not going to help mellow her opinion. He felt as if she were once again casting him in a group with all warriors, even though she had not specifically uttered a word about him. He did not want her to be reminded of the way she had once felt about his kind. But he could see from the prim expression of disgust on her face that it was too late to stop the process.

"Come," he said. "We must get rid of Gisba and Ral so we can move around Gorod more easily. I saw a packbird stable back near the entrance."

"All right," she answered mildly enough. But he could tell that she was still fuming over the incident she had witnessed.

They settled the dobbies in adjoining stalls, promising the stablemaster payment on their return. Sarak's skin was dark enough to pass for Jiboan but he did not have the distinguishing blue tattoos, so he kept his face covered, warning Phada to do the same. The proprietor of the stables was a Kargan male, although he was not a warrior. He was young, with a slender build, and his mannerisms reminded her a little of Jobus. He looked them over indifferently, then shrugged, unconcerned. Why should he be concerned? If they did not return, he could sell Gisba and Ral to the next desert-bound caravan and net a healthy profit. Phada did not trust him overmuch, but they had little choice. She felt marginally better when Sarak packed some of their belongings into a leather bag and slung it over his shoulder.

Once that was taken care of, he pulled her into a narrow tunnel, empty of foot traffic, at least for the moment. "I want to take a look around."

"It is too dangerous," she protested. "One glimpse of your face and they will know you are no Kargan. You are too big to pass for a Jiboan for very long."

"There is no other way."

"Yes, there is. If I could get a Kargan dress, I could easily pass."

Sarak sighed. Leave it to Phada to come up with another solution. Was it not in her nature to argue with anyone's suggestions, especially his?

"What about your hair?" he demanded.

"I realize that my hair is at the dark end of the spectrum when it comes to color, but it can still pass, I think, especially if I cover most of it with one of those head coverings and only allow the lighter ends to show. My eyes are rather dark too, but there is nothing I can do about that and at least they are blue."

"You cannot wander around here without an escort."

"Yes, I can. It is true, most of the women are

attached to males, but I have seen some walking about alone. We will be less conspicuous if we separate. Besides, we can find out more that way. In my guise as a Kargan, I should be able to pry where a Jiboan outsider could not."

He knew when he was defeated. Besides, she was correct in her deductions. They were in danger no matter what they did. It might be worse if she were to hang around in one area, waiting for him to return. They might as well try to cover twice the territory.

"All right," he agreed. "But you must promise not to wander off alone down any empty tunnels until we have a better idea of the layout of this place."

"I will be careful, Sarak. Believe me, I do not want to find myself in the clutches of some beastly Kargan."

"Neither do I," he echoed her sentiments wholeheartedly. "Here, hold this." He handed her the leather bag, flipping it open while she supported the bottom and removing a handful of koalnuts and dates. "I remember seeing a merchant who had dresses for sale. Let us see what these are worth."

It turned out they were worth enough to purchase the Kargan apparel. Sarak used his best bartering skills with the large, crafty Kargan merchant who tended the stall where they were sold. He was an older individual with gray streaking through his silvery blond locks, a startling effect when set off by his blue eyes, which also held a silvery hue. He seemed curious about why a Jiboan would want Kargan dress, but he was too busy trying to extract an extra koalnut, obviously a delicacy around these parts, to make mention of it.

Sarak convinced another merchant to part with a head covering with the veil attached in exchange

for the dates. He hurried back to where he had left
Phada. She was still standing there, much to his
relief, her sharp blue eyes taking in everything
around her. He wondered what she was thinking,
but when she turned toward him, her expression
was carefully blank.

"Oh, good," she said when she saw the material
in his hands. "I found a place where I can change
if you will stand guard."

She led him to an empty corridor that snaked
away into black nothingness. It was dirty and unlit, obviously unused. Sarak planted himself casually against one side of the entrance while
Phada slipped into its dark shadows. It was not
long before she reappeared, clutching her kanzu.
She looked beautiful in the garment, Sarak
thought as a jolt of awareness rocked his senses.
He had always seen her in the basic tan tunic of
the Keepers. He realized he had deliberately
bought a blue dress. The bright shade brought out
the color in her eyes, making them appear more
blue than gray and very beautiful. His gaze
dropped to the low-cut neckline where the tops of
her breasts were clearly revealed, almost down to
the nipple. Kargan males obviously liked to flaunt
their women. Sarak found he wanted to caress
her, to run his fingers across the soft, exposed
skin, so pale and creamy, so tantalizing.

As he watched, she placed the covering over her
hair and hooked the veil into place across her face.
She suddenly seemed even more mysterious and
foreign to his warrior sensibilities than she had as
a Keeper's apprentice, and very, very female. She
certainly did not look like the Phada he had first
noticed in the feasting hall, so prim and proper,
but indeed resembled the Kargan females.

She was right, the sun-lightened ends of her
hair could pass for the flaxen color of so many of
these people. And her eyes as well, although they

did not hold the submissive expression he had noticed elsewhere. Although her skin was pale, it was
not as white and translucent as a Kargan female's.
He only hoped she would not be stopped and
questioned because of it.

"Well, what do you think?" she asked, her
mouth pressed into a flat line. She had been very
much aware of the Kargan women, many of
whom were more amply endowed on top than she
could ever hope to be. Like the Jiboan females in
their filmy dance costumes, these antipodes females were used to displaying their charms and
did not blush every time they moved and their
flesh jiggled. Did Sarak think she had not noticed
him ogling them with a warrior's appreciation?
Would he now compare her to them and find her
wanting?

He finally lifted his gaze to her face, his eyes
burning. "It is fine," he said, sounding breathless.

"That is an easy statement for you to make," she
replied in a testy voice. "You are not the one wearing a cursed garment that exposes your anatomy
and allows everyone to judge you."

His eyes quickly darkened with anger. "It is an
easy statement for me to make because I have always worn just such a garment."

She bit her lip in dismay, hanging her head. "I
am sorry, Sarak. I have grown so used to seeing
you in that kanzu that I . . . I forgot about . . ."

"It does not matter," he interrupted, his tone flat
and emotionless. He turned away.

She groaned to herself, unable to believe her
roiling emotions over a simple dress. Here she was
covered from her head to her toes—except for the
generous display of her bosom—and she had
never felt more naked and exposed in her life.
How had Sarak been able to bear being stared at
and judged every moment of his life? Not that he
would come up lacking—he was everything a

male should be. But still, the thought of having her physical body on display was unnerving. Thank goodness her thoughts were still her own. She understood now why Sarak had developed that impassive expression he was so skilled at—it provided him with the privacy he needed.

And yet the way Sarak had stared at her chest had caused her to flush uncomfortably while warming her at the same time. Was he remembering how he had pressed his lips there before caressing her with his hands? She shook her head. Now was not the time to be thinking about such things. In fact, she could not believe she had become so preoccupied with mating, a subject she had never shown any interest in before. Of course, she had never personally experienced the act before either, so she supposed she should allow herself a period of adjustment for the newness to wear off. She wondered how long it might take.

"The sooner we get started, the sooner we can get out of here," he said.

"Fine."

"We will meet back here later, around evenfall, although I am not sure how we will be able to tell when that is."

"My stomach will probably tell me," she said lightly. She dared to reach out and touch his arm through the material of the kanzu. "Sarak. About what I said before—I truly am sorry. I sometimes speak hastily, without thinking."

He surprised her by grinning. "Yes, I have come to realize that you are impulsive as well as brave and beautiful." He touched her cheek. "Be careful, little wingbird."

She nodded, absurdly pleased at his compliment and his special name for her. "You be careful, too."

She watched him disappear into the crowd, finally losing track of him when he rounded the cor-

ner of a large merchant stall filled with colorful
woven rugs. She supposed she should be grateful
over her tantrum—it had kept her from acknowl-
edging her fear at what she was about to do. She
tucked her chin down and began to walk toward
the ledge from which all the Kargans had descended.

She kept her eyes averted whenever she passed
anyone. It seemed the proper behavior. Everywhere she turned, she noticed blustering Kargan
warriors, obviously the favored and ruling class.
They slapped each other on the back in greeting,
they strutted about like rockroosters, they shouted
insults at each other while their women followed
behind them, as docile as any packbird. Phada
wanted to rouse these females to rebellion, until
she remembered the way that Kargan warrior had
slapped his woman without remorse or regret, as
if she were a mere possession, as if it were his
right to inflict punishment whenever he desired.

No one challenged her as she began walking up
the narrow incline that led to the tunnel above.
The market was a thriving place, with much
shouted laughter and good-natured taunts—all in
masculine voices. The women seemed cowed and
silent, timid creatures who were completely dom-
inated by the warriors. Was this what would eventually happen in Mesara? She shuddered to think
that her beloved town would come to such a fate.
It was obvious, though, that Dalcor had modeled
the new Mesara on this example of might controlling everything.

She paced upward, her determination to discover the secret of the faral even more fixed in her
mind. A couple of the warriors stopped and stared
at her cleavage, not even bothering to disguise
their interest. She was not certain how to respond,
but she knew she had best quell the immediate
indignation their actions provoked in her. One of

them even had the audacity to comment on her physical attributes to his cohort.

"This one is ripe for the picking." He chortled, stopping directly in front of Phada so that she was forced to halt. He had blond hair the same shade as maize and a scar that slashed diagonally across his lip and chin. It showed a puckered pink color against the whiteness of his skin. Phada was forced to revise her opinion that a pale complexion was a delicate one as she took in the roughened texture of his arms and the shadowed skin of his face where his beard grew.

"Aye, Kracor. But you have already claimed your pleasure partner."

Kracor reached out to drag his forefinger across the soft flesh displayed just above the material of her bodice, his companion leering the entire while. Phada could not help the gasp that escaped her lips but retained enough presence of mind not to pull away. It took every ounce of willpower she possessed not to slap him across his smug warrior's face.

"That does not mean there is not room for another comely wench—that way I can use one to warm my chest and the other to warm my backside."

They roared with laughter at this inane comment, their coarse, horrible pale faces filled with the knowledge of their own invincibility. If this was an example of Kargan wit, it was sadly lacking.

Phada realized she was clenching her hands fiercely. She loosened her fingers, keeping her eyes downcast so the two Kargan brutes would not read the defiance in her gaze. She dared not leave and yet she did not know the proper protocol for getting herself out of this situation. Surely there had to be one.

Her rescue came from an unexpected source.

"This one has already been claimed, Kracor," a soft, feminine voice interjected.

Phada turned to see a female, a young girl by the sound of her voice and the boyish slenderness of her build, although it was hard to tell at first glance with the veil covering the lower half of her face. And then she noticed that the girl's dress was a more demure version of that worn by the women, sporting a more seemly scooped neckline that only exposed part of her collarbone and no cleavage because she had none to show.

The girl bowed her head, her hands clasped respectfully at her waist. She had soft, silver-gold hair that curled around her forehead and tumbled down the back of her rose-colored dress. "I would not want you to get in trouble for fondling her," she added respectfully.

"Who the fark are you?" Kracor demanded.

Phada flinched at his disrespectful tone but it did not seem to phase her rescuer. "I am Nalissa." She bowed again.

"Well, Nalissa. It is none of your farking business who I fondle, is it?" He asked the question softly, menacingly.

"No, Kracor." Nalissa kept her head down. She seemed calm, even unaffected by what Phada perceived as Kracor's soon-to-explode wrath. Phada decided it was best to follow suit and also bowed her head. Surprisingly enough, Nalissa's reply soothed the warrior's temper.

"Good. I am glad you know your place. I will excuse your temerity this time but do not dare address me in that manner again."

"Yes, Kracor."

The two warriors stalked away without a backward glance. Phada remained silent, unsure what to say, how much Nalissa knew or suspected about her presence here.

"Please come with me," she said in a low, urgent

voice, grabbing Phada's hand.

Phada had no choice but to follow the girl, not unless she wanted to make a scene, which she knew would be fatal. Nalissa led her through a labyrinth of tunnels, deeper and ever downward. They passed various homes cut out of the rock, along with shops and other rooms whose uses Phada could only guess at. The underground land of the Kargans seemed endless, the numerous tunnels and corridors twisting and confusing. Phada peered down one tunnel and saw that the walls were covered with huge, brown-capped mushrooms. Workers were industriously plucking them into baskets. The source of the faral?

Finally they ducked into another corridor. This one led to the inside of a small dwelling. Phada glanced around quickly. The furniture was crude but serviceable and there was a leather and cloth wall hanging that was quite pretty. Nalissa gestured her farther inside to a smaller room, obviously the girl's bedroom, for a sleeping pallet stood in one corner with a colorful woven blanket, probably of Jiboan origin. She pointed to a sturdy-looking chest at the foot of the bed, indicating that Phada should sit down.

As Nalissa began removing her veil, Phada got a good look at her eyes. To her surprise, they were not blue but a pretty shade of light brown. Her skin was also not as white as that of some of the other women she had noticed. Phada saw that she was correct, that Nalissa was only a young girl of no more than 12 or 13 cycles.

"We cannot stay here long," she said breathlessly. "My parents will be returning soon but I did not know where else to bring you. Do you not know what will happen if Adelard finds you?"

"Who is Adelard?"

"He is the chief warrior and the ruler of our people. He could have you sent to the slave mines. Or worse," she added meaningfully.

"Why are you helping me? You do not even know who I am."

Nalissa smiled wryly. Phada could see that the girl would someday be a beauty with her brown eyes and shining silver-blond hair, her pert nose and appealing features. "I know you are not from Gorod, although the odious Kracor was too thick-headed to realize it."

"My name is Phada and I must thank you for your timely intervention. You took a great risk in coming to my rescue."

"It was nothing," Nalissa said with a shrug. "Kracor knew he dared not abuse me because my father is a member of Adelard's advisory council."

"Still, it was very brave of you. I did not know how to handle such a warrior."

"Do you not have warriors where you come from?"

"Yes, but they are not allowed to bully and dominate ordinary citizens."

"That must be wonderful." Suddenly the girl burst into a torrent of words. "Oh, please, Phada, take me with you, take me away from here," she begged, her eyes pleading, her entire posture beseeching as she clasped her hands in front of her. "In four more years I must undergo the pleasure rites with a warrior chosen by my father. They give you a drug and then you belong to him and he can do anything he wants with you. I do not want to submit to such a fate. I would rather die."

She flung herself on the pallet and started weeping, quietly, despairingly. Phada thought her heart would break hearing the girl's wrenching sobs. She moved across the room to sit on the edge of the mattress. "Is there no other role that a woman can take here in Gorod?"

Nalissa raised her tear-streaked face from the blanket. "Yes, she can become a domestic slave.

You do not have to go to a warrior's bed, but it is a harsh life filled with drudgery for a domestic slave; she must do all the household chores and take care of any children her master might have and wear horrible, ugly clothes."

Phada recalled the women she had seen in the marketplace with their drab, colorless dresses and their unveiled faces; obviously anyone could look upon them because they belonged to no male. It was a harsh system for the females, but then it was a harsh land. She did not know what Sarak would say, but she yearned to tell this spirited young girl, who reminded her in many ways of herself at that age, that she could return with them to Mesara.

"Where are you from?" Nalissa roused herself to ask.

She was not sure how Nalissa would react if she spoke the truth, but some instinct told her not to withhold the information. "I am from Mesara."

The young girl frowned; then her mouth crooked up into a charming smile. "I know that cannot be. You are teasing me. The Mesarans were once our sworn enemies but the mighty warriors of Gorod vanquished them a long, long time ago, even before we came to live beneath the ground. Now we only fight with the renegade Kargans who live on the other side of the mountain in Tregor."

"If that is what they have told you about Mesara, it is not true," Phada replied gently. "Because that is where I am from."

Phada waited for her reaction. Nalissa sounded as if she were spouting Kargan rhetoric she had learned in a lesson chamber, especially since Phada was certain her tone of voice had shifted to subtle mockery when she had praised the Kargan warriors. It was evident she had no great love for their dominating ways. Still, Phada did not want to alienate the girl if she could help it.

"Our history tells us that the Mesaran warriors achieved victory over the Kargans and drove them here to the south," she added. "Why else would your people choose to live in such a barren place unless they were forced to do so?"

"You mean along with all the other hateful things the warriors do, they have lied to us all this time?"

There was no answer to this, so Phada remained silent, watching the play of emotions across Nalissa's expressive face. She would have to be careful when she grew older that she did not reveal her rebellious thoughts to the warriors. From what Phada had seen, they would have little patience with her and would make her life miserable.

It was hard to think in terms of enemies when she looked at Nalissa's beautiful blond hair and milk white skin. Kracor and his ilk, yes, they were as vile as she had ever imagined a hated Kargan to be. But she could never consider this young, vibrant Kargan girl her enemy.

"What is it like in Mesara?" Nalissa asked.

Phada smiled wistfully as she thought of the richness and abundance of her homeland compared to this barren place. She did not think it would do any harm to tell her new friend a little about it.

"It is a bounteous land, filled with vibrant green jungles, and it is very warm there. In fact, you have to be careful to stay out of the direct sunlight or you can get a bad burn."

"Sunlight? You mean you actually go outside into the sun?"

Phada frowned. "Yes, of course we do. Although we are always careful to cover ourselves or to stay beneath the protection of the jungle canopy. Do you not venture outside?"

"Never." She shook her head emphatically.

"Only the farmers and lanaherders are allowed out after nightfall, and of course the warriors. But that is because they patrol our boundaries. Prolonged exposure to direct sunlight is deadly to us."

She did not notice Phada's astonishment at this casually related fact of Kargan life. If this were true—and Phada had no reason to doubt the girl—then the Kargans were physically unable to cross the Calabian Desert. There had never been any threat of a Kargan invasion, or at least not for the countless orbits since Kargan and Mesaran had clashed, in the distant reaches of the past. Obviously, since their enemy had come to live at the southern antipodes, their skin had gradually lost its ability to protect itself from the sun.

"So tell me, how did you get here? Did you travel by night and hide in caves after sunrise?"

"Yes, I did travel quite a lot at night. But, Nalissa, there is nowhere to hide during cycle-light, not when you are crossing the Calabian Desert. You must be able to move about freely in direct sunlight in order to reach Mesara."

"How is that possible?" Nalissa asked, stricken. "Your skin is not quite as fair as mine but it is still very pale."

"I do not know for sure. I suppose it is because I grew up in a place filled with sunlight and so am used to it."

She did not bother to point out that perhaps Nalissa's unusual eye color suggested she might be different from the other Kargans and perhaps able to withstand small doses of the sun's rays, especially here at the southern antipodes, where the sun was not so powerful. But there was still no possible way this fragile, pale-skinned girl could spend cycles beneath the burning heat of the desert sun, no matter how many kentas she donned. Phada could tell from the anguished expression in her lovely, light brown eyes that she understood this.

"It does not matter. It . . . it was only a wild and foolish dream." She met Phada's gaze bravely, all signs of the weeping girl vanished except for the faint traces of redness around her eyes and nose. "You must have urgent reasons for traveling so far."

"Yes, I do. I am searching for information to help my people." She paused and then decided to risk telling Nalissa everything. The girl might know about the faral, and any knowledge she could provide would be invaluable. What other choice did she really have? "One of our most trusted warriors has reverted to his dominator side and betrayed us. He has forced every Mesaran to become enslaved to a spice that is only produced here in Gorod."

"Faral," Nalissa whispered, her eyes wide with horror. She stared at Phada for a long, timeless moment before speaking again. "So that is how Adelard has suddenly been able to provide us with all the fresh produce that has been pouring into Gorod. Oh, he is even more vile and horrible than I ever imagined."

"My mother, my sister Chelis." Phada stopped, closing her eyes as they filled with sudden, burning tears. She forced herself to continue. "They are all being made to work in the fields, growing crops in exchange for their allotment of the spice."

Nalissa straightened her shoulders. Her face glowed with determination. "I will help you obtain whatever information you need."

# Chapter Seventeen

Sarak pulled the kanzu closer around his face as he slipped into one of the smaller tunnels that appeared less traveled than the others. He did not think anyone had noticed him, but he waited just inside the entrance for a generous amount of time, just in case. When no one came to challenge him, he proceeded further into the depths, moving swiftly along the torch-lined corridor that slanted ever downward into the bowels of Elithra.

He still could not believe the vast reaches of the Kargans' underground city. The Mesarans had half-buried their buildings beneath the surface for the cooling effects, but it was nothing to compare to this. From what he could observe, it seemed as if they had started with the natural cavern where the marketplace was located and then built from there. It must have taken many orbits to hollow out the rest.

As he walked, he mulled over what he had learned so far. He had kept his eyes and ears open in the marketplace and had picked up a great deal of information about the Kargan way of life. It was not hard to determine that a small, select group of warriors held the reins of power. They seemed to roam the tunnels and marketplace in gangs, bullying the rest of the population as the whim took them and claiming the females who struck their fancy.

From some of the conversations he had eavesdropped on, many of the other Kargans worked in the fields on the other side of the entrance where he and Phada had entered the city, tilling and planting at night by the light of the blue moon. The merchants had freely discussed the new development of the sudden influx of Mesaran goods into Gorod, complaining that the new luxuries were driving them out of business. Adelard, their leader, was rumored to be amassing great profits, and would soon own everything he did not already have in his greedy hands.

The tunnel suddenly veered sharply. Beyond the curve, he could hear a slow, steady thumping noise, along with the sound of metal upon metal and various raised voices that seemed to be shouting orders. He slowed his pace, approaching the bend cautiously. He peered around the corner, then drew back quickly. The tunnel opened into a large, well-lighted area with a naturally high ceiling. He only had time to notice that there were crowds of men milling about down below, dressed in some kind of leather leggings, their chests bare. He dropped to the ground before crawling closer so he could peer over the edge of the rocky overhang where the tunnel ended.

This time he realized exactly what was going on in the scene spread out before him. These men were prisoners and the sound he had heard was the result of the movement of their leg chains dragging along the rocky ground as they worked.

A couple of Kargan warriors, dressed in fancier leggings trimmed with beads and fur, stood guard over the operation. Each had a sword by his side and a whip in his hand, although at the moment they were talking and laughing with one another rather than directing their charges.

Sarak wondered how these unfortunate males had ended up here, what laws they had transgressed in order to be condemned to such a fate. They were all pale-skinned Kargans, their faces and torsos streaked with dirt and sweat. One of them stood out from the rest because although his skin was as colorless as that of his fellow inmates, his hair was an unusual shade of red.

Over in one corner, four of the prisoners hacked at the footwall with huge mallets. Another group of three used smaller picks to attack the various pockets of freestone before them in a job that obviously called for a more delicate touch. Sarak wondered what they were mining, since he could not see any traces of mineral deposits streaking through the dull brown of the rock.

The sudden sound of a foot scraping against the ground alerted him to the fact that someone was approaching from behind. He sprang to his feet, searching desperately for a hiding place. Curse it, there was none to be found in the smooth walls of the corridor, nor could he slip into the mining pits, since the approach from where he was standing was too exposed. He would have to face whoever appeared and try to bluff his way out of trouble.

Much to his dismay he saw that it was another pair of Kargans, probably replacement guards for the ones in the mine since they carried whips along with the requisite sword strapped to their waists. Sarak's eyes narrowed as he watched them approach. The one on the right was built like Mizor, tall and broad with thick arms and a neck like a bulloxen. His white hair straggled around his face and down his back, uncombed and unkempt. Its color and texture reminded Sarak of the downy boll of the coxa plant. The Kargan warrior laughed at something his companion said, and Sarak noted that his teeth were yellow and decaying beneath the drooping mustache that framed his mouth.

He estimated that the other male was closer to his own size. His yellow locks were partially pulled back and tied with a leather thong. His pale blue eyes were set close together, a fact that the beard covering the lower half of his face seemed to emphasize rather than conceal. He looked cunning and quick.

They stopped talking when they spotted him leaning nonchalantly against the side of the tunnel, searching through the pack he carried. They would realize he was not Jiboan after one close glance, so he knew he had to try another tactic. "I am looking for Adelard," he said with a casual smile. He might as well bluff for all he was worth.

Both pairs of eyes narrowed suspiciously. "What do you want with him?" the cunning one asked.

"I am an envoy, sent by Dalcor," he explained as he threw back the hood of his kanzu. Their gazes raked over him, assessing his face and eyes, his brown hair and tanned skin. "I have a message from him for your leader. Can you direct me to his dwelling?"

"We will do better than that," the big brute said, baring his ugly teeth. "We will take you there ourselves, will we not, Drood?"

Drood nodded and Sarak's heart sank. He had hoped they would simply direct him back to the marketplace to await the leader. He was not certain whether he should come up with a way to immobilize the pair of them before they managed to reach Adelard or take his chances that the communication lines the two leaders had established were as unreliable as the Calabian Desert which lay between them. At least this pair had shown no surprise when he had claimed to be a messenger from Dalcor.

The choice was soon taken from him. Drood gestured to Sarak to precede him, and he had no choice but to do so as the two warriors fell into step on either side of him, both of them remaining a wary pace behind. From their caution and their unwillingness to speak further, he realized they did not trust him. Their positions precluded any immediate action on his part.

As they came closer to the main tunnel that led to the marketplace, Drood moved in front of him while Coxa Hair hovered at his back, never more than a step away. Sarak sensed the big warrior never let his hand stray very far from the hilt of his weapon. He thought about trying to make a run for it, into the chaos and confusion of the market, but he had noticed another of those small bands of warriors near the exit tunnel and he knew he could not make it that far without being captured. Besides, he could not leave, not while Phada was still wandering around the labyrinthine pathways of Gorod.

"Adelard!" Coxa Hair roared at the top of his powerful lungs. One of the males on the other side of the tumble of market stalls turned his head. Even from here, Sarak could tell that Adelard would be a tough opponent. His careless gesture as he signaled to Sarak's captors to cross the floor of the crowded marketplace showed that he was in total control of his underlings.

Adelard was not a young man, Sarak realized as Drood halted their little party before his entourage, stopping Sarak with a raised arm. He stared at the hawkish profile of the Kargan ruler with its beaked nose and a jutting chin his scraggly beard did nothing to disguise. And then Adelard turned to face him and Sarak had to stifle his indrawn breath of shock. The scar from a horrible sword wound slashed from his brow to his cheek, directly across his right eye, which was almost white in color and obviously sightless. The skin had puckered around the raised tissue, drawing that side of his face into a perpetual sneer.

To add to the overall effect, Sarak noted that the eye constantly watered. The fluid ran in streaks down the side of Adelard's grizzled face. Every so often, at almost regular intervals, the Kargan leader raised his arm and wiped his running nose and streaming eye on the sleeve of his shirt. A huge swath of the material was damp and crusted.

Adelard's pale skin had wrinkled with the passing of many orbits, although his body was straight and strong beneath the leather tunic and leggings the Kargans favored. There were traces of gray in the coarse strands of his dark blond hair, and two slashes of silver bracketed the beard around his mouth.

His good left eye narrowed on Sarak's face, sharp with animal curiosity and cunning. Sarak felt threads of uneasiness creep up his spine and along his limbs. Adelard's entire face glowed in an unnatural way, as though lit from within. His expression reminded Sarak of a tuskboar he had once seen on a hunt. The enraged creature had eschewed the chance to escape into the jungle, instead deciding to turn around and wreak revenge on its tormentors.

"What have we here?" Adelard asked, his voice sinuously caressing every syllable of the question.

Drood and Coxa Hair gazed at each other uneasily before Drood finally replied. "He says he has a message from Dalcor."

"I see." The leader flicked his fingers in a contemptuous gesture of disgust. "Did I not just send you to relieve my brother and Magnor in the mines?"

"Yes, Adelard." That was Coxa Hair. Even Sarak realized that the big male should not utter another word in his own defense, but he did not seem to understand the nature of his precarious position. "But we ran into this stranger and we thought we should . . ."

Adelard moved so quickly his entire form became a blur as he knocked the white-haired warrior to the ground with his fist, then planted a leather-booted foot on either side of his body. He drew his sword, allowing it to dangle carelessly from his right hand, its point hovering above the fallen male's chest. "You ignorant slimetoad! I do not keep you around to think but to obey!" he roared, his face twisted with rage.

Drood tried to back away but there was nowhere for him to go. His beady eyes darted around, looking everywhere but at Adelard's face. Coxa Hair remained sullenly mute, his fists clenched at his sides, his big body tense as he lay there.

Adelard did not hesitate. He slashed the downed warrior across the chest. A crimson line of blood immediately followed in his sword's wake. "Now get the fark out of here!" he screamed.

Coxa Hair jumped to his feet. Sarak had to admire his bravado, since he did not even glance down at the wound on his chest. Drood was already halfway along the path that led down to the floor of the marketplace. Amidst the guffawing of Adelard's entourage, Coxa Hair pivoted smartly on his heel and strode back in the direction of the tunnel that led to the mines.

Adelard turned to Sarak with a broad smile, switching abruptly back to their original topic of conversation. "I wonder what my Mesaran brother to the north has to say that was not included in the message I received from him yester-cycle?"

"Dalcor got word that there was a trap laid for the other messenger," Sarak improvised quickly. "A Jiboan tribe felt they had been cut out of their share of the latest faral profits and vowed to make trouble. So he decided to send me to Gorod as well."

"Yes." Adelard rubbed his hand along a smaller scar on his temple. By the look of the skin, it was another old battle wound, although who these Kargans fought with, Sarak had no idea. Probably with each other. "I would not want anything to ruin the mutually beneficial arrangement I have with Dalcor. Tell me, is all going well in Mesara?"

"Yes, all is well." Sarak tried not to choke on the words.

"I am glad to hear it." He glanced around at the five warriors. "Are we not all glad of this news?"

They nodded almost in unison, a couple of the hardened males grunting their agreement aloud. It would have been comical if they did not look so bloodthirsty, so ready to spring at a moment's notice. Sarak could feel the tension crackling in the air and he knew they were only looking for the merest excuse to do so. Something was going on here and he was not sure if it was because they did not believe him or because they did. He needed to get away from Adelard as quickly as he could without arousing his suspicion, not an easy task since the Kargan seemed to be wary of everyone.

"The population of Mesara is once again under the control of its mighty warriors, which is the way it should have been all along." Adelard raised his fist, punching at the air to emphasize his point. The effect was marred when he lowered his arm to wipe his running nose on the sleeve of his loose-fitting shirt. His harsh, grating voice grew louder as he continued. "How could you Mesarans have strayed so far from the ideals of logic and good sense? How could you have allowed weak, bookish males and even weaker females to dictate what you should do?"

Sarak shrugged indifferently. "It matters not, since their reign has now come to an end and that is the finish of it," he said.

Would the king and queen ever be reinstalled on their throne? It did not seem very likely. Sarak's insides tightened painfully as he thought of Riga and Pavonis, of the council and the Keepers, of the laws laid down orbits ago by the wisest of the ancients. No one claimed that the Mesaran system was perfect, but it was better than living in fear. He had noticed how the Kargan population scurried away from the roaming bands of warriors. He had witnessed incidents where they had bullied those weaker and unable to defend themselves, deriving amusement from the terror and humiliation of their victims. They held the entire city of Gorod in their thrall.

He knew he had to try to get away from Adelard before he said something that would give away his true feelings. If there was one thing he had learned since meeting Phada, it was how to restrain his emotions and control his urges. However, he did not think he would be able to do so for much longer.

"Since you have already received the communication, I will be on my way," he said with a brisk nod.

"I think not." Adelard jerked his bearded chin at the male to Sarak's right. Before he could react, the Kargan had drawn his dagger and placed the tip of the weapon against Sarak's throat. "You are Mesaran all right, but Dalcor did not send you." He stroked his mustache back from his lip. "You fell into my trap, dominator. We had no messenger yestercycle. We do not expect anyone for at least five or six cycles. Now who are you?"

Sarak saw no reason to answer. Instead he raised his arm and rammed his elbow into his captor's ribs. The male grunted, dropping his hold around Sarak's neck long enough for him to snatch the dagger from his hand. He whirled around, blade at the ready in front of him.

"Seize him," Adelard snarled.

Sarak gave a warrior cry as he ducked beneath the arms of the closest Kargan, shoving him into the others. It helped to buy him enough time to scramble up the path into a more defensible position. He slashed out with the dagger, managing to keep the others at bay, but it was only a matter of time. Suddenly, at Adelard's signal, three of the warriors rushed him at once. He slashed one along the arm while another had his side sliced open before they managed to overcome him. They grabbed his arms, twisting them behind his back and jerking them upward painfully as they dragged him over to where Adelard stood.

"I will kill you for this," the Kargan leader assured him with a hiss.

"Go right ahead," Sarak invited him, his voice laced with scorn for the Kargans. "I would rather be dead than to live in a world ruled by a pair of schoolground bullies like you and Dalcor."

Something flared in the depths of Adelard's eerie blue eye. Sarak thought the other warrior might run him through with his sword right where they stood. Then his mouth twisted into an evil smile as he pushed his face closer to Sarak's. "Better yet, I can have you sent to work in the mineral mines for the rest of your life. My brother is especially good with a whip. He can peel the flesh away from the bone at ten paces."

"A useful skill for those possessed of a cowardly disposition," Sarak retorted.

He met Adelard's furious gaze with no hint of emotion showing in his expression, even when the Kargan backhanded him across the face. Pain exploded inside his head and behind his eyes, spreading outward like ripples on the surface of the water. His mind was already in turmoil, his thoughts despairing as he considered the extent of Phada's desperate situation, thanks to his most recent blunder. Where was she now? Was she thinking about him? He hoped she had enough sense to remain hidden until he could think of some way to escape before they discovered that he had not come to Gorod alone. They had freed themselves from the Jiboans, had they not?

"Get him out of my sight." Adelard dismissed him with a contemptuous curl of his lip before turning his back on him completely.

It was of no further use to struggle. Two of the warriors tightened their grip on his arms; then two more joined them as they escorted him down endless corridors, moving ever deeper underground. The experience was unnerving, knowing that the only thing between him and eternal darkness was the light of the torches that burned at ever sparser intervals as they descended. Finally they tossed him into a dank, dark cell, their laughter ringing in his ears long after the last sounds of their footsteps had receded.

"They have caught him," Nalissa announced as she rushed breathlessly into the room.

"What? What are you talking about?" Phada had been resting on several rather lumpy bags of flour in one of Nalissa's father's storage chambers, but she quickly sat up.

"Your warrior companion. Adelard has captured him. The story is all over the marketplace."

Phada instinctively opened her mouth to deny the fact that she and Sarak had traveled together but she realized it was a useless strategy. Nalissa was too smart not to realize that she could never have gotten here from Mesara by herself. Besides, she knew she would not be able to hide her distress over this piece of news.

"What has happened to him? Where is he?"

Nalissa threw herself down next to Phada with the loose-limbed grace of the young. "In a prison cell, but I am not sure which one. Probably one of the holding cells where they keep anyone unfortunate enough to fall out of our leader's good graces. Later they will probably move him to the slave quarters—if they do not kill him first."

"Kill him!" Phada was aghast. "Oh, dear Goddess, no. They cannot!"

"I heard that he grossly insulted Adelard, and that is something he never forgives. He has a terrible temper," Nalissa confided, her light brown eyes wide with trepidation. "Why one time, in a fit of anger over a female, he even condemned his own brother to slavery in the mines. He had him whipped in front of everybody, right in the marketplace. And worse than that, he force-fed him faral on the spot, and that is something that is not done lightly. Jolf is lucky that Adelard later rescinded the order. People are usually quickly forgotten once they are drugged and sent to the mines."

Phada pounced on the sole piece of information in Nalissa's speech that was not disheartening. "He rescinded the order? What happened to Jolf?"

"He is back at Adelard's side, his chief adviser when they are not arguing."

"Yes, but what about the faral he took?"

"There have always been rumors that there is a neutralizer, although Adelard always denies it because he does not want the slaves in the mines to think they can free themselves from its deadly grasp. But it must be true because Jolf does not seem to be affected anymore." She wrinkled her nose in distaste. "He is drunk on vetch most of the time, but he shows no signs of being spice-controlled."

"A neutralizer. Where would he keep such a potion?" Phada asked urgently.

"I do not know. In his chambers perhaps. But, Phada, there is no way you could ever hope to retrieve it."

"I have to. It is the sole reason I came to Gorod. My entire world is being destroyed and if I do not free my people, there is nothing left for me. But first I must find Sarak."

"I can show you the way."

"Thank you." Phada jumped to her feet, automatically smoothing down the tight-fitting Kargan clothing that still felt so strange to her senses. She quickly donned her veil and headdress, even though it felt as suffocating as a harvest festival mask. At least she would be well disguised when she walked the pathways and tunnels of Gorod.

She followed Nalissa from the storage chamber into the tunnel, which she had learned was the main thoroughfare in the Kargan's underground world. She had only been here a cycle but already she missed the light and warmth of the sun. After the desert she never thought she would feel that way, but this perpetual threat of everlasting darkness was disquieting and demoralizing.

They did not speak much as they hurried past the small groups of people ambling toward the main marketplace. Phada was glad of Nalissa's assistance. She did not have the best sense of direction to begin with, but these endless intersecting tunnels were enough to confuse anyone.

Nalissa stopped walking and Phada paused with her. When there was no one in sight, the girl suddenly grabbed her arm and yanked her into a small tunnel to their right. She did not release her until they had rounded the first bend.

"We should not be here. No one is allowed to come here except for Adelard's warriors."

"Then you must return to the main passageway. I can go on alone," Phada assured her, although she was not so certain herself. But she did not want to draw this brave young Kargan girl into her problems any more than she had to.

"No, there will be a guard posted and you will need my help."

"I do not want to get you in trouble, Nalissa. What will happen if they catch you?"

"Do not worry about that. I have never had the opportunity to do something against the males who run all our lives and make us miserable. Do not deny me this chance, Phada. It is the only one I shall ever have and I intend to make the most of it."

Phada squeezed Nalissa's arm in gratitude. They continued along the tunnel, which slanted ever downward. There was enough room for the two of them to walk beside each other, but Phada still had the feeling that the walls were pressing in on her and might collapse. She would not make a very good citizen of Gorod if she had to traverse these corridors on a daily basis.

Nalissa held up a hand in warning. Just ahead, Phada could see that there were several torches burning, and in their light a Kargan warrior sat on a three-legged stool, his back against the wall. He appeared to be sleeping, although it was hard to tell from this distance.

"There is a guard here, which means that your friend must be in one of these cells."

"What do we do now?" Phada asked in a low voice.

"One of us will have to distract him," Nalissa whispered back. She bit her lip as she considered just how to accomplish the task, then brightened.

"You must be the one to do it, Phada," she said, leaning closer so she could speak directly into her ear. She glanced down at her flat chest with a giggle. "I do not yet have the feminine assets to pull it off. All Kargan warriors think women are pretty, mindless ornaments who are unable to think for themselves. He will not be surprised if you pretend that you have gotten yourself lost. He will be too busy looking down your dress to wonder what you are doing in this corridor. You must be sure to flutter your eyelashes at him and act helpless."

Phada chuckled. "I think I can manage that."

"Good. You must also get him to turn his back to me." Nalissa bent down to pick up a rock, hefting its weight in her hand as a slow smile spread across her face. Her eyes sparkled with anticipation. "It will give me great satisfaction to bash him over the head with this."

Phada smiled, shaking her head in admiration at the young girl's spirit and determination. Nalissa was definitely not like the other downtrodden Kargan females she had noticed during her short time here. "You are amazing."

Nalissa grinned, although Phada observed that it held a touch of sadness. "If I am, it is thanks to you. You have given me hope that there are other ways to live. I must tell you, I have never felt as alive as I do now. For once, I am acting instead of allowing things to happen to me. For once, I am not merely a helpless, subservient female. You have showed me that it is possible."

Phada frowned. "No, I do not agree. These things were inside you all along, Nalissa. You just needed a reason to bring them out and I happened to be the one who provided it. I can never repay you for all you have done for me. I only hope that you do not regret it."

"Be assured, I will never regret it. No matter what happens, I am glad I met you."

Phada touched Nalissa's cheek, realizing that she felt as close to this young Kargan as she did to her own sister. She had to swallow past the lump in her throat. They had no time now to wax sentimental. "All right, here I go."

She began walking toward the warrior, her heart pounding and her throat dry. Flashes of all the things she had done since leaving Mesara flickered through her mind, giving her courage. She knew she would attempt anything to save Sarak. She tried not to think about getting caught and having to spend the rest of her life in this horrible place, buried beneath the ground like a corpse, never to see cycle-light again.

The guard was sleeping, she realized as she drew closer, but not so deeply that he was unaware of her approach. He sat up quickly, his hand moving automatically to the hilt of his sword. When he saw it was a female, he relaxed his posture visibly. Hmph, Phada thought, insulted that he had already decided she presented no danger to him. *We will show you,* she promised him with satisfaction. *At least, I hope we will.*

"What is this?" he demanded.

She allowed her hands to fly up to her face in a flustered manner. "Oh! I . . . where am I? This is not the passageway I was seeking."

The warrior eyed her with a condescendingly amused smile as he rose to his feet. He was not as tall as Sarak, but he still topped her height by a good half measure. She had to tilt her head back to look at him, and as she did so she remembered to flutter her eyelashes. He perused her upturned features with approval before his gaze dropped to the exposed skin of her chest.

"You are a tender morsel," he growled softly. He probably thought he was using an irresistible tone of voice but it made Phada want to shudder. "Have you been claimed, sweetling?"

Phada was so flustered at this direct attack that she did not at first realize he was facing in the wrong direction. When she did, she tossed her head with a saucy motion as she walked past him, imitating as best she could the graceful mannerisms of the Jiboan dancers, swinging her hips inside the fitted dress in the most indecent way she could manage. She was relieved to note that he moved his position in order to follow her progress. Hurry, Nalissa, she thought.

She smiled coyly at the warrior before dropping her gaze to the ground. She was not altogether certain of how to reply to his query, but she quickly decided that to hold his interest she had best pretend to be unattached. "No, no one has claimed me," she said.

"Good. Then I do so now."

Before she knew what was happening the Kargan wrapped his arms around her waist and lifted her off the ground, pressing her entire body against his. She nearly gagged at the terrible odor that emanated from his body. He must not have bathed anytime during his entire adult life, and this close up she could see that his dark blond hair was that color because it was filthy. She could not stop herself from struggling.

"Aye," he muttered approvingly. "I like my females feisty. That way I get to tame them to my hand until they are skilled in what pleasures me. It will be most gratifying to teach you to do my bidding."

"I have changed my mind. I do not wish to be claimed."

He laughed in her face and his breath was as foul as the rest of him. "As if you have a choice in the matter. I will take it up with Adelard at the next council meeting." He lowered her to the ground, then bent down to nuzzle her neck. "Now, what is your name and who is your family?" He pulled back with a frown, his expression showing the first hints of suspicion. "I do not remember ever seeing you before."

A shadow moved on the wall behind him and then Nalissa's arm came briefly into view. She must have climbed onto the stool in order to get above her target. Phada smiled at the guard for all she was worth as a resounding crack filled the air. "That is because you probably have not," she replied as he crumpled to the ground at her feet. "Good work, Nalissa."

Nalissa scrambled down from her perch while Phada hurried to the door of the cell. "Sarak?" she hissed, peering into the small opening cut into the heavy wooden door. She did not know why she was whispering but it seemed the correct thing to do. Perhaps there was another guard stationed somewhere nearby who might hear them.

His face quickly appeared, although she could only see one eye and part of his cheek. "Phada?"

She could not help herself, she began babbling at top speed, a release from all the tension that had gone before. "Yes, it is me. We have come to rescue you. And I have found out that there is a neutralizer for the faral. Adelard has it, so it will not be easy to come by, but I am sure we can formulate some sort of plan. . . . "

"Phada, hush. One thing at a time." He managed to thrust his hand through the slot so he could touch her cheek. "I never thought to see you again." He gently feathered his fingers along her cheekbone before moving them to brush the hair back from her temple. Then he traced the line along the edge of her veil, ending at the corner of her mouth before pulling his hand back inside the cell.

Phada felt her insides melt. How did he manage to do that to her?

"We must get you out of there," she said urgently.

"The guard has a key," he told her.

She hurried back to where the Kargan lay unconscious. She hated to touch him but she had no choice. Nalissa hovered anxiously nearby as she rolled him until he was flat on his back. First she pulled his sword from its leather scabbard. Sarak would need a weapon. Next she discovered a leather bag hanging from his belt. Inside was a small quiver filled with darts and a dart blower. She had never noticed any of the other warriors wearing such a pouch and wondered what the darts were for. She searched the usual places one might have a key and finally found it on a metal ring he had placed around his wrist.

She stood up, key in hand. "Nalissa, you must leave. I cannot allow you to further endanger yourself."

The young girl nodded, her hair shimmering in the torchlight. "You must flee Gorod while you still can. I will see what I can gather to help you on your return journey. There is an abandoned tunnel just beyond the marketplace on the way to the outside. The entrance is half-filled with rocks and is easy to find. No one ever uses it. I will hide some food and supplies inside."

"Thank you," Phada said, her eyes and throat stinging with unshed tears. "You have been a wonderful friend."

She did not have the heart to tell the girl that they could not leave until they had at least obtained a sample of the neutralizer. They stood there staring at each other, and then suddenly they were hugging with fierce tenderness and genuine affection. Phada could not believe how fond she had become of Nalissa in the short amount of time she had known her.

"I am sorry we cannot take you with us," Phada said.

"I know." Nalissa stepped back and Phada saw the tears streaming down her face. The girl brushed them away with an impatient hand. "Please do not forget me when you are back in your warm, sunny land."

Phada's smile was filled with sadness. "I will never forget you. Now go quickly."

Nalissa turned and fled down the corridor. Phada watched until she disappeared from view and then hurried back to the door of Sarak's cell. "I have the key."

"Well done." She found herself flushing at his praise. "Who were you talking to?"

"A young Kargan girl I met named Nalissa. Without her aid, I would never have found you."

It took a while to fit the heavy metal key into the lock and even longer to force it to turn. She thought he must be growing impatient with her clumsiness but he did not utter a word of reproach; he did not even urge her to hurry. As she yanked at the recalcitrant door handle, she found herself faintly embarrassed at her unseemly haste in wanting to see Sarak again. Did he not feel the same? He had seemed glad of her presence when she had first appeared, when he had caressed her face, but of course who would not appreciate his rescuer?

She finally managed to shove the door open. Her gaze roamed hungrily over him, checking for injuries. They had taken his kanzu and he was clad only in his dominator's breechcloth. She could not believe how good it was to see him. He seemed more handsome than she remembered, although his face and chest were streaked with dirt and one side of his face was swollen and bruised.

She wanted to hug him, dirt and all, and even

found herself starting forward until she realized that he had not made a move in her direction. Why did he not reach for her? she wondered, feeling hurt and dismayed. Of course they had no time for such things, but it would have been nice to know he had been thinking about her the way she had been thinking about him.

"Are you all right?" she finally asked. She could not stop herself from lifting a hand toward his injured cheek.

"I am fine." He swayed in her direction, and then suddenly he backed away as though remembering his place. "No," he said. "You must not touch me. I am filthy with mud."

"I do not care." She pressed her fingers to his face, her thumb resting just beneath his jaw. His hand quickly came up to cover hers.

The sound of pounding footsteps filled the corridor. Phada's head automatically swiveled in the direction of the noise. She gasped in dismay when she saw a small band of Kargan warriors running toward them, their swords brandished. There had to be at least five of them.

"You there! Halt!" the male in the lead shouted.

"Come on, this way." Sarak grabbed her hand and together they bolted down the tunnel in the opposite direction.

# *Chapter Eighteen*

Phada thought her lungs would burst as she stumbled along behind Sarak. He had released her hand ages ago when the second tunnel they had turned into had narrowed, making it impossible to run side by side. She was not even certain anymore if they were heading up toward the light or down into the depths of Gorod. Her legs automatically pumped up and down, propelling her forward along endless corridors. How did the Kargans survive in such a warren? She wanted to ask if Sarak knew where they were going, but she could not summon the breath to do so.

Thank the Goddess, Sarak had managed to lose their pursuers somewhere down that last corridor. There had been a choice of directions, a three-way crossing point. Just past another sharp bend in the passage, he pulled her close to the wall, where they would not be easily seen.

"Do you know where we are?" she gasped the question, slumping over in a desperate, but futile effort to catch her breath.

"This place is impossible, like something out of a nightmare. I was too busy trying to stay ahead of those warriors to watch which way we turned. We could be back where we started for all I know." He had his hands on his knees but otherwise did not seem nearly as winded as she was. Well, what did she expect? she thought with a grimace. He was a trained warrior, after all.

She gazed over at him. "What are we going to do?"

He held up his hand for silence. Phada swiveled her head from side to side, unable to hear anything. And then her eyes widened in horror as she realized there was an unnatural quality to the stillness that suddenly washed over and around them.

Sarak gestured for her to follow, placing a finger to his lips to reinforce what she already knew, that she should remain silent. They crept carefully along the corridor; the only sound Phada could hear was her own ragged breathing. Just ahead a large boulder jutted into the middle of the passageway, its pitted sides streaked with some sort of shiny rock deposit that gleamed in the feeble light of the torch. She realized that there was very little in this dark underground world that sparkled or gave any other indication of life and vitality. In any case, she did not like the looks of this particular boulder or the possibility that a group of Kargans might be poised on the other side, waiting to pounce.

The faintest noise, perhaps the scraping of a booted foot against a pebble, halted them in their tracks. Sarak gestured for her to back away from the boulder. And then pandemonium broke loose.

"Run," Sarak yelled. He pushed her ahead of him, whirling around to face their enemy, the sword she had taken from the guard gripped in his hand. "Get out of here while you can. I will hold them."

Phada hesitated. Four Kargans slowly advanced on Sarak, their swords drawn and their faces grim. She did not want to leave him, but if they were both captured they would have no chance at all. And yet suppose they killed Sarak?

"Adelard wants this one alive," the brute on one end said with disgust, jerking his chin in Sarak's direction.

"Go!" Sarak cried again.

That was all Phada needed to hear. She whirled on her heel and started to run down the corridor, the sound of clanging swords echoing behind her. She wanted to sob, to pivot around and dash back to Sarak, but she knew she should not. If she could only find her way out of this passageway and back to the areas where the Kargans went about their daily lives, she might be able to find Nalissa. She knew the young girl would help hide her until she could think of some way to free Sarak once again. It was a slim chance but as far as she could tell, it was their only one.

She burst around the corner and ran smack into a Kargan warrior who stepped casually into her path from a side tunnel she had not noticed. He caught her by the arms and spun her around so quickly her feet barely left the ground. Then he pushed her forward, forcing her to march back toward the fighting.

"Oh, Goddess." She muffled a sob with the back of her hand when she saw Sarak, flat on the ground with two Kargans standing over him. One of them had his foot pressed into Sarak's back, and the other had laid the tip of his sword against Sarak's temple.

"Well, well, Mesaran dog, we meet again." The harsh, grating voice had a nasal quality that should have lessened its authority but somehow did not. Its owner stepped closer to the light and Phada felt her heart drop to her feet at the sight of the marred face of the Kargan warrior before her. He had lost the sight in one eye and the scars from that wound disfigured the entire half of his face. He was dressed like the others, but the golden circlet encrusted with precious stones that hung around his neck proclaimed that this must be Adelard.

His gaze suddenly focused on her. "And what have we here?" he asked softly. Frissons of alarm raced up and down her spine at the avaricious gleam in his one good eye. "Another Mesaran visitor. We are honored. So honored in fact, that I will personally make you welcome to Gorod." He chuckled and the blood chilled in her veins. "What is your name, little one?"

Coming from his lips, the sweetly cajoling tone was a mockery of everything decent in the world. Phada knew they would receive no mercy at this warrior's hands. She wanted to spit in his ugly face, and yet something warned her not to—at least not just yet. She did not have much faith in her powers of persuasion, but she could tell that he desired her and as long as she was alive there was always a glimmer of hope that circumstances would change in their favor. She knew instinctively that she should not give Adelard a reason to suspect her deep feelings for Sarak.

"Do not answer him," Sarak hissed. He grunted in pain as his words earned him a thudding kick in the ribs.

"I am called Phada," she replied. She tried to catch Sarak's eye, but his second captor was using Sarak's neck as a footrest and his face was smashed into the ground. She forced herself to move her eyes away from him before her emotions unmasked her.

"Phada." Adelard tested the name and obviously

found it pleasing, because he smiled. Or at least Phada figured that the grimace that stretched his twisted features was supposed to pass for a smile. "Well, Phada, I have decided to claim you. You are going to pleasure me."

"If you touch her, I will kill you!" Sarak hissed in fury. He tried to jerk himself away from the foot planted on his neck, but to no avail.

Phada pressed her lips together, her throat tight with emotion. So much for keeping their feelings secret. She knew he would give his life to ensure her well-being and it made her want to cry at the injustice of their fate. Was this how goodness and honor were rewarded? She had begun to think perhaps the ancients were wrong in their assessment of warriors, but her own experience was forcing her to the same conclusion. Every warrior she had ever known—except for Sarak—was a brute and a bully.

Adelard laughed at his reaction. "I think we can find some use for all that energy and anger. A little entertainment is in order, Mesaran, before I claim your female for my own. Tell me, is she a good pleasure giver? Does she moan and writhe enough to excite?"

"You sun-cursed bastard," Sarak spat in defiance. Phada thought he had never looked more magnificent, like a cornered clawcat snarling defiance in the face of impossible odds. He would die fighting, and he put every other male around him to shame.

Adelard snorted vigorously in an effort to clear his clogged nasal passages. Then he wiped his nose on his sleeve with a gesture she was already beginning to loathe with every fiber of her being. "To the victor go the spoils," he said, shrugging carelessly. "Take him to the arena. We will see if he is as much of a warrior as he thinks."

Phada sat on the cold stone bench staring help-lessly down at the small, enclosed arena below with its packed dirt floor and thick, wooden walls. Adelard sat by her side, his incessant sniffing setting her teeth on edge. She did not know whether to thank the Goddess that his sightless eye was on the side farthest away from her where she did not have to look at it or despair because he could see every move she made.

At least for the moment his attention was diverted to what was about to happen below. He had stopped trying to grab her hand and touch the flesh above the low neckline of her revealing Kargan clothing. Just the memory of his ogling glances at her breasts still caused the bile to rise in her throat. She could never allow him to touch her intimately, to mate with her, not after what she had experienced with Sarak. But she did not know how she was going to be able to stop him.

He had promised her a spectacle she would never forget and she was afraid he was about to deliver on that promise. A door clanged open and Sarak was shoved into the arena so hard he stumbled. He soon righted himself, his gaze immediately sweeping the seating area until it came to rest on Phada. His dark eyes were eloquent with unspoken emotion, although his expression remained stoic. Phada did not know how he could appear so totally unperturbed at his predicament. Her lips parted but she did not know what to say to him. She wanted to tell him how special he was, to thank him for changing her life, but she knew that would only incite Adelard to think up further torments and humiliations.

She continued to stare down at him, her mind reeling. She realized she might never get another chance to say what was in her heart. "Sarak!" she cried, jumping to her feet.

Adelard grabbed her and jerked her into his lap.

His hand came up to cover her mouth just as a Kargan warrior strode into the arena, placing himself between Sarak and the overhanging seating area where Phada struggled to free herself. He held a gleaming sword in one hand and a shield in the other. Phada's movements became less frenzied, her horror growing as the implications of what she was observing began to sink in. Dear Goddess, were they going to slaughter him right before her very eyes?

She finally ceased her useless resistance altogether. In response, Adelard released her. She was furious, her head pounding with the force of her anger.

"Do not cry out to him again or you will regret it," he snarled at her.

She slumped back in her seat. Another warrior entered the arena to hand Sarak a sword. Even from here, Phada could discern that it was old, the metal dull and pitted with heavy use. She turned to Adelard, her voice dripping with sarcasm. "You must be very fearful of him that you handicap him with a poor sword and no shield."

She had thought to at least shame the Kargan leader into giving Sarak a better weapon, but he only chuckled. "I said I wanted entertainment, not a fair contest."

"You are a brute and a coward," she cried out, heedless of the consequences. Her hands clenched into tight fists, her fingernails pressed painfully into her palms. She could no longer suppress her anguish and she no longer cared.

"Save some of that feistiness for the mating pallet," he told her with a grin.

She did not bother to reply to his jibe, nor did she try to hide her shudder of revulsion. "Why do you not just kill us both and be done with it?" she asked bitterly.

He sniffed long and hard before answering,

grinning at the look of deep-seated disgust that crossed her face. "Ah, Phada, that would be much too easy. Now sit back and watch your companion fall." He leaned forward to raise his voice in a shout. "Tyrkar, show him how it is done!"

Tyrkar let out a roar as he charged at Sarak, his feet driving into the dirt floor so hard they sent up little clouds of dust. The sound of clanging swords soon filled the arena, echoing off the stone walls, bouncing from the ceiling. It was strange and horrible to sit there, the only witnesses to this spectacle of blood.

Phada did not want to watch, but she could not seem to tear her gaze away from the pair of battling warriors below. And then to her utter amazement, it was over, almost before it had begun. Sarak feinted to his left and then slashed his opponent with a clean, slicing motion across the stomach. The Kargan fell to the ground, clutching his injury and moaning.

Phada released the air she had been holding in her lungs. It was the first conscious breath she could remember taking since the contest had begun. Sarak stood quietly in the center of the dimly lit arena, his rusty sword held tightly by his side, ready for whatever else Adelard might send his way. Phada spared a brief glance for his opponent. The sight of the Kargan's blood gushing between his pale fingers was shocking in the contrast of dark and light. It spread in an ever-widening pool, garishly red against the whiteness of his skin.

She was barely aware of the two warriors who came to lead the injured male away, so relieved was she that it was over. She turned to observe Adelard's reaction, surprised to discover that he did not seem angry or upset. Instead he grinned that horrible, death's-head grin at her and signaled to the warrior guarding the door below. He opened it and another Kargan stepped into the ring with a confident stride.

This one looked even more fierce than the first, Phada decided in dismay. He was dressed for battle in dark leather leggings and a sleeveless tunic that bared his pale, brawny arms and a good deal of his chest. He had pulled his long, light brown hair into an elaborate nest of braids that hung down alongside his bearded face and moved every time he tossed his head, which he did as often as the vainest female. He grinned up at her, his teeth large and flashing as they caught the torchlight, his expression filled with arrogance.

Sarak stepped forward, undaunted, to challenge him. "I do not suppose you would release the female if I best this next warrior," he called out wryly. Phada did not know how he could jest about such matters.

Adelard sniffed as he squinted his eye consideringly. "I do not think you can beat him," he said with a smirk. "Is that not right, Vibald?"

"I will enjoy watching his pitiful efforts to try," the braided warrior shouted, pumping his shield up and down like a bellows. "And then I will kill him."

Adelard chuckled as he turned to Sarak. "All right, Mesaran. If you can conquer Vibald, I will allow your Phada to walk away from here."

The promise of a warrior was sacred, but somehow Phada did not believe the Kargan leader would keep his word. Sarak's eyes narrowed as he nodded briskly in response to this offer. He hefted his sword, adjusting his grip, then immediately began circling the other male like a wary clawcat. He danced lightly on the balls of his feet, his weight ready to shift in any direction at a moment's notice. Vibald dropped into a crouch, feinting with his shield, then his sword, in what he obviously considered a dazzling display of bluffing his opponent, although Sarak hardly blinked an eye at his maneuvering. He certainly did not fall for the ruse; Phada could tell that he was not about to be lured into attacking before he was ready.

"Why do you wait?" Adelard cried to his own fighter. "Do not play his cautious game. That is the coward's way. Attack! Attack!"

Phada gripped her hands together as Vibald let out a high-pitched, hissing screech and surged forward. She could not prevent her body from jerking in terror at the first impact of sword against sword. Adelard continued to scream contradictory instructions to his warrior. Phada was no battle-hardened veteran, but even she could tell that Adelard had no sense of timing and certainly no innate skill in the finer nuances of battle. All he seemed to want was to hear the loud noises produced from the clanging of weapons, like a little boy whacking a spoon against his mother's stewpot.

She wanted to boast aloud of Sarak's prowess as it became more obvious with every passing millimark that he was beating Vibald badly, but she did not want to do anything that might jinx the outcome. Adelard had ceased his instructing, thank the Goddess, and now sat beside her, grunting aloud as his warrior began to tire, but making no comment about Sarak's superiority. He scowled when Vibald finally fell awkwardly on his side, a victim of a particularly graceful and lightning-fast maneuver on Sarak's part.

"Your warrior has lost in the most disgraceful manner possible," Phada commented. She took a large degree of pleasure in the communication and did not hesitate to show it.

Adelard snorted, unabashed. "It does not matter about Vibald. He was a braggart and a liar when he promised me victory. If I send in enough warriors, one of them will defeat him."

She was shocked and disgusted at this further evidence of his bullying attitude. "You act as if such a one-sided battle would make you proud."

"Why should it not?" he asked. "A victory is a victory, no matter how it is achieved."

"That is the vilest sentiment I have ever heard from the mouth of a so-called warrior, even a Kargan one," she muttered scornfully.

She stared at his ugly face with its unnatural, sneering expression that reflected the bitterness in his sun-blackened soul. What did it matter if she provoked him? She and Sarak were both doomed in any case. She met his angry gaze and realized she did not care anymore what happened to her. The situation had passed beyond hopeless and she knew it. It might not be a bad thing if she could goad him into putting her out of her misery.

"You are all cowards as well as weaklings," she said, tossing her head in a show of bravado that took her by surprise. She might not have as many braids as Vibald, but she thought the end result was passably effective. She could only conclude that some of Sarak's bravery had rubbed off on her.

"I see you do not appreciate Kargan cunning," he countered. "We have always been prepared for Mesaran treachery, especially now that we deal on a regular basis with our brother, Dalcor." He leaned closer, his arm touching hers. She flinched away but he only laughed. "See the leather quiver strapped around that warrior's waist and the small dart blower beside it?" He gestured toward the two warriors who were helping Vibald stagger to his feet.

She shrugged disdainfully. "So?"

"So, those darts are tipped with faral. That way we cannot lose no matter how unequal the fight."

"By the holy name of the Goddess, you have no principles, no honor," Phada retorted, horrified at this further example of the Kargan leader's low standard of ethics. "You are a disgrace to the warrior code."

He laughed uproariously. "Who cares about honor or the warrior code when winning is everything?" He rose to his feet. "I grow tired of this. Volsung! Ospak! Come, collect the prisoner."

The warriors who had dragged their fallen comrades from the arena came forward to disarm Sarak before hauling him closer to their leader. This time Phada noticed the dart blowers and shuddered. Sarak avoided her gaze, all his attention focused on his mortal foe.

Adelard's mouth lifted in a nasty smile as he leaned over the parapet to address him. "You were lucky to vanquish my warriors. Then again, any cornered tunnelrat might accomplish the same." He chuckled at his own wit before continuing. "I am going to give your Phada a tablet laced with a pleasure drug that induces a mating frenzy in the recipient. After it takes effect she will be my Phada and she will eagerly spread her legs for me. She will forget you entirely. In fact," he assured them both with a raspy laugh, "she will lust for me to the exclusion of reason."

"You stinking Kargan bastard," Sarak roared, lunging toward the wall as if his willpower alone would allow him to fly over it and grab Adelard by the throat. The two warriors quickly restrained him, one by delivering a blow to Sarak's head with his fist. Phada rushed to the edge, reaching out a beseeching hand. Below her, Sarak continued to struggle in spite of the blows that pummeled his head, stomach, and ribs. Phada could hear the visceral thud of each blow as though it were striking her own body.

"Stop it," she screamed, throwing herself along the high rock wall that was the only obstacle separating her from Sarak. "Stop it, do you hear me!"

Before she could say another word, Adelard grabbed her by the hair, yanking her back. She yelped as burning shards of pain exploded along her scalp. She had to admit his tactic was effective, if barbaric. She held herself utterly still, not even bothering to wipe the tears that trickled down her cheeks.

Adelard reached inside his vest and pulled out a pouch. Untying it, he quickly withdrew a small square that looked like pressed straw, only it was dark brown in color. "Eat this," he commanded her.

"No. You'll have to kill me first."

"Have you ever seen bulloxen castrated?" he began slowly, stroking the scraggly hair of his bearded chin. "It works such wonders on their temperaments. They become as docile and biddable as children. I do not know if castration has the same effect on a warrior, but it would be interesting to find out, do you not think so?" He paused just long enough to allow the horror of what he was suggesting to sink in. "Take the drug, Phada, or I will have your companion castrated right now, while you watch."

"No," she quickly interjected. "I . . . I will take it." She could not best him; she wondered why she bothered to keep trying. His cruelty would not allow him to lose. She was the defeated one. She reached out a shaking hand for the square, taking it and popping it quickly into her mouth before she lost her courage. It tasted mostly like dried grass, but as she chewed she could detect the underlying taste of faral. Hope, unbidden and eternal, sprang up in her breast as she tried not to gag. No one knew of her body's rejection of the drug. Could she somehow use this to her advantage?

"That is better," Adelard crooned. "You are going to be quite a handful, but I intend to enjoy your ultimate surrender. And surrender you will, sweetling."

Phada hardly heard his threat, so busy was she trying to plan the best course of action. She wondered if her body would also reject the pleasure drug and if not, how powerful its effect might be. She would have to wait and see. In the meantime, she decided she had to remain docile; it was the usual result in individuals who had consumed the spice, and it was what Adelard would be expecting. She must take care not to give herself away.

"Dose him with faral!"

Adelard gave the order to his minions as though it were of little consequence. Sarak cried out in protest, redoubling his efforts to escape, but one of the warriors reached into his quiver and pulled out a dart, stabbing him in the arm before he knew what had hit him. Oh Goddess, Sarak, she thought, her eyes filling with tears as she watched. She began to cry then, quietly and hopelessly, hot tears running down her face as she remembered how valiantly Sarak had struggled to break the hold of the spice over his mind and body, how much and how bravely he had suffered. Now he would be helpless once again, a slave to his body's insistent craving.

She whirled to face Adelard, forgetting the plan she had laid out for herself, instead pounding her fists against his chest in her fury and helplessness. He only laughed as he subdued her easily, wrapping his arms around her and clamping her flailing limbs to her sides.

He eyed her with a puzzled frown. "The faral usually works more quickly than this," he said.

He proceeded to haul her out of the arena. Phada bit her lip until it bled, trying to regain control over her rampaging emotions. She had to remain calm or she would ruin whatever small scrap of a chance they still had. She allowed her feet to drag, as if she did not have the energy to move them herself. Adelard grunted with satisfaction, running his hands in the most revolting and familiar fashion over her body. He slyly fondled her breast. She could feel him waiting for her reaction. It took every ounce of willpower she possessed to do nothing.

When they reached the top row of stone benches that encircled the arena, Adelard stopped. "When he is docile, send him to the mineral mines," he called over his shoulder. "We will see how long the Mesaran lasts under Jolf's whip."

He then turned back to Phada, his one eye gleaming. "Come. The time of waiting is over."

# *Chapter Nineteen*

Phada followed submissively behind Adelard as they traversed more tunnels and corridors. Her cooperation had earned her the release of her hand from his sweaty grip before she lost control of her urge to snatch her squashed fingers away, a small victory but encouraging nonetheless. He believed that the faral was taking effect; she must make sure that he continued to do so.

Finally they reached his chambers. They were located in a section of the underground stronghold that she could not remember viewing before. He jerked his head to indicate she should enter. Such a charming man, she thought with disdain, as he closed the heavy wooden door behind them

She gazed around at the elaborate interior of his quarters. The room was filled with brightly colored rugs on the floors and hanging from the walls. It reminded her of the Jiboans' tents, and indeed, the woven mats were definitely from the various tribes of the desert people. The furniture

334

was made of a beautiful light-colored wood streaked with darker markings. Someone had obviously taken great care with its design and construction, and the polished finish gleamed in the light from the wall sconces. There were two chairs and a couch, all of them covered with an artfully careless array of colorful pillows and cushions, mostly in shades of blue and green. The long, low tables displayed small statues of animals, some of them with jeweled eyes, along with other decorative items.

Phada was amazed. The overall effect was light and airy and more beautiful than anything she had seen in Gorod so far. Even the dwelling of Nalissa and her parents, although comfortable, was nothing to boast about. She could not imagine that Adelard had had anything to do with the design or layout of this room, unless she had been sadly misled about his character and talents.

"Your dwelling is lovely," she said.

Her comment seemed to please him, although he spoiled the effect by stating, "Kargan warriors deserve only the best." He reached for one of the statues, bypassing the snarling tuskboar and the hissing serpent to choose a bright-eyed leporus with long ears and gentle brown eyes of gleaming topazine. He held it out to her.

"It is exquisite, wondrous," she whispered in awe as she examined its intricately carved lines and curves. And indeed it was. The artist had captured the quivering alertness of the small creature, so that Phada swore she could almost see its nose twitch. Even the wood felt warm and alive as she cradled it in her hands. "I have never seen anything like it."

"Yes." He seemed embarrassed at agreeing with her praise. He suddenly sniffled loudly, breaking the spell.

Phada drew in a deep breath, surprised that she

had experienced even that brief moment of connection with the despicable Kargan leader. The pleasure drug must be softening her natural aversion to him. She felt much better when he reverted to his usual behavior, ripping off his filthy leather vest, wiping his nose on it one last time before tossing it over the clean cushions without a care. She knew she had not been mistaken in her original assessment of him, but she restrained herself from advising him of the fact. She needed to remain in his good graces, especially if she hoped to carry out the newest plan that was slowly forming in her mind.

"Come." He grabbed her hand and tugged her toward a doorway.

Phada tried not to show her reluctance by dragging her feet, but it was difficult, especially when she caught a glimpse of a sumptuous sleeping pallet over his shoulder. It sat on a raised platform, the centerpiece of the room. As they moved further inside, she swallowed hard at the sight of the elaborate draperies that hung from rods in the ceiling. They girded the raised mattress and could be pulled around the pallet for complete privacy.

There was a huge tapestry on the far wall, the likes of which Phada had never seen. Had the women of Gorod made it? The wall hanging depicted beautiful scenes, perhaps half-imagined, since the landscape outside the caves was uninspiring and this tapestry showed sylvan glades covered with green grass and blooming vegetation. It did not resemble the oasis or the jungles of Mesara. She wondered where this place was located.

Adelard drew her to a halt. He peered into her face and she tried to summon the expression she had seen so many times on the faces of her mother and sister, an unfocused withdrawal from the world around her. He seemed satisfied.

"I . . . May I have some time alone to prepare?" she asked, bowing her head slightly. She could not quite feign total subservience to this male, but the sharp pains that had recently begun to twist her insides helped her to focus. "I would like to wash off the dirt from the tunnel."

He eyed her suspiciously for a moment, but when she kept her gaze meekly downcast, he finally grunted. "All right. There is a washing chamber through there. But do not think you can escape, for it has no access except to this room."

She nodded, ignoring his comment about escaping. "Thank you, Adelard," she replied.

Her use of his name made his eyes gleam with cockiness. He thought she had totally succumbed to his nasty drugs. She wondered if anyone in this darkness-cursed place ever did anything of his own free will, without being coerced with faral or pleasure drugs. Did these Kargans not know that what was taken through force was never as good as something given freely? She could not help feeling sorry for them.

She went into the washing chamber, closing the door behind her. The racking pains were growing more forceful by the millimark and she gazed wildly around for any kind of receptacle. She noticed a sink cut into the rock with a drainage hole in the bottom. She barely reached it before her stomach flipped over, wrenching painfully as it rejected all traces of the faral. She hung weakly from the edge of the basin, her legs shaking with the violence of her reaction, her skin covered with a sheen of rapidly drying perspiration. She squeezed her eyes closed and shivered.

She stayed there as long as she dared before finally rousing herself. She spotted a pitcher of water. She poured some into the sink, washing away the evidence of her temporary illness, and then splashed some into a nearby basin that sat on the counter. Before washing she quickly investigated her surroundings for anything that could be used as a weapon. The only thing remotely portable was the chamber pot, which was located in a cabinet at the far side of the small space. She chuckled ruefully. She did not think she could slink into the sleeping chamber clutching that in her hands without Adelard noticing something amiss.

"Sweetling?"

Phada started at the muffled sound of his voice. "Yes?"

"If you do not come out of there right now, I will come in and drag you out," he said.

Phada grimaced. So much for the doting suitor. And why should he cater to anyone but himself? That was the way of these Kargan warriors. They held all the advantages and everyone else was forced to do their bidding. She quickly splashed some water on her face and arms, then dried them on the cloth lying next to the basin. Then she hurried into the sleeping chamber.

The sight of him lounging completely naked on the pallet was a shock. "It is about time," he growled. "Now strip off your dress and climb up here."

She avoided looking at him, her mind racing. He was not jesting when he told her to climb onto the mattress. She noticed that there was a stool next to the side of the pallet. As a weapon it left a lot to be desired, but she could not afford to be choosy. It was now or never. "I am not schooled in the ways of the mating pallet," she said. That was still basically true. "If you do not mind, I will leave my clothes on for now."

He laughed. "I will have the farking dress off you soon enough," he said with a gloating leer at her bosom and hips. "Now get over here."

Goddess, do not abandon me now, she fervently prayed. She crossed the room and stepped onto the stool. She sat on the edge of the mattress, but before she could reach down for the stool, Adelard pounced on her, tangling them both in the pallet coverings as he pinned her beneath the considerable weight of his body. He grabbed her hands and pushed them to either side of her head, leering down at her from his superior position. This close up his injured eye was milky white, and his breath smelled of stale vetch.

He began touching her hair, her face, her breasts. Phada felt the stirrings of something deep inside her, in spite of the horrified protests of her mind. Had the pleasure drug been absorbed into her system more quickly than the faral? Was it already having some kind of effect on her senses? Adelard touched her against her will, and yet she could not deny the beginning of a physical response. She wanted to cry out in disgust. Was she no better than some cowox in heat?

She thought of Sarak, of how he had pleasured every inch of her body. She could not imagine doing any of those things with this vile Kargan. She did not want to do them. And yet her body reacted to his maleness in a way she abhorred. She tried to calm herself as Adelard pawed at the neckline of her dress. It was too tight-fitting for him to free her breasts from their confinement, thank the Goddess, so he contented himself with slobbering over what he could reach of them, panting in his excitement and sniffling at the same time.

She began slowly inching her way back toward the side of the pallet where the stool was located. Adelard was too busy to notice. As she pulled herself along, using her elbows, she concentrated her thoughts on Sarak, not his physical attributes, which pleased her senses, but his other qualities, such as his bravery, his kindness and caring, the things that had touched her heart.

She suddenly realized all her concentration was

focused on reaching her goal and she no longer felt any sexual response to Adelard at all. She was able to reach her arm over the side of the mattress, groping about until she touched the stool, grasping its leg tightly in her hand. With a mighty effort, she swung her arm up and cracked him over the head.

He rolled off her immediately, clutching his head and groaning loudly. She did not waste any time, leaping from the pallet to the floor and kneeling by his discarded leggings. Yes, there they were, the dart blower and the quiver. She snatched one of the faral-tipped darts and returned to the mattress. Without the least hesitation, she stabbed the needlelike point into his upper arm so hard that it drew blood. He gave out a yelp, his good eye widening in horror as he realized what she had done.

"You bitch," he yelled at the top of his lungs. "I will kill you for this!"

She dodged him easily as he half-lunged, half-fell from the mattress. Because of his head wound, his balance was faulty and he fell to the floor with a heartening crash. He did not move for a long while after that. Phada took the opportunity to pull the belt from his leggings, using it to bind his arms behind him. She was not sure how long the clumsy knots she managed to tie in the thick leather would hold him, but it was better than nothing. She could see his eye glazing over as the force of the faral hit him. The first dose always had the greatest effect, as she well knew.

She dragged him into a sitting position against the wall. Then, for good measure, she plunged a second dart into his other arm. He hardly made a sound of protest, his head lolling toward his chest as he slumped toward the floor, a foolish expression softening his twisted features until he looked almost normal. It was nowhere near the revenge she wanted to take on him for reacquainting Sarak with the spice, but it would have to do.

She crossed to the door, making sure it was locked, and then quickly searched the room. Her gaze landed on a locked chest. She found the key in the pouch Adelard had discarded with his clothes and opened it. Inside, she found what she was looking for—two small vials. She hoped it was the neutralizer.

She crouched down next to Adelard, who was crooning to himself under his breath. She held one of the vials directly under his nose until he finally sensed her presence and opened his eyes. The good one immediately focused on the vial.

"The neutralizer." He laughed uncontrollably for long millimarks, then shook his head weakly, unable to master the spasms of mirth that continued to rock him at uneven intervals. "It will do you no good," he assured her, gasping for breath.

She wanted to knock the silly smirk right off his face. "Why not?" she demanded.

"Because that is . . . all . . . there is." He chuckled. His nose had begun running until it was now dripping into his moustache. He did not appear to notice, although he sniffed every now and again.

"How is it made?"

"Oh ho, my sweet Mesaran lady. That is for me to know and for you to discover." He actually giggled this time, and then his expression grew crafty. "I cannot afford anyone getting their hands on it and fomenting a rebellion of the mine slaves, nor do I wish to have someone sneaking in here and making off with it . . . like you!" He burst into loud guffaws.

Phada rolled her eyes in disgust at his giddiness. She decided that the meaner the individual, the harder he fell to the powers of the faral. At least he was answering her questions—the problem was that it was taking too long. She could not afford to spend much more time here. Someone who did not know he had made off with his female captive might come searching for him. She would have to take the neutralizer and try her chances in the corridor.

"No one has ever freed himself completely from the faral," Adelard told her in a chatty manner, as if they were at a social gathering. He did not seem at all embarrassed by his nakedness. "It is more than just a physical craving. The mind grows used to being released from all its cares and always tries to have that feeling again."

Sarak had done it, she thought to herself. Ah, yes, Sarak with his indomitable willpower. She ignored Adelard's lecture, instead picking up the pouch that had contained the darts and stashing the precious vials inside. She slipped the cord over her head, letting it drop against her chest, where it hung like an unattractive, but practical, necklace.

He peered up into her face, suddenly frowning. "How is it that you are not affected?"

She did not dare answer. The less he knew about her, the better, especially since he possessed a direct link with Dalcor.

"I know," he continued in a cheerfully slurred voice. "You stuck a finger down your throat and made yourself vomit. I heard you, although I was not thinking clearly enough at the time to realize what it meant. No, no, my mind was preoccupied with other things." He straightened his back, smugly tossing his hair from his eyes. "The spice will eventually affect you whether you like it or not. And then you will come crawling back to me for more of it."

"Oh, shut up," she finally hissed.

She crept over to the door, lifting the latch and pulling it carefully open. Before she knew what

was happening someone launched himself into
the breach, knocking her to the floor and falling
on top of her. The air was forced from her lungs
by the weight of the intruder's body.

"Phada!"

Thank the Goddess, it was Sarak. Between the
lack of air and the continuing press of his body
smashing her into the floor, she was well and truly
speechless. How in the name of Mother Elithra
had he managed to escape?

He seemed in no hurry to get up. Instead, he
lifted his head, gazing around the room. She knew
when he spotted Adelard because every muscle in
his body tensed. "Are you all right?" he asked, suddenly grim.

"Yes, I am fine."

"Did he . . ."

"No," she quickly assured him. "I cracked him
over the head with a stool so it never got that far."

"Thank the Goddess." He suddenly grinned, a
rueful expression that lifted one corner of his
mouth in a most appealing fashion. "I see that you
are as resourceful as ever," he said. "Here I
thought I was coming to your rescue and you have
already nicely rescued yourself. You are an amazing female."

"Thank you," she gasped. "Now let me up before
you smother me and ruin everything."

He chuckled as he rolled to one side and slid to
his feet in one easy, graceful motion. She quickly
scanned every inch of him. He appeared unscathed, besides the cuts and abrasions he had
sustained in the arena.

"How did you get away?"

"It was not difficult. They thought I was spice-
controlled."

"But . . ." She stared at him, suddenly realizing
what had been bothering her about his appearance. He looked as alert and aware as he had since

he had weaned himself from the spice. How was that possible when she had seen the Kargan warrior plunge a faral-tipped dart into his arm? "Why are you not affected?"

He laughed, his teeth gleaming whitely against the tanned skin of his face. He was dressed in his dominator garb and he had never looked more wonderful to her. "I do not know, but so far it has had no effect on me. Perhaps it takes longer the second time around."

Phada frowned. It was not a pleasant thought to contemplate that he might succumb to the faral at any moment.

"Or maybe," he added, "once a person has been controlled by it and then conquered the habit, his body becomes immune."

"Oh, yes, I like the sound of that." She straightened her clothes and brushed the stray strands of hair back from her face. "Do you think it is possible?"

"I do not know. We can only hope it is true, but we must not count on it," he told her solemnly. "In any case, we do not have time to discuss the matter. Let us go."

"What about him?"

Sarak crossed the room to stand over Adelard, who continued to hum tunelessly beneath his breath, the sound rising and falling in a meaningless pattern. The Kargan seemed unaware that Sarak hovered above him. "What in the name of the Blessed Lady did you do to him?"

Phada grinned. "I gave him a taste of his own cursed drug. And look." She rummaged in the pouch to produce the two vials, proudly holding them out for his inspection. "I found the neutralizer. He says he only makes up a small amount at any one time. He is a suspicious sort and wants no one to be able to use it to gain control. This is all there is."

"It will have to do. Now come, we cannot stay here any longer."

Adelard stirred himself enough to speak. "There is only enough neutralizer for a couple of days for two people in those vials," he reminded them with a grin. "You will not make it across the Calabian Desert before the craving comes back—for both of you."

"He is right about one thing," Sarak interjected. "We do not know how long I have before the craving hits me again. We must get out of here quickly, while I am still upright."

He rummaged through one of the chests until he emerged with a piece of gaily colored cloth. He gagged Adelard, who only struggled in protest for a short time before resigning himself to his fate. Sarak stepped behind the Kargan. Before Phada knew what he was about, he brought his hand down with a chopping motion, knocking the unsuspecting Adelard unconscious. His suddenly limp body slumped to one side before sliding bonelessly down to the floor.

"We cannot have him calling out for help," Sarak explained with a shrug. "This will buy us more time to escape."

"You do not have to apologize to me for slugging that piece of Kargan vermin."

"I am glad to hear it." He returned to the chest, digging inside. "Do you still have your veil?"

She nodded. "It is in my pocket."

"Good. Then put it on."

"What about you? You cannot stroll around the corridors of Gorod dressed like that."

"I know." He held up a pair of leather leggings and a beautiful white lana-wool coat. "These will have to do for now."

He quickly tugged on the pants and slipped into the coat. It had a hood that he pulled forward over his head and around his face. He began to shuffle toward the door, his back hunched over as though with age. "Come on." He gestured her to fall into step behind him.

Phada laughed. "It may take us an entire cycle to reach the main tunnel, but your disguise is very effective."

She followed him into the hall. This part of Gorod, where Adelard and his cronies lived, was deserted. Phada estimated that it was sometime postzenith, although it was hard to keep track of such things underground. They carefully worked their way along the various tunnels. Sarak went into his crouching old man routine whenever people appeared, but otherwise they moved at top speed down the deserted passageways.

She was completely at a loss about their direction, but Sarak seemed to have a good idea of which way to go. She wanted to question him about it, but decided she would wait until later, when they were safely out of Gorod and on their way back to the desert. Surprisingly she thought longingly of the heat and burning desert sun. It would be wonderful to be above the ground's surface once again, no matter what the temperature.

She realized Sarak must have been correct in his reckonings, since they were definitely moving upward rather than down. However, their pace was much slower now because they were in the sections where people gathered. If they could only reach the marketplace, they should be able to exit the main tunnel easily. She hoped Adelard was still unconscious. Once he awakened and alerted the other warriors, their hopes of escaping might be dashed, and this time they would not be able to fool their Kargan captors so easily.

The sound of voices grew louder until they finally emerged into the marketplace. They were on the side farthest away from the tunnel that led outside, but Phada felt her heart lift and her pulse race with excitement. She wanted to run, but Sarak continued his slow, halting pace and she stayed alongside him, holding his arm as though assisting him. Several Kargan women sent pitying glances in her direction. They probably thought her warrior was on his last legs. Little did they know, she thought with a small chuckle at the feel of Sarak's coiled strength beneath her fingertips.

"What do we do now?" she inquired briskly.

"We need to find the packbirds. Without them we will never make it home."

*Home.* Phada whispered the word to herself, tasting it on her lips. She had forgotten the sweet, soft sound of it. Just the thought of Mesara filled her with yearning. Would she ever see it again? With Sarak by her side, she believed she would. He could do anything he set his mind to, anything. She had never felt such invincibility before, such certainty. He was a warrior beyond all warriors, beyond all other males. She loved him with all her heart.

Phada blushed beneath the veil but she did not even bother to deny her feelings. It was too late. She had been slowly but irrevocably falling in love with the warrior at her side since the moment she had first laid eyes on him in the feasting hall. She knew it was wrong, a sin, to feel the way she did, but she could not seem to muster up the righteous indignation she had once felt about involvement with the warrior class.

"Wait here," he told her.

She nodded. She did not need to ask him what he was going to do. Whatever it was, she trusted him utterly. He would get them out of here if anyone could. She followed his slow, torturous progress through the crowded aisles between the various merchants' stalls until she lost sight of him. He was headed in the direction of the stables where they had left Gisba and Ral. Phada hoped the birds were all right. It seemed like ages since they had first entered Gorod, but it was only a few cycles. They had accomplished everything they had set out to do, a fact that astonished her.

Would their luck continue to hold? It seemed a lot to ask after everything that had already happened, but she prayed that nothing would hinder them now that escape was within their grasp. She waited, suddenly impatient and sorry she had not accompanied Sarak. She had an uneasy feeling that left her shaken. Where was he? He should have returned by now.

A hand touched her shoulder, and she gasped. The blood rushed from her head so quickly she felt faint even as her heart hammered painfully in her chest. Her entire body froze. Was this how it was all going to end, with a tap on the shoulder? Slowly she turned to face the inevitable.

It was Nalissa. "I have been waiting for you," she hissed. She grabbed Phada by the hand and began dragging her toward the passage that led to the outside. "You must leave quickly. There is no time to lose. I just came past the inner council chamber. Adelard has summoned all his warriors to arms. Even now he is on his way to block off the exit. Oh, why did you not leave when you had the chance?"

"We had to find the neutralizer." She patted the pouch that hung around her neck. "And we did."

"I am so glad for you," Nalissa said over her shoulder as she continued to pull Phada along in her wake.

Suddenly an arm snaked out and grabbed the girl by the throat, pulling her into the entrance of an unlit corridor. Oh Goddess, what now? Phada thought in alarm, staring at the empty space where the girl had just been. She hesitated, unsure whether she could best help Nalissa by making a run for it or by trying to free her from whomever had taken her. She decided she could not leave.

The sounds of struggle came from inside the passageway. Phada took a deep breath and rushed inside, hoping the surprise of her bold action would confuse whoever was holding Nalissa into releasing her. Perhaps the two of them together could handle a single warrior.

It did not work. Except for her shimmering silver-blond hair, Phada could barely make out the squirming form of the young Kargan girl. Nalissa was wrapped in the arms of a Jiboan male, the voluminous folds of his kanzu fluttering around her like a spider's web. Phada thought she knew a little about that contemptuous breed.

"Let her go," she hissed between clenched teeth, furious that this desert trader had the nerve to try to kidnap her friend. She kicked him in the knee, wringing a satisfying grunt of pain from him.

"Hold, Phada, it is me." It was Sarak's voice. "Holy Mother, what a wild clawcat you are."

"Sarak, release that girl at once. She is Nalissa, the one who helped me to spring you from that cell."

Sarak dropped his arms, then bent down to rub his tender shin. "I am sorry." He turned toward Nalissa. "I thought you were trying to bring Phada to Adelard."

Nalissa sniffed indignantly. "As if I would ever do anything to help that ugly, sniveling monster."

Sarak's teeth gleamed in the faint light that filtered in from the marketplace. "I can see why the two of you got along so quickly and so well. Nalissa, I thank you for your aid."

"It will all go for naught if you do not make a run for it now, before Adelard arrives. There is a shortcut that the warriors use so they do not have to cross the marketplace. If Adelard reaches it before you do, you will be trapped."

"Then let us go. Phada, I have secured our pack-birds."

A stifled squawk and a scuffle was the only warning Phada received before a huge shadowy form leapt toward her from the deepest shadows of the small cavern. "Gisba," she cried, throwing her arms around the dobby's neck. She smoothed the sparse head feathers affectionately, then moved lower to scratch her beneath her chin. It was her favorite spot and Gisba cheeped happily. Ral pushed forward for her share of petting.

"I have placed some supplies in a small alcove just before the last bend in the tunnel," Nalissa explained. "It is on the left-hand side, half-hidden by a boulder that covers a good portion of the opening. I do not think you will miss it."

"Thank you, Nalissa." Phada hugged the girl, turning away before she could become overly emotional. There was no time for that, not now. Later she would grieve for the valiant young Kargan they could not take with them.

"Goddess bless you," Sarak said, squeezing her arm. He turned to Phada. "Come. We must leave."

He grabbed Ral's reins and strode from the dark cavern into the noise and light of the marketplace.

"Think of me sometimes, Phada, as you walk in freedom beneath the sun."

"I will," she promised.

She hurried along behind Sarak with Gisba's head hovering over her shoulder like an anxious mother rockhen. She cringed at every untoward movement, every sound. They crossed the market area at a hurried walk, not wanting to draw too much attention to themselves. They made it without mishap and entered the final tunnel that led to the blessed outside. She did not know where the warriors' shortcut opened onto the exit tunnel but she kept visualizing Adelard around every bend in the corridor, waiting to attack them.

They stopped very briefly at the alcove where Nalissa had hidden the supplies. Sarak tossed the bundle onto Ral's back, securing it quickly with one of the tassels on her saddle. They did not have time to do more.

She could not see Sarak's face, but she could feel the determination in his every step. Ral chirped and Gisba answered as though the two dobbies sensed they were on their way back to the desert. Sarak glanced over his shoulder and smiled encouragingly at her. She could still not believe that he was unaffected by the faral, but she was not about to question their good fortune. If only it would hold for a little while longer.

Even though the exit was not yet visible, she could see light filtering in from the outside. Already she had to squint her eyes against its brightness after the gloomy passages and shadowy corners of Gorod. The scent of rain drifted in as well, sharp and pungent after the light, almost odorless air of the tunnels. She could even smell traces of vegetation. It was a heady sensation and she realized how much she missed the natural world of sunlight and open spaces.

Suddenly a shout was raised. She swiveled her head. Thank the Goddess it came from behind them and not ahead, but her heart sank to her heels when she saw that there were at least 20 warriors heading at an all-out sprint in their direction.

"Run," Sarak cried. He gestured her to move in front of him and she did so as quickly as her legs would carry her. As Phada passed, he handed her Ral's reins, leaving his hands free to pull the sword from the packbird's saddle as she trotted by, frantic to keep up with her companion.

Gisba had already accelerated into an awkward loping gallop that would have made Phada laugh were she not so busy fleeing for her life.

Something hurtled past her, the whining sound loud and horrible in her ear. Oh no, they were shooting those cursed faral-tipped darts.

There was only one guard on duty. He must have heard the shouts of alarm because he leapt out from the hut with a bloodcurdling scream, directly into Sarak's path.

"Keep going," Sarak told her tersely as he whirled to face this new threat. "I will be right behind you."

She did as he instructed, although she could not help slowing her pace somewhat. The sound of clanging swords filled her ears, but it stopped almost as quickly as it had begun. She heard Sarak's footsteps pounding behind her as he made up the lost distance.

Her lungs burned as they tried to suck in enough air to keep up the grueling pace. They ducked around the final corner, where the piercing light of day broadsided them into temporary immobility. Phada stumbled to a halt, her arm automatically rising to press against her eyes in an effort to mitigate the pain of the sun's brightness. She was totally blinded.

"Do not stop," Sarak shouted from somewhere near her ear. He fumbled until he found her hand and then dragged her along behind him. She kept her eyes squeezed tightly shut, allowing him to lead her like a child.

Sarak's body jerked and he let out a startled grunt. "What happened?" she asked breathlessly.

"It is nothing. Be careful; the path is strewn with rocks."

He helped her down the steep road that led to the floor of the valley below. Phada gingerly opened one eye. She could see shapes and shadows now, although it was still painfully bright. Thank the Goddess, these were only the weak rays that shone on Gorod and not those of the fiercely burning desert sun. She breathed another prayer of thanks that it was not yet night, when the Kargans could easily pursue them beyond the mouth of their cavernous world.

They reached the bottom of the path. Sarak stopped, releasing her hand. Phada leaned against a large boulder, gasping for breath but giddy with the realization that they had escaped.

"We made it," she chortled gleefully.

Sarak did not reply. She watched, puzzled, as he grabbed his arm. A dart peered out from between his fingers along with a smear of blood on the cloth of his kanzu. He had been hit.

# *Chapter Twenty*

Sarak pulled his kanzu tighter against the biting wind that tugged playfully at its folds like a houndpup worrying a bone. They had been traveling for more than a cycle, and if he recalled the landscape correctly, this plateau they were on would soon give way to the flatter scrub that signaled the edges of the desert. He realized he was looking forward to its heat. Anything was better than this cursed Kargan climate.

He did not know what was the matter with him. He should be feeling pleased with his warrior prowess and proud of the way they had managed to accomplish their goals. They had escaped from Gorod with the neutralizer, although there was not very much of it, and they were on their way back to Mesara. There had been many close calls, but they had been truly blessed in this mission.

So why was he feeling so heavy-hearted?

He glanced across at Phada as she paced along steadily by his side, her slender body completely hidden by the kanzu he had insisted she wear. He could not help smiling to himself at the sight of her. Her tame packbird hovered protectively at her back, her beady black eyes slitted in contentment as she followed her mistress with all the devotion she could muster. Everyone else considered the creatures to be simpleminded beasts of burden. Who would have ever thought one of them could have such a winning personality? Phada had a talent for drawing all manner of living beings to her with her gentle nature and kind heart and bringing out their best qualities.

She had certainly performed the same service for him, he realized ruefully. She had poked and prodded and shamed him into making this journey. More than that, she had believed in him until he, too, had believed that nothing was impossible.

He wished he dared get as close to her as Gisba did. Of course she had not asked him to do any such thing. He knew that fact was at the root of his strange melancholy. Since she had told him of her ordeal with Adelard in his chambers, he had watched her actions carefully. She did not seem to be behaving any differently toward him. In fact, she did not seem disgusted with him at all. But he knew she must be. She was simply too kind to let him know her true feelings. After all, she had seen the dominator character taken to its worst extreme. Whatever she had felt for him on the journey here must surely be dead after witnessing the actions of Adelard and his henchmen.

He did not know what would happen to them once they returned home and tried to outwit Dalcor, but he had enough sense to realize that everything between them would be over. He could not jest with her and see her smile at him with that soft expression in her beautiful gray-blue eyes. He would not be able to touch her in any way, let alone intimately, which meant he would never again experience the soaring ecstasy of joining their bodies together in the mating act, a pleasure beyond anything he had ever known.

Obviously the ancients had done the right thing in segregating Mesara's warriors, he thought sadly. No doubt they were correct in formulating laws forbidding any dominator to have a relationship with a town woman, and most especially a Keeper. Every step that brought him closer to Mesara seemed a death knell for the forbidden hopes and dreams he had begun to carry in his heart. It was tearing him apart.

"Can we stop soon?" Phada asked. "I find I am more than a little weary after all the running we did."

It seemed a modest request, and yet she dropped her gaze as if embarrassed or uncomfortable. Sarak eyed the top of her cloth-covered head with a faint frown. "Yes, we can set up camp just ahead. I want to check over our supplies as well as whatever your friend Nalissa has provided. And we will need to fill the water bags before we reach the desert."

She must be feeling the awkwardness of knowing she would have to be inside a shelter with him once more, he decided. He could not blame her, but it still felt like a zirconian dagger wound to the chest.

They reached an acceptable area behind a grouping of rocks that cut the wind. The ground was sandy and pretty much rock-free. He unloaded the dobbies, spreading the contents of the saddles on the ground in piles as he examined everything. Nalissa had included enough food for a small army, as well as a pair of thickly woven blankets. He should be able to make a nice, cozy shelter from them.

He set to work at once. Phada disappeared behind the rocks to take care of personal matters.

When he finished, he stepped back to admire his handiwork. It was not quite the same as a Jiboan tent, but it was not half bad either. He had tried to provide as much space inside as he possibly could, for Phada's benefit, but it was still going to be tight quarters. He only hoped he could handle it. It would not be easy to go back to the way they had been at the beginning of the trip, but he had to force himself to forget the liberties she had allowed him.

He felt her presence behind him. "Please go inside." He knew he sounded terse, so he tried to cover his awkwardness with a gracious gesture. He failed miserably. "I will return shortly."

He spun on his heel and stalked off toward a cluster of boulders in the opposite direction from the one she had taken, but not before he caught a glimpse of her puzzled, hurt expression. He wanted to soothe her, to tell her that she had not done anything wrong, but he was simply not calm enough to explain any further.

When he returned, he paused outside the shelter to take a deep breath before squatting on his haunches and crawling inside. Phada had changed from the Kargan clothing back into her tunic. He found he missed the brightly colored dress and the way it highlighted her eyes. He was ashamed to admit he also missed the nicely revealing glimpse it had offered of the upper curves of her breasts. He quickly banished the thought before Phada could see the longing and desire that he knew must be clearly visible in his expression.

She had spread out the kanzu she had been wearing, rolling up the blue dress and placing it at one end for a pillow. He saw that she had spread the makings of a simple meal on the side closest to him. "Are you hungry?"

"A little," he replied, his voice still gruff as he tried to force his confused emotions into enough

order so that he could command them. He felt odd
about doffing the protective folds of the Jiboan
garment, although that was crazy. He had spent
most of his life dressed in next to nothing. Why
should the naked contours of his own body em-
barrass him now? He pulled the material over his
head, scowling all the while. The sooner he got
back to normal, the better.

He shook out his kanzu, hefting it into the air
and allowing it to float down to the ground.
Somehow it did not look as inviting as hers did,
but he lowered himself onto it anyway. The
ground was rockier than he had anticipated, and
it took him several moments before he found a
spot where the pebbles did not dig into his flesh.

She handed him a chunk of bread and some
slices of goat cheese. Again she averted her gaze
and again he felt the shock of her refusal to meet
his eyes directly. Had he suddenly grown two
heads? he wondered sourly. He bit into the bread.
It was tough and chewy, being mostly crust, but
he was hungry. When he added some of the
cheese, it became more tolerable.

He sat with one leg bent comfortably at the knee
and the other stretched out in front of him. Phada
continued to concentrate on her food. She was so
close he had only to reach out his arm to touch
her. But he knew he would not do so. She was
making it clear how she wanted their relationship
to proceed from this point on, and he thought he
should honor her obvious, albeit unspoken, request. He owed her that much and more.

She cleared her throat. "Do you think the Kargans will pursue us, now that the sun has gone
down?"

"No. I made sure we traveled more than a cycle's
journey from Gorod. They cannot risk straying
that far from the protection of their city."

"It is hard to imagine that they must always stay

inside, that they cannot ever feel the sunlight on their skin. In a way it makes them less fierce than I had always imagined them to be."

"It also means they are not the ones who have been raiding Mesara all these cycles."

She gasped. "I never thought of that. Who else could it possibly be? The Jiboans?"

"The Jiboans are too lazy to carry out that kind of extended campaign, not to mention too greedy to risk weapons and other equipment when they could make more money by selling it to the highest bidder. No, whoever engineered those attacks was a mastermind at planning. That is why we were never able to catch them at it, no matter how many traps we laid."

"Perhaps it was those people the Jiboans mentioned to us, the ones whose kanzus they said we were wearing."

"The Tuargas? Perhaps."

Suddenly he felt a surge of anger at the impersonal direction of their conversation. He did not want to talk about Kargans and weapons; he wanted to delve into the depths of Phada's heart, to discover how she felt about him. Did she ever think of those marks they had spent in each other's arms? Did she totally regret her impulsive behavior, or was there even the smallest part of her that was glad they had flouted the laws?

Curse it, he would not allow her to shut him out like this. They might have trespassed beyond the bounds of all propriety by their actions on the journey here, but that did not mean they could not remain friends—of a sort—at least until they reached Mesara. He did not want to pass the entire trip with these awkward moments of togetherness and the uncomfortable silences they had engendered.

"Phada . . ." He halted, closing his eyes against the surge of emotions heating his body. He barely managed to stop his hand from reaching out for her. By the Goddess and all that was holy, he could not deliberately cause her unhappiness by forcing himself on her. He simply could not do it.

She moved closer. "Yes?"

"It is nothing. We had better go to sleep."

"Is that what you really want, dominator?" she asked softly, tauntingly. "Have things between us changed so completely since we were last in the desert?"

"You must know it is not that. . . ."

She pressed her small, soft hand against his chest. The feel of it made his heart beat heavy and hard against his ribs, until it sounded like the excited pace of an antelope-skin drum at the warrior initiation ceremony. She opened her fingers as wide as they would go, rubbing them back and forth against his suddenly burning flesh.

"I have learned a thing or two about mating during our trip to Gorod," she told him softly. "I know what pleases a male." She leaned down and kissed his shoulder, her mouth lingering as she brushed her lips back and forth. "If you do not wish this, you may stop me at any time."

It was sweet torture and he had no desire for it ever to end. She pushed him with her fingertips and he went down as easily as if she had struck him a mortal blow with the deadliest weapon. He suspected that it was the residue of the Kargan pleasure drug that was making her act this way. What else could explain her actions? He groaned, writhing in excitement as she kissed his stomach and caressed his hips. He was torn between pulling away from her now or enjoying this night in her arms. He was not a fool; he knew that once they crossed the desert he would never be allowed to touch her again.

He found he could not resist her, not when she was so warm and pliant and his body had been aching for her. She raised herself to her knees until she was poised above him, her weight resting on her hands, which she placed on either side of his head. He reached up to grasp her waist, sliding her over until she was on top of him. He gasped as the warmth of her feminine core pressed against his loins.

When she bent forward to kiss him, he found there was no choice at all. He was so delirious with pleasure, he even thought he heard her say "I love you." And then he knew nothing else as he allowed her to carry them both into sweet oblivion.

The return journey passed all too quickly. They spent the nights walking because it was cooler and the cycle-light in each other's arms. The sun stayed in the sky a little longer with each passing cycle, another sign that they were nearing Mesara. Much to his surprise, Sarak showed no signs of reverting to spice-controlled behavior. He was at a loss to explain it, but neither of them had any desire to question this lucky break.

They only saw two Jiboan caravans, and these they were easily able to avoid, although Sarak insisted on raiding one for extra water and food. One of the small satchels that he thought held grain contained faral instead. Just one whiff of the potent drug and he wanted to toss the contents to the desert winds. Surprisingly, Phada protested this decision, saying that her Keeper's intuition warned her not to act too hastily. Sarak believed strongly in such things, so he packed the container away with the rest of their dwindling supplies.

In an odd sort of way they had become a family, with Gisba and Ral like two unruly but sweet-tempered children. He hated to see the intimacy end, but he knew it must when they began seeing more and more signs that they were nearing the end of the desert. They pressed onward right past the next cycle-rise until they reached the scrublike vegetation that marked the farthest boundaries of Mesara.

They were finally home.

They camped on the far side of the jungle that postzenith. Sarak pulled her into his arms hungrily, knowing that this was their last night together. They had made record time across the desert, because they knew the way. Now that they were back in Mesara, there was no time to waste, not when a message from Gorod could arrive at any moment, warning Dalcor of their imminent arrival. They needed the element of surprise. In fact, they needed every advantage they could get, because they were so sorely outnumbered.

"How far do you think the neutralizer will go?" Phada asked as they shared the evening meal. "Will we be able to free enough warriors to retake Mesara?"

Sarak blew out his breath thoughtfully. It was a question he had been turning over in his mind since they had escaped from Gorod. "I do not know," he finally replied. "We have no idea how effective Adelard's potion really is."

"He said that the contents of these two vials were enough to free two people from the effects of the spice for a couple of cycles."

"Then we should be able to free a group of fifteen warriors for a few marks." Sarak frowned. "Dalcor has a core regiment of about forty warriors. We will have to disable as many of them as we can and we will have to work fast."

"There must be something I can do to help," she said thoughtfully. She glanced over at the container of faral they had stolen, her expression brightening. "And I know what it is."

*        *        *

Phada hovered at the crossroads that led to the center of Mesara, clutching her satchel. Sarak had already bid her good-bye. He slipped off the pathway, heading toward the back of the palace where prisoners were always kept, the vials of neutralizer with him. She felt bereft as she watched him disappear into the thick jungle undergrowth, as though she had lost a huge part of herself. She threw back her shoulders and took herself firmly in hand. There was no time to waste if she hoped to carry out her end of the plan.

Her insides still clenched with terror every time she thought of what they intended to do. She realized there was an excellent chance that they would be captured or even killed before they ever saw each other again. And yet she did not regret a single moment.

She began walking in a parallel direction to the one Sarak had taken, hoping to reach a little-used side entrance to the palace without running into any of Dalcor's warriors. She sighed as she moved through the jungle, her mind filled with images and impressions of Sarak as he had mated with her last night. She might have been able to convince herself that they had done nothing wrong before, but this time they were within the boundaries of Mesara; this time there could be no doubt that they had truly broken the sacred laws laid down by the ancients generations ago.

Sarak had not responded when she told him she loved him. She knew he cared about her, but perhaps a warrior was as incapable of love and bonding as everyone had always believed. Perhaps he simply did not know how to deal with such unwarriorlike sentiments. It did not matter, because she had been unable to stop herself from saying the words. She wanted him to know the way she felt, just in case.

The palace loomed out of the tangled green vegetation immediately ahead. Phada glanced cautiously around, but there was no sound, no movement to indicate a guard. It was easier than she ever would have believed to hide her things and slip into the palace unnoticed. Obviously Dalcor felt secure in his power, because there were no guards inside either. She moved along the corridors that led to the kitchens, her throat tight with memories of another life as her senses were assailed with all the familiar smells, sights, and sounds of her home.

The delicious scent of roasted rockhen filled her nostrils, along with a myriad of cooking odors. There must be some sort of feast tonight. Or, for all she knew, this could be business as usual in the new kingdom of Mesara. Runners moved in every direction, although their pace was slow because of their spice-addled condition. Phada pressed her lips together at the sight of their glazed expressions. Perhaps that was why there were so many of them, because it took more to get the job done in the same amount of time. Pray Goddess she and Sarak could pull this thing off—it was the only possible way to alleviate the plight of her fellow town dwellers.

She slipped easily among the throng, working her way to the heart of the kitchens without mishap. She did not think anyone would recognize her, since she was not in her Keeper's apprentice tunic. She had also fixed her hair more elaborately, pulling it away from her face with a ribbon and allowing it to cascade down her back and shoulders. In spite of her precautions in the desert, the long, shining mass had lightened beneath the searing sun, especially the tendrils around her face. No, even her own mother would be hard-pressed to recognize her now.

How similar and yet how unlike Gorod her home was, she mused as she observed the familiar, beloved surroundings. Both societies used Mother Elithra to shelter their people from the harsh conditions on the surface, and yet the Kargans never came aboveground to reach the sunlight and share in the Mother's other gifts. Had it always been thus in Gorod, or had they simply grown so used to remaining beneath the ground that their bodies had lost the ability to protect themselves from the sun?

She jostled past a runner carrying a tray with pitchers of vetch. She knew they contained the Jiboan ale because some of the liquid sloshed over the side and she could smell the potent brew. She slipped her hands into her pockets. The two pouches of faral were still there, ready to ensnare more victims.

No one challenged her when she crossed the room and began to stir the various pots. All the kitchen staff were so slow-witted from the spice themselves that it was easy to slip some faral into the dishes that were to be served to the warriors in the main feasting hall. The only problem was that she was forced to use such a tiny amount. Its distinctive aroma was so strong, it would give the game away should Dalcor or one of his dominators detect it. She prayed that it would be enough to weaken them or at least knock them enough off balance that they grew confused and disoriented in the face of what she hoped would be Sarak's unexpected attack. She had to take the chance; it was the only way she could help.

She did not dare protest when she was pressed into serving the meal. As she walked slowly down the corridor that led to the feasting hall, she swallowed nervously. *No one will recognize you and no one will know you are not dazed with faral if you are careful,* she assured herself. And yet it was one thing to work behind the scenes and entirely something else to place herself directly in Dalcor's line of vision, where there would be no escape.

The sound of male voices grew louder until it was almost deafening, especially when combined with the music of a group of blowpipers and drummers. Phada's eyes widened and she could not help gaping for a moment at the sight that greeted her before she quickly closed her mouth. The feasting hall looked as if a pack of warriors had chased a tuskboar through the place. Many of the tables were wrecked and the chairs overturned. The floors were covered with dirt and other unidentifiable debris and looked as though they had not been swept since she had left Mesara all those cycles ago. Talk about a mudhog's sty.

And the smell. Phada's head reeled from the barrage of odors that assailed her senses. Plates of leftover food from earlier meals decorated the few upright tables in one corner of the room. Did they move from area to area until a new place could be cleared? Phada wondered in disgust. The noise, the smoke, and the pungent smell of vetch were overwhelming. It looked like a combination of the Gorod marketplace and the interior of a Jiboan tent—it certainly displayed the worst of both those worlds.

She maintained her slow pace, surreptitiously turning her head to glance at the head table. Dalcor slouched there, downing a huge mug of vetch in one long, continuous swallow while his fellow warriors hooted their approval. She was not sure how many of the males had been served the farallaced dishes, but she could see no outward effect from the spice on any of them. Some, however, were well on their way to becoming drunk; Phada did not know if it would be enough.

She must think of something else. If Sarak and his warriors arrived now, the odds against them would be more than overwhelming. She needed to take some drastic action, but what? An idea popped into her head full-blown, but it was so out-rageous she did not know if she dared try it. And then she realized that for Sarak, she would dare anything. She quickly slipped from the feasting hall, running down the maze of corridors, and out into the cool Mesaran evenfall to where she had hidden her satchel.

Less than a quartermark later, she was heading back to the hall, clad in the revealing Kargan dress, her face veiled. She could feel that her cheeks were flushed, a combination of embarrass-ment and excitement. Suddenly she found she was looking forward to pitting her wits against Dalcor and his gang of jungle scavengers.

No one noticed her immediately when she en-tered the hall, but before she had crossed half the room she could hear the rumble of interest and feel it pulsing in her direction. Several of the war-riors rose to their feet shouting provocative com-ments about her anatomy as they hooted and hollered and poured more vetch down their throats. She let their words flow right over her head—she had a job to do.

As she drew closer, she signaled to the musi-cians. They appeared as groggy as everyone else, a daze compounded by the loud clamor of their instruments, but they eventually picked up on her wish to play something stirring. Phada almost grinned when she heard the first notes of an old Mesaran fighting song with a singularly provoca-tive beat.

She began to dance. She could feel that the muscles of her body were stiff from nervousness, but she could not seem to relax them. After all, she had never done anything like this in her entire life. But as she danced, her limbs became freer, moving more suggestively. She tried to remember everything she could about the way those Jiboan females had twined and writhed in front of Sarak.

They had seductive dancing honed to a fine art.
She even went so far as to pretend that she was
dancing for Sarak, trying to entice him into coming to her pallet. After that it grew much easier.

Most of the warriors had dropped back into
their chairs. Several of them clapped their hands
or stomped their feet in time to the music, while
others simply nodded their heads. After the sight
of so many blond-haired Kargans with their pale
skin and light blue eyes, these males looked dark
and dangerous and all too capable of flying into
an unprovoked violent rage. Goddess above, there
were so many of them. She shuddered and then
quickly forced such comparisons from her mind.
She had to think in a positive way, to believe to
the utter depths of her soul that it was possible to
fool the dominators of Mesara. If Dalcor had once
managed to do it, then so could she.

Besides, she had nothing to lose. She grew
braver, stepping closer to the head table, deliberately catching Dalcor's eye. He scrutinized her
from head to toe, the expression in his eyes filled
with intensity. Her entire body went on alert. And
then it occurred to her that this was exactly the
reaction she should have been praying for, because it meant that he was not going to be difficult
to handle. He only wished to have a good time, no
holds barred, and he had decided that his good
time now included her.

If the unbridled lust gleaming in his eyes had
not already warned her of his intentions, his next
action did. He rose to his feet, thrusting aside the
female who had just planted herself in his lap as
all his attention focused on Phada. He did not
even notice that the poor woman tumbled to the
floor at his feet, nor that the warrior sitting next
to him immediately snatched her into his arms to
claim her for his own.

Phada moved around the table until she was directly in front of the renegade leader. Reaching past him, she grabbed a piece of roasted fowl from his plate and teasingly hand-fed it to him. She tried not to shudder when he nibbled on her fingers as he took the meat from her with all the finesse of a ravenous clawcat. The assurance that he could have her whenever he wanted was evident in his expression. Phada knew he was not a patient man. She had to keep him eating and entertained or be carried off to his chambers.

She continued to gyrate to the steady, throbbing beat of the music. Dalcor was already growing impatient—she could see it in his eyes and in the predatory grin that stretched his mouth. She pushed the material of her dress from her shoulders, baring them and allowing the bodice to dip even lower. Dalcor growled suggestively, obviously hoping it would fall off altogether. She reached for another slice of meat, this time placing it between her teeth and bending over backward to offer it to him. It gave him a bird's-eye view of her cleavage, but then, that was the point. Shouts of approval and suggestions on how things should proceed filled the air around her.

She had not realized just how creative she could be. She wanted to laugh at how easy it was to handle a lust-filled dominator. They certainly did not think with their minds at times like these. The subtle smell of the spice suddenly became nauseating to her. She was not sure how much longer she could keep this charade going.

From her upside-down position, she noticed that several of the women were imitating her actions with their respective males. Blessed Mother in Heaven, one of them was her sister! Phada almost swallowed the meat between her teeth at the shock of seeing Chelis again. Her sister looked intensely shocked herself at the vision of her one and only older sibling writhing like a Jiboan slithersnake across the feasting-hall floor. And yet there was also approval in her eyes along with the beginnings of hope. Their gazes locked and an arc of understanding passed between them. Thank the Goddess that Chelis realized something was going on, Phada thought. She was certainly doing her best to help, even coaxing the other women into playing the game of feed-the-warriors.

The call went up for more platters of meat. Phada was growing tired of dancing, not to mention the fact that her stomach was growing increasingly queasy from the scent of faral.

She was about to reach for another piece of roasted fowl when Dalcor grabbed the platter and flung it across the room. A howling pack of hounds raced to catch the falling slabs of meat before they even hit the floor, snarling and fighting over the choicest bits. Dalcor grabbed her by the hand and yanked her into his lap. Before she could catch her breath from that stunning maneuver, he began nuzzling her neck and pawing at the front of her dress. He certainly had nothing on Adelard when it came to obnoxious manners.

"What is your hurry, mighty warrior?" she asked, leaning down to croon the last words right next to his ear. "Believe me, Dalcor, when I am finally through with you, you will no longer be able to stand on your own two feet." *And that is a promise,* she added to herself.

"You are spirited as well as beautiful. I like that in a female," he said with a deep, knowing chuckle. "All the other women are so dull-witted . . . . " He stared into her eyes, suddenly frowning. "It is almost as if you are not . . ."

She swooped down and kissed him, hard, on the mouth. The feel of his lips grinding against hers made her want to gag, but she knew it was necessary to stop the dangerous direction of his thoughts. Curse her carelessness. In all her efforts to get him to eat more faral, she had almost given away her own nonaddled condition. *Where are you, Sarak?* she wondered as Dalcor obligingly remained diverted, kissing her neck and moving down toward her barely covered breasts. Waves of desperation washed over her, overcoming her original spirit of optimism. If Sarak did not come soon, she was going to be hard-pressed to avoid being tossed over Dalcor's shoulder and carried away.

There was a clatter of feet and the metallic sound of swords. Sarak burst into the room, followed by a small band of warriors. His gaze immediately took in Phada sitting on Dalcor's lap. Even from here she could see his jaw clench with anger. With a mighty shout, he launched himself directly at the Mesaran leader. Dalcor shoved her aside, but she was prepared for it, only stumbling a little as she regained her balance. She quickly stepped back at Sarak's shouted warning, scurrying around the table to where the other women had retreated, sobbing and clinging to each other in their fright.

"Chelis! It is so good to see you." Phada hugged her sister, then pulled back. Chelis looked terrible, even worse than Phada remembered. Her eyes were sunken into her head and ringed with black circles of fatigue, her color even more pale and unhealthy than previously. She had tried to fix her hair but it hung lifelessly alongside her thin face.

"What is happening, Phada?" she asked in a plaintive voice filled with fear. Phada could see that her sister did not have much left to give. Chelis grimaced as she covered her ears against the loud shouts and clanging of swords. "Oh please, make it stop."

"Everything will soon be all right. But you must help me." Phada grasped her by the arms, giving her a small shake to gain her full attention. "Sister, do you think you can lead these women to safety? Perhaps the kitchen would be a good place to hide. I will come for you when this is all over."

Chelis nodded weakly. She moved closer to one of the women, placing an arm around her shoulders. "Come, Pila, we must go from this place."

Soon the other women were following her as they made slow but steady progress toward one of the exit corridors.

Phada turned back to the battle, which had continued to rage behind her while she talked to Chelis. She immediately spotted Sarak, slashing his sword at one of the renegade dominators, dropping him to the floor with ease. The newly freed warriors were highly motivated, while the usurpers were half-drunk with vetch. Some of them had also succumbed to the spice and now lay slumped over the tables. Sarak and his followers appeared to be overcoming the opposition without too much trouble. At this rate, they would soon have control of the hall.

Phada had done a quick head count when she first entered the place. She figured that only a few of Dalcor's dominators remained at large, probably in the barracks. They should not give Sarak much trouble now that the main force was defeated. However, she did not see Dalcor anywhere. Had Sarak already killed him? As she carefully skirted one of the overturned tables on her way to the front of the hall, someone grabbed her. She started to scream but a hand reached around to clamp over her mouth, cutting off her cry for help. She fought hard, twisting and kicking, but it had no effect on her captor. He dragged her to one of the side corridors, pulling her away from any immediate hope of rescue. He continued to haul her like a sack of grain for another 20 measures until she knew they had passed out of calling distance as well. Had Sarak seen her? She prayed he had.

She could hardly breathe. Her assailant finally released her and she twisted around to see who held her.

Her heart sank. It was Dalcor who grinned back at her.

# Chapter Twenty-one

Phada rubbed her bruised arms as she took in the barely contained rage on Dalcor's face. "You will not get away with this."

"We shall see," he snarled.

He looked as if he wanted to slay her on the spot. Phada decided she had better hold her tongue for the time being. She made no protest when he motioned her to continue down the corridor. She found she was growing tired of bullying males. One of the torches sputtered loudly, but otherwise all was quiet. Where was everybody? She supposed Sarak and the others were too busy securing the defeated warriors to notice anything amiss.

As they turned another corner, she realized that they were heading for the queen's chambers. Dalcor shoved her through the doorway, where she stumbled to the center of the large, well-lighted room. This was the queen's hideaway retreat, where even Pavonis had to request admittance.

Riga had decorated the place simply, yet there was a quiet, understated elegance that suited her personality to perfection. A lovely tapanu-wood desk stood in one corner. Above it, a woven wall hanging in pretty, pale shades of violet, yellow, and blue added an aura of sunlight and flowers to the windowless chamber.

There was no sign of anyone here either. Dalcor crossed the carpeted floor to rifle through the contents of a large, hand-carved chest. To Phada's dismay, he pulled out a vial of the neutralizer. She waited quietly until he came to retrieve her, then flailed out with her fists, hoping to send the vial smashing against the wall. Her ploy was not successful—Dalcor was too strong for her. She could see his eyes already glazing over from the initial effects of the faral, but she also noted the determination that gleamed in their depths. He would rather die than allow himself to be captured, and that made him dangerous.

He grabbed her by the wrist, jerking her back into the corridor. Still no sign of rescue. Only millimarks later, they stepped into the jungle outside. It was quiet; evenfall had turned into the semidarkness of night. The cry of a lone kwara bird rang through the still air. Palm fronds rustled in the faint breeze. The wonderfully familiar scent of green vegetation, with its moist undercurrent of decay and the sacred cycle of life and death, filled her senses, poignantly reminding her of how much she had missed her home. And yet being here felt alien in many ways, perhaps because she had changed so much. She realized she did not know what to believe or where she belonged anymore, except that it was not with Dalcor.

In spite of the drug, he easily pulled her along the trampled dirt pathway leading out of Mesara. She dared not dawdle, not when any moment he might decide that she was no longer necessary for

his escape and kill her. When they had put a siz-
able distance between themselves and the palace,
he halted abruptly, swinging her around so that
they were face-to-face.

"Who the hell are you?" he demanded. He did
not release her, but instead dragged her even
closer, glaring at her from his superior height.

"I am Phada."

"So, you are the little Keeper's apprentice I keep
hearing about, the one who somehow managed to
escape from Mesara faral-free, the one who rescued Sarak from exile." He jerked her arm, forcing
her to emit a small gasp of pain. "You do not look
clever enough to have accomplished such incredible feats."

His comment infuriated her. "You are not the
only one who can plan a rebellion," she retorted,
all previous notions of behaving cautiously flung
to the four winds. This denigration of her abilities
simply had to stop. First it was Adelard and now
Dalcor. She was sick and tired of trudging from
pole to pole only to be insulted and underestimated by bragging, puffed-up warrior leaders
who were not fit to wield an eating utensil, let
alone a scepter.

"How did you manage to get your hands on
enough neutralizer to free all those spice-addled
warriors?" he asked.

She said nothing, instead pressing her lips together in mute resistance. She had no intention of
revealing that the liberators' faral-free condition
would only last another mark at best. Whatever
happened to her, Mesara no longer remained under this warrior's hateful domination. "What does
it matter? The deed is already done and you have
lost."

Dalcor scowled at her. "You are correct; the information will do me no good now. Better to con-

centrate on my escape and my future plans to reclaim Mesara."

"Sarak will see your soul cursed to the black depths of Elithra for all eternity before he allows that to happen," she assured him.

"Close your mouth or I will do it for you."

Phada knew she had said enough for now. They continued along the pathway. She turned her attention to trying everything in her power to slow down their pace, but Dalcor was ready for her every tactic. He showed no mercy as he jerked her along behind him, his fingers squeezing the flesh of her upper arm until it became white and bloodless. Her forearm had long since gone numb, although she knew that when he finally released her, the pain of returning sensation would be excruciating.

"Where are you taking me?" she demanded in haughty tones. She still could not believe that he had kidnapped her so easily.

"You, my lovely, are going to Gorod with me."

"You will never make it across the desert with only that one vial of neutralizer."

He snorted derisively, his upper lip curling into a sneer reminiscent of Adelard's contorted features. He did not bother to turn around to look at her when he replied. "Then I will stay spice-addled until I can reach the Kargan stronghold. I do not care if I have to sell you to the Jiboans for more faral. Or better yet, perhaps after I have tamed you with a nice, tasty dose of the spice, you will be willing to do anything to get more."

Phada tossed her head disdainfully. "If that is your strategy, you will be fighting a losing battle," she taunted.

They skirted a large koalnut palm only to discover Sarak planted in the middle of the path, waiting for them. Phada could not stop the huge smile that wreathed her face, nor the brightness that sparkled in her eyes at the sight of him.

"Sarak," she breathed.

He raised his drawn sword and pointed it at Dalcor. "Release her."

Dalcor glanced from one to the other. "Ah, so the wind lies in that direction," he said, his eyes filled with cunning. He jerked Phada against his chest, pulling a dagger from the belt at his waist and holding it to her throat. "Do not doubt that I will kill her. She means nothing to me except a means of escape."

Dalcor used the tip of the dagger blade to caress the tops of Phada's breasts where they spilled out of the Kargan dress. She swallowed hard but otherwise remained as motionless as she possibly could, watching Sarak closely, waiting for a signal or any other kind of instruction of what he wanted her to do. They could not allow Dalcor to escape, not when he had so much to answer for.

"Now that you have had a taste of real freedom, why do you not come with me, Sarak? Together we can make all of Elithra a warrior's paradise as it is in Gorod."

"If Gorod is a warrior's paradise, I want no part of it," Sarak spat in disdain. "Mesara may not be perfect, but despite its flaws, our system is based on fairness."

"Fair!" Dalcor's mouth twisted in bitter amazement. "Is it a fair system that reviles its strongest males? We were the ones who defended Mesara from danger and we were treated like dirt because of it, segregated and looked down upon by every town dweller, male, female, and child. Is that the system you are so eager to embrace again?"

"I have pledged myself to protect and serve the queen."

"What about your little Keeper playmate here?" Dalcor sneered. "Do you think they will allow you to hold on to her? If you do, you are much mistaken."

The blow hit home. Sarak flinched, but he did not back down. "I know my place."

"You are worse than spice-addled; you are a fool," Dalcor retorted, his voice laced with scorn.

"And you are a coward to use a female as your shield." Sarak braced his legs and tightened his grip on his sword. "Release her and face me like a warrior."

"Why should I do that? I have been dosed with faral, thanks to your little pallet partner here," he snarled, suddenly furious. He gave Phada such a vicious shake, it brought tears of pain to her eyes. "It would not be a fair fight."

"Was it fair when you had Sarak dosed with the spice against his will?" Phada cried.

"Silence!" he roared. And then he calmed down enough to shrug. "I know you well, my former second-in-command. You will not fight me. It would go against your sense of honor." He spat out the word like a curse. "Now, drop your weapon if you want the female to remain alive long enough to view another cycle-rise."

Sarak hesitated, obviously torn, but he finally tossed the sword onto the ground near his feet.

"What are you doing?" Phada cried, aghast. "Are you mad? This is not time to worry about your honor. Fight him."

Dalcor jerked her to silence before grinning in triumph. "Now, move away from it. Good. Step off the path and into the jungle."

Sarak complied. The jungle undergrowth immediately reached out as though to tangle him in its harsh embrace, scratching his arms and legs. Phada could see the blood beginning to trickle along his limbs.

She gasped in shock when Dalcor shoved her into the brush as well. Luckily Sarak caught her

in his arms before she hit the jungle floor. His
muscles trembled as he held her above the bram-
bles and vines that tried to score her delicate flesh.
They were so busy with their own plight, they
could do nothing except watch helplessly as Dalcor strode boldly away.

Sarak managed to keep her safe long enough to
rip his way free of the brush. Phada cried out in
dismay at the sound of the sharp thorns tearing
into him, but he was heedless of his own bare skin.
She could hear Dalcor crashing through the jungle farther ahead. He must have jumped off the
path and taken a shortcut.

"Sarak, go after him," she pleaded. "Have you
forgotten what he did to you, to all of us? You
cannot allow him to escape."

Sarak shook his head, defeated. "He is right. In
spite of everything, I cannot fight him in his weakened condition," he explained wearily. "It does not
matter now. We have Mesara back."

Phada stared down the pathway, sighing deeply.
She supposed Sarak was correct. Nothing mattered anymore except returning Mesara to what
was left of her former glory. She realized with a
heavy heart that nothing would ever be the same.
The faral had ripped everyone's life apart and they
could never go back to the way things had been.
She smiled crookedly. "He and the Kargans deserve each other."

Sarak had not yet released Phada's arms. He
gazed into her eyes and his entire heart was revealed in that look. She sensed that he wanted to
kiss her, but he held himself back. She supposed
he did not dare, not here on the main thoroughfare of Mesara. She smiled sadly at his restraint,
knowing it heralded the end of her time with
Sarak.

She reached out to touch his chest, just above
the line of lacerations that made swirling patterns

on his skin. "You look terrible," she said, trying not to cry. It was true; there was blood everywhere, running freely down his arms and legs, dripping into his breechcloth. Some of it had smeared onto her clothing as well.

"It is not as bad as it appears," he replied with a small, wry smile.

She knew he was remembering their conversation about warriors and their stoic acceptance of injury and pain. It seemed a lifetime ago. Her heart squeezed painfully. "Of course."

Not knowing what else to do, she turned and began walking toward the palace. Sarak fell into step beside her. Neither spoke for a long while.

"There is a lot of work to be done before Mesara is restored to normality," he finally commented.

"Yes." She could not believe they were conversing about this subject when her heart cried out that they should be talking about themselves, about how they could manage some kind of a future together. Did he not long to be with her? Her heart ached when she realized that even if he did wish for them to be together, he would not fight against the system to which he had pledged his loyalty. He knew his place; had he not just said so?

She trudged along beside him, feeling as heavy and sluggish as a muddy jungle river after a rain. Mesara was free. But she had just lost everything that mattered to her.

Sarak made another circuit of the perimeter, trying not to allow his gaze to stray to where Phada sat on one of the benches, her mother and sister on either side of her. The feasting hall was packed to the rafters this evenfall with jubilant Mesarans. The familiar sound of neighbors shouting greetings and children giggling as they chased each other around the tables almost made it seem like the Mesara of old. But there were other, less cheerful indications that things had changed irrevocably, most especially the distinctive odor of faral that wafted across the hall along with the faint movement of the air trickling in from the outside.

It had not been an easy task to wean people away from the Kargan spice that ensnared the mind as well as the body. Even though the Keepers had discovered the main ingredients of the neutralizer and were now able to produce it in sufficient quantity, many Mesarans were still unable to free themselves from the clutches of the addicting spice. The first thing Queen Riga had done on regaining her throne was to declare all faral illegal. In spite of her edict, a thriving Jiboan black market had sprung up on the outskirts of town. There, anyone with enough coin could obtain the forbidden condiment.

So much for the terrible aftereffects of Dalcor's grab for power. Sarak allowed his anger at fate to flow as his gaze swept the hall. So many things had happened since he had last been posted on duty. He had realized from the start that it was better to feel anger than the horrible, empty sense of despair that overwhelmed his senses whenever he let his guard down. No matter how many times he told himself that Phada was lost to him forever, it did not stop the pain, nor did it temper his eagerness to see her. He had thought that time would blur the memories, maybe even erase them, but it was becoming more difficult with each passing cycle to force himself not to recall what he had once shared with her.

She looked beautiful sitting there, in spite of being clad in the drab tunic of the Keeper's apprentice. Her long hair was neatly braided and hung down her back, almost to her waist. He would never forget the sight of that hair swirling around her slender body like a beautiful, tawny cloud, its sweet scent filling his head—nay, the very core of his being—with the intoxicating possibilities of life. It had been a truly glorious fantasy, but it was over now. After his many orbits as a warrior he should know better than to allow himself to dream of things that could never be.

He was glad she had not revealed the extent of their transgression, that she was still studying to become a Keeper. She would make a fine wise woman, strong, courageous, and fair-minded, all traits he had witnessed in her firsthand. He had no doubt that she would guide Mesara toward a brighter future, free from any further subjugation to the kind of warrior rule she had observed in Gorod.

He frowned as the volume of noise grew more deafening. On the surface everyone seemed to be having a good time, but it did not take much insight to discern the unhappiness that lay beneath the surface like rotting jungle vegetation, just waiting to crumble away. Too many Mesarans stared blankly into the distance, lost in a spice-induced fog. Those who had managed to break the habit of using faral appeared drawn and tense, their eyes haunted and sunken as they battled their desire for the oblivion it offered.

He took up his station on the platform behind the queen, his hand hovering over his sword even though he knew they had nothing to fear from a Kargan attack. Who would have ever guessed that their hated enemies were unable to cross the desert all these orbits, victims of their own pale complexions? Even if Dalcor had reached the southern antipodes, there was little he could do to threaten the integrity of Mesara, not without the support of his warriors, who now languished in the palace prison.

The throne beside Riga was empty. Sarak knew

that Pavonis was totally broken, a shadow of his former self. It was questionable whether he would ever return to help Riga govern. Palace gossips whispered that seeing his wife in the hands of Dalcor had shattered his sanity beyond repair. Sarak could well understand such an intense reaction; all he had to do was think about Phada and what revenge he might have exacted on Adelard had he managed to place more than his filthy hands upon her.

The queen rose and lifted her hand for silence, glancing over her shoulder at Sarak as she did so. It pained him to see how thin she had grown, how tired and worn she appeared, like a woman twice her age. Her royal purple tunic had been crafted by the finest seamstress in Mesara, but it hung from her shoulders with as much style as an empty grain sack. All in all, he supposed, she had weathered her humiliation and abuse at Dalcor's hands as well as could be expected—certainly better than her mate had done. She was another of the strong, brave females Mesara seemed to breed. Her mettle had been tested in the fires of adversity and not been found wanting, much like another female he knew. Sarak was proud to be on the same platform with her.

She gestured for him to move closer to the front. Although he was puzzled by her request, he moved forward immediately. "Citizens of Mesara," she began, her voice clear and brimming with a hard-won authority it had not previously possessed. "It is good to be back in the feasting hall with you."

A halfhearted rumble of approval went up at this sentiment, primarily because a large portion of her subjects were barely functional and unable to pay attention to anything beyond their own sweet stupor. Those who were alert enough to understand what was going on around them did not feel much like celebrating, knowing their loved ones still hovered so precariously between throwing off their shackles to lead a Goddess-blessed life or sliding even further into servitude to the mind-numbing Kargan faral.

"Our captivity was harsh, but we have come through those hard times together," Riga continued. "Thanks to the Goddess and the special liberator she chose to rescue us from slavery, the light of freedom shines on our fair town once more. We are again able to live our lives as we choose and not under the cruel, punishing heel of a tyrant."

Up until this time, the hall had been deathly quiet as all listened to their queen. Sarak saw numerous heads in the sea of upturned faces nodding in agreement with Riga's words. Others shed tears; he could see them glistening in the light of the torches. A few spice-addled citizens actually sobbed aloud. The response steadily grew, building from a faint murmur of sound to shouted comments, sporadic clapping, and finally a wholehearted standing ovation.

However, they returned to their subdued state quickly. Riga's smile held more than a touch of sadness as the quiet descended once again. Mesarans were not known to be temperate in their enthusiasm. But at least they had roused themselves to respond, which showed hope for the future. The queen smoothed down the sides of her tunic, the graceful, feminine gesture a reminder of the carefree young queen she had once been.

"I spoke about our liberator. I am sure you all know who it is. Therefore, I would like to make an announcement. I wish to bestow the position of first-in-command on Sarak, who saved Mesara from Dalcor. He went above and beyond the duties and obligations of a warrior. His bravery and courage should ever stand as a shining beacon

and an unparalleled example of the kind of behavior to which every Mesaran should aspire."

Riga bowed to him, her hands clasped in front
of her, her body bending deeply from the waist.
Sarak knew this was a singular sign of honor from
a sovereign to her subject—and most especially a
dominator. The applause was hesitant at first and
then became louder and more boisterous as Riga
held up the gold-and-blue sash of first-in-
command; preparing to slip it over his head.

Sarak knew he looked as uncomfortable as he
felt. He did not know what to say, how to tell the
queen that he could not accept the honor she
wished to give him. She did not know how little
he deserved it. He had broken so many Mesaran
laws he had lost count, not to mention his greatest
crime of all—falling in love with a tan-haired,
blue-eyed Keeper's apprentice.

"I thank you, lady Queen," he said stiffly, "but I
cannot accept."

He could see the confusion in her eyes. And then
she laughed and moved toward him, again holding out the sash. She obviously thought he was
being modest. Sarak sank to one knee and bowed
his head in obeisance, then rose to his feet. With
another bow, he crossed the platform and climbed
down the stairs, eager to leave the hall as quickly
as possible. He spared a quick glance in Phada's
direction as he paced along the side wall. She
looked positively stunned. Did she really think he
had so little sense of honor and duty that he would
accept this boon? She alone knew how low he had
fallen. He would not shame himself or her by accepting such an honor.

He stopped short when he realized that he was
still on guard duty. He could not add deserting his
post to all his other crimes. He hovered in the
shadows at the rear of the hall, his hand on the
hilt of his sword, remembering the intense, gut-

wrenching emotions he had experienced when Dalcor held his dagger to Phada's throat. That was when he had realized that he loved her—more than life itself, that he would have done anything to save her, sacrificed everything, including his pride, to keep her safe. He wished he could ask her to bond with him, to keep her forever, but the only thing he could offer her was a Jiboan desert ceremony, which was not even binding under Mesaran law, and after that life as an outcast. She deserved so much more.

He took full responsibility for his actions in the desert as well as hers. She was a female after all, tenderhearted and loving, and she had not known from one cycle to the next whether she would live or die. Who could blame her for her curiosity and her actions? He, however, should have known better.

His heart started pounding when he noticed Phada marching in his direction. Her expression was grim, her mouth drawn taut with anger. He braced himself to meet her.

"Why are you doing this?" she hissed furiously, her blue eyes flashing. "Is it because of me, because of what we did?"

"It is that and more."

"Well, you cannot refuse the queen's offer. You were born to lead the warriors. You are smart and brave and wonderful and you deserve every accolade she bestowed upon you."

"Phada, you do not know what you are talking about," he muttered, pulling her closer to the wall before anyone at the nearby tables could hear the direction of their conversation. "I am not fit for the job. In the face of temptation, I could not abide by the codes."

"What does that matter now? You saved Mesara, Sarak."

He scowled at her in amazement. By the Goddess, she was a stubborn female, as well as dead wrong. She was talking as if he had saved the place single-handedly. He would never have made the journey without her, never have weaned his addled senses from the faral or pressed himself to attain such lofty pinnacles of courage had she not pushed and prodded him. Had she not been by his side—and eventually in his pallet—he would never have achieved any of it. She was the one Mesara should be honoring.

The crowd around them was beginning to disperse, although several people stared at them curiously. Phada clapped her hands sharply and the noise level around them immediately dropped. The queen was leaving the platform. "My lady Queen!" she cried out. She sounded like a herald announcing a festival. "Please wait. I have something I must tell you."

Sarak reached for her. "Phada, no."

She slipped from his grasp and ran to the front of the feasting hall, tripping up the platform steps and onto the dais. She stood a respectful distance away until the queen motioned for her to approach.

"I must speak with you," she said. "Sarak must also be present, for it concerns him."

At the queen's nod of approval she marched to the edge of the royal platform and called his name. He cringed inwardly but stepped forward to stand just below her on the feasting hall floor. Several Mesarans hesitated, mesmerized by what was unfolding before them.

"Sarak, please," she pleaded as she gazed down on him. "You must not refuse Queen Riga's offer." When she saw that he was not going to change his mind, she turned back to the queen. "My lady, this warrior risked his life for me, for all of us, time and time again. He accomplished what no one else could, what no one else dared, traveling to

Gorod to obtain the neutralizer and then returning to overthrow Dalcor and his minions. He is
brave and stalwart and more than worthy to lead
the warriors of Mesara into whatever the future
holds for us."

"I could not agree with you more," Riga said,
smiling.

Sarak groaned, his hands clenching at his sides.
"Phada, stop," he muttered between clenched
teeth. "Do not force this issue. You know better
than anyone why I cannot accept that sash."

"Why should you not be able to accept a position that is by all rights yours, while I am allowed
to continue blithely on the Keeper's path?"

He shook his head mutely, despairingly, refusing to answer. Why did she not cease? Did she not
realize that she was about to ruin everything for
herself? He did not think he could bear it if Phada
were discharged from her training. It was what
she wanted, what she was born to do.

"I must confess, my lady, that he is refusing because of something that is my fault, and he must
realize that he is wrong for doing so. Mesara needs
him, perhaps more than he will ever know."

"Tell me what you mean," the queen invited,
gesturing for Phada to step closer.

Sweet Goddess, no, he thought frantically. He
lunged for the hem of her tunic, hoping to catch
her before she moved out of his range. He could
tell by her eyes that she was going to confess
everything. She again evaded his grasp. He leapt
onto the dais. "Do not listen to her, my lady. She
has not fully recovered from her journey to Gorod."

"Hold, Sarak. I must speak. Lady Queen, I am
no longer qualified to be a Keeper's apprentice. I
have already been to see the head Keeper this very
evenfall and informed her that I can no longer
train."

By the blue moon, she had already been to see the Keepers. Sarak bit his lip to keep from keening like a mortally wounded clawcat. His throat clogged with grief and he could not see past the sheen of tears that had formed in his eyes. Why did she want to give up everything that had given her life meaning when he had tried so hard to keep her free from the taint of his transgression?

He stepped forward. "I have broken Mesara's sacred laws. That is why I refused your gracious offer and that is why I am not fit to be first-in-command." He threw his shoulders back, drawing in a deep breath so he could continue. "I forced her, my lady. She was an innocent and she trusted me and I used it against her."

"Sarak!" Riga's eyes widened in shock. "Are you saying that you mated with this Keeper's apprentice?"

"Yes, my sovereign. And I willingly accept any punishment you wish to mete out."

Riga turned toward Phada, astonishment still plainly etched on every delicate royal feature.

"That is not true; it did not happen in quite the way he says it did," Phada stated calmly. She went to stand next to Sarak. "If you are going to punish him, then you must also punish me. He did not force me, my lady. He would never commit such a heinous act. I went to his pallet willingly because I wanted to mate with him, and I do not regret a single, wonderful moment of that experience."

Now Sarak was just as speechless as the queen. He stared at Phada, feeling both pride that she would admit to such a deed in front of the queen and shame that he had allowed her to break the law. Her next words shocked him right down to his sandaled feet.

"I have fallen in love with him. I consider him my bonded mate. There is another, even more urgent reason why I am no longer qualified to become a Keeper. I am carrying his child."

"Phada!"

Sarak's gasp mixed with several others from the citizens standing nearby. Dear Goddess in heaven, Phada was pregnant with his babe. His heart soared even as his spirits sank. She looked beautiful and brave standing there, confessing her conduct to the queen, defying everything she had been brought up to believe. And she loved him. He had never experienced such happiness and such despair in his entire life. He thought it would tear him apart before she was done.

"I will follow him into exile if that is what you command, my lady," she finished quietly. "For I find that I cannot live without him."

Rudela, the palace healer and one of the most respected Keepers in Mesara, stepped forward. "May we speak, Queen Riga?"

The queen looked bewildered, but nodded graciously.

"I could not help overhearing what has just occurred. Peace has been restored to Mesara, thanks to these two young people. But we have all been changed forever. Even now, even when the ingredients of the neutralizer have been analyzed so we can prepare it ourselves, many are still addicted to faral and perhaps always will be. The web of community has been broken and it will take orbits of hard work and much effort to restore it to its former glory. But I hope it has taught us a lesson as well. We must be ever vigilant against allowing one segment of society to dominate another. We must ever listen to all our people if we are to grow, neither exalting one nor denigrating the other.

"We have had much discussion in the Keepers' Sanctuary. One of the things we feel must be overturned is the law forbidding a warrior to bond. A warrior needs something more than scorn for his task of fighting to protect us all. Besides, dominators are also part of the web of life, a proper masculine counterforce to the feminine energy of the Keepers. Perhaps we went too far in the other direction when we segregated them. They should be able to bond and integrate into the life of the community, not be kept separate and unequal any longer."

Sarak was astonished to find Riga nodding thoughtfully before smiling over at him. "I believe you may be correct. Perhaps you would draw up the decree for me to sign." She slanted an encouraging smile in Sarak's direction. "And perhaps Sarak and Phada wish to be the first to take advantage of such a law when it is passed by the council, as I am sure it will be."

Sarak opened his mouth, searching desperately for words with which to reply. He was still in shock at the sudden turn of events. Phada beat him to it. "He has not asked me to bond with him."

He reached for her hand, engulfing it in his larger one and pressing it to his heart. "Phada, I do not know how a Mesaran male asks such a vital question, but I ask it of you. Will you bond with me, be my mate for as long as we live? I cannot imagine life without you."

Her smile rivaled the brightness of the sun and moon combined. "Yes."

"Think about this carefully," he cautioned. "I do not have much to offer in the way of a bonding gift."

"That is not exactly true. What about Gisba and Ral? I am sure they would wish to be included in any dealings between us. With them we have the makings of a fine trade caravan."

"Annoying packbirds," he said, heaving a mock sigh. His fingers caressed her captive hand. "As if you would ever force them to work for their supper."

"As long as you do," she said with a grin. "Do

you agree to the terms or not?"

"Indeed I do." He pulled her into his arms, feeling awkward at first with Rudela and the queen looking on, and then not caring as his mouth closed over Phada's in a searing kiss.

Rudela watched them, smiling. When they finally came up for air, she asked. "Is it true that you are carrying the warrior's child?"

Phada blushed and nodded.

"As you know, we are not sure why your body rejects the faral. Whether or not your child inherits this same characteristic will tell us much," Rudela said, pursing her lips, her expression thoughtful. "The great mystery is why Sarak did not succumb when he was reintroduced to faral by Adelard. I think I may know why."

"You do?" Phada's eyes widened in surprise. "Tell us, please."

"Sarak did not fall prey to the effects of the drug the second time around because of the way he weaned himself from it," the Keeper explained. "Without the help of the neutralizer, his body was forced to produce its own defenses rather than relying on outside intervention. It is the only explanation that makes any sense."

Sarak met Phada's gaze. "You saved me in more ways than one, little wingbird," he said. "And created a new life in the bargain."

"We each carry something of the other."

"Yes." He pulled her close, laying a gentle hand over her stomach. "I never expected to have a child. I have no words to express my joy."

She smiled as she laid her head against his heart. "The child of a Keeper's apprentice and a warrior. I can think of no better herald of hope for the future than that."

# ELIZABETH CRANE

**Don't miss these passionate time-travel romances, in which modern-day heroines journey to other eras and find the men who fulfill their hearts' desires**

*Reflections In Time.* When practical-minded Renata O'Neal submits to hypnosis to cure her insomnia, she never expects to wake up in 1880s Louisiana—or in love with fiery Nathan Blue. But vicious secrets and Victorian sensibilities threaten to keep Renata and Nathan apart...until Renata vows that nothing will separate her from the most deliciously alluring man of any century.

_52089-3                                    $4.99 US/$6.99 CAN

*Time Remembered.* Among the ruins of an antebellum mansion, young architect Jody Farnell discovers the diary of a man from another century and a voodoo doll whose ancient spell whisks her back one hundred years to his time. Micah Deveroux yearns for someone he can love above all others, and he thinks he has found that woman until Jody mysteriously appears in his own bedroom. Enchanted by Jody, betrothed to another, Micah fears he has lost his one chance at happiness—unless the same black magic that has brought Jody into his life can work its charms again.

_51904-6                                    $4.99 US/$5.99 CAN

**Dorchester Publishing Co., Inc.**
**65 Commerce Road**
**Stamford, CT 06902**

Please add $1.75 for shipping and handling for the first book and $.50 for each book thereafter. NY, NYC, PA and CT residents, please add appropriate sales tax. No cash, stamps, or C.O.D.s. All orders shipped within 6 weeks via postal service book rate. Canadian orders require $2.00 extra postage and must be paid in U.S. dollars through a U.S. banking facility.

Name _____

Address _____

City _____ State _____ Zip _____

I have enclosed $_____ in payment for the checked book(s).

Payment <u>must</u> accompany all orders.☐ Please send a free catalog.

# BITTERROOT

# VICTORIA CHANCELLOR

### Bestselling Author Of *Forever & A Day*

In the Wyoming Territory—a land both breathtaking and brutal—bitterroots grow every summer for a brief time. Therapist Rebecca Hartford has never seen such a plant—until she is swept back to the days of Indian medicine men, feuding ranchers, and her pioneer forebears. Nor has she ever known a man as dark, menacing, and devastatingly handsome as Sloan Travers. Sloan hides a tormented past, and Rebecca vows to use her professional skills to help the former Union soldier, even though she longs to succumb to personal desire. But when a mysterious shaman warns Rebecca that her sojourn in the Old West will last only as long as the bitterroot blooms, she can only pray that her love for Sloan is strong enough to span the ages....

_52087-7           $5.50 US/$7.50 CAN

# A GLIMPSE OF FOREVER

## TIMESWEPT

# LINDA O. JOHNSTON

Her wagon train stranded on the Spanish Trail, pioneer Abby Wynne searches the heavens for rain. Gifted with the visionary powers, Abby senses a man in another time gazing at the same night sky. But even she cannot foresee that she will journey to the future and into the arms of her soul mate.

Widower Mike Danziger has escaped the L.A. lights for the Painted Desert, but nothing prepares him for a beauty as radiant as the doe-eyed woman he finds. His intellect can't accept her incredible story, but her warm kisses ease the longing in his heart.

Caught between two eras bridged only by their love, Mike and Abby fight to stay together, even as the past beckons Abby back to save those trapped on the trail. Is their passion a destiny written in the stars, or only a fleeting glimpse of paradise?

_52070-2                                    $4.99 US/$6.99 CAN

# THERE NEVER WAS A TIME

## GAIL LINK

**"Gail Link was born to write romance!"**
**—Jayne Ann Krentz**

Sitting alone in her Vermont farmhouse, Rebecca Gallagher Fraser hears a ghostly voice whisper to her. But not until she stumbles across a distant ancestor's diary do the spirit's words hold any meaning for her.

Drawn by inexplicable forces, Rebecca journeys to the once resplendent Southern plantation where her forebear loved and lost a Union soldier. And there, on a jasmine-scented New Orleans night, she discovers that passion unfulfilled in one lifetime can defy fate and logic and be reborn so much sweeter in another.

__52025-7                                        $4.99 US/$5.99 CAN

# A Gift of Wild Flowers

## GEORGIA BOCKOVEN

# Harlequin Books

TORONTO • NEW YORK • LONDON
AMSTERDAM • PARIS • SYDNEY • HAMBURG
STOCKHOLM • ATHENS • TOKYO • MILAN

To Nancy Elliott, Debbie Gordon and Martha Sans—
wonderful and talented friends who badgered,
prodded and talked me through my first,
and I sincerely hope my last,
case of writer's block.

Published May 1985

ISBN 0-373-25157-2

# 1

BRIAN ROBERTSON STEPPED deeper into the pulsating spray coming from the shower head, letting the near-scalding water work on the tension-filled muscles at the back of his neck. If today was supposed to be the biggest day in his life—as so prominently proclaimed in the morning paper—why in the hell was he having trouble even getting started with it?

Slowly he tilted his head back until the water cascaded over his thick brown hair. He let the rushing sound engulf him in isolation, taking him far away from the reality of a world he no longer found joy in inhabiting. Where was the sense of accomplishment, the gratification he should feel? Why the knot in his midsection, the constricting band around his chest?

Disgustedly he turned the chrome faucet handles to their off position, reached for a towel and began drying himself. With droplets of water still sprinkled across the smooth expanse of his back and sparkling on the soft mat of brown hair that covered his chest, he walked out of the bathroom, leaving a trail of size-thirteen footprints on the cool tile floor. As his Aunt Matilda had prophesied to a distraught preteen, he had eventually grown into his big feet. When he'd finally stopped growing, at six feet three inches, they no longer seemed the embarrassing twin boats they had seemed when he was twelve.

Bypassing the dining room, which still held the remnants of his breakfast and the morning newspaper with his photograph displayed on the front page of the business section, Brian went into the living room. Seeking beauty to calm his disquiet, he walked over to the window to watch the deep blue water of Lake Michigan far below him as it responded to the new day. While he stood staring at the lake and then at the early-morning Chicago traffic, he absently adjusted the bath towel that had begun to slip from his waist—a waist as narrow and firm now that he was thirty-four, as it had been when he was on the wrestling team at Harvard.

Lost in thought about the day ahead of him and his peculiar reluctance to get started with it, he was startled by the intrusive ring of the telephone. He stared at the molded piece of plastic, his chestnut eyes filled with resentment. Unable to think of one person he wanted to speak to that morning, he considered letting it ring. He made it to the fourth insistent summons before he relented and picked up the receiver. "Yes?" he said, his voice gruff despite his attempt at civility.

Paula Michaelson ignored the gruffness. "Hi, sweetheart. Daddy wanted me to remind you about tonight."

Never once in the ten years he had known Roger Michaelson had Brian ever forgotten an appointment...or a party.

"And I wanted to remind you about lunch." Her voice turned sultry. "I thought we might go to the Easterbrook and celebrate your promotion in a very special way. I have a suite reserved for us." She paused. "Does that sound as yummy to you as it does to me?"

Brian closed his eyes in a mental sigh. "Paula, I told you last week that I would be having lunch with the board in the executive dining room today. As the newest member, I can't possibly get out of attending."

"Would you like me to see if I can get daddy to excuse you a little early?"

The mental sigh became physical. "No, Paula...I would not like it if you talked to your father." He knew from experience that she had just formed a pout on her carefully glossed lips.

"How am I going to give you your present, then?"

Brian rubbed his eyes. "We're seeing each other tonight." When she didn't answer, he said, "Why don't you meet me in my office after the board meeting. I'll arrange for us to have a few minutes alone. If you can't give me what you had planned, you can at least give me a congratulatory kiss."

"See?" she said triumphantly. "I just knew you would come up with something."

"I have to go now, Paula."

"Brian?"

"Yes?"

"Have I told you how very, very proud I am of you?"

He smiled. "No, I don't think you've mentioned anything like that up to now."

"Oh, you rat. I've told you at least ten times each and every day since the first itty bitty hint of your promotion."

"Well, now that I think about it, perhaps you have made mention of the fact once or twice. I have to get going, Paula," he reminded her. "Either hang up or I will." Brian listened for her click before replacing his own receiver. Paula had a "thing" about hanging up first. Threatening to beat her to it was the one sure way to get her off the phone.

Paula Michaelson was going to make a perfect corporate wife, a real asset to his career. Having spent her entire life in the elite social circle of the upper echelons of the Chicago business community, she was completely comfortable there.

It was he who was the intruder. Son of a construction-worker father and bookkeeper mother from Denver, Colorado, he had been far more familiar with backyard barbecues than afternoon lawn parties. He had been someone whose entry into Harvard and the rarefied world of Harvard graduates had been unplanned, unforeseen. Without the insurance money given to him after his father's accidental death, he would never have been able to afford the tuition and would probably have gone to a local school. Would he have been happier as the manager of a branch office of a bank somewhere in Colorado? It was a question he had contemplated more frequently lately.

Using the insurance money had put an incredible, self-imposed burden on him to do well. Consequently, he had graduated in the top ten percent of his class, allowing him to pick and choose among the crème de la crème of job offers. Amercoast Bank had been his first choice, and it had been a wise one. Or so it would seem today. At ten o'clock he was to be made the youngest full vice-president in the bank's history. With the promotion came a seat on the board and another round of limelight in the local press, a press that seemed to have come to think of him as their own, to be summoned, interviewed and photographed whenever they had space in the business section to fill.

His rise to the top had occurred with dizzying speed, leaving no time at each brief stop on the rung of the promotional ladder to get to know the people around him. Only recently, in the quiet hours of early mornings, had he acknowledged the terrible price his success had exacted. He was rich with acquaintances, impoverished of friends. And then with the last promotion had come Paula. He was amused at the number of people who gave her the credit for his meteoric rise in the hierarchy of the nation's fourth largest bank. That he hadn't met her prior to last year seemed to make no difference to the gossips—only that she was the daughter of the chairman of the board and therefore bound to be a strong influence in his favor.

Their courtship and subsequent engagement were strangely hazy in his memory. It wasn't that he felt as if he'd been maneuvered into doing something he wouldn't have done on his own. What nagged at him on sleepless nights was the possibility that Paula, like the seemingly endless promotions he had earned, might be a path he walked because it was the one of least resistance.

Brian reached up to rub his neck. He stared unseeingly at the shimmering beauty of Lake Michigan. Supposedly he had it all. Why, then, wasn't he happier? How many thirty-four-year-old men faced the world each morning with the feeling that all the challenge, all the excitement in living was behind them? Was he so unusual? Brian brought his eyes back into focus to cast one final look at the sun reflecting off the water of the lake, then turned and headed for the bedroom. He wasn't sure what he was going to do to change things; he only knew that it had become absolutely necessary that he do something. The sudden, heartfelt truth of his feelings made his step more determined. Life was too damn short to continue to live it as unhappily as he had been doing.

Less than a half hour later he was ready, dressed in blue jeans and a tweed jacket, to leave for the towering Amercoast office building. The unofficial banking uniform he had worn for twelve years—charcoal gray pin-striped suit—was lying in a heap at the foot of his bed.

The man who walked back through the rooms less than thirty minutes later was not the same. This new man had a satisfied smile replacing the lines of tension that had been around his mouth; his step was light, his eyes shone with determination. Like a bear waking from a long winter's hibernation, Brian had shaken himself free from the lethargy that had gripped his soul for the past decade. He felt as though he could breathe again—deep gulping breaths, not the faint, proper sighs he had learned to use in the stuffy offices and boardrooms of Amercoast.

If he had been a dancer, he would have kicked up his heels; a singer, he would have gone for a high C. Because he was Brian Robertson, widely proclaimed boy genius of the banking world, whose routine was as predictable as a sunrise, he dismissed his waiting limousine and walked to work, privately exulting at the feel of air around him that was not artificially climate controlled. Such a small thing. How had he so completely lost touch with the man he had once been—a man who had grown up breathing crisp, clean mountain air.

By the time he arrived at work, he was fifteen minutes late for the board meeting. The eyes that turned his way when he opened the large oak paneled doors into the room reflected more than irritation—there was shock. Brian met their gazes unflinchingly, basking in the knowledge that it was for the last time. He nodded his head in greeting. "Gentlemen." Three of the less influential members nodded back.

With deliberate slowness, savoring every hostile and curious glance sent in his direction—he had not risen through the ranks without creating animosity along the way—Brian walked the length of the table to the empty seat at the other end.

Glaring at the slow-moving Brian, Roger Michaelson impatiently cleared his throat. "Since it would be inconvenient for the rest of us to wait while you went home to change clothes, Mr. Robertson, kindly hurry up and be seated and we will get on with the business at hand."

Brian grasped the back of the chair that had been left vacant for him. "Before you begin the scheduled meeting, I have something I would like to say."

"Couldn't it wait?" Roger Michaelson's icy tone was not questioning, it was a command.

"I'm only asking for a few minutes. Fair exchange, I think, for the twelve vacationless years I have given Amercoast."

Roger Michaelson leaned back in his chair. Impatiently he began to tap first one end and then the other of his thin gold pen against the padded leather armrest. "Make it as brief as possible."

Brian smiled. The methodical tapping was meant to intimidate, but he knew the smile he sent in return would infuriate the father of his bride-to-be. Slowly he let his gaze travel around the table, pausing a moment to make direct eye contact with each man present. When at last his gaze returned to

Roger Michaelson, he nodded slightly and said, "As briefly as possible, gentlemen . . . I quit."

A collective, audible gasp greeted the announcement. Even Roger's mouth dropped open in surprise. It was the single most satisfying moment in Brian's career with Amercoast. With everyone still too stunned to speak, Brian again walked the length of the table and left the room. He rode the elevator down two floors to his office, stopped to kiss his secretary of eight years, then went inside to clean out his desk.

Barbara Halsted hadn't remained secretary to banking's boy genuis for eight years by being slow on the uptake. It took her less than thirty seconds to recover from the first kiss her boss had ever given her, leave her desk and follow him into his office. Still working a year and a half after she could have retired, she had nothing to lose by saying what was on her mind. It was one of the things Brian liked best about her. Even before she had reached retirement age, she had never minced words, given false praise or pretended to be anything but the crusty, extremely efficient executive secretary that she was. In return for saving his backside on countless occasions when he had been young and green, Brian had made sure she had received a raise every time he had, making her the most highly paid secretary employed by the bank.

Now this powerhouse of efficiency and intuition stood facing him, her back pressed against the closed door. "Well?" she said.

Brian looked up from his desk, the grin he could no longer contain spreading across his face. "I quit."

Barbara's eyes grew wide. "You did what?"

"I quit," he repeated for her.

She folded her arms across her chest. After staring at him for a few seconds, she shook her head. "Well, bully for you."

He winked at her. "I knew you would understand."

"I'm probably the only one who will."

"You and my mother. She's been telling me for years that all work and no play was turning me into an old man."

"She's a smart—" The door shoved against Barbara's back. Before she had a chance to move out of the way, she was struck again.

"Brian!" Paula's voice screeched. "I know you're in there, Brian. Don't try to keep me out by blocking the—" With that, she came hurtling into the room.

Barbara sent Brian a furtive "see you later" look, stepped around Paula and discreetly closed the door.

Clasping her heaving chest, Paula looked as if she had just run a marathon. "How...could...you?" she choked. "How could you...do...this...without talking to me...or at least saying something to daddy first?"

"Paula." He came around the desk. When he reached for her she jerked away. He let his arms fall to his sides. "I only decided to quit about an hour or so ago—"

"How could you do this to me?" she wailed.

"To you?"

"Yes, dammit, to me." For the first time since he had known her, Paula started to cry. "How will I ever be able to explain this to my friends?"

Brian leaned against the desk. "Should any real need to explain anything to anyone ever arise, you can tell whoever asks that I got tired of riding the merry-go-round and decided to get off."

She let out a heart-wrenching sob. "That doesn't make any sense! People will think I'm engaged to someone who's lost his mind." She started to run her hand through her sleekly cut shoulder-length blond hair, then stopped as if realizing she might disturb the tortoiseshell comb.

"Paula, stop whining for a minute and listen to me. When are you going to realize that there are some things in life more important than what others think or say about you?"

"You're wrong, Brian. There is nothing more important than being thought well of by one's peers."

"If you sincerely believe that, we have a real problem."

She looked at him, her blue eyes outlined in big black circles of tear-smudged mascara. "Oh, Brian," she sobbed. "You've broken my heart." She accepted the handkerchief he offered. Several sniffs later, she raised hopeful eyes to meet his. "There's still a chance...." She reached for his arm, a pleading look in her eyes. "You could tell them it was all a terrible mistake. They would be angry, but eventually they would forgive you. Daddy would see to it." When it became obvious that he was not going to do as she asked, she moved closer to snuggle against him. "Please, Brian. Do it for me—for us?"

"I'm sorry, Paula...."

She pulled away from his loose embrace. Her voice turned cool, her words clipped. "Is that your final word?"

"Yes."

"Then you leave me no other choice, Brian." She reached for the pear-shaped diamond on her left hand. "I waited a long time before I decided to hitch myself to a star. I thought I had finally found the one that would go the highest and burn the brightest when I met you. But obviously I was wrong." She handed him the ring. "I have too high an opinion of myself to let this happen to me. I refuse to let you take me down with you."

Brian looked at her for a few seconds before he took the ring and slipped it into his pocket. He grasped her by the shoulders, brought her to him and kissed her lightly on the forehead. "I'm not sure I know how to thank you for this magnanimous gesture, Paula," he said, sarcasm hiding the hurt. "It's so kind of you to release me. If there's ever anything I can do in return—"

"Leave Chicago," she spat, her look scathing. "Slither out of here as quickly and as quietly as you possibly can."

"Ah, my beautiful Paula. How can you say something so cruel after all we've meant to each other?" Brian felt a detached trace of truth in his sardonic reply.

"For you to do what you did this morning proves that you never really loved me at all."

"Paula, please try to understand that what I did had nothing to do with you. Today was just the culmination of something I've been feeling for years." How could he possibly communicate the emptiness he felt, the necessity of his actions? "I've been withering away inside. I have to see if I can find a way to make myself whole again. If we can't remain lovers, could we at least part friends?"

"You can go to hell, Brian Robertson. The last thing in the world I need is a friend like you!" Again her eyes filled with tears. "I hope I never see you again for as long as I live." She turned and left, slamming the door behind her.

Brian stared at the closed door, trying to summon a sense of loss. That he had let himself become involved with a woman like Paula was telling in itself. The man he had once been would have had no trouble seeing her for what she was. What had happened to him to cause such blindness?

A light tapping sound snapped him out of his musing. "Yes?" he called out.

Barbara peered around the door. "Mind some company?"

"Whose?"

"Mine."

He gave her a weary smile. "Come in—a friendly face would be a welcome sight."

"I take it all did not go well with the fair lady Paula?"

"It seems she thinks her knight in shining armor has developed a terminal case of rust."

"Would I be out of line if I said good riddance?"

He raked his hand through his hair. "I've been struggling, but I keep reaching the same conclusion. I guess I don't want to accept just how far I've let myself drift."

"Well, I'll say this for you—when you decided to get back on track, you certainly did it with a bang. You might be interested to know that word has already reached the papers. You've had three requests for interviews. I told them you'd get back to them as soon as possible."

"Do you think any of them believed you?"

"Not to the point that they aren't on their way over here right now. If you want to escape them, I'd suggest you snap to it."

Brian glanced back at his desk.

"I'll do that," Barbara told him. "It will be my final official act as your secretary—and as an employee of Amercoast Bank." He eyed her quizzically. "You don't think I'd stick around here without you, do you? I've got a whole passel of grandchildren I've been ignoring. And then there's a cruise around the world I've been promising myself I'd take before I got too old to enjoy it."

Brian shoved his hand in his pocket and withdrew the diamond engagement ring Paula had given him back only minutes earlier. "Would you do me one last favor?"

"For you? Anything."

Brian smiled. "Years from now when I think back on all these events and the memory looms before me like a giant mushroom cloud, the one island of sanity will be you wearing this look on your face." He reached for her hand, opened it and placed the obscenely expensive stone in her palm. "I want you to take this as a going-away present. Wear it, sell it, do whatever you want with it. Knowing you had put this particular piece of carbon to pleasurable use would do my heart a world of good."

Barbara looked at the ring and then smiled at Brian. "You can count on it," she said softly. She kissed his cheek. "Now get out of here."

LATER THAT EVENING as Brian stood in his apartment, drink in hand, looking down at the lights of Chicago, the sense of euphoria began to fade. A terrible feeling of sadness settled through him, its tentacles reaching into hidden corners of his mind. Where had he lost the way? At what point in his life had he traded emotions for promotions, a sense of wonder for power?

Quitting had been the first step to rediscovering

himself. Now if he only had some idea where to look for the second. He felt cut loose—a boat adrift without wind, sail or rudder. Chicago was his home, but without a job and the contacts it necessitated he was a stranger. There was no one he wanted to see, no one in the circle of acquaintances he had established who would understand his reasoning. He had done far more today than quit a job; he had abandoned a life-style.

A life-style for a life—the trade seemed more than worthwhile. Brian set the half-empty glass on the table, stretched and walked into the bedroom. He absently twisted and then poked the gold initial cuff links with the classic roman-style letter *B* on them through his cuffs and then laid them on the dresser. The cuff links had been his father's, the only real jewelry he had ever owned, given to Brian because he and his father had shared the same name.

He glanced at the old photograph of his family perched on the dresser. The picture had been taken a year before his father's accident, when they were on the last backpacking trip they had taken as a family into the Colorado wilderness. Brian remembered how proud he had been that year to have finally reached his father's height. His mother, a head shorter, her hair a cap of blond curls, her arm lovingly placed around her husband's waist had been particularly happy that day—they had surprised her when they stopped for lunch with a slightly crushed birthday cake complete with candles.

His brother, Tom, only an inch or two shy of Brian's shoulder in the photograph had wound up topping his own six-foot-three-inch height by the time he had reached eighteen. Almost five years had passed since he had seen Tom and his marine-biologist wife who lived in Anchorage, Alaska, with their four cildren.

And then there was Sally. Born almost seven years before Brian, she had challenged both her brothers to be the best they could be, had taught them to wrestle and was a better coach than any they'd had throughout school. Because she could outhike, out-run and outsmart them, they had had sense enough to let her take over when things fell apart for their mother after the accident. Sally had married her high-school sweetheart just out of college and be-come the mother of three children in four years. She currently lived in Maryland, worked for the govern-ment and still, at least twice a year, made a point of checking up on him.

They had been a magnificent family, one filled with love and laughter. With the loss of his father, the laughter had died. It had taken them months just to learn to smile again. All because someone had tried to save a little money by cutting back on the steel-and-concrete supports in a high-rise office building. The nearly completed structure had col-lapsed just as the crews were coming to work. Brian's father had been one of twelve people killed.

How often could a man look back to one point in his life and say with conviction that he would have been a different person if that day had never hap-pened? Without the self-imposed pressure to suc-ceed—to make something of himself in memory of his father—Brian would never have gone after his degree or his job with such single-mindedness. And the tragedy of it all was something he only now un-derstood. His father's idea of a successful man was one who also took time to enjoy and to savor life. To him, sharing a sunset with a friend would have scored far higher on the scale of a good life than gaining a seat on the board of directors of Amercoast Bank.

BRIAN SPENT the next few days purposely avoiding reporters and putting his feelings into a semblance of order. When, at the end of the third day, he felt ready to make contact with someone, the first person who came to mind was Phil Stewart. Phil was Brian's one friend from college he still made an effort to see. Whenever Phil's job brought him to Chicago, which was at least twice a year, he would stay at Brian's apartment and they would renew old ties, happily discovering that despite neglect, the bonds that had created their friendship continued to be as strong as ever. After two unsuccessful tries, Brian finally reached Phil at his home in Phoenix, Arizona.

"Brian, why haven't you been answering your phone?" Phil demanded. He didn't wait for a reply. "What in the hell is happening up there?"

"I don't know—I haven't been paying much attention to the news lately."

"I'm talking about *you*!"

"You heard something about me all the way down there?"

"We get cable news all the way down here, remember? You happen to be a hot item in certain circles."

Brian mentally groaned. He had minored in journalism in college, had even worked at a paper during one summer break, so he had an appreciation for the journalist's job. He was just terribly weary of being a "hot item." "Phil, could you put up with a houseguest for a few days?"

"You know you're always welcome. Haven't I invited you often enough?"

"Well, I'm finally going to take you up on the offer."

"Brian...."

"Yeah?"

"I've got to warn you...."

"I know." Phil's job as editor for a group of in-flight magazines was a natural extension of his innate curiosity. Friend or foe, if there was a story, he would ask. "I'll tell you all the boring details when I get there. I promise you'll be disappointed."

"Let me know when your flight arrives. If I can't make it, Alice will pick you up."

Brian said he would call as soon as he had made the arrangements. After he'd hung up the phone he looked around his apartment, realizing it would probably be one of the last times he would do so. Perhaps, he decided sadly, given enough time he might miss the collection of rooms he had never thought of as home...but he sincerely doubted it.

# 2

"FORGET IT, PHIL. I'm not going to drop everything and go chasing into the woods to photograph some back-to-nature freak." Kelly Stewart shifted the phone to her other ear, grimacing as she watched the kittens she had been preparing to photograph tear her backdrop apart. "Phil, I've got to go."

"Wait!"

"There's nothing you can say to change my mind, so you might as well give it up."

"Reinhart Travel?"

She hesitated. He had found the magic words. She had been trying to get in to see someone about doing the advertising photography for Reinhart Travel for over a year. The ad agency that handled their account refused to even look at her portfolio, saying they were completely satisfied with their present photographers.

"Templeton's?"

Only the most exclusive women's dress shop in Phoenix.

"I can get you in to see the right people..." he coaxed.

"How?" Her voice dripped suspicion.

"Two weeks ago they decided to advertise in three of the in-flights. I've had lunch with the agency people several times since then."

Kelly caught her lip between her teeth, something

she frequently did when deep in thought. Flipping
the single tawny braid she wore when working back
over her shoulder, she said, "All right, tell me something about the guy."

"His name is Brian Robertson. He was a room-
mate of mine at college. He's thirty-four, wickedly
handsome, has a dynamite personality—"

"I'm not looking for a date, Phil. Just tell me why
you're doing an article on him."

"About two weeks ago, on the day he was supposed to be promoted to full vice-president of Amercoast Bank and given a seat on the board of directors,
he quit."

Kelly frowned. "Are you sure this guy's caboose is
attached?"

"I'm positive. He just spent the past seven days
with me. I have an exclusive on his story. I've never
seen him look better. Better than in college even."

"It's not his looks I'm asking about, Phil." The
older she became without any marriage prospects in
sight, the more her brother described men to her in
terms of their physical attributes. Whenever she
pointed this out to him, he told her she was imagining things.

"Kelly, this is really important to me—"

"So important that you'd send your only sister off
to the wilds with some nut?"

"He's *not* a nut. And besides, as I recall, you're not
my only sister."

"I hope you're not trying to reassure me." She
turned her back on the kittens, now systematically
destroying the set she had worked all night to construct. "Tell me again why you need me to do this.
What's wrong with Dave?"

He let out a frustrated sigh. "Dave is in Tucson

covering a rodeo. Henry is in Gila Bend, inaccessible by phone, doing God knows what. Rhonda is in the hospital having her fourth kid. None of the free-lancers we've used before, who I could trust to do this right, are available." His voice had grown progressively louder with each statement. "Now do you understand why I am on bended knees to you?" he said, shouting so vehemently that she tilted the phone away from her ear.

"When would I have to leave?"

"This afternoon."

"How long would I be gone?"

"Four days—five tops."

"You'll give me prominent photo credits? Not like the last time when I had to get a magnifying glass to read my name?"

"I promise."

"How about mentioning my name on the mast-head?"

"On the *masthead*?"

"It was worth a try."

"Kelly...." There was a pause covering just enough time for him to slowly count to ten. In a deceptively calm voice he asked, "How long do you plan to make me wait for your answer?"

"I've never backpacked," she said, ignoring his question. "I don't have any equipment."

"You can go over to the Broadway Sporting Goods store and either rent or buy whatever you need. I'll reimburse you. As for never having gone backpacking before, I can't imagine why you'd worry about something like that. Anyone who works out at a gym three times a week is in good enough shape to do anything."

"How strong is your contact with the ad agency?"

"First class."

"If the thing with Reinhart and Templeton's should fall through, will you arrange something else?"

"Anything you want."

"Something tells me I would be an idiot not to hold out for more. I think I've got you over a barrel."

"Dammit, Kelly, will you go or won't you?"

"If this Robertson guy turns out to be some crazy who hates women photographers, my death will be on your conscience."

"You can come back and haunt me if you want."

"Don't think for a minute that I won't."

He let out a deep sigh. "Thanks, Kelly. You're a sweetheart. I owe you one."

"You owe me more than one, big brother. Let's not forget the last time I saved your neck when that boxer was in town."

"I'll arrange your flight and pick you up at three with all the pertinent information," he said, pointedly ignoring her reference to the pugilist.

"I can't believe this," she mumbled. "I've agreed to go on this idiot adventure and I don't even know where I'm going."

"California. I told Brian a photographer would meet him at nine o'clock in the morning at the Kearsarge Pass trail head."

"One more thing, Phil. . . ."

"Yes?"

"Why didn't you simply take his picture while he was here in town?"

There was a long pause. "Since when have I ever done things the easy way?" Again there was a pause. "At the time, I thought Dave would be available to go with Brian. If I'd had any idea things

would get so complicated, I would have at least ar-
ranged a few head shots before he left. As it is, the
story is scheduled and I don't have so much as a
snapshot. This piece is really important to me, Kelly.
I want it to be a dynamite layout, at least as good as
the story. In-flights don't come by exclusives very
often, and I want to do this one up right. Be sure you
shoot something for the cover."

More magic words. Magazine covers looked impressive in portfolios. "Well, I guess if I'm going to
do it, I'd better get a move on."

After Kelly had hung up the phone, she steeled
herself to turn and face the damage the kittens had
done to her set. It was a wreck—worse than she had
feared. And the culprits were nowhere to be seen. It
was a good thing there was no hurry on the ad she
was putting together for The Wool Barn; she would
have to start all over when she returned next week.
Now, if the kittens would cooperate and stay small,
everything might work out.

Bending over to retrieve a skein of yarn, Kelly felt
a shiver of excitement crawl up her spine. Getting in
to see the right people at the ad agency could be the
break she had been looking for. It might also mean
that her work would be seen by the numerous firms
that had accounts there. One commission could lead
to another and then another. She might make a
name for herself before she turned thirty, after all—
she still had two and a half years.

Staring at the mess around her, she shook her
head. She was ready for success, but was success
ready for her?

Kelly hurriedly cleaned the studio, returned the
kittens to her neighbor's daughter and headed for
the sporting-goods store. Broadway's turned out to

be a small shop catering primarily to college kids. They carried equipment for a vast number of outdoor activities ranging from mountain climbing to kayaking. Every available corner and cupboard was filled to overflowing with odd pieces of gear that Kelly finally gave up trying to identify while she waited for the clerk, settling instead on perusing the book rack.

When the only other customer in the store left, the clerk, a young man with silvery blond hair and a deep tan, turned to her. "Can I help you?" he asked.

Kelly explained her predicament.

He shoved his hands into his back pockets. "It would really be better if you could come back this afternoon," he said. "My uncle is the backpacking expert. He's the one who should help outfit you."

"I can't come back this afternoon. I have to catch a plane. Surely you know enough to get me started. I'm not going to take this up as a permanent hobby. I only need equipment enough to get me through a few days."

"It's a little more complicated than that, ma'am."

He could have stuck out his tongue at her and Kelly would have been less surprised. Never in her twenty-seven years had someone called her "ma'am." She had to fight an urge to glance at her reflection to see if she had somehow dramatically aged in the past half hour.

"Not only does the pack have to be properly fitted, but also the boots—by the way, where did you say you were going?"

"California."

"What part?"

"I'm not sure, but I think it's somewhere near the Yosemite National Park."

"They have some terrific white-water rivers in California. That's my sport—kayaking. The wilder the river, the better. Of course, there's not much chance for me to practice around here.

Kelly smiled. "If I happen to see any wild rivers, I'll be sure to come back and tell you all about them."

The clerk blushed. "I guess you'd like to get started, huh?"

"I would be truly grateful if you could get me out of here in record time. I have a dozen things I have to get done before I leave this afternoon."

Shaking his head, he grimaced. "I sure wish you could come back later. I'm just the summer help around here and you really need—"

"Stop worrying. You'll do just fine. How complicated can it possibly be?"

They started with her feet. After a quick check through a book of topographical maps to see what kind of terrain Kelly would be hiking in, they decided she should buy an extrasturdy pair of boots. When she chose her pack, she took the largest one they could get on her in order to hold the extensive camera equipment she would be carrying. The sleeping bag he insisted she would need for that elevation was a down-filled beauty, navy blue with a hood to keep her head and neck warm. The whole thing stuffed into a bag smaller than a decorative sofa pillow.

The food was the toughest decision; it all sounded and looked ghastly. She solved the problem by taking something different for each meal. That way she would only have to choke down something particularly bad once.

When all her purchases were scattered across the counter, including new socks, shorts, a lightweight tent, stove, fuel, first-aid supplies and a snake-bite kit, she began to have a few doubts. How was that huge mound of equipment ever going to fit into that tiny pack?

After Kelly arrived home and tried packing, her fears became reality. With her cameras, lenses and backpacking gear in small piles around her, she was forced to admit that she could not possibly take everything she had earlier thought absolutely necessary. But what to leave behind? She began making new stacks, starting with "essentials" and ending with "sure would be nice to haves." The first thing to go was her makeup, the second, her bulky lamb's wool sweater. When she reached the point where only the "essentials" were left, she began to pack.

The sky-blue pouch was filled to bursting when she rocked back on her heels in frustration. Around her lay almost half of her "essentials." She glanced at the clock. It was getting late.

Ruthlessly she yanked the contents out of the zippered pouches. The six fresh changes of undergarments became one—she would just have to wash a pair out every night. All snacks were discarded next—she needed to lose a few pounds, anyway. Then the first-aid supplies came under scrutiny. She was healthy, had never been accident prone and sincerely believed that if she left snakes alone, they would leave her alone. That left insect repellent. Did insects live in elevations over ten thousand feet? She took the plastic squeeze bottle in her hand; it wasn't as large as her palm and weighed little more than a packet of freeze-dried food. If Phoenix insects considered her particularly delectable, it seemed reasonable that California's would feel the same. The repellent went in the pack.

Her camera equipment came next. After careful consideration, she settled on one body, three lenses and twenty-five rolls of film, knowing everything she left behind would at one time or another become a source of teeth-gnashing frustration.

Phil arrived just as she pulled the last zipper closed on the pack.

Settling herself in the front seat of the station wagon for the trip to the airport, Kelly lifted the heavy hair from her neck to let the car's air conditioning flow across her nape. It would feel good to be out of Phoenix's summer heat for a while. When Phil was seated beside her, she let her hair fall back over her shoulders and reached for her seat belt.

Dressed casually in jeans and a Western shirt, Phil looked more native than the lifelong locals. His naturally light brown hair carried streaks of unruly sun-bleached blond that made him look years younger than he was. Because of his hair, his naturally impish grin and sparse frame, he was frequently mistaken for her younger brother. Kelly glanced at him. They were much alike in their builds and coloring, but as different as an abacus and computer in their personalities. He was a worrier; she couldn't be bothered. He needed people around him; she enjoyed the solitude of the darkroom. He was nervous because she was unmarried and nearing thirty; she enjoyed the freedom of being single.

When they were on their way, Kelly turned to Phil. "How about giving me some more background on this Brian Robertson guy? Why'd he quit a promising career, what he's going to do now—that kind of thing."

"He told me he woke up one morning, asked himself who he was, what he wanted and where he was going. When he couldn't come up with a satisfactory answer, he figured it was time to find out."

"Isn't thirty-five pretty young for a midlife crisis?"

"He's thirty-four and I wouldn't call what he did a midlife anything. Brian is the kind of guy who is unstoppable when he decides to do something. I've known him since we were freshmen at college. If I hadn't liked him so much from the very beginning, he would have driven me right up the wall. He started out to be every bit as big a goof-off as any of the rest of us—until we got our first set of grades. As I recall, he averaged a high C, nothing to brag about but nothing to be ashamed of, either. He must have spent two days looking at those marks and thinking about them. When the next semester started, he told me that he was through messing around, that he owed someone who had been special to him better than a C average. The incredible part was not how he felt or what he said, it was what he did. Like I said before, if Brian Robertson sets his mind to do something, nothing stands in his way."

"Some people call that particular trait pigheadedness."

Phil glanced at her, a smile curving his mouth. "Isn't there an old saying that goes 'it takes one to know one'?"

Kelly gave him a haughty look, her square jaw tilted up, her smoky blue eyes slightly hooded. "I can't imagine what you mean."

Phil's smile became a chuckle. "If being stubborn was a crime, you'd have been locked up for life the day you were born."

"How can you say such a thing? Especially after I capitulated so easily to your pathetic pleading this morning."

"By any chance does this lapse into vulnerability mean I'm off the hook if the ad-agency thing falls through?"

A slow smile settled on her lips. "How is it that we lived together all those years and I never knew you had such a wonderful sense of humor?"

IT WASN'T UNTIL Kelly was on the plane and heading for Los Angeles that she remembered Phil's charming sense of humor had always come in a poor second to his deviousness. After a quick perusal of the packet of information he had given her, she leaned her head back against the seat and silently swore that somehow, someday, she would get even with her conniving brother.

While Phil had told her that she was to meet Brian Robertson at 9:00 A.M. the next morning, he had failed to mention how complicated it would be for her to get to their rendezvous on time. She had all of fifteen minutes to change planes in Los Angeles for some place called Bakersfield. Once there, she was to rent a car and drive the route carefully marked on the map of California included with her packet. Since the red line traversed some suspiciously tall passes, she had sense enough not to allow its relative straightness to lull her into thinking the hundred and fifty miles she would travel necessarily translated into a simple three-hour drive.

Refolding the map and set of instructions, she

tried to tuck them back into the envelope but they wouldn't slide inside. After her next attempt also failed, she turned the packet over and gave it a shake. A piece of notepaper fell out onto her lap.

Dear Kelly,
   If I failed to tell you before you left, let me do so now. You are the most wonderful, considerate, thoughtful, beautiful and understanding sister any man could ever hope to have. I'll never be able to express how much it means to me that you were willing to jump right in like you did and help me out of a jam. You will be proud to know that since I am confident you'll come back with dynamite pics, I'm going ahead with the layout for the article.

Hurry home,
Phil

P.S. Should anything happen in the next week that might precipitate your having unkind thoughts toward me, just remember this letter. Guilt will instantly assail you, and the urge to come after me with weapon unsheathed will soon pass.

Despite her attempts to prevent it, to maintain her righteous indignation over being so blatantly manipulated, a smile crept across her face. Although she would never tell him so, she knew that given enough time, Phil could talk her into investing in oceanfront property in Kansas.

SEVERAL HUNDRED MILES, a half dozen assorted mishaps and twenty exhausting hours later, Kelly was feeling hard put to remember the warm feelings she'd had

for her brother on the flight to Los Angeles. Not
only had her patience been put to every imaginable
test, her heart had been in her throat ever since she
had crossed the Sierra Nevada and picked up Route
395 headed north. Although she had valiantly tried
to keep her gaze from wandering off the road, she
had failed miserably. Having lived her entire life in
the desert, she found the soaring mountains that accompanied her path through Owens Valley almost
overwhelming. They reminded her of drawings she
had done as a child—simplistic artistry where sheer
inverted ice-cream-cone-type mountain peaks always met flat grasslands. There were no gently
rolling foothills to serve as stairsteps to these haughty heights. It was snow-streaked mountain and high
desert valley and nothing in between.

Backpacking, Phil had called it. Ha! Backpacking
was something ordinary sane people did for relax-
ation in benign, welcoming environments. For anyone to purposely set out to climb *these* mountains,
there had to be a touch of insanity somewhere in his
or her psyche. Fragile, breakable human beings had
no business messing around with Mother Nature on
these battlegrounds where snow still lingered in
June. A backpacker perched on the side of one of
these spires of granite was about as significant as a
drop of rainwater clinging to the Sears Tower.

# 3

By the time Kelly reached the town of Independence, where she was to leave the main road and drive the eleven miles to the trail head, her fingers were gripping the steering wheel so tightly she had to relax them consciously before she could engage the turn signal. Leaving the four-thousand-foot high valley floor, the road began a steep continuous climb that had her yawning and swallowing to try to clear her ears by the time she reached the hikers' parking lot—a climb of five thousand feet. She was in the middle of a particularly huge tonsil-touting yawn when she pulled into an empty parking space, looked up and saw a glowering man pacing the pathway in front of her car. Their gazes met. Her mouth snapped shut with tooth-clacking force.

For interminable seconds they continued to stare at each other. His light brown eyes, emphasized by thick brows bunched close in a deep intimidating frown, radiated ill humor.

Instinct? Premonition? Or just plain bad luck? Whatever it was called, she knew as surely as if he had been wearing a flashing neon sign around his neck that the disagreeable looking lump of humanity standing in front of her was none other than Brian Robertson.

Their brief eye contact ceased when Brian turned and glanced down the road Kelly had just traveled.

His scowl deepened. She saw his lips move in an easily discerned expletive. A shiver of apprehension passed through her, raising goose bumps on her arms and the hair on the nape of her neck. She closed her eyes in a weary mental sigh. The day was obviously not going to be one of her better ones. First had come a range of mountains any Sherpa would have thought twice about climbing, and then a traveling companion who had turned out to be about as companionable looking as a gorilla.

She steeled herself to get out of the car. *Come on, Kelly,* she prodded, *remember those new accounts. Think rich and famous.* If everything went according to plan, in just a few short years clients would be calling from all over the state or the country. If she was going to dream, why not dream big—the world!

Certainly for something this important, she reasoned, the end justified the means—spend a week working with someone who was a few cents short of a dime and get the chance to make a real name for herself in advertising. After all, nothing ventured, nothing gained. She groaned. She had better make her move before she ran out of clichés. It was now or never. A smile curved her mouth. Apparently there were more clichés in her repertoire than she had realized. Swinging her jeans-clad legs out of the car, she stood and stretched, stalling for time. A soft moan escaped her lips as muscles complained at the abuse she had put them through the past day and a half.

Her movements caught Brian's eye, and he glanced her way. Somewhere in the back of her mind she heard her brother's voice saying, "He's wickedly handsome...." A tiny part of her responded to that handsomeness, but the rest, the reasonable part, saw him as a formidable obstacle straddling the path she must travel to reach fame and fortune.

Now that she had actually seen him, something told her that he was not going to like the idea of a woman photographer accompanying him. She sensed she was going to have to do some fast talking to get him to agree to let her go along. Squaring her shoulders, she stepped around to the front of the car and smiled her most charming smile. "By any chance are you Brian Robertson?" she said, immediately gaining his full attention.

"Yes...I am," he answered, his quick examination and questioning eyes demanding she explain herself.

Kelly ignored his lack of warmth and thrust out her hand. "Hi, I'm Kelly Stewart." When it was apparent her name meant nothing to him, she added, "Phil Stewart's sister?" When he still failed to make the connection, she said, "The photographer you've been expecting?"

It was probably the tiny flare of his nostrils when he finally realized who she was, more than the cool handshake, that made her suspect their meeting was going to go straight downhill.

"Phil sent you?" he said, his voice deceptively calm. "His sister? *You're* the award-winning nature photographer?"

Kelly tried to hide her surprise with a quick smile. *Award-winning nature photographer?* What kind of line had Phil used on this guy? As far as she knew, not only wasn't the description applicable to her, but it didn't fit any of the people who normally worked for Phil, either. The closest she had come to photographing anything to do with nature was during her senior year at college when she had harrassed some poor spider with a waterfilled spray bottle trying to get an "artsy" dew-filled shot of his web.

The way she saw it, there were two ways she could handle the mistake in identity—lie or tell the truth. She opted for something in between. "Since you mentioned it, and it seems to matter to you," she said, "I have won several awards...." Not exactly a lie. She had won three blue and two white ribbons for her work on the college newspaper. Her chin rose slightly, defensively. "If you're really interested, I'd be willing to name them for you. Otherwise—" she made a dismissive gesture "—I find that sort of thing rather boring."

"Since listing your awards bores you, we'll skip them and move on to something that interests me. Perhaps you wouldn't mind telling me why in the hell you're so late. You were supposed to be here at nine o'clock." He looked at his watch. "It's going on twelve-thirty."

If he had asked her in something close to a reasonable tone, she would have told him about her backpack going to Sacramento while she went to Bakersfield and the long frustrating wait at the airport while it was found and returned. And then, when she had figured she still had a chance to make it to their meeting on time if she drove all night, there had been the flat tire she'd had to change on the blind side of a curve on a mountain road. But his attitude made her spine stiffen as stubbornly as if he had backed her up against a stone wall.

"As a matter of fact," she began, making her voice sound sweetly apologetic, "I found this lovely little Indian jewelry store that had this great big Sale sign in the window in one of the towns I passed through this morning. You know how it is with us women...I just *couldn't* resist stopping." She shrugged helplessly. "I simply lost track of the time."

He shoved his hands deep into the pockets of his tan walking shorts. "I guess I deserved that."

"Every word."

"It's just that...." His gaze quickly swept her. "Look, I don't know any other way to say this... you're not what I expected." He paused, collecting his thoughts before going on. "When Phil told me about you, somehow he forgot to mention that you were a woman. Frankly—and I don't understand how I could have been so completely wrong about this—I was expecting a man."

Kelly dropped her gaze, knowing if she continued to meet his eyes, he would be able to see the guilt in hers. Complications were setting in faster than she could handle them. She was going to have to admit that she had been sent as a substitute. "I think maybe we had better—"

He didn't let her finish. "Before you go on, there's something we should get straight between us. This trip means a lot to me. I only agreed to let a photographer come along after Phil spent three days wearing me down with promises he would send someone who was not only a top-notch cameraman, but also an experienced backpacker."

He raked his hand through his short-cropped hair, started to speak and then stopped. He stared at her for a minute before looking down at the pavement between them. In a troubled voice, he said, "I feel I have to be honest with you about this. If Phil had told me that you were a woman, I wouldn't have agreed to allow you to come along, no matter how experienced you were." He glanced up again, meeting her wide-eyed gaze. "But since you're al-ready here . . . well, if you're half as good as Phil said you are, we shouldn't have any problems."

If she could have gotten her hands around her brother's neck at that precise moment, she would have gladly choked him. He could have at least warned her about what she was getting into. Forcing a smile that was a feeble mockery of the expression, she said, "Yeah . . . well, at least there's one thing you can count on. I'm not going to stick around any longer than absolutely necessary. I'm as anxious to get back to my work as you are to have me gone."

"Great, then let's get started." As if to soften his abruptness, he said, "Since we're getting such a late start it's important that we go as soon as possible in order to get over Kearsarge Pass and to our first campsite before nightfall."

Involuntarily her eyes moved to look at the steep granite walls behind him. She swallowed. "How far is this Kearsarge Pass?"

"About four miles."

Kelly breathed a silent mental sigh of relief. When she had been "into" jogging, she had gone twice that distance before breakfast. "That's not so far," she remarked with a dismissive tilt of her chin, her confidence rising.

His only answer was a tiny smile before he turned and started back up the hill where he had left his own pack leaning against a tree. He had a shaky feeling about this Kelly Stewart. She looked fit enough, but there was something about the way she kept glancing at the mountains that bothered him. Every instinct told him he should insist she take whatever pictures Phil needed for the article right there at the trail head. From previous experience with magazines, he knew there were rarely more than two or three photographs used with the kind of article being done on him, anyway. He would then be free to proceed on the trip alone as he had originally planned. Having anyone accompany him was an intrusion on the healing solitude he was seeking in these mountains; having a woman along was not only an intrusion, it was also complicating and somehow awkward. But how did he go about saying so without sounding like a chauvinistic jerk?

His position became indefensible when he reminded himself that he had been willing to go along with the arrangements when he thought the photographer was a man. She was only doing her job. He could not with a clear conscience deny her that right.

Reaching the tree where he had left his pack, Brian grabbed the shoulder straps and swung the seventy pounds up onto his back. When the belt was securely fastened at his hips and the weight had been properly adjusted, he headed back to Kelly's car.

He found her sitting on a rock struggling into her boots. After he'd watched her actions for a few more seconds, his eyes narrowed suspiciously. Just as he started to say something about the foolishness of breaking in a new pair of boots on a climb like the one they were about to take, she looked up and flashed him a smile that made him choke back the criticism. With that smile he truly saw Kelly Stewart for the first time. She was, quite simply, beautiful. Her hair was caught in a thick braid that lay against her back, quick blue eyes flashed an innate intelligence...and she had that incredible smile. She was as different from the women he had known for the past ten years as the buildings of Chicago were to the mountains around him.

Abruptly she stood, brushed off the seat of her pants, which he noted covered a decidedly lovely derriere, and headed back to the car. When she opened the trunk she was temporarily hidden from his view. He used the time to think about the humorous side to his uncharacteristic musing. He couldn't remember that Paula Michaelson had ever stirred such basic, unabashedly lusty thoughts. Obviously the mountain air had already worked some startling magic on him. He had been right to come to this place.

When the trunk lid thunked closed, Brian's face sported a self-satisfied smile. The smile quickly faded, however, when Kelly stepped around the car and he saw her in full regalia.

Her boots weren't the only new thing she had purchased for the trip. Everything, from the pack to the Ensolite pad strapped across the top smacked of new, as in novice, as in never having backpacked before in her life.

His eyes flashed an ominous message as he curled his hands around the padded straps that rested loosely across his shoulders. "You can forget coming with me," he said, his voice tight, keeping his temper under control with conscious effort. "If you really wanted to make me think you had backpacked before, you should have had sense enough to rent your gear. That way at least it would have looked used. There's no way I'm going to spend the next week baby-sitting someone who's stupid enough to think they can take a hike like this without knowing what they're doing." He turned to leave, then stopped and faced her again. He knew he should just walk away, and in the serenity of the mountains forget everything that had happened here this morning, but his anger had started to nudge fury. "When you get back to Phoenix, tell that brother of yours that if he ever tries to con me again—"

Kelly felt her face flush and then her ears start to burn. In response to his browbeating she skipped anger altogether and went right to fury. "If you think I've come all this way to be dismissed like some underling, you're crazy," she began, her voice a low warning. "I have a job to do, and I'm going to do it whether you like it or not!" What was she saying? She should grab the opportunity to get out of going with him and head back to Phoenix as fast as her little rental car would take her.

"Crazy?" he shouted. "I'll tell you crazy. Crazy is some feather-headed blonde thinking she's Wonder Woman because she can bounce around longer than anyone else in her exercise class."

So much for the niceties. "Wrong guess, Robertson. I don't 'bounce' at all. It so happens I lift weights." Purposely she let her gaze travel the length of him. "Something that might do you some good." Who was she trying to kid? "Not to mention getting a little sun once in a while." She gave him a superior sneer. "It must be tough to figure out where those legs of yours leave off and the sheets begin when you go to bed at night. Decidedly pale, don't you think, for someone who purports to be in such constant communion with nature?" He started to answer her, but she wasn't through and wasn't about to let him speak. "And while I'm at it, how is it that you can make judgments on my backpacking abilities by looking at my equipment when yours is every bit as new as mine?"

She had him on that one. Except for his own boots, fowarded by a mother who, thank God, never threw anything out, every other piece of his gear was also recently purchased. He crossed the short span of asphalt that separated them. Looking down at her five feet five inches from his own intimidating height, he said, "All right...just how many times *have* you been backpacking?"

Kelly tilted her head back to stare up at him. "Give me one good reason why it should make any difference and I'll tell you."

"That does it." He reached for her shoulders and moved her out of the way.

When Kelly realized what he was doing, she dug the keys out of her pocket, locked the car and hurried after him. She was out of the parking lot before she realized she was still carrying her tennis shoes. If she took them back, he would get impossibly ahead of her. Rather than just drop them beside the trail, she reached up and tucked them into the pad she carried on top of her pack, then broke into a light jog to make up the final distance separating them. They were several hundred yards along the trail when he turned to face her, a threatening scowl making his eyebrows one continuous line. "We are not playing some adolescent game here, Ms Stewart. This trip means a lot to me, and I refuse to let it be ruined by some lying, manipulating—"

Kelly matched him glare for glare, scowl for scowl. "I'd be careful with the name-calling if I were you, *Mr. Robertson*. We have several days to spend together and I can be incredibly unpleasant when properly provoked."

"Why doesn't that surprise me?"

"Look here, Mr. Big-shot Executive. There's something you should try to get through your thick skull right now. This intimidation stuff might have worked for you in the banking business, but it doesn't faze me in the slightest. I'm the youngest of six children. I've been worked on by experts." She stepped closer and to emphasize her point pressed her index finger against the middle of his chest. "It just so happens that this next week means more to me than it could possibly mean to you, and there's no way I'm going to let you screw it up for me. When I'm gone, you can hike in solitary splendor to the North Pole for all I care. Until then, I'm a part of the scenery."

Without saying a word, Brian reached up, removed her finger from the middle of his chest, turned and started walking again.

SEVEN HOURS and thirteen excruciating miles later, the trail dropped down to skirt a small lake still sporting scattered islands of ice. Even through her fog of fatigue, Kelly's senses responded to the grandeur of the stark shadow-filled crags and grass-softened meandering shoreline. Everywhere she looked, light or its absence played a role in contrasting patches of lingering snow and ice to its surroundings. She reached for her camera, methodically releasing the hooks that had held it snugly against her chest as she walked.

At the sound of her shutter clicking Brian turned. "There's no need to rush. We'll be staying here for the night."

Kelly swallowed the sarcastic retort that teetered on the edge of her tongue. She wanted to ask him what had made him give up trying to make it all the way to the next trail head, but the last thing she wanted to do was harass him into changing his mind about stopping. She had no doubt that she could manage another mile or two tonight—for the past hour her legs had been operating on automatic, anyway. What she was really afraid of was whether or not she could get moving again in the morning.

About halfway up the ascent of a place Brian had called Glenn Pass—a charming little stroll he had casually mentioned was only twenty feet short of twelve thousand—she had stopped being aware of every little nerve ending in her legs. A blessed numbness had set in, which had allowed her her finest moment of the day when they had reached the summit and Brian had asked if she wanted to rest. She had given him a wide-eyed expression of surprise and replied, "No. Do you?"

Slowly, throughout the long afternoon, she had seen a begrudging admiration replace the doubt that had been in his eyes in the beginning. Noting the transformation and taking foolish pride in it had made her go on long past the point her body had screamed in protest.

Because he had gained several yards on her while she stopped to photograph him walking, Brian reached their evening campsite first. He dropped his pack and then pressed his hands against the small of his back and stretched, his body extending in a graceful arching line. Suddenly he straightened and began slapping at his arms and neck. As Kelly came closer she realized why. Voracious, impossible to discourage mosquitoes began attacking her with the enthusiasm of a school of piranhas. She unbuckled then quickly shrugged out of her pack. Reaching into the side pocket where she had stored the repellent, she said a silent prayer of thanks that she had decided to bring it along. If she were going to donate blood, she preferred a worthier cause.

The oily substance she squeezed out of the plastic bottle onto her palm smelled terrible and felt worse on her skin, but it did what it promised on the container. The mosquitoes left her alone. Left her alone, but seemed to double their attack on Brian. Confused by his actions, Kelly watched him put on his down jacket, turn up the collar and tightly tie the hood. Undaunted, the mosquitoes simply concentrated on his exposed hands and face as he went about setting up camp. Finally her curiosity got the best of her. "Why don't you use your repellent?"

She couldn't understand his mumbled answer. "What?" she prodded.

He turned to face her. Slowly, carefully pronouncing each word, he said, "I forgot to bring any."

Kelly caught her lip to keep the one-upsmanship smile she felt hovering from becoming a big, flashing grin. She succeeded with the smile but was unable to keep the amusement from her eyes. Plucking the repellent from the rock where she had placed it, she tossed the plastic bottle to him. "Please ... be my guest."

His eyes flashed a silent thanks. When he had finished applying the lotion he looked up and said, "I have to admit I'm impressed."

"And well you should be." She caught her knee with her hands and leaned back against a rock.

He lobbed the lotion back to her. "You're not going to ask me why I'm impressed?"

"Something tells me I'd be better off leaving it to my own imagination. But I'll go for it. So tell me, just why are you impressed?"

"You had a perfect opportunity to slam me about forgetting repellent and yet you didn't."

"And here I thought you were going to say something nice about my athletic prowess."

A slow smile changed his expression to warm and responsive. "That, too," he said softly.

Something told her that a cantankerous Brian Robertson would be infinitely easier for her to handle than the one she had just glimpsed behind that smile. She busied herself returning the repellent to her pack. "It was nothing," she answered, hiding her sudden confusion with bravado.

When she looked up again, Brian was in the process of putting together his stove. She glanced at the sky, quickly calculating how much daylight remained. Her growling stomach would have to wait. Whatever time was left was better spent on photography.

When Brian's dinner had reached the point that it could be left alone to finish cooking, she asked him to stand on one of the rocky points reaching into the lake like fingers on an outstretched hand. As they waited, what she had hoped would happen did. The setting sun turned the sky a brilliant orange and the lake became a patchwork of gold and white. She shot him in silhouette, his hands resting comfortably in his pockets, his face turned in profile.

Symbolically it was the ideal photograph to tell the story of a man who had traded the gold of one world for another. A perfect cover shot, one that she had a feeling would turn out to be a particular favorite of hers. Slowly she lowered her camera and looked at Brian. For the first time, she wondered about him as a person apart from the superficial subject of her assignment. What had pushed him, what crises had occurred in his life that had made him walk away from such a promising career?

He turned and caught her staring at him. "All through?"

She blinked. "Pardon me?" And then realizing what he had asked, answered, "Oh...yes." Now that her work was finished for the day, her arms suddenly felt as heavy and useless as her legs. She walked the short distance back to their camp and laid her camera beside her pack to be tucked into her sleeping bag later when she went to bed. Keeping the camera above freezing was the only way to prevent static lines when she changed or advanced the film, should she want to go to work first thing in the morning.

As she reached for the side pocket that held part of her cache of food, Kelly saw that her hands were trembling. She had realized her body was operating on reserves, but she'd had no idea those reserves had gotten so low. When her shaking hands couldn't function well enough to open the foil pouch of freeze-dried apples, she used her teeth. As the package tore, a heady aroma hit her nostrils, making her mouth water. In her haste she fumbled and dropped the package, spilling the contents on the slab of granite beside her. Not even bothering to brush it off, she popped one of the cinnamon-spiced apple slices into her mouth. Her eyes closed as she chewed, her teeth making a satisfying crunching sound on apples that because of their special processing no longer even remotely resembled the real juicy thing. She breathed a contented sigh. Steak and potatoes had never tasted as good.

"Hungry?" Brian queried, stepping past her.

Kelly looked up at him. She shook her head. "I've

passed hungry. I'm to the point now that if it hops, crawls, slithers or slinks anywhere near me, I'll eat it." His laugh, wonderfully deep and warm, surprised her. It wasn't a sound she had expected to come from him; it was, in fact, a radical contradiction to the image of Brian Robertson she had formed in her mind. With a laugh like that, he could hardly be the humorless oaf she thought him. Obviously she would have to cut another facet on the stone that she had pictured him to be.

"As I remember, most of this dehydrated stuff tastes as if it could fall into any one of those categories." He gave his simmering dinner a quick stir. "If you're brave enough to chance some of this questionable concoction," he said, indicating the stew cooking in front of him, "I'm willing to share."

Kelly started to protest that it wasn't necessary for him to share his food. She had brought plenty of her own, after all. But just then the wind shifted slightly, and the most incredible smell drifted her way. "Are you sure you have enough?" she asked over the sound of her growling stomach.

"If not, we'll open something else."

She was too tired and too hungry to let the fact that she was supposed to be angry with him stop her from eating his food. "Thanks," she said, taking her mess kit out of her pack and going over to sit beside him. When he glanced up at her, she purposely met his gaze. "How come you're being so nice to me all of a sudden?" she asked.

He gave her a lopsided grin. "Afraid I'm going to drug you and then sneak off?"

"Now that your mention it."

He turned back to the stew. "Maybe it's just my way of saying I'm sorry for the way I behaved earlier."

She thought about his peace offering for a minute. "Well," she finally said, "considering the circumstances, it sure beats sending flowers."

Brian reached for her metal cup and began ladling stew into it. "I guess if you're going to turn nice on me," she went on, "then I have to come clean and admit there are apologies due you, too."

"Oh?"

"I'm not the photographer you were expecting."

Handing her the cup of stew, Brian began dishing up his own. "I see," he said softly. He paused a minute to look at a still-shriveled carrot, wondering if he had given the vegetables enough water and cooking time to recapture their moisture and become tender.

Kelly watched him. It was suddenly very important to her that Brian did not get the wrong impression. "Substitute is not necessarily synonymous with second-rate, you know. I'm very good at what I do. Just because I've never done anything quite like this before doesn't mean that I won't do it well."

"Why didn't you tell me this earlier?"

"Think about that a minute."

He did and after a while nodded. "I see what you mean. I didn't give you much choice, did I?"

She took a bite of stew. Although it was not completely done—the carrots were chewy, the peas on the tough side—she would have ranked it right up there with any meal she had ever eaten in Phoenix's Grande Maison restaurant. "My compliments to the chef," she managed to mumble between bites, deciding it was best to put their conversation back on more neutral ground.

He bowed his head in acknowledgment. "It was nothing, mam'selle."

"Oh, but you're far too modest, *monsieur*," she

playfully returned. "Look how far I've come just for the opportunity to partake of this sumptuous meal. What greater testimonial could you desire?"

"How about an offer to do the dishes?"

"I walked right into that one." She started to get up, but he reached out and put his hand on her arm.

"It can wait," he said. "First, why don't you tell me just who you are since you're not who I originally thought you were."

"Except for the award-winning-nature-photographer part, the rest of what I told you was the truth."

"You really are Phil's sister?"

"The youngest of his two sisters."

Brian thought a moment. "When we were roommates I remember Phil talking a lot about his family, but not about a sister named Kelly."

"How about one named Kathleen?"

Dawning filled his eyes. "Kathleen the Horrible? The Terror of Talman High School?"

"Ah, I see you have heard of me," she said dryly. "In my own defense, I think it behooves me to add that being called the Terror of Talman High School was an affectionate nickname coined and used by only a few very close friends."

"As I remember it," Brian went on, his eyes hooded in concentration, "Phil said the principal called you that at some sort of assembly in front of the whole school. And that you were fit to be tied about it."

She shot him a disgusted look. "You must be terrific at trivia games. Like I said . . . a few close friends. When you spend enough time in someone's office, you're bound to get to know them pretty well after a while."

"What could you possibly have done to earn a name like that?"

"Which time?"

"There was more than one?"

"There were more than a dozen. My particular favorite was the one that got me in the most trouble." She stared down at her outstretched legs. In high school her bids for attention had ranged from the ridiculous to the sublime. "The school officials insisted there weren't enough funds to let the swimming team have a bus for a meet across town, but I knew—because I was going with one of the guys on the team—that the football squad was being taken to the same school later that night. In a flush of youthful indignation, I took all the wires from the engine compartment of the bus and didn't return them until the next morning."

"I can see where something like that might have made a few people testy."

"To put it mildly. I had no idea what a can of worms I would open with that particular stunt. Special meetings were called by everyone from the athletic boosters club to the PTA, all of them demanding to know why the football team received preferential treatment. My notoriety didn't do a thing for me when it came to making my punishment any easier, though. I had to spend every afternoon for an entire month cleaning up the school yard."

"I'll bet if your punishment had been left up to the football team, you would have been on yard duty for the rest of the year."

She reached up to toss her braid back over her shoulder. "Needless to say, that was the last time I ever went out with that particular boyfriend."

Brian stood and stretched. While they'd been talking, the sky had steadily darkened until all that remained was a blanket of stars. "I'm sure there was another one waiting to take his place."

"Ah, flattery. My favorite form of repartee." She sighed. "But it was not to be . . . not in high school, at least. Once you get a reputation for being a rabble-rouser, guys think you're fun to know, but social suicide to date." She stifled a yawn. She felt like a cat sated with cream, her stomach full. All she could think about was curling up somewhere and going to sleep.

"If you started walking on the wild side in high school, I shudder to think what you were like by the time you were in college."

This time she did yawn. "Pretty tame actually. I took a class in photography in my freshman year because it looked like an easy A. After that, I was so tied up taking or printing pictures, I had little time for anything else."

"Not even boyfriends?"

Kelly's eyelids had closed; purposely she forced them open again, knowing that without concentrated effort she would be sound asleep within seconds. Readjusting herself so that she sat straighter and less comfortably, she answered him. "There was only one boyfriend who was anywhere close to being serious, and he was an on-again-off-again kind of thing. His name was Eric Warner. . . . He wanted to be a war correspondent." A sad smile curved her mouth. She looked down at her outstretched legs and brushed the dust from her knees. "It was a strange experience for me, the world's number-one pacifist, to be around someone who was terrified there wouldn't be any wars left by the time he graduated." Afraid she had given the wrong impression about the man she had once loved, she added, "It wasn't that Eric was a warmonger...he just craved some excitement in his middle-class life. I don't think he had any real idea what war was actually all about."

Her voice softened as she dipped into seldom-spoken memories. "He thought we would make a great team. I'd take the pictures, he'd write the story. It didn't faze him or in the least discourage him that I didn't want to photograph people being killed. He said I'd toughen up, even get used to it in time." She glanced up at Brian but with the starlight behind him and his face in shadow, she couldn't see his expression. "Can you imagine anyone thinking you would get used to something like that?"

Kelly didn't bother to add that she and Eric had been together almost her entire four years at college, or that when he finally found his war in a Central American country, he was killed the week after he arrived.

"No...I can't." As he answered, Brian started cleaning up the mess from dinner. "But then I was raised in a household where we were expected to capture insects and return them to the out-of-doors unharmed."

"Hey," Kelly protested, noticing Brian scraping out a cup. "That's supposed to be my job." She made a halfhearted attempt to get up to help him.

"Stay put," he commanded. "You can do it twice tomorrow."

Feeling as she did, she decided it was foolish to argue. "Now that I've bared my soul to you," she said, pausing for another yawn. "It's your turn to tell me something about Brian Robertson."

He hesitated, as if carefully considering her request. "What would you like to hear?"

"For starters, I'm curious how you rose to the top of Amercoast as fast as you did." Whether she could get him to talk candidly about himself, at least enough for her to see a glimpse of the man hidden behind the public facade, could be a determining factor in the quality of the work she turned in.

Brian snorted. "You've chosen an incredibly boring subject. Are you sure you wouldn't rather hear about my wild and wicked college years?"

Kelly shook her head. If Phil had told her the truth about the time Brian spent at college, it had consisted of days equally divided among the library, classroom and dorm. Hardly the kind of scintillating listening material she needed to keep her awake or give her any insight into the man. "Why don't we save 'wild and wicked' for tomorrow's campfire chat?"

Reluctantly, unable to understand why anyone who wasn't remotely involved would be interested in hearing how someone else had climbed a corporate ladder, he began. He told her about being recruited directly out of college and the tough beginning years when he felt as if he was just another steer in the junior executive barnyard—struggling to find a way out, constantly shuffling for position.

As Kelly listened, she valiantly waged a losing battle with fatigue, periodically pulling herself together enough to ask an astute question, encouraging him to go on with his story.

When Brian reached the point in his abbreviated version of the life and times of the boy wonder of banking at which he had to decide whether or not to tell Kelly about Paula, he paused and heard the unmistakable sounds of heavier than normal breathing. Shifting closer, he bent low to study her face. His own became suffused with a grin when he realized she had fallen asleep.

He unsnapped the hood from his parka, folded it and put it behind her head before he finished cleaning the campsite. When the dishes were finished and everything was ready for them to go to bed, he gently nudged Kelly to wake her. She moaned and tried to snuggle closer to the rock.

Brian glanced over to the sleeping bag he had taken from her pack and laid out across from his. He was sure there were personal things she would want to take care of before going to bed, but he was just as sure that she would have a hard time waking up enough to do them. Deciding there was nothing that couldn't wait for morning, he sat down in front of her and took off her boots.

*My God, no wonder she's exhausted,* he thought in amazement. He held her boots, one in each hand, calculating their weight. He guessed them to be nearly five pounds apiece. He looked closer at the heavy soles and full leather tops. They were beautifully made and sturdy enough to protect her from anything short of an avalanche...far more boot than she needed.

He turned them over again, noting their careful stitching. They reminded him of the pair of boots he had saved money from his paper route to buy when he was a teenager. When his father had discovered his plan, he had insisted on accompanying Brian to the store. As gently and as patiently as he could, his father had explained why Brian should not buy the boots he'd had his heart set on. Telling him that every pound he carried on his feet was equal to ten on his back, his father had finally made him understand how something as beautiful as the boots he had saved so long to buy could hold the potential for considerable misery.

Hefting Kelly's boots again, Brian shook his head. She might as well be carrying a pack loaded with an extra hundred pounds of rocks. He dropped the boots and moved back, letting the glow of the newly risen moon shine on her so that he could see her more clearly.

With her usually flashing eyes closed and her expression guileless and unguarded, she looked strangely vulnerable. She had touched a part of him long dormant...the boy who had stayed up nights to feed orphaned baby robins...the teenager who had, for a year, given up his other friends so that he could be with one who was dying of leukemia. It had been such a long time since he had felt the need to reach out to someone that he had assumed the need was no longer a part of him. Why had it come back now? And why with Kelly Stewart?

His hand moved to touch the tawny-colored braid that lay across her shoulder like a thick silken cord. Staring at her as if somehow his answer might magically appear if he looked long enough, he noticed a muscle twitch at the corner of her mouth. She frowned. Her hand came up and bumped into his. She pushed him away.

"So," he said softly. "Even in sleep you would hold me at arm's length." And then he understood a portion of his fascination with her. She was the first person in years who had stood up to him. By doing so she had insisted that he consider her an equal. Who he was or had been meant absolutely nothing to her. They could communicate; they could become friends without the suffocating rules and social mores of the life he had left in Chicago.

There were times like these when Brian felt as if he had not truly escaped by quitting; he had only unlocked the door. He had yet to see it swing open or to walk free.

A soft cry brought his attention back to Kelly. He looked at her and saw the utter exhaustion that had put her in such a deep sleep. Since discovering the burden she carried on her feet all day, he was more than a little red-faced that he had even insinuated she wasn't fit enough to keep up with him. And not only had she kept up, but she also could have gone on when he would have stopped to rest.

Brian slipped an arm underneath Kelly's knees and one across her back and then gently lifted her. She was remarkably light for her size. He smiled. Obviously much of her size was illusionary. To someone who had never seen her at all, someone who had only been on the receiving end of one of her tirades on the other end of a phone, she probably seemed six feet tall.

He tried to remember particulars of conversations he and Phil had had in college about "Kathleen," but the details were sketchy and confused with stories of other members of the family. After they had spent all those years as roommates it seemed wrong that they didn't know more about each other. But then it wasn't the years they had spent together that had lacked anything, it was what he had allowed to happen afterward. He had much to make up, friends to see, nieces and nephews to form bonds with, a family to hold close again.

# 4

THE NEXT MORNING Kelly awoke to the smell of cooking oatmeal. With her eyes open wide in confusion, she stared at her surroundings. The where and why returned on daintily shod feet, the who came back wearing cleats. Her heart gave an uncomfortable lurch when she saw Brian standing by the lake, bare to the waist, his thick brown hair glistening with moisture. She let out a disgusted sigh. Give her a half-naked man who looked like an Adonis and she forgot all about how ill-tempered he could be. How easily her veneer of being "above such things,"—the very line she used on Phil every time he tried to fix her up with a date—disappeared when she was faced with someone who looked like Brian Robertson?

Someone who looked like Brian Robertson? Fat chance. There wasn't another person she knew who looked remotely like him. Oh, there were a few movie stars who came close, but then the right camera angles could do wonders for someone's profile. Because she had tried, she knew that there wasn't a camera angle that would make Brian look less than breathtaking.

Glancing around the campsite, she noticed that he had already packed his sleeping bag, which meant that once he had eaten and cleaned up, he would be ready to go. A sense of panic struck. She turned over on her back. An involuntary moan rumbled deep in her chest. Never, not once in all her twenty-seven years, could she remember feeling this sore. Not even after the forty-eight-hour skate-a-thon her niece had talked her into participating in two years ago to raise money for the children's wing of St. Anthony's Hospital had she felt this bad.

Tentatively she tried to raise her legs and was amazed when they responded to her commands. Again and then once more, she went through rudimentary motions of movement, frantically trying to work out some of the stiffness before Brian returned for his breakfast. After she had gone on and on the night before about her physical fitness, to ask him to slow the pace now would mean biting off a larger dose of pride than she wanted to swallow. Would she never learn to keep her mouth shut?

By the time Brian started back up the hill she had worked herself into a sitting position. She watched him cover the distance between them with a long-legged, easy stride. He had put on a red plaid shirt, tucked it into his jeans and casually rolled back the sleeves. She tried to imagine him in a tailored suit, sitting behind a desk and was surprised when she couldn't.

He noticed her looking at him and smiled. "Good morning," he said, his voice caressing her. "Did you sleep well?"

She returned his smile, trying to remember all the reasons she should ignore the way he made her feel special by simply asking an ordinary question. "Like a log—I don't think I moved once all night."

"Neither did I, and I'm afraid I'm going to pay for it today. I feel like an arthritic old man after a night on a park bench. There are places hurting on my body I didn't know could get sore."

It was an interesting observation to contemplate,

especially for anyone with an active and creative imagination. She felt a blush warm her cheeks. "I'm not sure I can come up with an appropriate answer to that," she stammered.

Brian laughed aloud. "I'm talking about the back of my head, Kelly. I must have adjusted my pack wrong yesterday because I have a sore spot where the frame comes up behind my neck."

"Oh...." To say anything more would perpetuate an already embarrassing situation, so she changed the subject. "Will we be covering the same kind of country today?"

His eyes held a knowing gleam. "Pretty much. But the hike will be easier. We don't have as far to go and more time to do it in."

"You don't have to slow down on my account." What was she saying?

"I'm not," he assured her. "Each day's hike is planned around a place I picked to spend the night. Some days that will mean walking all day, others for only a couple of hours."

"Oh...I see." Then he hadn't been testing her after all, simply sticking to a schedule. She wiggled a little farther out of her bag. Seeing her jeans-clad legs reminded her of something she wanted to tell him. "I'm not sure in what order I should say this, but...thanks for putting me to bed last night...."

"It was my pleasure," he said.

"And I want to apologize for falling asleep while you were telling me your life story."

"Forget it. Other than the snoring occasionally interrupting the telling, your falling asleep hardly slowed me down."

A grin tugged at the corners of her mouth. "Well, as long as I didn't stop the soliloquy entirely—"

"And you needn't worry that you missed anything. Not only did I note at what point you nodded
off, but I made sure I saved the best part—the year I
spent in Europe studying the financial structures of
Swiss banks—for tonight."

*"Wonderful!"* she groaned. "Swiss banks are my
all-time favorites."

He threw his sleeping pad at her. She caught it,
stared at it a moment then succumbing to temptation, wiggled back down in her bag and tucked the
rolled-up pad beneath her head, to use as a pillow.

Brian ignored her as he went about dividing the
oatmeal into two portions. When he had finished
adding a sprinkling of brown sugar and cinnamon,
he poured the coffee. Picking up one oatmeal and
one coffee, he started toward her. Several feet short
of her reach, he stopped and set her breakfast on a
flat rock, stood back and smiled. "It's ready when
you are."

Kelly stared at him. "I'm beginning to understand
how you operate, Robertson. Hit 'em in their weaknesses."

His answering smile personified innocence. "Remember, you're on cleanup this morning," he said,
returning to his own food.

Grumbling, Kelly wiggled back out of her bag.
When she was seated at the makeshift table she
brought the coffee up to her nose and breathed
deeply. Opening her eyes, she saw Brian looking at
her, an inexplicable expression on his face. She met
his gaze a few seconds longer. "If there is something socially unacceptable about my appearance
this morning," she said formally, "it would be extremely impolite of you not to find a gracious way
to tell me."

"I was simply noticing how the sunlight made your hair look like a halo."

She flashed him an impish grin. "It's the back-lighting, a trick we photographer types employ all the time. Properly used, it can make the most monstrous child look angelic."

"Or an already incredibly beautiful woman even more so," he said softly.

When Kelly realized he wasn't teasing her she didn't know how to answer him. Nonplussed, she hid her confusion by concentrating on her oatmeal. "This is good," she remarked between bites, seeking to hide her feelings in the mundane.

Actually she hated oatmeal. It made her think of Oliver Twist and orphanages.

"The only time I ever eat cooked cereal is when I'm backpacking," he said.

"And how often is that?" When he didn't immediately answer, she glanced up to see if he had heard her.

"Not as often as I would like."

"Oh? How often?" she asked, suddenly suspicious.

"In the past fifteen years?"

"Fifteen is a good number."

"Twice."

*"Twice!"* she choked. "You had the audacity to browbeat me about being a beginner when you've only gone backpacking twice in the past fifteen years?"

"I'm not quite as green as it sounds, Kelly. There were at least thirty trips before that."

"If this isn't the kind of thing you do much anymore, why are you here now?"

"Getting off by myself seemed like a good way to

try to figure out who I am and what I want to do with the rest of my life. As for doing it in California...this particular trip was one my father planned that he never got to take. I decided it was time that I went for him."

"This trip obviously means a lot to you. I don't understand how you ever let Phil talk you into having someone tag along."

Brian smiled. "I'm still not sure; but then I'm not surprised, either. Phil has always been able to talk me into doing things no one else ever could."

"You too, huh? I didn't want to be here any more than you wanted me."

"And now that you are?"

If he had asked her that yesterday, her answer would have come quickly. This morning, she wasn't so sure. "First tell me how you feel about my being here."

He hesitated, bringing his coffee up to his mouth, using it as a prop to delay answering. He had a gut feeling it would scare her if she knew how quickly and completely he had changed his mind about having her along. He sipped at the now-cool liquid, then poured the remainder onto the ground. "Since I will have another month to go it alone after you're gone, having you along for a few days isn't the total disruption I thought it would be in the beginning."

"Thanks...I think."

"And you?"

She smiled. "I'll let you know tonight. I figure by then I'll know which Brian Robertson is the real one."

"I guess that's fair, all things considered." He looked at his watch. "How long do you think it will take you to get ready?"

Kelly thought about the process she would like to go through—a long soak in a hot tub, wash her hair, facial, steam room, massage, sauna.... "Two hours?"

"How about fifteen minutes?"

"Half an hour?"

"You're on the clock."

NEARLY THIRTY MINUTES LATER Kelly stiffly made her way back up the hill from the lake to their campsite. Despite her concentrated efforts to walk normally, she could not hide the limp caused by the pain that radiated from her feet up her legs. Yesterday she had been aware that blisters were forming, she had felt the sore spots at her heels and toes. But she hadn't been prepared for what she saw this morning when she pulled off her socks to wash them and her underwear. Only her arches and the very tops of her feet were totally free of the huge water-filled bumps.

She considered telling Brian but when she realized there was nothing he could do, she decided against it. If she had made it through yesterday, she could make it today and then the next. Besides, what real choice did she have? It wasn't as if she could catch the next taxi home.

Thank heaven she was blessed with a high pain threshold, an asset nurtured and developed early in life when she discovered her brothers wouldn't let her play with them if she cried when she got hurt.

Brian looked up from the book he was reading. "Are you all right?" he said, noticing her limp.

She forced a smile. "I'm fine. Just a little stiff."

He closed the book and laid it in his pack. "There's something I've been meaning to ask you—"

"Shoot."

"Do you really lift weights?"

"Twice a week when I'm busy, three times when I'm not."

"Do you have any long-range plans, uh, I mean...."

"I know what you mean. You want to know if I'm planning to enter body-building contests." It seemed everyone asked her that question sooner or later.

"Well...are you?"

Slowly she turned so that her back was to him. Then, when in position, she struck a classic body-building pose. Twisting slightly so that she could look at him over her shoulder, she smiled and winked. "What do you think? Would I make it?"

Brian folded his arms across his chest. "As I recall, the contestants usually wear less clothes when they pose." He shrugged. "I really don't feel I can judge properly under these conditions."

Shaking her head sadly, she turned to face him. "And here I thought you were a man of imagination."

Her words and the thoughts they provoked sucked the wind out of him. He could imagine all too well how she would look without the flannel shirt and snug jeans. From the moment they had met, he had noted the gentle swelling of her breasts and the sensual curve of her hips. And then there was the wondrous way she had felt in his arms when he carried her to her sleeping bag the night before. "I think we had better leave my imagination out of this," he finally said.

Realizing how unintentionally provocative she had sounded, Kelly stammered an answer. "Listen...I didn't...what I mean is—"

Brian reached for her hand, which still grasped her wet laundry. "Kelly, you must stop taking everything I say so seriously. I've never seen anyone blush as easily as you do."

"Just another of my many endearing traits." Her short laugh came out strangely high-pitched as she struggled with nervousness. "How do you think I'll go over as Kelly the Blushing Body Builder?"

He released her hand and bent to pick up his pack. When he looked at her again, his eyes sparkled in amusement. "I assume that will be tattooed in an appropriate place?"

"How about matching places?" She flashed him an impish grin.

He laughed aloud. "Ah, sweet Kelly. I'm beginning to think you're better medicine than a mountain ever could be."

To hide the inordinate swell of pleasure his words provoked, Kelly moved past Brian and busied herself putting the biodegradable soap she had used for her laundry into her pack. When the last of her dishes were also put away she hung her socks and underwear from the straps and cords that crisscrossed her pack. She had to smile at the odd juxtaposition of gray wool and fuchsia silk and lace.

IT WAS LATE MORNING before they returned to the subject of weight lifting. Kelly welcomed the chance to think about something other than her pain-racked feet. With each step she silently said a prayer for the numbness she had experienced the day before to return. Instead, only stronger and stronger flashes of agony shot up her legs.

Forcing herself to concentrate on Brian's questions and then on her answers, she explained how important it was that she work out on a regular basis to stay strong enough to lug her own equipment around. Not only was it expensive to hire photographers' assistants, but also good ones weren't plentiful in Phoenix. She was describing a particularly heavy lighting setup that normally took two people to carry when Brian stopped short in front of her and she almost ran into him.

"There it is," he said, wonder in his voice. "Isn't it beautiful?"

Kelly peered around his shoulder. Her mouth dropped open. In front of them, cutting directly across their path, a wildly rushing river cascaded down the mountainside. "My God," she breathed. "What are we going to do?"

"First we're going to stop here for a minute or two while we tell each other what a dynamite postcard this scene would make. Then we're going to cross over to the other side and continue on our way."

"We're going to cross that raging river? How?"

"Kelly...that 'river' is hardly big enough to be called a stream."

Her chin rose. "In Arizona, *that* is a river."

"In *California*, it's only a step above a trickle. And in case you haven't noticed, we happen to be in California."

She folded her arms across her chest. "Just how do you propose we get across this trickle?"

He grabbed her hand and gave her a tug. "Come on, I'll show you."

She caught her breath and swallowed the cry of pain that his exuberance caused as she tried to keep her balance. When they came to the stream's edge, Brian told her to take off her boots. She backed up and stared at him. "You can't be serious. Look at that current. One wrong step and we'll be swept down the mountainside."

He reached for her chin, then turned her head so that her gaze followed the water's path. "Should that unlikely event occur, the farthest we could possibly be 'swept' is that pool down there, twenty feet away at the most."

"All right," she grumbled, giving in because it was her only option. They certainly weren't going to turn back, and she hadn't the stomach to climb up the mountain to try to find the headwaters. She moved away from him, seeking a place to sit while she unlaced her shoes. As she took off her boots and then her socks, she was forced to admit that she was very close to reaching her unusually high threshold of pain. Purposely she did not look at her feet, concentrating instead on rolling up her pant legs and tying the laces of her boots together so that she could carry both of them with one hand.

Acutely conscious of every pebble, Kelly carefully walked up to the water's edge to stand beside Brian. He turned and eyed her. His face changed from openness to a frown. "Are you absolutely sure that you're all right?"

She took a deep breath. "What you see on my face, Robertson, is unadulterated fear. Not a pretty sight, is it?"

He shook his head. "I'm beginning to think you chose the wrong side of the camera for your career." His gaze left her face. As he focused on an object behind her, the frown returned, except this time it was one of frustration and was accompanied by a lamenting groan. Suddenly he reached up and took something from her pack.

"Brian, what is it?" she asked, instinctively recoiling, positive he was rescuing her from imminent attack by some heinous creature.

"This!"

The way he'd said, "This," she was sure he was about to produce something even worse than she had first imagined. Instead what he showed her was a fistful of fuchsia lace and silk.

"Every time I look at you I see these," he muttered, opening a side pocket on her pack and stuffing them inside. "To put it mildly, my sweet Kelly, they are driving me slightly crazy."

"Those little bitty things?"

He shook his head. "The amazing thing is that you can ask me that with such wide-eyed innocence."

"I can't believe you haven't seen women's underwear before."

He stared at her long and hard. "I think we've pursued the subject of your underwear as far as it should go. Now give me your hand."

His voice, the way he looked at her, his words, all combined to send a warning shiver down her spine. His reply had been as intimate as a physical caress and had left her as shaken. She placed her hand into his outstretched one.

"Now watch where I put my feet and then when I move, put yours in the same spot. If a rock will hold me, it will certainly hold you." He had become cool and businesslike again. When he turned to study the rushing water, she wondered if she had imagined what had just passed between them.

Carefully he tested the first foothold and then took a step. "Brian—wait," she cried, stopping him from going farther.

He turned to look at her, one foot on the shore,

the other submerged, water coming up to touch his calf.

"Don't take such big steps," she said softly.

He glanced down at the distance he had covered and then at her legs. "Sorry," he replied, moving his foot to a flat rock closer to the shore. But instead of taking a second step, he turned back to her again, his eyes filled with compassion. "Why don't I just take our packs to the other side and then come back and carry you across?"

It was on the tip of her tongue to agree, but pride wouldn't let her. "Don't be silly...I've just been giving you a hard time. I'm not really afraid."

"Are you sure?"

"I'm positive." She made her mouth turn up at the corners in what she hoped was the semblance of a confident smile.

"All right, then...let's go."

Kelly nodded. Concentrating on the rock that had held Brian's foot, she stepped forward. The shock of the freezing water hit her, stealing her breath away. Dizzying waves of pain blurred her vision. She began to sway as she desperately fought to keep from passing out. Her heart pounded in her ears; her chest tightened convulsively.

Blindly she followed him as he gently tugged her forward. Twice she tried to cry out for him to stop, but no words came from her mouth. The water that inched up her legs was so cold she could not distinguish it from heat and imagined for an instant that she had been plunged into fire.

Because it was a stream they crossed and not a river, they were quickly on the other side. "See," Brian said, as he stepped onto the opposite shore. "That wasn't so—" The words ceased the instant he saw her. "Kelly?" he breathed. "Kelly...?" The whisper became a fearful demand. "What's the matter with you?"

Tears coursed her cheeks as silent sobs shook her shoulders. "My...my...f-f-f..." she stammered.

Brian pulled her on shore. He held her by the arms, frantically searching her face. "Kelly, I don't understand. What is it?"

She tried to catch her breath. "My...f-f-feet," she at last managed to gasp.

Brian stepped back to look at her feet. When he couldn't immediately see what was wrong, he knelt down, and then he understood. Large pieces of skin torn from ruptured blisters hung from her feet like tattered bits of cloth. Unreasoning anger shot through him. Why hadn't she told him this was happening to her? Why in the hell hadn't he guessed?

Afraid of what he might say, he said nothing. Instead he stood and flung off his pack and then removed hers. Picking her up, he walked several yards down the trail until he found a rock that was only slightly lower than his waist. He sat her on the rock. Opening his shirt, he gently reached for her feet and placed them against the warmth of his chest.

Kelly swiped at her face with the back of her hand and tried to control her tears. "You don't have to do that," she got out. "I'm okay now."

"Shut up!" he barked in reply.

Her head snapped up. She glared at him. "Don't you dare...tell me to shut up...you big—"

"What's the matter?" he said, his voice low and dangerous. "Can't think of something suitably nasty to call me? Well, I have a few choice words for you, starting with stupid."

A fresh wave of tears filled her eyes. She bit her lip to try to prevent them from spilling over her lashes, but that had about as much effect as trying to stop a rainstorm with an umbrella. Unable to bear facing his anger any longer, she dropped her gaze to her lap. Since she had been a small child, she'd been at her most vulnerable when she was hurt...physically or mentally. It was a time more than any other when she needed uncritical, loving arms around her. Without someone to provide that special care, she would inevitably build an enormous, unreasoning case for feeling sorry for herself. That would usually result in a crying jag, which always left her with a stuffed-up nose and one dilly of a headache.

"Damn you, Brian Robertson," she choked, her chin quivering. Before she was even aware of what she was going to say next, it was out. "I need to be hugged, not screamed at."

Brian looked at her tear-streaked face, her eyes filled with hurt, her mouth pursed in pain. Could a heart really melt? If so, his just had. Tenderly he took her feet from his chest and reached for her. Picking her up in his arms, he cradled her against him as she forlornly sobbed the required tears necessary to bring her back to normal again. He pressed his lips to the top of her head while he crooned unintelligible calming phrases and wondered how big a bruise her camera lens would leave on his ribs.

When Kelly's sobs had turned to occasional sighs, she said, "You can put me down now." Brian returned her to her rocky perch. Embarrassed by her emotional outburst, she stared at the ground as she worked to clear the traces of tears from her face with trembling hands. "I owe you an apology," she began, struggling to sound normal. "I'll bet in your worst imaginings you never thought you'd wind up with a hysterical female."

Brian pulled a handkerchief from his pocket and began wiping her face. "You're right," he agreed. "But then, if you recall, I had no idea there was even the possibility of a female traveling companion."

"I feel like I've let the entire women's movement down."

He bit back a smile. "I wasn't aware that you were a spokesperson."

"Every woman is...all the time...in everything she does."

"That's quite a burden. No wonder your feet gave out."

"I should have known."

"What? That I would give you a hard time about chastising yourself for doing something *human*? Since when are blisters a sexist issue?"

"Blisters aren't. Crying about them is."

Brian cupped her chin with his hand, bringing it up and making her look at him. "Kelly," he said softly, "there's only one way I could irrefutably prove to you that I might behave the same way under the same circumstances. I think you would agree that to do so would be going to extremes to prove a point." He waited to see acceptance for what he had said reflected in her eyes. When he was satisfied that she understood what he was trying to tell her, he went on. "Now, since it looks like we're going to be spending more than the couple of days we had first thought in each other's company, I think it would be a good idea if we both took the chips off our shoulders and relaxed. You can stop trying to prove you're as tough as I am—" he smiled "—and I can stop trying to prove that you aren't."

"Have you really been doing that?"

He nodded. "And I'm pretty damned embarrassed about it, too."

"As well you should be." A hint of a twinkle shone from her eyes.

Resting a hand on each of her knees, he leaned forward to press a kiss to her forehead. "Friends?"

"Yes," she answered. "I'd like that."

"Me too." He straightened. "Now stay put. I'll be right back."

He brought over their packs and leaned them against the rock where she sat. After a few minutes of searching, he found her parka and removed the hood, then did the same to his. Using the cords as laces, he fashioned a pair of slippers, one dark blue, the other bright red. "You won't be able to walk in them, but at least they'll keep your feet warm," he said, surveying his handiwork.

"They're charming. Maybe I'll start a new fad."

"With the marmots?"

"Hmm." She pretended to give the idea serious thought. "There are distinct possibilities here. Think of the profits—marmots have four feet."

Brian groaned. "Since you're obviously feeling better, I'm going to leave you and hike up the trail a little farther to see if I can find a place to set up camp."

She watched him walk away, could not stop watching him until he had disappeared behind a wall of granite. A tiny twinge of loss fluttered in her chest. She took a deep breath; it came out as a sigh.

To pass the time she concentrated on the majesty of her surroundings. As her gaze swept the ancient peaks, a sense of being truly and totally alone came over her. It was an alien feeling. And because it was so unknown and powerful and had taken her by such surprise, she was at first frightened. Uneasily she admitted that everything about this place intimidated her. It seemed so harsh and unforgiving. Even the pines that valiantly nudged past the tree line had grown twisted and gnarled for their efforts, as if they were being punished for not keeping that place. Sterile rocks had crevices that sheltered snow so old it had turned into miniglaciers. The streams and lakes were so cold they brought pain to those who would use their water. She could not understand Brian's love of this place or how he hoped to find the peace he sought here.

And then the most incredible thing happened. A yellow-and-black swallowtail butterfly flew past and landed on a patch of snow that still lingered in the shadowed depression of the rock beside her. The startling appearance of something so fragile in an environment seemingly intolerant of anything not its equal made Kelly catch her breath in surprise. Automatically she reached for her camera.

But it wasn't taking a photograph that consumed her thoughts as she looked at the sharply contrasting colors of butterfly and snow through the viewfinder. When she put the camera aside, she looked at the world around her differently. For the first time since entering these mountains she felt their majesty embrace her with a sense of wonder instead of fear. There was room here for the ephemeral, for that which was never meant to challenge eternity. The cascading stream lost its menacing sound and became merely the music of falling water on its way to create a river; the crisp wind became something to stimulate one instead of something to huddle against.

By the time Brian came back to get her, Kelly had almost settled her quarrel with what she had considered the inhospitability of the Sierra Nevada. While she still had not heard them call to her as Brian had, at least she no longer felt they wished her gone.

She avidly watched Brian's progress as he followed the trail back to her. Finally, unable to contain herself any longer, she loudly called out, "What did you find?"

He smiled. "It's a surprise."

She returned his smile, openly pleased to see him. "Well, I have a surprise for you, too." As he drew closer, she warned him. "Walk gently or you'll scare her."

"Her?"

"Look." She proudly pointed to the butterfly as if it had been her creation.

He gave the insect a cursory examination then glanced at Kelly, a twinkle in his eyes. "I'm glad to see she made it."

"And what is that supposed to mean?"

"We passed each other on the trail and I asked her to come up here to keep you company."

It was an indication of how her feelings had changed toward Brian that a part of her considered the possibility of what he told her being true. She decided to play along. "How thoughtful of you, kind sir." She gave him a tiny bow.

"'Twas a mere token of my deep feelings for the fair lady Kathleen." He bowed in return. "Now then, fair lady, may I show you to your quarters before that fine derriere of yours freezes and becomes permanently attached to that rock?"

"Again how kind of you." She inched forward to

slip down. "I had begun to notice a slight numbness setting in."

"What are you doing?"

"I'm going to get my tennis shoes out of my pack. I figured they would be easier—"

He placed his hands on either side of her on the rock and leaned so close they were almost nose to nose. "So that we understand each other right off— until your feet no longer look like raw meat, I'm in charge around here. I have no doubt that with your stubborn streak keeping you upright, you could make it part of the way before you keeled over from the pain, but when you finally did pass out and I had to carry you, I would have to carry dead weight. Now if we start out right in the first place, it will be a lot easier on me."

"You're exaggerating. There's no way I'm going to pass out. I've never passed out in my entire life. I'm not the type."

"Oh, no?" He backed away from her. "Step down."

She did. Despite doing so as gingerly as possible, excruciating pain shot up her legs, taking her breath away and making her sway dizzily. She reached for Brian.

"I don't think you realize just how badly you've messed yourself up with your little macho routine," he said gently, setting her back on the rock.

Kelly had never known a time when her body could not respond to her commands. Being virtually helpless put her in an uncomfortable position. She had not been totally dependent on anyone else for anything since leaving home. The implications were mind boggling.

Intuitively Brian reassured her. "In a couple of

days you'll be up and around again." He tucked a tendril of hair behind her ear. When he continued, there was a teasing quality to his voice. "As I figure it, there's only, say, a thirty or forty percent chance you won't heal properly and we'll have to set up a permanent residence here. But fear not, fair Kathleen, I shall be steadfast and remain by your side until you finally succumb to your terminal case of obstinacy."

"Oh, thanks. That certainly makes me feel better."

"Anytime I can be of help." As naturally as if they were longtime friends, he kissed her. It was only a quick meeting of their lips, with barely more pressure applied than that of a husband bussing his wife as he hurried off to work in the morning. But it was enough to bring a surge of response swelling throughout Brian's body. Stunned, he hid his reaction by turning his back to her and saying, "Hop on."

Kelly stared at his broad shoulders, her hand touching her lips, her eyes wide in surprise. She was glad he had turned and could not see how strongly she had been affected by his innocent kiss. She shook her head, trying to rid herself of the strange feelings traipsing around in her chest and exploding in her mind. Obviously being tired and hungry and injured had chipped away at her defenses and left her susceptible to ordinary men masquerading as gallant knights. There was no other logical reason for her to feel as she did. After all, it was only a kiss.

"I'm waiting," he said, snapping her out of her musing.

"But what about the packs?"

"I'll come back for them later."

She wiggled closer to him, wrapping her arms

around his neck as he caught her legs against his waist. When she was securely in place, he started walking. Nodding to the butterfly as they passed, he said, ''You can go now.''

The final thread of spun gold wove itself into their magical fabric of time at the top of the hill when the wings of black and yellow started to move at Brian's command. The butterfly rose and circled the couple once before disappearing. For an instant Kelly found herself believing that Brian had indeed summoned the tiny enchanted creature. Then her reasoning returned, and she decided even insects could get cold and that they would have sense enough to move on when that happened. It was only a coincidence that the two events had happened at the same time.

# 5

As KELLY WAITED once more for Brian's return, she thought about his kiss. She tried to analyze her reaction rationally, to put what she had felt into proper perspective. Every time she almost succeeded, she would remember the flood of warmth, the awakening ache. It was crazy. But then, all things considered, maybe it wasn't. He was the kind of man who could make a woman's heart beat faster simply by catching her eye in a crowded elevator. Why shouldn't she react as she had?

Purposely she made herself think of something else. Brian had left her in a meadow on a grassy mound where she could watch the trail he would be taking back into the valley. It also afforded her a sweeping view of the pines and lake. He had chosen an area just enough lower than the main trail that it was in the height of its brief spring. When Brian returned with the backpacks, she would put the macro lens on her camera and use her time here to take pictures of the wild flowers and perhaps pick up some extra money selling the photographs later to card and calendar publishers.

The harder she tried to concentrate on her surroundings and the technical aspects of capturing the pristine quality on film, the more often she cast furtive glances to the place where she expected Brian to appear. At last her efforts were rewarded, and he was there waving and calling her name. Her hand rose in return greeting. She no longer noticed the cold or felt lonely.

He covered the ground between them quickly, dropped their packs and came to stand in front of her. "Miss me?" he asked, his face flushed from the exertion, his eyes sparkling.

"Were you gone?"

"Ah, my sweet Kathleen. How am I ever going to work my way into your heart?"

"Feed me."

He laughed. "So that's the secret, is it?"

"It's one of the shortcuts."

"And the others?"

"Ah, my sweet Brian," she echoed, "would you have me lose my air of mystery?"

"Yes... I would." He reached for his pack and began rummaging around inside. "By the time we leave this place, I plan to know all there is to know about Kathleen Stewart."

"Kathleen *Maureen* Stewart."

He sat down in front of her, opened a small first-aid kit and reached for her foot. Kelly winced when he removed her makeshift slipper. "So talk to me, Kathleen Maureen Stewart. Tell me about yourself. Where you were born... what you dream about at night... your favorite movie stars."

She understood what he was doing. The trick was an old and honored one, used as effectively for extracting splinters from tiny fingers as cleaning pebbles from scrapped knees. Distract her by making her talk about herself and she wouldn't be so aware of what he was doing. But she considered herself a little too old to fall for a ploy used on children. "Brian... whatever it is you're planning to do, I'm sure I can handle it myself." She tried to pull her foot from his grasp. "You've been wonderful and I appreciate everything you've done for me, but—" She saw the stubborn set of his jaw and knew she was getting nowhere. "You're not listening to me, are you?"

He shook his head.

"I'm wasting my breath?"

This time he nodded.

"What if I told you that it embarrasses me to have you messing around with my foot?"

"I'm not 'messing around,' I'm medicating."

"Whatever! It's something I'd rather do for myself."

"Why?"

He wasn't going to give up easily. "I happen to think my feet are singularly unattractive, and I would prefer to keep them—"

He propped her heel against his thigh and looked at her. "Since I know it would be useless for me to argue how attractive your feet are or aren't, I'm not going to bother. But since I *am* going to take care of these blisters, you might as well lean back and relax."

"Brian, you're starting to get pushy again."

His answering smile was quick and devilish. "I'll return to warm and loving as soon as I've finished."

Damn! Her cheeks had started to burn again. One *slightly* suggestive comment and she flashed instant sunburn. She gave up trying to argue with him and relaxed her leg, letting her foot lie easily against the hard muscles of his thigh. After all, it wasn't as if she was in some stupid beauty contest and he was the judge. When she finished this assignment, they would probably never see each other again. "I was born in Phoenix and will probably die there," she began with a resigned sigh. "Unless, of course, I happen to expire prematurely in California."

"Not a chance." He took a small pair of scissors from the first-aid kit and began cutting loose skin. "How about movie stars?"

"Meryl Streep, Jessica Lange, Robert Redford, Harrison Ford—ouch!"

"Sorry. Go on."

"More movie stars?"

"No. Dreams."

She thought for a moment. Her dreams were personal. They were hidden away in a secret place she seemed to visit less and less frequently lately. It might feel good to take them out and dust them off. "I want to take pictures so spectacular they make people stop and look and then come back to look again."

"In any particular field?" He opened a tube, squeezed a yellow cream on his fingers then rubbed it onto her feet.

"Advertising."

Brian returned his first-aid kit to his pack and took out a pair of socks. The striped tops stopped just short of her knees. "So what's holding you back?" he said, his hands now familiarly cupping the backs of her calves.

"Phoenix is controlled by a half dozen photographers who have done the advertising work there for years and years. Just trying to get someone to look at my work has been a series of frustrations."

"Why don't you go to a city that's more open to new talent?"

Why indeed? "I have stock answers I drag out

whenever I ask myself that same question, but they're getting weaker every time I use them." She hesitated. She had never said out loud before what she was about to tell him. "I'm beginning to wonder if maybe it isn't easier to stay in Phoenix and have a hundred reasons for not succeeding than it would be to move somewhere else and have only one for failing."

"It sounds like the real enemy you're fighting is yourself."

"I keep thinking that one morning I'll wake up and know it's time to go for it, and I'll pack my bags and take off."

"And until then?"

"I'll work at what jobs I can get and learn my craft so well that when the momentous day finally does come, I'll be ready."

An emotion stirred inside Brian, one he hadn't felt since he had been a recruit learning the banking business. Kelly's dream made him remember the one he had once nurtured. To be the best, to rise further and faster than anyone in banking ever had before. When had the dream turned into a nightmare?

Kelly saw Brian drifting. "Sorry you asked me?" she teased.

He blinked away the soft focus of inner thought. "I wish you could walk."

"Tired of being stuck with me already?" She made her tone purposely light to hide the sudden, inexplicable hurt.

He ignored her question. "I would like to hold your hand and spend the afternoon leisurely walking around the lake with you." Long seconds passed before he continued. "I can't remember the last time I held anyone's hand and went for a walk."

"Well, at least you were half right in your choice of partners. I may not be able to walk, but I'm a toucher from way back. My nieces and nephews all think I can't cross the street unless someone is attached to me." She reached down and took his oversize hand into hers. The instant her fingers wrapped around his palm she knew she'd made a terrible mistake. The tension that had been developing between them since they had first exchanged angry stares yesterday morning quickly became a nearly tangible thing.

As Brian's hand slowly closed around hers, the contact set up a chain reaction of need and wanting. Suddenly the memory of her thighs resting around his waist and the feel of her breasts pressed against his back overwhelmed him. What in the hell was he thinking? Could he really be contemplating making love to Kelly Stewart—his best friend's sister?

He released her hand. "I'd better get some lunch in you," he said brusquely. "We can't let your body waste away while we're waiting for your feet to heal."

Kelly struggled with an overpowering, useless urge to flee. She understood the feeling that had passed between them. It was basic, universal...and one she wanted nothing to do with. Besides being grossly unprofessional, getting involved with Brian could lead to all kinds of complications. And the kind of complications that came with a man were definitely not ones she needed cluttering up her life right now. "I don't remember electing you chief cook and bottle washer," she said, forcing a lightness to her voice. "Why don't you let me prepare lunch while you take that walk by yourself?"

He needed to get away from her, to spend time thinking about what had just happened. "Have you ever put one of these stoves together before?"

"No, but mine still has its instructions. I'll manage."

He should stay, at least long enough to see that she didn't need him.

"Go on," she urged. "I'll be fine."

"You're sure?"

"Yes."

He stood. Looking back down at her, Brian realized that getting away for a while was the only way to keep what had started between them from going any further. What he needed was to go somewhere alone to think, to find a way to get his head back on straight before he did something really stupid. "All right," he said. "I won't be gone long." He started to walk away, then remembered something and came back. Withdrawing a shiny aluminum whistle from beneath his shirt, he tossed it to her. "If you need me, just whistle."

Kelly looped the cord over her neck. "So, you're an old movie fan."

He gave her a blank stare. "I'm afraid you've lost me."

"You mean you weren't intentionally quoting Lauren Bacall talking to Humphrey Bogart in—"

"There's something you don't understand about me, Kelly," he said slowly. "I can't converse intelligently about new movies, let alone old ones. The only films I've attended for the past ten years have been those premiered in Chicago for charity benefits. I own a television set but with the exception of the news, I can't remember the last time I watched it. I have lived such a myopic existence that in a party situation the only way I can sound reasonably well-rounded is if the general conversation never gets more complicated than the information I try to find the opportunity to glean weekly from *Time* or *Newsweek*. I have led a completely self-centered life—even to the exclusion of friends and family." He shoved his hands in his pockets. No longer able to look at the stunned expression in her eyes, he stared at the gently swaying grasses beside her. "I've come here to these mountains to try to find the man I used to be...." He let out a sigh. "I'm not sure what I'll do if I can't because I don't like the man I've become."

He turned and walked away, not waiting for a reply. As he neared the lake, the ground became spongy, and with each step tiny waves of water came up to lap against the soles of his boots. He stopped to slap at a mosquito and then turn up the collar of his shirt. Several hours had passed since he had last applied Kelly's repellent, enough time to encourage the more determined insects. The occasional bite would be enough to distract him and keep him from completely sinking into the mire of depression that hovered every time he thought of his life and how much he had wasted of it.

His unorthodox reaction to having Kelly around was confirmation of his fears that he was not ready to merge back into the "real" world. He desperately needed human contact, to have interaction with someone who had nothing to gain by knowing him and nothing to lose by not liking him. He had moved so long in the company of people who used others that he had almost forgotten what it was like anywhere else. Oh, he needed Kelly and what she could give him, all right. But she sure as hell didn't need someone like him.

AFTER TEN MINUTES of concentrated effort, the instructions in one hand, the stove parts in the other, Kelly smiled triumphantly at her fully assembled masterpiece, its shiny aluminum pot perched on top waiting her decision what to put inside. She started going through packages of freeze-dried and dehydrated food, finally settling on macaroni and cheese. Within a surprisingly short time, the bright orange concoction was ready.

She looked across the lake at Brian and then again at their steaming lunch. Even if he started back right then, the food would be cold by the time he arrived.

"What brilliant planning, you idiot," she grumbled, giving the macaroni another stir, trying to keep it from congealing into one large lump. A noodle stuck to her finger; she absently popped it into her mouth. Her stomach responded with a sound reminiscent of feeding time at the zoo. Glancing over at Brian, she carefully ran her finger around the inside of the pot, gathering onto her finger the sticky sauce that clung to the sides. Normally, macaroni and cheese was not something she would purposely choose to eat and she could have resisted nibbling without any effort—but this stuff was either exceptional or she was exceptionally hungry.

Soon an occasional dip for a single cheese-encrusted noodle turned into one moderate spoonful and then another. Before the meal had ever had any real chance to cool, she convinced herself she would be doing Brian a favor if she went ahead and ate what had already been prepared. That way, as soon as she saw him coming back, she could start something else and he, too, would have a fresh, hot meal. Nowhere in her reasoning did she stop to consider that she had used the last of the water accessible to her.

Later, when she saw Brian turn and start around the lake and realized just what she had done, she wished for a hole to open in the ground beside her big enough for her to crawl in and hide. She felt rotten. Once they had surmounted their rough beginnings, Brian had been nothing short of wonderful, consistently taking care of her needs first. And as soon as she had the chance to reciprocate, what had she done? She had behaved like someone who had learned her table manners at a trough.

Halfway around the lake Brian stopped and bent over, distracted by something on the ground. For long seconds she stared, trying to figure out what had caught his attention. *Oh, no,* she mentally groaned. *Please don't do that, Brian. Don't pick flowers for me; I don't deserve them.*

But he did. And as he drew closer, she could see the small bouquet of lavender and gold he held clutched in his hand. "Lunch ready?" he called out to her.

"Yes," she choked. "Sort of...or at least it once was."

"I know...I owe you an apology for being so late. I lost all track of time. Is everything ruined?"

"That depends on how you look at it."

Still several yards from her, he stopped. A puzzled frown drew his brows together. A quick glance around the campsite took in the empty pot, the incriminating spoon sticking out of it at a jaunty angle and a chagrined Kelly. "Got tired of waiting, did you?" he said, the frown becoming an easy grin.

"Got carried away with the tasting is closer to the truth. You know how it goes...one bite leads to another...and then another...and another...." She shrugged. "I'm really embarrassed about this."

He laughed. "I'll bet you are. Here." He handed her the flowers. "Hold these while I get some water." He was still smiling when he returned with their jugs, took a tin out of his pack and dropped a tablet into each of the plastic containers.

"Why did you do that? Surely the water here can't be polluted."

"Sadly enough, it is. And from what I learned at the ranger station the other day, the experts are afraid it's going to be like this from now on."

"How can that be? I thought a lake would recover if given enough time."

"Usually that's true. But not here. At least not anymore. It's gone beyond a simple problem confined to a single area. The animals in this region have become infected with this new bacteria. They're the ones that have become the carriers. Consequently, even the most isolated free-flowing stream is no longer safe."

"But I didn't put anything in the water I used last night."

"I did it for you."

Kelly shook her head. "You and my brother. Who did you take care of before I came along?"

"For longer than I want to remember, no one."

"Is that why you're going overboard on me now? Because you have all this big-brother stuff stored up inside you just dying to get out?"

"Perhaps—" he winked at her "—but then I never dared to hope I would find someone as needy."

"We make one terrific team, you and me. You bring out the absolute worst in me and it happens to suit your needs perfectly."

"Do I really bring out the worst in you?"

"You can't think I'm always like this."

"Kelly, you don't seem to understand what I've been trying to tell you all afternoon. When I look at you, I like what I see...very much."

There it was again. The flush of warmth burning her cheeks. She fought to cover her embarrassment. "Boy, if I look good to you now, you'd have gone crazy if you could have seen me when I had a full-leg cast and crutches."

"Kelly—"

"And then there was the time I fell asleep while I was sunbathing in the nude. For over a week all I could do was stand up or lie down on my stomach."

"Oh?" A grin tugged at the corners of his mouth.

"Don't say 'oh' in that tone of voice. It was all perfectly innocent. I was house sitting for one of my brothers. He has a very private pool in his backyard."

"What finally woke you?"

She hesitated. "The next-door neighbor just happened to look over the fence and see me. He assured me that it was the first time...."

Brian chuckled. The chuckle became a laugh that didn't stop until there were tears in his eyes. He came over to sit beside her, a doubting look on his face. "I didn't believe him, either," she admitted.

Cupping his hands on either side of her face, he kissed the tip of her nose. "Kelly...." The way he said her name was like a caress. "I can't remember the last time I laughed like that or tell you how good it makes me feel inside."

"Does this mean I'm forgiven for eating all the macaroni and cheese?"

"Yes."

"There's one other thing, Brian," she said shyly. "It's taken me a long time to try to find a way to ask this with some aplomb. In fact, I'm beginning to fear I may have waited too long."

He pressed his finger to her lips. "Say no more, fair lady. I should have thought of it earlier." He stood up. "I'll leave the decision about the way you want to be carried up to you."

Kelly patted her pocket to be sure the tissue paper she had put there earlier hadn't worked its way out. "In your arms, please. And very, very carefully."

Brian took her to a secluded area in the pine trees and told her to whistle when she was ready for him to come back to get her. She did and he immediately returned. He behaved so matter-of-factly about a situation that mortified her, she was able to get through the episode and still feel comfortable in his presence. When she thanked him, he answered her with a smile of understanding.

Back at their camp, Brian eventually started dinner while Kelly lay on her belly and propped herself up on her elbows to shoot wild flowers in the early-evening light. They passed the time in comfortable silence, the way of friends or lovers who had known each other a long time. After a while Kelly's arms grew too tired to hold the camera without movement, and she decided it was time to quit.

Brian looked up from the book he held. He had been watching her as she lay in the grass, engrossed in her work, noting the gentle swell of her buttocks and the graceful shape of her legs. But more than seeing her physically, he had raptly watched the intensity of her expression as she went about her work. It was obvious she loved what she did. Her eyes sparkled with the challenge and excitement of finding a new way of recording an oft-photographed subject. He could not help but wonder how those smoky blue eyes would look at the man she loved. He tried to imagine them filled with passion and then in satiation. The result brought a powerful stirring to his loins. He laid his book aside. "Can I help?"

She handed him her camera. "Thanks...playing snake isn't as easy as it looks. But I think the impersonation was worth it." She brushed loose grass from her sleeves. "Now it's hurry up and wait—the hardest part for me. I've been at this long enough that there aren't usually too many surprises when the transparencies are developed, but every once in a while a picture comes through that can make even the most terrible day seem exciting."

"I used to feel that way about bringing in a particularly difficult account. There was a special sense of accomplishment when I knew I had made a difference to someone, or in the case of a corporation that needed financing to keep the doors open, a lot of someones."

"What happened that made you lose the feeling?"

"I stopped working with people and started working with machines. The higher I went, the less contact I had with anyone outside the bank. When I reached 'status' position, I realized all my contacts, both inside and outside my job, had become strictly that...contacts. They looked at me as I looked at them, as a means to an end."

"That's sad."

"Yes, it is," he said softly.

"And this is what you're running away from?"

"I prefer to think I'm running to something. It sounds better somehow."

"I guess I'm lucky. I have a large family in Phoenix, one that grows larger every year. Even if I tried, they would never allow me to become as isolated as you did."

"I take it you've never been married?"

"Close...once."

"The war correspondent?"

She nodded.

"What happened?"

"He found his war and it killed him."

He had guessed as much. "And there's been no one since then?"

"No one serious. I go out occasionally with a guy who works for the *Phoenix Gazette* and one who is an architect; but mostly my weekends are spent in the lab working."

"Do you ever get bone-deep lonely, Kelly?" he asked, not realizing how much he told about himself by posing such a question.

"No," she answered automatically, defensively. But it was a lie. "Yes," she quietly admitted. "Especially when I see my brothers and sister with their families. Even if they're all quarreling, the underlying love still shows through. Most of the time it doesn't bother me...the loneliness...but every once in a while I have trouble going home to an empty apartment. I think how nice it would be to have someone waiting for me." She shrugged. "I'm sure you would hear the same thing from anyone who lives alone. How about you?"

"An empty apartment never bothered me; I went there to recover from the other world I lived in. Sort of like a wild animal seeking its cave." He hesitated. "The times I felt the most alone I was in a group of people."

"You didn't leave anyone behind? A wife? Girl-friend?"

How could he explain Paula Michaelson? "For the last year—right up until the hour I quit—I was engaged to a woman considered by many to be the most beautiful in Chicago."

Kelly pushed her braid back over her shoulder, wishing she was prettier and hating herself for the thought. "You two must have made quite a pair. Cinderella and Prince Charming."

"We were regular fodder for the society pages, if that's what you mean."

Without thinking about her actions, Kelly hiked her knees up to rest her chin on them. Her feet exploded in pain with even that small amount of pressure on them. As she straightened her legs again, Brian reached for her foot. "Time for more ointment," he said, his change in tone dismissing their more personal conversation.

But Kelly wasn't ready to let go. "Is she waiting for you?"

There were a dozen ways he could answer her, ranging from sarcastic to sad. He chose the simplest. "No. My quitting was hard on her."

"Oh...I see."

He glanced up from examining her foot. "Do you?"

"She probably thought you betrayed her."

"As I recall, the way she worded it was that she refused to hitch herself to a falling star."

Kelly winced. She couldn't understand how the Brian Robertson she had come to know these past two days could have been involved with someone so insensitive. A sudden quick pain shot through her chest, making her catch her breath. She was jealous of this woman he had once loved—a woman he possibly still did. She forced herself to smile dismissively at the ridiculousness of her reaction. She felt sorry for him, that was all. She wanted to give him comfort, to be a shoulder for him to lean on. He had done as much for her.

From the back of her mind a voice asked whether it was truly Brian she wanted to comfort against the pain of loneliness ... or herself.

THE NEXT DAY Kelly spent the early morning and late afternoon photographing Brian, wild flowers and several deer that came to share their meadow. She used an entire roll of film shooting Brian as he fished, casting a fly into the lake filled with golden trout that rose to capture swarming mosquitoes. During the hours she worked, she photographed him from every angle and in every light. She witnessed pensiveness, humor, and mischievousness on his face. She saw his mouth curve in smile and purse with thought. His eyes fascinated her. They were the most expressive she had ever seen, beckoning one minute, closing her off the next.

She watched and she listened and she felt herself falling ever so slightly and impossibly in love with a man she knew she'd probably never see again.

# 6

A BREEZE PULLED long strands of hair from Kelly's grasp as she futiley tried to rebraid the thick mass into its former neatness. Brian lay across from her, staring at clouds drifting across the early-evening sky. Every once in a while he would take a deeper than usual breath, trying to identify and again become familiar with the elusive mountain scents carried by the soft wind. Pine was easy, as was the occasional smell of grass that came from the crushed blades beneath him. But there was one scent that frustrated him, defied every memory he had of mountains.

Turning to his side and propping his head up with his hand, he took a minute to watch Kelly. The four days they had been together had done wondrous things for his spirit. Just seeing her work with her hair, fluffing it with both hands and then a comb as she tried to get it to dry after her swim brought a sense of rightness to him.

He smiled as he thought about the glimpse he had seen of her gliding through the crystal water. He should have known better than to mention that their lake was far warmer than the one they had camped beside the first night; not only were they at a lower elevation but the lake was also shallow enough to absorb and hold some of the sun's heat. After he'd admitted he had gone swimming earlier, it had taken her less than a minute to insist he take her out on one of the flat rocks jutting into the water so that she too could swim and wash off the accumulated grime of the past few days. She hadn't stayed in the water long, but when Brian came back to retrieve her, she had told him the marvelous way she felt had been worth every goose bump.

Kelly looked down at her feet, still encased in Brian's wool socks. The blisters were healing faster than either of them had expected. Judging by the few tentative steps she had tried earlier that day, she knew it would soon be unnecessary for him to carry her everywhere. She had convinced herself she was looking forward to getting along without his help and was therefore confused at the strange feeling of loss that greeted every new accomplishment. She lowered her arms and let out a frustrated sigh. "This is a worse mess than the one I had before."

"Why do you have to braid it? I like your hair free. It gives you a mysterious Gypsy quality."

"That's okay if you're a Gypsy, but it's a real pain for we photographer types. When I wear my hair loose, it constantly gets in the way."

"Are you going to do any more shooting to-night?"

She paused a moment. "I see your point." Nimble fingers untangled the twists.

Brian thought about their day and how completely absorbed Kelly had been in her work. "Until I met you I had no idea photography was such an exacting profession."

"I suppose that like most people you figured it was all point and shoot."

"Something like that."

"Actually, what happens in the field is only a

small part. It's the processing and printing that really make the difference. The most incredible shots can look ordinary and vice versa with skillful dark-room techniques. Especially when you're working with black and white."

Brian asked her another question. He told himself it was because he was truly interested in the answer, but he knew it was more than that. He asked because he wanted to hear the sound of her voice as she answered. Last night sleep had come to him slowly and late as he lay awake and listened to the soft sounds of her breathing. Trying to imagine what it would be like to have those sounds close beside him, within the circle of his arms, had set up a series of thoughts that made going to sleep extremely diffi-cult. Then as now, he ached to touch her, to feel the texture of her hair, the smoothness of her skin. And he ached as deeply to have her touch him. Being with Kelly for even a short time had taken the in-tense need he had to reach out to someone and made it grow until it had become an all-consuming thing. It took every bit of the self-control he had so dili-gently learned in banking to maintain his facade of indifference. For his own sanity, he knew it would be far better if he were to hurry their parting rather than to look for ways to delay it. Yet even thinking about the day he would tell her goodbye grew pro-gressively more difficult.

"Why do I have the feeling you're not listening?" she said, breaking into his thoughts.

"I heard every word."

"Repeat the last three."

He pulled a piece of grass and stuck the tender end into his mouth. "Technically . . . 'are not listening,' would be correct. However, since the 'are' was part

of a contraction, I suppose 'you're' could be considered—"

She playfully threw her comb at him, hitting him
in the chest. As if mortally wounded, he groaned
and rolled backward, striking the corner of his pack
and knocking it over on top of him. The aluminum
frame landed on his head, his nose taking the brunt
of the blow. He sat up, his hands covering his face.

Kelly gasped. "Brian, are you all right?"

"I'm not sure," he mumbled, his hands now gingerly touching his nose. "I think maybe it's broken."

"Oh, my God." She crawled over to him. "Here,
let me see." Pulling his hands away from his face,
she gave a sigh of relief. "At least it's not bleeding."
She reached up to press her fingers to a spot she
thought slightly swollen.

"Ouch!"

His loud cry of pain startled her. "I'm sorry," she
breathed. "Oh, Brian, I hardly touched you. It must
be broken."

"Don't worry," he said, a terrible grimace of pain
distorting his face. "I'll be all right." He paused to
catch his breath. "If we aren't able to reach civilization in time to have my nose properly set, I can always go through the excruciating torture of having
it rebroken again and—"

She glared at him. "There's nothing wrong with
your nose, is there?"

A devilish twinkle lit up his eyes.

"You rat!" She tried to give him a shove. He
caught her hands and held her, staring deeply into
her eyes before slowly bringing her to him. The look
he gave her had lost its playfulness.

Tentatively their lips touched with only the light-
est pressure, as if each was aware of the dangerous

new territory a deeper kiss would plunge them into. But then yearning superseded caution and rationale disappeared. A groan came from Brian's throat as he pulled her closer and she willingly came.

Holding her, touching her, was as he had imagined. And yet he knew he could never have dreamed something as intense as the feelings that gripped him. His hand cupped her face, and his fingers fanned into her hair, separating its silky strands. Parting his lips, he took her into him—her breath, her taste, the velvet feel of her tongue. His hands traveled down her back and then around to the curving swell of her hips. He inhaled deeply, and became intensely conscious of the smell of her. *She* was the elusive scent he had tried to identify earlier—a clean natural smell subtly interwoven with minute traces of soaps and shampoos and perfume.

A long-ignored ache burst in Kelly's chest, sweeping aside all lingering traces of being sensible. The mindlessness of passion caught her in its maelstrom and she ignored her internal panicked warnings that what they were doing was a horrendous mistake. Her arms went around him, and she intimately felt the sleek body she had already come to know through her camera lens. Her hands followed the muscles of his back as she drew him closer.

Brian turned, lifting Kelly and then gently placing her on the down-filled sleeping bag. He sighed her name as his lips moved from her mouth to the base of her throat. Cushioning his cheek against her breast, he listened to the thundering of her heartbeat and rejoiced that it echoed his own. He had never wanted a woman with the intensity that he wanted Kelly. Not even when he'd been in his teens and in the middle of his sexual awakening had a need as overwhelming possessed him. The preambles of courtship, the rituals that would have guided their behavior had they been in Chicago or Phoenix had been left behind with the other trappings of civilization. Now a new, more primitive and basic conduct guided him.

His fingers worked the buttons on her blouse, creating first a plunging V and then an opening. Exposed to the cool air and the heat of his consuming gaze, Kelly's nipples rose to rigid peaks beneath her silk bra. Brian unhooked the clasp to caress the turgid mounds, then undid his own shirt and drew her against him.

When Kelly reached up to put her arms around his neck, her hands hit the backpack that had fallen on Brian earlier. The simple action broke the magical spell and brought the real world crashing back. It was as if she were suddenly able to step outside her body and see what was happening from an observer's viewpoint. Stunned by the implication of what she knew they were about to do, she put her palms against Brian's shoulders and pushed. "My God," she gasped, "what's happening to us?" Embarrassed by both her behavior and her nakedness, she turned away from him and began buttoning her blouse.

Brian sat up. He blinked and then shook his head as if physical effort could clear the confusion. "I'm sorry, Kelly," he finally said, fighting for control. While he could vividly remember their teasing exchange, he couldn't pinpoint what had precipitated the passionate embrace. To lose control was as alien to him as failure.

"There's no need for you to apologize...it wasn't your fault."

"Oh?" Despite his best efforts to appear out-wardly calm, Brian's fingers shook too much to guide the buttons back through the holes in his shirt. "Does that mean you're accepting complete responsibility?" he gently bantered.

Kelly tried to answer in the same teasing tone. If they could find a humorous side to what had just happened, it would provide a shelter for them, a way to remain friends. "I've decided it has to be the water. If you don't get physically ill, you behave ir-rationally." Irrational or not, she couldn't deny the intense feeling of loss. It was as if she'd been given a beautifully wrapped package...and then returned it unopened. In defense of her actions she reminded herself how foolish it would be to allow something to happen between them, when in only a few more days, each would be going his or her separate way...alone.

"I appreciate what you're trying to do, Kelly," he said, his voice low, his words barely above a whis-per. "But it isn't necessary." He turned to look at her. "And...I promise you it won't happen again." He would promise her anything in order not to lose her trust and the marvelous spontaneity between them. He brushed the hair from his forehead. "I'm going to go for a walk; do you need me for anything before I leave?"

Numbed by all that had just occurred, Kelly sim-ply shook her head. When he reached beside her to get his jacket and his shirt fell open, revealing the matting of hair that had so recently caressed her still-aching breasts, she caught her breath in sur-prise at the deep flush of yearning that swept over her. Forcefully she controlled the urge to reach out and touch him. The instant passed, with her hands still clutching the front of her blouse. She watched him walk away, unable to say the words that would have made him stay. Never in her life had she considered the possibility of engaging in casual sex, so why now? And if it wasn't a casual relationship she was contemplating, what then? It was madness to think there could be anything else between them.

EVENING SETTLED IN QUICKLY after Brian left. Stars and an almost full moon filled the smog-free valley with light brilliant enough to create deep shadows. Kelly watched and waited for Brian's return, not giving up her vigil until her head began to nod with fatigue.

When she awoke the next morning to sunshine and the sounds of wind whistling through the pines, her gaze immediately went to Brian's sleeping bag. It was empty! Fighting panic, she scanned the campsite. Everything looked the same. Maybe he hadn't returned. With her hand shielding the sun from her eyes, she searched first near the trees and then farther out toward the lake. When she found him beside the water she uttered an audible sigh of relief. Moisture pooled in her eyes. Angrily she blinked it away. What was happening to her? The thought had become an echo. She was behaving like an out-of-control adolescent who had a crush on the science teacher.

When she found herself watching Brian and remembering how soft his lips were and how his bare chest had felt against her own, she groaned in disgust and purposely looked away.

At the lake's edge Brian shivered against a sudden gust of cool air. He glanced down at the fish he had already caught that morning and measured his growing hunger against the time needed to land a few more. He had decided on fish for breakfast when he woke up before Kelly and couldn't keep his eyes or thoughts off her. During the long walk he had taken the night before and the subsequent time he had sat on a boulder a hundred yards from their camp while he waited for her to fall asleep, he had gone over and over the arguments for maintaining a platonic relationship between them.

When he tried to make sense out of what was happening to him, it all came back to the simple fact that he was falling in love. He grimaced at his image reflecting in the shimmering lake.

Rationally, he realized too much had happened to him lately to even contemplate the prospect of falling in love; it was too soon after Paula...after leaving the bank. How could he possibly give himself to Kelly when he hadn't any idea who "he" was anymore?

How could he not? The arguments, the reasoning, the protests were a facade. He was already too much in love with her to ever back out unscathed.

The same arguments that had surfaced the night before were destroyed with the same answers. Logic played a small role where emotions were concerned. What did it matter that they had known each other less than a week, when she made him feel more alive than he had felt in years? She was stubborn and hotheaded and sexy—a volatile combination that excited and challenged him. Somehow, she had also tapped a deep-seated protective streak he hadn't known still existed and made him feel more like a man than he had felt in a long time.

He smiled at that. What would Kelly say if she knew she had inspired the "me Tarzan, you Jane" syndrome in him? He had a feeling she wouldn't be impressed. She wasn't the kind of woman to play Jane to anyone's Tarzan.

A tug on the line brought his thoughts back to fishing. A glance toward camp and he forgot about everything else, save Kelly. She was sitting up, watching him. He smiled and waved, then retrieved their breakfast and headed back up the slope.

Tentatively Kelly stood, testing her feet, wanting to show Brian how she was progressing. She tried a few steps and then several more. There was pain, but it was bearable.

"Not bad," he said, hiding his true feelings about her rapid healing behind a mask of cheerfulness.

"I thought you would be pleased. Give me another day or two and I'll be good as new. Then you can get rid of me and continue with your trip."

He forced a smile. "And here I've been scouting around for permanent homesites."

"I told you I was tougher than I look."

"I remember, the Incredible Hulk in drag."

"Watch it. You don't want to make me mad. You know what happens...."

He cocked his head and quickly looked her up and down. "I don't know, it might be kind of fun to see you turn green and shed your clothes."

She shifted her balance to try to remove the pressure from her left heel and caught her breath as pain shot up her leg. Instinctively she reached for Brian. He dropped his gear and caught her in his arms. Bending, he picked her up. It was a mistake. Without preamble he was thrust back into the gut-wrenching need of the night before. "Kelly," he murmured, his ache for her eloquently expressed in the way he said her name. It wasn't necessary to say anything else.

Time ceased as they looked into each other's eyes. Subliminally Kelly acknowledged that the fight in her was gone. She abandoned reason for feeling and placed her arms around his neck.

Kelly's sudden capitulation made Brian hesitate. He knew if he allowed himself this hour with her, there would no longer be a place for him to hide from his loneliness. "There's something we have to get straight between us before this goes any further, Kelly." She had to understand that he wanted more than physical release from her—he wanted commitment.

She couldn't bear to hear the words she sensed he would speak, so she stopped him by pressing her lips to his. To know that what was about to happen between them was no more than the coming together of two lonely people was one thing, to actually hear it from him was another. Simply by being the man he was, Brian had made her acknowledge that beneath her facade she was also lonely. If only for the short time they would be together on this trip, she needed him. She yearned for his tenderness and warmth, his compassion and caring. He had listened to her dreams and in the listening made them fresh and possible again.

Despite her desperate wish that it wasn't so, she recognized they were too different to ever have a permanent life together. But for a day or two, before the real world intruded on them again, they could give each other happiness and create memories that would warm them on all their lonely nights to come.

"I know what you want to tell me, Brian," she answered softly. "I feel the same way. We don't have to put what's happening between us into words." She kissed him. "Sometimes if something is analyzed or talked about too much, the magic disappears."

"Between us?" he murmured, feeling an indescribable surge of joy as he drew her back to him. "Never...." He would wait to tell her he loved her if that was what she wanted. Waiting didn't matter anymore; they had a lifetime.

Brian met Kelly's upturned mouth. Their lips touched and then yielded. An eloquent moan vibrated his chest as his arms closed tightly around her, drawing her closer to him. She was as he remembered—an incredible combination of soft and pliant, firm and resilient. His heartbeat thundered in his ears, yet he clearly heard the music of the meadow.

Her mouth opened slightly in invitation. His tongue touched her lips, her teeth, the erotic depths beyond. His world started to spin, closing off all other sights and sounds, making ever smaller circles that irresistibly drew him to a center composed exclusively of his overwhelming need.

He hadn't dared to hope she might be feeling the same seeds of love that had grown in him. He felt like shouting his joy while whispering his incredulity lest it all be a fragile dream.

Brian carried Kelly to his sleeping bag. When she lay beneath him he reached up to touch her hair, letting it slip between his fingers. "Did I tell you that bright sunshine makes your hair look like burnished gold?"

She smiled and adjusted herself to his outstretched length so that she could unbutton his shirt. "If you did, I don't mind hearing it again." She moved her hand lower, then followed with her mouth, traveling from his slightly abrasive, lightly bearded chin to the place where his heartbeat pulsed at the base of his throat. She moved lower still, pressing her face against the light matting of hair on his chest, letting the tactile sensation it produced carry her on a sensual journey. Her hand dipped beneath his shirt and across the expanse of his chest to his waist. She heard him softly sigh her name as he reached for her, capturing her mouth in a kiss filled with his growing need.

"Kelly...I'm so afraid of hurting you."

Her hands held the sides of his face. She pressed her lips to his eyes, the corners of his mouth, his temples. "I'm the tough one here, remember?"

His breath softly caressed her neck. When he answered, his voice carried none of her playfulness. "I need you, fair Kathleen...more than you could ever imagine. I'm afraid my need is so great it will suffocate you."

She touched his cheek with her fingertips, tracing the flesh beneath the bone, following it into the richness of his hair. "Oh, Brian," she murmured. "No one has needed me for such a long time. I want you to need me...I have so much to give."

He pulled her shirt from her jeans and slipped his hand inside, seeking the feel of her flesh at her waist. Now his hand moved higher, unerringly finding the place that would make her breath catch in her throat—cupping and stroking her silk-covered breasts with achingly tender movements. He kissed her throat, then pressed his lips where his hand had been, his breath sending a demanding, heat-filled message to the hardened, waiting nipple.

Their clothing soon grew into an irritating barrier, a source of frustration in their desire to give and receive the intimacies of lovemaking. Kelly finished opening the buttons on her shirt; Brian eased the material from her shoulders, tasting the honey of her skin as he did so. When she started to unhook the clasp at the front of her bra, he caught her hand. "You are beautiful beyond my imaginings," he whispered, looking at her as his finger lightly traced the line of lace at the top of her breasts. Slowly his hand moved to the smoothness of the cup and the hard peak that pressed erotically, invitingly against the thin fabric. He took the beckoning bud between his thumb and finger, then lowered his head to press his face into her breast.

"Brian..." she murmured, his name becoming a seductive cry. He slipped the hook from its clasp and moved the silk cloth aside. Gently he drew the nipple into his mouth, holding it lightly with his teeth, stroking with his tongue.

Kelly felt an urgency building in him and she responded, communicating her own growing need. He paused to rid himself of his clothing; she did the same with the last of hers.

A breeze swept her nakedness and she felt a chill; he touched her and she was warm again. Brian made love to her as she had never been made love to before. Infinitely tender, passionately involved, he let her know how he reveled in her touch with whispered sighs and softly spoken words. She felt herself a full partner, able to give or to receive pleasure without shyness or hesitation.

When he moved to enter her and she eagerly accepted the weight of his hips on hers, she felt a sense of rightness and was able to completely release herself to him.

Patiently, lovingly Brian brought Kelly with him on the culminating journey. She caught her breath in surprise and softly whispered his name in an expression of wonder. He cradled her in his arms, holding her while she slowly came down from the heights of passion to the reality of their surroundings.

When her breathing had neared normal, she let out a sigh and stretched before snuggling deeper into his embrace. Brian kissed the top of her head. "Shall I tell you how I feel after that wondrous experience?" he asked.

She tilted her head back to meet his gaze, her own eyes still dusky with a trace of lingering passion. "You can find the words?"

"Mmm...." An incredulous smile pulled at the corners of his mouth. "I can't believe what looking at you just did to me. Thirty seconds ago I was feeling this smug sort of contentment. And now it's like the last half hour never took place."

Kelly touched the tip of her tongue to his slightly parted lips. "Half hour?" she murmured. "I don't remember any half hour."

Brian moved to pin her beneath him. With a welcoming groan he took her teasing tongue into his mouth. His hand moved across the flatness of her belly and then to the place between her thighs that harbored a reawakened need. She readily responded to the intimacies of his touch, without shyness, as if they had always been lovers. For an instant he saw a glimpse of their future together and the promise of it made his mind reel. He felt like shouting his gratitude, but he didn't know whom to thank. Was there an angel somewhere who tallied such things—an angel who determined that a certain amount of unhappiness was enough?

# 7

SLOWLY, AS THEY LAY in each other's arms, the real world intruded on the one they had created with their lovemaking. The wind chilled, hunger nudged. Brian brushed a strand of hair from Kelly's cheek, his eyes following its path back to rejoin the mass.

Abruptly his loving expression changed to a curious frown. "It appears we have an audience, my love," he said, his voice purposely low. "A trio of voyeurs is even now blatantly staring at your lovely derriere."

"You're kidding,' she gasped, burrowing against him. "What a rotten thing to do! How could they?"

"Kelly." A laugh rumbled in his chest. "You can save your blushing for later. Our inquisitive visitors are the four-legged kind."

She glared at him. "You did that on purpose, didn't you?"

"Who? Me?"

Coming up to a sitting position, she glanced around. "Where are they?" Brian pointed to an area behind her pack. Once she knew where to look, she had no trouble finding the plump balls of fur. Their frankly curious black eyes and bold posture made them seem far more tame than any of the previous wild animals they had encountered. "They look like squirrels with glandular problems," she whispered, enchanted.

"Careful...you don't want to sound insulting. Remember, you're looking at the sum total of your slipper market for these parts."

"*That's* what a marmot looks like?"

He softly cupped her chin with his hand and turned her to face him. "And this is what a man in love looks like," he said. "We are going to make a great team, Kelly. After we finish my odyssey...."

Her smiled faded; her heart slammed against her chest. "I...I don't understand," she stammered. "I thought—"

Brian watched her struggle with confusion. How could she be surprised by his pronouncement of love? Hadn't she said she understood, that she felt the same way he did? My God, he mentally gasped, she wasn't talking about love at all. He felt as if he had been hit in the stomach. "It seems we have had a slight misunderstanding," he said, his voice cool and controlled, betraying none of the crushing disappointment that tore at his insides. Needing something to do, he reached for his clothes.

For the second time in as many days, Kelly wished for a hole to open in which she could hide. How could they have been so far apart in their thinking?

"Brian...I'm sorry. I thought—"

"Not now, Kelly," he murmured. "We'll talk when I get back." He pulled on his jeans and then his shirt.

"Where are you going?"

"For a swim. I need to get away by myself for a while."

She recoiled at the pain she saw in his eyes. *Oh, Brian, I would love you if I could. Don't you know that?* "Do you want me to start breakfast?" How easily she used the mundane, how calculating and unfeeling it made her sound.

"Kelly...." He jammed his hands into his pockets, glanced toward the sky and took a deep breath. When he looked down at her again, his face was composed. Only his eyes gave a clue to his torment. "Go ahead and eat without me. I'll fix myself something when I get back." He turned and walked the few steps to the place where he had hung his parka on a tree stump. Glancing back at her, he said, "Do you need anything before I leave?"

Why couldn't she do what she ached to do and ask him to stay? "No...I'll be fine."

He eyed her a moment longer, then nodded and quietly left.

BY THE TIME BRIAN RETURNED, it was almost noon. A flood of relief washed over Kelly when she saw him walking toward her, rapidly covering the distance between them in his now-familiar long-legged stride. Again her heart increased its beat at the sight of him; and again she insistently attributed her peculiar reaction to his unusual handsomeness.

She wondered how she should act and then decided to leave the tone of their meeting up to him. It would be better for both of them if she simply reacted to his mood instead of trying to set one. When she realized her hands were nervously twisting in her lap as she knotted and then unknotted the string from her parka, she shoved them under her thighs to keep them still.

Brian stopped directly in front of her. "I think we should talk," he said without preamble.

She nodded. His hair was still damp and she noticed his beard had become more pronounced. Looking at him made her breath catch in her throat.

"So that we really understand each other this time,

let's not leave anything to supposition," he added.

Again she nodded.

"Am I correct in assuming you do not feel the same way about me that I do about you? In other words," he said evenly, "you do not love me and have no intention of staying with me any longer than necessary."

It was on the tip of her tongue to qualify what he said. Instead she softly replied, "I like you very much...."

A weary smile shone from his eyes. "What did you think I was trying to tell you this morning?" His veneer of detachment developed a tiny crack as his feelings forced their way to the surface.

She struggled to find the words. It was important he understand. "What has happened to us up here," she began slowly, "could never have happened anywhere else. If we had met at a party or run into each other at Phil's, we probably never would have seen each other again. This has been a magical time for both of us. We've been existing in a Shangri-la kind of place for the past few days. If we try to take that specialness with us, or if we try to continue what we have started here, it will be destroyed. We won't even have the memories."

"How can you be so sure?"

"We're so different from each other. As long as we're somewhere that's alien to both of us, we're all right. But the minute either of us tried to step into the other's world, everything would come apart. You're running away from the very things I'm still seeking—success, stability, ordinariness." She pulled her hands from beneath her legs and tucked them under her arms to warm them. "If I stayed with you after we left these mountains, your personality and

your needs would overshadow mine to the point
that they would disappear." She hoped he understood what she was trying to say.

"Stop and think about what's happened between
us in only four or five days. Really think about it,"
she urged. "I've never behaved this way before. I've
always thought that making love with someone was
a serious commitment, and yet I made love with
you—a virtual stranger—with no more provocation
than a kiss. Can't you see? Neither of us is behaving
normally or rationally. This thing between us isn't
real."

He reached for her hands. It was foolish for him to
try to deny what she said. His arguments would be
as filled with suppositions as hers were. "I never
thought pragmatic was a dirty word before now."

She blinked away threatening tears. "I'm not
ready to give up my dream," she said softly, "even to
follow another."

"Are you so sure you would have to?"

Anger shot through her, stiffening her spine and
making her pull away from him. "What are you going to do when you finish this trek?" she demanded.

"I haven't decided yet. All I do know is that sometime in the next few months I want to make contact
with my family and a few old friends again. Real
contact. I want to spend some time with them, get to
know them again."

"And where would I fit in?"

"You would come with me."

"And my studio?"

Brian rubbed his temples. One of the advantages
of being successful was being catered to. And he had
been *very* successful. He was shaken that there was a
possibility she might be right. "It would only be for
a few months—"

He couldn't have proved her point more effectively. "I didn't think you took me seriously," she said tonelessly.

"You're demanding answers to questions I haven't had time to consider. I didn't come into this with a game plan. Five days ago falling in love was the last thing on my mind."

"But don't you see, that's just what I've been talking about. Given the circumstances, what happened between us was almost predestined—a man going through a traumatic, disruptive change in his life, a woman injured, vulnerable. It was natural that we would reach out to each other but...it isn't real." Why was it so hard for her to tell him these things? Why the terrible sadness over the truth? "If we try to make more out of this than it is, we'll wind up destroying what we've had."

"Look at me." He touched her chin. "I'm a grown man, not someone in the flush of first love. There have been other women before you, even some I thought I loved. None of them made me feel the way you do. I have never been so sure of something as I am this."

"How do I make you feel?"

He hesitated, uncertain how to put abstract feelings into words. "When I'm with you I feel at peace with myself...satisfied. Suddenly there's an enthusiasm for life growing inside me, which I thought had died."

How she wanted to believe him. It would be so easy to take the heady ride he offered. She almost capitulated. But then reason reared its forceful head. Could she really give up everything she had worked so hard to achieve, just as it was all starting to fall in place? Especially when deep inside she knew their time together would necessarily be fleeting? When

Brian finally disappeared from her life, what would she have left? Where would she go to heal the hurt? "I'm sorry..." she whispered. "I can't."

He silenced her by touching her lips with his thumb. He could see the confusion, the unhappiness in her eyes and wanted to spare her more pain. Unexpectedly, he smiled. "If I can't bowl you over in a place like this with my devastating charm, I guess I'll have to win you on more familiar territory and by more conventional methods. Until then, for as long as we're together here in the mountains, we'll just be friends. I won't put any pressure on you for anything else... but I won't settle for less. I want you to know, my beautiful Kathleen, I have not given up on us."

Startled by his abrupt change, Kelly studied his face, seeking a clue to his thinking. She didn't find the defeat she had anticipated. Instead there was a steely glint of determination in his eyes. Her heart skipped a beat. Could it be that the hard-driven, calculating genius of the banking world was a man who believed in miracles?

KELLY HAD FEARED the remaining time together would be awkward for them, but it only proved how little she knew Brian. During the next two days they spent in the meadow he was as open and friendly as he had been before—but that was all. He behaved as if they'd never made love.

Finally, despite her feet still not being completely healed, they could delay leaving no longer; Kelly had work waiting for her back in Phoenix, and she knew Phil would be frantic if she didn't show up soon.

They left the meadow and continued hiking. This

time they walked in short easy stretches, Kelly wearing her tennis shoes, Brian carrying most of her load in his own pack. On the third day they left the main trail and headed for the ranger station at the Larkspur trail head.

Their descent was unusually quiet. After a few attempts to engage her in conversation, Brian abandoned the effort and withdrew into his own sense of impending loss.

As they walked, Kelly kept telling herself that what she was feeling was not a heavy heart, it was fatigue. But a voice deep inside mocked her easy answer.

They rounded a final sweeping bend in the trail, and the ranger station came into view. Brian tried to decide which of the dozen speeches he had mentally prepared the past few miles he should use. He wanted just the right one to let her know he had not changed his mind—he still loved her and sincerely believed he always would.

Kelly stared at his back as they walked, mentally absorbing these last images of him. She had tried over and over, but she couldn't think of a way to say goodbye. Were there prescribed phrases in a book somewhere that told how to end something as special as the time they had shared on a properly upbeat note? Was there a way to tell Brian she wished their interlude had never ended, without making it sound as if she thought they should pursue the relationship?

Nearing the parking lot, Brian spotted a van being loaded with backpacks. Three men and two women he estimated to be in their early twenties stood around the vehicle. As they came closer, one of the women looked up and saw them. She spoke to the man beside her and then motioned to Brian and

Kelly. "We're headed for the Kearsarge Pass trail head and then on down to Rawlins. Do you need a ride to either place?" she asked, her smile open and friendly. "There's room enough for two more if you don't mind doubling up."

"Yes...thank you," Kelly quickly answered, relieved at how easily she had found transportation back to her car. They went over to the van and after introductions—she learned her benefactors were college students from Los Angeles—she and Brian transferred her gear from his pack to hers and then loaded it into the van.

As she turned to say goodbye, a sense of panic gripped her. What they had shared deserved a better ending than a hurried farewell in a parking lot. She hesitated leaving, unable to take her gaze from Brian while all around her the others climbed into the van. Trying to swallow a huge lump that had suddenly appeared in her throat, she extended her hand.

He gave her a wistful smile. Seconds that seemed like an eternity passed as they stared at each other, oblivious to all else. Then ignoring her outstretched arm, he came toward her and placed his hands on either side of her head, letting his fingers comb through the thickness of her hair. Slowly he lowered his mouth and kissed her, expressing in the touch of his lips what he could not find the words to say aloud.

And then it was over, and Kelly was in the van heading back to a life that had become unalterably different in spite of her stubborn refusal to admit it had changed at all. What she had intellectualized, that their coming together was a once-in-a-lifetime interlude and nothing more, had not yet completely filtered down to her heart.

# 8

THE DAY KELLY TOOK to return to Phoenix was the most desolate she had ever known. Arriving at her apartment in the middle of the night, she dropped her equipment in the living room, stumbled down the hall, stripped off her clothes and collapsed on her bed. The next day it took the repetitive nagging ring of the telephone to drag her out of the depths of sleep.

"Hello..." she murmured, rolling over onto her back, flinging her arm across her face.

"Where in the hell have you been?"

"Hi, Phil," she said, ignoring his ill humor. "How's it going?"

"I've been worried sick. You were supposed to be home days ago. If you hadn't answered your phone just now, the police were next on my list to call."

"Has it been this hot all week?" She had neglected to turn on the air conditioner when she arrived last night, and now her bedroom felt like an oven.

"For God's sake, Kelly...what happened to you? Where have you been?"

"Hang on a sec, will you?" She heard him shout her name as she laid the receiver on the pillow. "I'll be right back," she hollered, swinging her legs over the side of the bed. She sat on the edge for a moment to clear her head before attempting the trip down the hall and into the living room to flip the switch on the thermostat. By the time she was back in bed, reasonably cool air had started to come out of the overhead diffuser.

"What time is it?" she asked, putting the phone to her ear again.

"Six o'clock," he answered tightly.

"*Six o'clock!* What an ungodly hour to call someone."

"In the evening, Kelly."

A soft groan passed her lips. How could she possibly still be tired after nearly fifteen hours of sleep? "Did you know you were shouting at me, Phil?"

"You'd be shouting, too, if you'd spent the past few days frantically worrying about—"

"That's sweet," she purposely interrupted. "Have you really been worried about me?"

"Never mind that now." He let out a pent-up sigh. "Did you get the pictures?"

"Aha, now the truth comes out. It wasn't me you were worried about at all. It was the photographs."

"Well? Did you get them?"

"Yes. . . ."

"And?"

"They're good."

"How good?"

"Probably the best I've ever done."

"Kelly, I could kiss you."

"You can forget the sentimentality. Just get me the appointments you promised."

"How does nine o'clock tomorrow morning sound?"

"With who?" Her eyes flew open. She reached for the pad of paper and pencil she kept on the nightstand.

"Templeton's."

"Their agency or the store itself?"

"The agency."

All traces of lingering fatigue vanished. Now that her decision to leave Brian had proven to be the right one, after all, she felt an odd mixture of euphoria mixed with sorrow. "Thanks, Phil," she said, her voice little more than a choked whisper.

"Anytime." There was a short pause. "I didn't think it was appropriate to tell you this before—for obvious reasons—but I want you to know that I had planned to put in a good word for you all along."

"I figured as much."

"Kelly, you know it's perfectly all right to let me feel magnanimous once in a while. We big-brother types thrive on things like that."

"I guess I'm just spoiled. Since you've always had this overwhelming urge to look out for me, I've come to expect certain things."

"Let me know how it goes tomorrow."

"I'll process the film as soon as the interview is over and bring it right to the office." She said goodbye and started to hang up when she heard Phil's voice calling to her.

"You never told me what you thought of Brian."

There it was, that tightness in her chest, a feeling that had come to her so often in the past few days it had started to become familiar. "I'll tell you some other time."

"You didn't like him?"

"I don't want to talk about this now, Phil."

"I was so sure you two would hit it off."

Sudden suspicion shot through her. "Was Dave really tied up in Tucson shooting a rodeo?"

"Are you accusing me of setting you up?"

"Did you?" If he had, she would be a long time forgiving him for this one.

"No...I swear to you the whole thing was on the up-and-up." When she didn't immediately reply, he added, "You can ask Dave." Again there was a pause. "Kelly? Are you all right?"

She took a deep breath. "I couldn't be better. I'm just a little bewildered by everything that's happened. After all, tomorrow's a big day for me. This could be the break I've been waiting for."

"I'm not sure you should be putting so much hope into these interviews. Whether you get anywhere with these guys or not, it isn't going to change the fact that you're a fantastic photographer. It would be a shame if you let someone else be the final judge of your talent."

"You haven't given me that particular pep talk in months. It's nice to see you aren't losing your touch."

"Don't get carried away," he countered, returning to the customary bantering tone of their conversations. "It was a recording. I keep the tape player constantly on the ready right here beside the phone. With a manic-depressive for a sister, I'm never sure when I'll need it."

"I love you, too, Phil. Now hang up and go help Alice with the dishes."

"I cooked."

"Goodbye, Phil."

"Sure you don't want to talk some more?"

"I'm hanging up now."

"I don't have anything else to—"

"Goodbye, Phil." She dropped the receiver into its cradle, rolled onto her back and stared at the ceiling. If she had stayed in the mountains with Brian, they would probably be setting up camp about now. She had a strange feeling in her chest. A new and compelling reason to have everything go well at the agency tomorrow morning gripped her. Without an especially demanding project to keep her busy, the transition period of putting Brian from her every thought could turn into a long and agonizing one.

THE INTERVIEW with the vice-president of the Alexander Agency almost went too easily. After his perfunctory perusal of her portfolio, she was speechless when he told her he was going to give her an assignment for Templeton's on speculation. He agreed to pay her a basic fee for the work and then if they decided to go with the campaign, she would receive a bonus.

Driving from downtown Phoenix to her studio on the outskirts of the city, Kelly suddenly realized she had no memory of leaving the agency or walking to her car. Quite simply, she had been in a state of shock. And as the shock receded, an incredible surge of excitement took its place. At last . . . it had finally happened. She'd knocked on a door and it had opened.

As soon as she reached the studio, Kelly flipped through her appointment book, mentally rescheduling her bread-and-butter accounts to make room for Templeton's. While the four or five days she had originally planned to be gone on assignment hadn't thrown her into a tailspin, the extra days she had spent nursing her blisters had put her impossibly behind.

When, after an hour's work, she finally came up with a schedule that allowed her time to sleep but little else, she sat back in her chair and eyed the piece of paper. Instead of the anticipated groan of fatigue at the thought of all the work she had ahead of her, she let out a tiny sigh of relief. She had used work as an antidote for problems before, but never with such enthusiasm. Getting over her brief affair with Brian was going to be easier than she had dared to hope.

Later that afternoon while processing transparencies, she mentally patted herself on the back for her decidedly unemotional resolution to what could have been a devastating problem... until she took her first roll of film from the drier into the workroom to view it on the light table. Even without the magnifying glass she normally used when working with 35mm, her eyes focused on Brian's image until it filled her field of vision. The tiny form of a man triggered her memory until the very essence of him occupied not only her mind but her senses.

The roll she had arbitrarily chosen to view first was one taken the day after they had made love. Her gaze drifted from frame to frame, following his progress through the riotously flower-filled meadow as he walked back to their camp with fresh water. Then the scene changed to one filled with shimmering blue as a near-naked Brian broke the surface of the lake with a graceful reaching stroke.

Her focus blurred as she remembered how cold his lips had felt later when he gave her a quick, chaste kiss after coming up to sit beside her. In her mind's eye she saw him as clearly as if he were again standing in front of her.

In the short time they had been in the thin air of the mountains, Brian had started to turn a golden brown, completely skipping the normal pinks and reds of sunburn. Each day his beard had grown a little, subtly and then dramatically changing his appearance from somewhat unkempt to ruggedly nat-

ural and unaffected. By the time they parted it
seemed he had merely walked into the wilderness,
casually shrugged and completely discarded civilization's trappings. The man who had softly touched
her cheek as he told her goodbye was not the same
one she had found pacing the walkway beside her
car a week and a half before.

In a way, the dramatic change had disturbed her.
Every time she found herself even considering the
possibility of abandoning her known life to step into
the unknown with Brian, she forced herself to consider how dramatically he had already changed and
how likely it was that that was only the beginning.

Kelly shook herself free from the memories and
turned off the light behind the milky glass. Suddenly
overwhelmingly tired, she paused to rub her eyes.
Trying to swallow the lump in her throat, she silently wondered yet again if she should have stayed
with Brian. Had she, like Robert Frost, found a significant fork in the road? How tragic her life would
someday seem if she ever regretted the path she had
chosen.

No, dammit, she wouldn't let herself fall into that
trap. Life was full of decisions. You made them and
then you went on. Looking back was foolish, futile....

She had known Brian for little more than a week.
In her heart she had held and nurtured the dream of
touching people's lives with her talent far longer
than she had yearned for a man who would have
tossed her dreams aside by the sheer force of his
presence. Perhaps the day would come when she
would wistfully wonder about him, but she would
*never* allow herself to doubt that her decision had
been the right one.

PHIL WAS ESTATIC when she went over to his office later that afternoon to show him the slides. Without guidance or encouragement, he chose the picture of Brian standing beside the lake at sunset to put on the cover.

"You done real good, kid." He was beaming and gave Kelly's shoulders a quick squeeze.

"That envelope you so casually laid aside," she said, hiking herself up to sit on the corner of his massive walnut desk, "happens to contain my bill."

"Tsk, tsk, Kelly. Why would you want to mention something as crass as money at a time like this?"

"It comes hand in hand with a vulgar need I have for food and shelter. Outfitting myself for this little adventure of yours devastated my checkbook balance. I need to be reimbursed as quickly as possible." She nudged one of the transparencies with her finger. "By the way, what would you like me to do with all that backpacking stuff?"

"Did you check to see if you could return it for credit?"

Kelly shook her head. "Nope. As I recall, trying to go cheap wasn't part of the deal."

"I don't suppose you would like to keep everything as partial payment of your fee?"

Kelly purposely looked around Phil's office. While not the most opulent she had ever been in, it was a far cry from her own, which contained secondhand furnishings and a remnant carpet. "What do you think mom would say if I told her that you wanted me, your little sister, to accept *used* backpacking equipment in lieu of rent and food money?"

"I should have my head examined for thinking there could ever be a purely business relationship between us."

"Oh? And when are you going to make the appointment with the psychiatrist? Before or after the next photography crisis I have to bail you out of?"

He gave her a crooked, engaging grin. "Go on, get out of here. I'll see you get your money by the end of the week."

"And Reinhart's?"

"Check with me tomorrow morning. I'll try to get you an appointment within the next few days."

She pushed herself off of the desk and headed for the door. "Remember...prominent photo credits."

"Wait a second," he said, ignoring her crack about the credits. "You still haven't told me how you and Brian hit it off."

She paused, her hand on the knob, poised for flight. "Some other time, Phil. I have a hundred things to do this afternoon." She pulled the door open.

"I'm not asking for a dissertation. Just tell me — did you like him or didn't you?"

"I don't think 'like' is the right word," she said softly, cryptically.

"Such eloquence."

"Hey, I just take the pictures. You'll have to hire someone else to write the story."

"You didn't do anything to offend—"

"For crying out loud, Phil. What always makes you so quick to assume *I* would do something? How do you know that Brian didn't—"

"Because he's not the type."

*"But I am?"*

Phil's expression went from teasing curiosity to a frown. "Are we talking about the same thing?" Uneasily he leaned forward in his chair, resting his hands on his desk. "Kelly, he didn't...."

"No." She sighed. "Brian didn't try to rape me or anything like that."

He visibly relaxed. "That's not what I meant. I just thought that maybe—"

"I'll see you later, Phil."

"Why don't you come for dinner Saturday?"

"Let me get back to you, okay?"

She saw him nod and reach for the transparencies as she closed the door. If she couldn't find some way to get Phil off her back about Brian, it wasn't going to be nearly as easy to exorcise him as she had first thought.

ON THE WAY BACK to the studio, Kelly swung past the animal shelter to find a kitten to use in The Wool Barn project. In the weeks she had been gone, her neighbor, Charlene Boyers had put an ad in the paper and given away the kittens Kelly had hoped to borrow again. Seeking something long-haired, with an air of genteel aristocracy, she was faintly annoyed at the persistent actions of a pugnacious-looking orange-and-white tabby as it reached out and snagged her blouse whenever she passed too close to his cage. When he finally caught her and she tried to remove his claw from the cut lacework on her sleeve, he quickly countered and gained a better hold by digging into the flesh beneath. Kelly gasped as needlelike tips sank into her arm.

"Here, let me help you." One of the workers spotted her predicament and came up to the cage.

Kelly forced a smile. "He seems a little overeager to find a new owner."

The elderly woman looked at the paper attached to the cage. "If I were him, I'd probably be a little anxious, too."

"What do you mean?"

"As much as we'd like to keep 'em all, we just don't have the room. Unless they're real special, they usually only get to stay a few days."

Kelly felt a sinking sensation in the pit of her stomach. So much for soft and sophisticated, she inwardly groaned. She stared at the kitten, now staring back at her, his face pressed to the bars. A touch of deep orange on either side of his nose gave him a permanent look of jaunty disdain. When she reached up to touch the top of his head with her finger, he artfully caught it with his paw, brought it to his mouth and caressed it with a moist pink tongue. "All right," she murmured with a sigh, knowing it would take a considerable amount of work to make this hauty creature look "cute." "You win." Turning to the woman beside her, she said, "I'll take this one."

Determined not to allow the kitten any firmer grasp on her heartstrings than absolutely necessary, Kelly decided not to give him a name. She would leave that chore to his next, more permanent owner. As soon as she finished the work for The Wool Barn, she would put an ad in the paper and find the kitten a real home. Fair pay for a day's work, considering the possible alternatives.

LATER THAT WEEK as Kelly stood at the door to her studio staring at the second set the Beast had destroyed in as many days, she felt the first niggling doubts begin to take hold that she would ever be able to inflict that animal on anyone else. What if the person who answered her ad had priceless antique furniture or happened to bleed easily? What if they had children? Could a child cope with a cat that liked to take unannounced rides attached to his leg—especially if that child wasn't wearing long pants at the time?

As if equipped with a sixth sense, the Beast seemed to know when Kelly had reached the end of her patience. Then, with uncanny accuracy, he would do something that would make her fall back under the spell of his charm. Whether he was unexpectedly snuggling up on her lap or tilting his head to one side and talking to her with a plaintive meow, the cat seemed to have perfect timing.

Kelly stepped into the room carefully, making sure the door closed tightly behind her. Still not spotting his now-familiar orange-and-white coat, she avoided walking near his favorite hiding places, hoping to reach the dressing room where she would slip out of her panty hose before he had a chance to greet her. The appointment with the owner of Reinhart's Travel Agency had been a disappointment, but not a devastating one. At least he had given her portfolio far more than the cursory examination it had received at the Alexander Agency. And his comments had been astute as well as complimentary. The problem with hiring her was simple. Just that week Reinhart's had decided to stop using photographs and to go back to artwork in their advertising. With a promise that they would be in touch should the agency ever decide to go back to photography, he had shown Kelly to the door.

That left Templeton's to concentrate on. As soon as The Wool Barn was out of the way, she planned to rearrange the studio to accommodate her regular work in one corner, and to keep the rest free for the Templeton project. She was anxious to get started. Although they hadn't given her a firm due date, she certainly wouldn't be given a second assignment until the first was finished.

A wide smile of excitement and pleasure hit her face just as the Beast struck her ankles.

# 9

THE END OF JULY passed with little notice. While most
of the citizens of Phoenix turned darker from the
sun's unrelenting presence, Kelly's tan faded. With
rare exception, her life for the past month had consisted of time spent at the studio working and at her
apartment sleeping. The Beast seemingly grew larger
by the hour, silently confirming her worst fears that
his sire had been part mountain lion. At least once a
day in a fit of pique, she reached for the telephone,
loudly threatening a by-then-cowering feline that
she was going to put an ad in the paper to get rid of
him. In one of her moments of fury she had even
mentally composed an ad. *Free to good home: kitten of
questionable lineage. Would be perfect companion to extremely mean child or ex-gladiator. Hurry! Only one left.*

Deeply concentrating on the problem of photographing a jelly doughnut for a local bakery so that
it looked freshly baked, Kelly wasn't aware that
someone had entered her outer office until the Beast
lifted his head and growled in that direction. She
stepped over the trailing electrical cords lying scattered across the floor like thick black spaghetti and
lunged for the door, closing it behind her a fraction
of a second before the Beast could follow. "Charlene!" she cried, surprise and delight in her voice.
"What are you doing here?"

"I've given up trying to catch you at home." Her

neighbor reached into her huge straw purse, pulled out a package wrapped in brown paper and handed it to Kelly. "This came for you almost a week ago. Since it wouldn't fit in the box, I told the mailman I would make sure you received it, in order to save you a trip to the post office. At the time, I had no idea it would be so hard to get hold of you. You're *never* home anymore."

Charlene Boyers was the same age as Kelly, and despite their numerous differences in life-styles, they had become immediate and close friends when Kelly moved into the same apartment complex four years earlier. Tall and still slim after three children in five years, she had recently started modeling for local fashion shows to add money to the "house" account she and her husband, Andy, had started just after they were married.

"I appreciate the effort, but you didn't have to come all the way down here; you could have called. I would have made a point of stopping by or—"

"I was in the neighborhood, anyway." She shifted from one foot to the other. "Well, aren't you going to open it?"

For the first time Kelly really looked at the package. She turned it over to see her name handwritten in unfamiliar bold script. Automatically her gaze shifted to the upper left-hand corner. Her breath caught in her throat. Written in the same bold script was the name...B. Robertson. The address blurred as she fought to hide the intensity of her reaction from Charlene. With studied nonchalance, she tossed the package on the counter. "It's nothing important. Just something left over from a job I did a few weeks ago. I'm sorry you had to go out of your way to get it to me."

"Oh...." The word came out as a disappointed sigh. "I thought...well, I don't know what I thought. It's just that unopened packages drive me nuts whether they happen to be for me or not."

Kelly's heartbeat pounded loudly in her ears. "Do you have a few minutes to visit? There's coffee in the—" A loud crash came from the back room.

Charlene jumped. "What was that?"

Kelly rolled her eyes in disgust. "From the whooshing sound that came just before the thud, I'd say one of the portable rolls of paper just fell over."

"All by itself? Aren't you going to check to make sure?"

"Not until I can walk in there without homicide on my mind." Kelly went on to explain her increasingly tenuous relationship with the Beast, blatantly hinting that the cat was available for adoption.

"Why don't you take him back to the animal shelter?"

"Because in my heart I know it would be his death sentence. There isn't another person in this city crazy enough to put up with a cat that thinks it's a Doberman pinscher." Charlene gave her an uncomprehending stare. "He's attacked three deliverymen, two mailmen and one poor guy who just happened to stop outside the front door when it was open," Kelly explained. "He gives his victims a three-second warning signal that sounds something like a lizard clearing its throat. After that, if they haven't had the good sense to leave, the Beast attaches himself to the nearest part of their anatomy." She tossed her braid back over her shoulder. "The funny thing about his weird behavior is that I honestly think *he* thinks he's protecting me."

"What does he do to women?"

"I don't know. I've been afraid to find out."

Charlene thought a minute then grinned impishly. "I'll be sure to forewarn Andy. There are certain parts of his anatomy I most assuredly do not want injured."

Kelly laughed aloud. "I said my cat was mean, not maniacal."

"In this case, I'd rather be safe than sorry." She turned to leave. "When you decide to stop all this work nonsense for a little fun, call me."

"Give me another month."

Charlene waved through the window, then headed for her car. As Kelly watched her friend drive away, the frozen smile she had maintained melted into a look of apprehension. Slowly she walked back to the counter; her trembling hand touched the innocuous-looking package. For long seconds she stared at her name, studying the sureness and clarity of Brian's handwriting.

Why now, she wanted to scream. After four weeks she had considered herself well down the road to forgetfulness. Her finger touched the package's edge, moving thoughtfully along the six-inch length and then across the four-inch width.

Fleetingly she considered finding a felt tip pen and writing Return to Sender in broad slashing letters, obliterating her own name with the message. Instead she took the package from the counter and held it against her chest. Mechanically she walked back into the studio, poured herself a cup of coffee, stepped around the roll of paper the Beast had knocked over and sat down on the overstuffed sofa she sometimes used for a bed. The thoughts and memories of Brian she had ruthlessly shunted aside during the past month refused to be held in abeyance any longer. They overwhelmed her, insistently letting her know that for all her denials she was still terribly vulnerable where he was concerned.

Taking a deep breath, she set the coffee aside, turned the package over on her lap and ran her finger along the taped seam. Once the paper was pushed aside, she immediately recognized the familiar reddish-brown cover of the book Brian had carried with him on their trip. She looked at the title, stamped in gold, *Starr's Guide to the John Muir Trail & the High Sierra Region*. Puzzled, Kelly removed the rest of the paper, seeking a note of explanation. Nothing. She started to open the book when she noticed the pages were oddly separated, as if something had been stuffed between them.

She let the book open naturally. A soft cry of surprise caught in her throat. Pressed between the pages was a bright yellow wild flower. Her gaze went to the margin where she saw a note written in a now-familiar hand. And arrow pointed to the text where a section had been underlined.

Found this flower here the day after you left. Its color reminded me of our first morning together when the sun made your hair look like strands of gold.

And then at the bottom of the opposite page....

Breakfast. I made oatmeal—enough for two. Even the marmots turned up their noses at the leftovers.

The three marmots that had visited them in the meadow hadn't been nearly as fussy. They had eaten anything and everything, whether offered or not.

But then, after that first morning when Brian had shared his oatmeal with her, she hadn't been quite so fussy, either. At the end of a week and a half, she had actually discovered she was beginning to like his "stick to the ribs" breakfast.

The Beast hopped up beside Kelly, poked his head under her arm and peremptorialy curled up on her lap. She gave him a moment to settle in before she leaned the book against his vibrating back and turned the page.

An arrow pointed to a section of text.

Found a lake here. It was so clear I was sure the water couldn't be more than a foot or two deep—it was well above my head. Thought about you and the times you went swimming... how beautiful you looked... how graceful.

Farther down the page....

Camped next to this stream. Looked at the stars and wondered if you were looking at them in Phoenix. Picked out the brightest and made a wish. Didn't sleep well after that.

She felt a warmth in her loins. Since returning from the mountains, she had known several similiar nights.

The afternoon slipped away on padded feet as Kelly slowly turned the pages of Brian's book, gathering a bouquet of pressed wild flowers and a heart full of poignant messages. With beautifully cryptic prose he had taken her along with him as he traversed sheer cliffs, climbed peaks still covered with snow and camped in lush meadows. Each day he had stopped to write something, to give a part of himself to her. In his written words were unspoken messages of love. The messages were never demanding but were gifts from himself expressed openly, freely and naturally.

If he had come to her and tried to force his way into her life she could have used her stubbornness to resist him—this way, she was defenseless. Her dreams didn't seem to matter when weighed against the ache he created inside her. Had he used a bulldozer, she would not have succumbed. But his weapon had been a whisper, and she had an overwhelming need to hear the rest of what he would tell her.

She flipped the wrapping paper over to read the return address. Denver, Colorado. Hadn't he told her that his mother lived in Denver? If she were to call him there, what would she say? Hi, this is Kelly. Can you come to Phoenix so that I can figure out whether I really love you or whether what we have is only an incredible example of biological urges gone crazy?

The Beast stirred on her lap, stretching his legs and poking her in the stomach with his back feet. Absently she scratched his ears, setting off the loud rumbling purr again. Purposely she let her gaze travel around the studio. She had worked so hard to get where she was, sacrificed vacations, clothing, a social life—even chosen to live in a Spartan, utilitarian apartment in order to buy the state-of-the-art equipment that filled these few rooms. Never once during those years had she ever considered that someday giving it all up might be the price she would have to pay to love someone. Give it up? No. She wouldn't even consider that possibility. What she was contemplating was really nothing more than an extended vacation.

"Get up, Beast," she said, giving the cat a nudge. This time when he stretched, his claws dug lightly but meaningfully into her leg. "Keep that up and you'll be looking for someone else's lap to warm," she warned, her voice threatening. As if it had been his intent all along, he pulled in his claws and gracefully stepped aside.

More out of conviction that her actions had somehow been predestined rather than a compulsion to perform them, Kelly headed for the phone to call Brian. After two tries she found a sympathetic operator who was willing to spend the time it took to match the single last name of Robertson with the address Kelly supplied. Not giving herself time to reconsider, she immediately pressed the eleven numbers that would connect her with Brian.

A friendly sounding female voice answered. "Hello."

"Hi." Now what? "My name is Kelly Stewart...." Suddenly she felt as if her mouth had filled with cotton and her throat contained a huge lump. "I'm... uh... a friend of Brian's. Is he there, by any chance?"

"Oh, I'm so sorry—you just missed him. He left two hours ago to visit his brother."

"Will he be back soon?"

"Well... yes, however, I'm not sure when. Brian's brother lives in Alaska, you know. Since they haven't seen each other for quite some time, I don't expect him back for a while."

"Alaska?" she breathed, unable to hide her acute disappointment.

"Is it an emergency that you get in touch with him?"

"No...I only wanted to thank him...for a present he sent me."

"I can give you Tom's address in Alaska if you'd like to write to him there. Or perhaps you'd prefer the phone number."

"No...."

"Well, I'm sorry you missed him."

"Yes...I am, too." She needed time to think. She thanked the woman she had assumed to be Brian's mother and hung up, declining to leave her number for a return call.

Only minutes ago she had been filled with such anticipation. And now it was as if she'd suddenly been drained of everything that made the day worthwhile. She felt exhausted, numb. If only she had gone home a little earlier this past week. Charlene would have given her the package sooner, she would have called Brian before he left.

*If only!* Words for people who weren't strong enough to accept the consequences of their actions. She had been crazy to try to call Brian in the first place. What was the point? What would she have done if he had asked her to come to him? Take off and leave her clients without their promised advertising copy? Not to mention the work she had already put into Templeton's.

Kelly glanced at her watch. She had already spent an entire afternoon in never-never land. It was time to get back to the real world again.

She left Brian's book on the front desk. Out of sight, she reasoned, out of mind.

The cat raised his head when she entered the studio, momentarily interrupting his ritualistic groom-

ing to stare at her. As she moved past the draped
table where she had left the setup for the bakery ad,
she paused a moment, confused. Seconds later she
realized what was wrong. Her frustration had found
a target. The jelly doughnut was gone!

"Dammit, Beast," she raged. "This is the last
straw. You have committed your final sin around
here." He continued to stare at her. "You can save
the wide-eyed innocent look for the next poor jerk
who's stupid enough to be taken in by it—I'm immune."

As if realizing that he had finally gone too far, the
Beast shook himself, answered her venom with a
plaintive meow and padded across the studio to rub
against her legs.

"It won't work this time. We are absolutely, reso-
lutely, unequivocally through." Kelly went into the
lab to get the keys to the studio. When she stormed
back through a few minutes later on her way out to
get a replacement doughnut, she paused at the door.
"If there is one thing out of place when I return,"
she warned, "you may not even make it back to the
animal shelter."

Instead of cowering in fear, the Beast blinked and
then yawned. Kelly slammed the door hard enough
to knock her prized diploma from Gibson Photography Institute off of the wall.

WHEN KELLY RETURNED a half hour later, a strangely
quiet Beast was at the door to greet her. She pointedly ignored him and headed for the workbench to
start the intricate surgical process necessary to make
the new doughnut look as if someone had just taken
a bite out of it. Once the small half circle was cut, she
would use a pastry tube to carefully add the jelly.

That morning it had taken three tries to get what she considered a satisfactory combination; she mentally crossed her fingers that everything would come together on the first try this time. She was tired, sticky from the heat and hungry... not to mention irritable.

With the "bite" precisely cut and ready for the jelly, Kelly carefully studied the doughnut from every angle to make sure the powdered sugar was evenly distributed and would photograph with the proper density. Bending for one last look from the angle she would shoot, she backed up and stepped on the cat. "Dammit, Beast," she grumbled, pushing him aside with her foot. "Stay out of my way."

Before she had finished yelling at him, he was back, butting his head against her shin. "All right, that's it. I'm locking you in the office." She bent over to pick him up. Just as her hands curved around his stomach, she saw the mouse in his mouth. She screamed; he bolted; the mouse landed on her foot.

Fighting back the urge to scream again, Kelly closed her eyes and counted to ten. Then without looking at what she was doing, she gingerly slipped her foot out of her loafer. With a deep breath to fortify her, she picked up the shoe and carefully transported the precariously balanced rodent to the trash can. The Beast watched her pass from behind a stool. She glared at him. "If you think you won any points with this, believe me, you can think again."

The mouse made a small thunking sound as it hit the bottom of the metal container. Kelly gulped. She looked at her shoe; knowing she would forever see the mouse perched on its end, she tossed the loafer into the trash can, too. She leaned against the wall and sighed. The idea of spending the next half hour squeezing bright red jelly into a doughnut made her nauseated. It was time to go home.

Gathering her belongings, she turned to the cat. "Front and center, Beast," she said, her voice low, ominous. "You're coming with me." Head down, tail dragging, the cat crossed the room. "Cut it out. Your melodramatics won't work this time. I told you, we're through." Still, despite her command, he followed her with all of the animation of a wilted flower.

By the time they reached the animal shelter, it was closed. A sign indicated there was a place to leave animals for the night but despite her anger, Kelly couldn't bring herself to put the Beast inside.

"Well, you lucked out," she said, getting back into the car. "You've won a fourteen-hour reprieve. Make the most of it."

BRIAN PACED the narrow walkway in front of Kelly's apartment, repeatedly telling himself that he had no business being there. If she had wanted to see him, she would have called. He had given her plenty of time to make up her mind—more than a week after the book should have arrived. Yet here he was in Phoenix uninvited. So much for maintaining subtlety in his supposedly cleverly planned courtship.

Staying away had been torture. At each trail head he had fought the same battle—whether to continue the journey or leave the mountains and go to her. In the end he always remained, not because he wanted to but because he felt it was important to give her time alone to think about him.

He had been so sure she would have changed her mind by now and would want to see him again. But she hadn't...and still he had come. Loving her, wanting her, had become so much a part of him that he simply could not stay away any longer.

He wondered if Phil had told her he called to get her address. Could that be why she never answered her phone? Could this be him, thinking such paranoid thoughts? He glanced at his watch. Four minutes had passed since the last time he checked.

Maybe she was on assignment somewhere or on vacation. There was always the remote chance that something had happened and she hadn't even received the book yet. He let out a disgusted groan. He was really reaching for an explanation. A car door slammed behind him just then. From the same direction he heard, "Get out of the car. And if you know what's good for you, you won't try anything funny. This is absolutely your last chance with me."

Brian raked his hand through his hair. What in the hell had he walked in on? A lover's quarrel? In all his planning, he had never once considered the possibility he would find her with another man. Just then Kelly came around the corner, nearly colliding with him in her preoccupied, head-down, stride.

"Brian...!" she breathed, his name a whispered exclamation.

"Hello, Kelly," he said, watching, waiting for her eyes to tell him he was welcome.

"What are you doing here? I thought—"

"You had heard the last of me?" He tried to inject a light touch to cover the awkwardness. He couldn't believe how beautiful she looked.

"I thought you were going to Alaska."

"How did you—"

"Your mother told me—"

"When did—"

"This afternoon." How handsome he looked with

his beard now fully grown and carefully trimmed. Dressed in slacks, a short-sleeve shirt and a tie that had been loosened, and carrying his jacket slung over his shoulder, he presented quite a different image than the one she had carried in her mind these past four weeks. Now, for the first time, she could see the executive in him and it was terrifically sexy. "I called to thank you for the flowers."

She had received them, and she had tried to reach him. "You're welcome," he said softly. For long seconds they stared at each other, exchanging thoughts, desires, memories in the energy of their gazes.

Suddenly Kelly stiffened. From somewhere behind her, she heard the Beast growl his warning. "Brian," she cried. "Watch out!" But it was too late. The cat had attached himself to Brian's thigh with all four paws.

"What the . . . !" Brian exclaimed.

"*Beast*, let go," Kelly ordered, grasping the cat by the scruff of his neck.

"Kelly, please," Brian gasped. "Let *me* do that." He reached down and pulled the cat from his leg. Holding it at arm's length in front of him, he said, "He's yours, I take it?" He glanced from the cat to Kelly and then back to the cat again. Suddenly the strange one-way conversation he had overheard moments ago made sense. "Quite a welcoming committee you have here."

"Are you hurt?" she asked with concern.

"Would it mean tender loving care if I said yes?"

She finally relaxed and returned his grin. "Every bit as tender and loving as would be given to someone who had two feet full of blisters."

"Then I am mortally wounded." He readjusted his

hold on the squirming cat, grasping him more firmly at the shoulders. "Does he have a name?"

"I call him the Beast, for obvious reasons."

"Is he always this protective or does he have a thing about ex-bankers?"

"He won't let any man get near me."

Tilting his head slightly to one side, Brian studied the cat for a moment. "How interesting. I think we might become friends, after all." With a quick, graceful movement he tucked the Beast under his arm and started to scratch him behind his ears.

To Kelly's amazement, the cat began purring. She shook her head. "I give up. I'm not even going to try to understand what just happened."

"It's nothing mysterious. He's had time enough to figure out that I'm not planning any immediate harm to you and since you seem to have accepted me, he's decided he might as well, also."

"And how is it that you happen to know so much about cats?" He was constantly surprising her.

"Whenever I needed extra money in high school— which was all the time—I'd work for my aunt. She was the only vet in town who specialized in felines. For some reason I've always been able to handle the meanest of them without coming out too badly abused. And let me tell you, there are some cantankerous, stubborn cats in this world."

"Oh, really?" She purposely eyed the Beast. "I would never have guessed."

Brian laughed. "I take it that the two of you have had a bad day?"

"I'd rather not talk about it, if you don't mind." She stared at him a moment before going on. She liked the idea that he had worked with animals and had such tolerance for their idiosyncrasies. "There's so much about you I don't know."

"If you would invite me into your apartment, we could start working to change that."

She gave him an embarrassed smile. "You mean you didn't come all the way down here to stand around visiting with me on my front lawn?" She turned to walk the few steps to her door.

"Kelly?" he called, stopping her.

She turned around. "Huh?"

"Why are you only wearing one shoe?"

"It's a long story," she said, giving the Beast another pointed look. "Come in, and if there happens to be one of those painful pauses in the conversation when neither of us can think of anything else to say, I'll tell you all about it."

# 10

BRIAN FOLLOWED KELLY into her apartment. He waited for her to close the door, then released the cat. When she turned she found him staring at her. "I've imagined seeing you again so many times that I can't quite believe it's finally happened," he told her.

She smiled softly and held out her hand. "You can touch me if you want," she invited. "Just don't pinch."

Brian took her hand and brought it to his lips.

Shaken by the feelings his simple gesture produced, Kelly fought for control. "Are you hungry?" she asked, seeking something, anything, to say and not realizing how suggestive her question might seem until it was too late.

"No..." he answered, fighting his own battles. "At least I don't think I am. Are you?"

She took a deep breath. "I must be. I haven't eaten all day."

"Is that why your hand is shaking?"

"My hand?" She hadn't realized her nervousness had manifested itself in such a painfully obvious way. Normally she could hide her emotions from even the most discerning person.

"This thing I happen to be holding." He gave her fingers a gentle squeeze. "It's trembling." Quietly he added, "Why don't we conduct this reunion on safer grounds and go out to dinner somewhere? I want to talk to you."

"About what?"

It would be foolish to lie, to try to pretend he had come to Phoenix for anything but the reason he had. "About you and me and the possibility that if we work at it, we might be able to find a way for us to go on seeing each other." Still, despite his supposed honesty, he had made his explanation sound a lot better than it really was. What he truly hoped was not to talk her into an occasional date, but into leaving Phoenix and going with him. He wanted her to meet his family and them to know her. But most of all, beyond all the trumped-up practical reasons, he had a deep abiding ache just to have her with him.

"You don't give up easily, do you?"

"I never have." Especially not when the stakes were so incredibly high.

WHILE HE WAITED for Kelly to get ready, Brian read the titles of the books on the shelves that lined the back wall of her living room. Several rows were taken up with volumes on photography, the rest were filled with a haphazard assortment of subjects ranging from history to science, Westerns to romance. He realized with a start that he knew no more about this woman he professed to love than she knew about him. What kind of person curled up in bed at night with *Understanding Einstein*?

Kelly came up behind him. "You can read anything that appeals to you but you'll have to do it here," she teased. "After repeated bad experiences, I've learned not to lend my books."

Brian turned. His quick reply died in his throat when he saw her. Dressed in a loosely belted lightweight jersey that clung softly to the hills and valleys of her body, she literally took his breath away. She had unbraided her hair and pulled the sides back, allowing the shimmering tawny mass to lie full and free, softly caressing her shoulders. "That's a good color for you," he said, noting how the dress made her skin seem to glow, her eyes shine with smoky blue fires.

"I'm never sure whether to call it peach or apricot." She had chosen this particular dress because it was new and made her feel pretty...and it had suddenly mattered very much that she look pretty for Brian.

"Shall we go?" If they stayed, he was afraid he would lose what little control he had left. Where her breasts pressed against the material, he imagined them pressed against his chest; where her hips gently swelled below her waist, he imagined their feel under his exploring hand.

Kelly didn't want to leave. She wanted to stay in the cocoon of her apartment with Brian and forget, if only for an evening, all that divided them. "Do you have a preference...."

"For?" he softly queried.

"Any special cuisine?"

Brian slipped the book he had been holding back into the shelf. Unable to keep from touching her any longer, he reached out and gently caressed her throat, letting his fingers move higher to follow the curve of her jaw. "I don't think it makes much difference. We could eat pizza or the finest steak in Phoenix and tomorrow I doubt that I would remember any part of the meal other than you sitting across from me."

Kelly swallowed. "Mexican is, er, pretty hard to forget."

Oh, how desperately he wanted her—for now, for always. "Mexican it is, then; lead the way."

"I'll just be a minute...I have to get my coat." Kelly started toward the bedroom, stopped and then turned back to face him. With a sheepish smile she said, "I don't think there's much chance I'll need a coat tonight. Not after it reached 107 degrees in the shade only a few hours ago."

Brian walked over to her and took her hand. "You never know about these things," he said, gently teasing her. "But you needn't worry about it, should a cold front move in while we're in the restaurant, I'd be happy to lend you the jacket I have out in the rental car."

"Do I detect a note of skepticism in your voice?"

"Not at all. If I've learned anything about you in the time we've known each other, it's to never—"

"Stop! I can't handle praise on an empty stomach. And I'm absolutely sure it was praise you were about to give me, wasn't it? Wait, don't answer. Let's just get out of here so we can eat."

Brian laughed and reached for the door. "I thought you said the mountain air created that voracious appetite of yours."

"So you've caught me in one little tiny white lie. What's something like that between friends?" She winked as she stepped past him. "Unbridled gluttony is such an unfeminine trait. Can you blame me for trying to keep it hidden?"

KELLY'S FAVORITE MEXICAN RESTAURANT had a forty-five-minute waiting list, so they went to a place called The Clarion, a secluded, out-of-the-way establishment that specialized in prime rib. Over candlelight and white wine, spinach salad and steak cooked medium well, they talked and laughed and learned more about each other. Kelly discovered that Brian was allergic to red wine and when he was three, he had almost died from a spider bite. She told him about her unreasoning fear of crickets and that she had stood in line for eight hours to see *The Empire Strikes Back* the first day it hit the theaters.

When the dishes were cleared away and coffee served, Brian reached across the white linen table-cloth and took Kelly's hand. "I've missed you," he said softly. "When you first left, I had a terrible time believing you were really gone. I'd be walking along the trail and see something—a flower, a waterfall—and I'd turn around to tell you about it." His eyes expressed the confusion, the terrible disappointment he had felt at the time. "It was such a shock when you weren't there."

"The time we spent together was special, magical, rare." Again, as she had in the mountains, she tried to make him understand something she couldn't fully comprehend herself.

"You're wrong, Kelly. It wasn't just the time we were together before that is so special...it's when-ever and wherever we happen to be, whether it's here in Phoenix or traveling around the world. That's what I've come to prove to you." His thumb massaged the back of her hand.

"Tell me what the rest of the trip was like," she prompted, trying to steer him back to safer, more neutral ground. Somewhere they would not be forced to stand on opposite sides of an emotional fence. "What did you see? Did you meet anyone?"

Of course he knew what she was doing and con-sidered the possibility that she was right to react the way she had. The subject was still beyond them at the moment. Nothing had been settled past the knowing that they had desperately missed each other. He leaned forward, his elbows resting on the table, his eyes filled with understanding. "I saw the most incredible country, Kelly. There were water-falls that echoed through canyons like runaway freight trains and streams that passed right beside me with hardly a whisper. I saw grouse and golden trout and yellow-legged frogs. I met a couple of hikers who were on their way to a High Sierra wedding and walked a few miles with them." He paused. "And with every step I took, I thought about you," he finished.

"Probably because you could feel me thinking about you," she finally admitted as much to herself as to him. "At night I would close my eyes and try to imagine the place you were camping. In the daytime I would wonder what meals you had prepared and try to imagine the country you walked through."

He stared at her a moment longer before releasing her hand and signaling for the check. "I want you to show me your studio," he said. "I think it's about time I saw my competition."

KELLY UNLOCKED THE FRONT DOOR to the office, flipped on the lights then quickly went over to a closet to shut off the burglar alarm. She motioned for Brian to follow her into the studio. "Well... here it is," she said, stepping aside to let him pass, an unmistakable note of pride in her voice.

Brian moved past her, his gaze sweeping the room. He had never been inside a professional pho-tography studio, but because of his long-ago sum-mer job at a newspaper, he knew a little about the profession. There were lights everywhere—overhead, on stands—both round and rectangular. Umbrellas and large white reflector sheets used to soften or heighten the effects of the lights sat in a corner. Against one wall, attached to the ceiling, were large rolls of different-colored paper to be lowered like movie screens and used as backdrops. On one side of the room was a table draped with black cloth, on another side there was a Chinese jade figure sitting on a long wooden bench, encircled by a forest green piece of silk. A sofa and chair took up the third wall, a workbench the fourth. On the workbench was the remnant of a doughnut. "Left over from lunch?" he asked as Kelly came over to stand beside him.

"It's a long story." She laid her purse on the bench. "Come on back to the workroom. I'll show you what I've been doing lately."

Brian started to follow, then stopped when he spotted her missing shoe in the trash can. When he bent to retrieve it, he saw the mouse. He glanced up at Kelly, a puzzled look in his eyes. "I know...he was after your doughnut and you killed him with the only thing at hand."

She grinned. "It's another—"

"You don't have to tell me, it's *another* long story." He dropped the shoe and continued down a short hallway and into a long, narrow room. There were black-and-white and colored pictures of every size covering the walls; the surfaces of the tables that lined both walls were meticulously free of clutter.

Kelly turned to him, her eyes sparkling with excitement. "Do you remember me telling you how hard it was to get lucrative assignments in Phoenix?"

"As I recall, you said the prime accounts were locked up tight against new talent."

"Well...." She playfully leaned close to him and in a stage whisper said, "I don't want to say this too loudly for fear I might jinx the whole thing, but thanks to Phil, a crack in the shield has developed and I'm going to squeeze through. One of the area's top ad agencies has given me an assignment. The most exclusive dress shop in Phoenix is bringing in a shipment of silks in the late fall and they want a really dynamite series of photographs to advertise them." She could no longer keep the smile from her face. "Would you like to see what I've done so far?"

"Sneak previews are my favorite kind," he told her solemnly.

"I think you're a reasonably safe risk not to tell the competition." She opened a locked drawer. Inside were three large boxes containing two-and-one-quarter-inch transparencies and several eleven-by-fourteen pictures. Kelly took out the stack of photos, laid them on the table and stepped back.

Brian moved to take her place. He picked up the top photograph and studied it. Just below center was a partially filled fishbowl containing two brightly colored fantail goldfish. Carefully draped over the bowl was a cloth of sheerest silk, delicately embroidered with yet more fantail goldfish. The longer he looked the more illusionary the photograph seemed, until it became difficult to tell which fish were silk and which were real. The result was a stunningly simple photograph that spoke volumes about the quality of the silk scarf.

"That one was a real bear to shoot, but I'm really pleased with the results." She laughed lightly. "You have no idea how tough it is to get fish to pose for you. Or how to keep from cooking them under the hot lights when they won't pose."

Brian didn't respond to her animated monologue. He simply laid the first photograph aside and moved on to the next. This one showed a man and a woman from just below their waists to several inches above their heads. The woman's back was to the camera, the man's hand was placed in the center as if they were dancing. Their heads were in muted shadow so that the focus of the photograph was the man's hand resting on the shimmering royal blue silk dress.

"The agency gave me the captions they wanted to use and left the artwork up to me. The copy for this one reads, '*Nothing* feels like real silk.'"

Brian was glad that he was standing with his back to Kelly. He would have hated to let her see the look of stunned surprise he knew was in his eyes. She was good—damn good. Never once had it occurred to him she had this much talent. It made him sick to his stomach that he had so cavalierly dismissed her abilities without ever having seen any examples of her work.

He finished looking at the remaining photographs, only subliminally hearing Kelly's comments as he sunk deeper into a despair of his own making. What a supercilious, egotistical bastard he had been. He had come to Phoenix with the single-minded intent of sweeping her off her feet and taking her away from her everyday, humdrum existence. She had been right to turn him down a month ago...she was right to turn him down now.

"Well?" Kelly prompted, her voice betraying her anxiety at his continued silence.

Slowly, carefully he regrouped the pictures, taking far more time than necessary to put them into a perfectly even stack. He was stalling for time because he had no idea what to say. In showing him these pictures, Kelly had forced him to stand back and look at himself...and he had been appalled at what he had seen. He had never been a self-sacrificing person; no one could have achieved what he had as fast as he had by putting the needs of those around him first. For as long as he'd been an adult, if he saw something he wanted, he went after it. And now, with Kelly, that was no longer possible. He loved her too much to put what he wanted above what was best for her.

"Brian?" she urged softly, her confidence slipping at his persistent refusal to answer.

"They're spectacular, Kelly," he finally said. "If these photographs don't put you on the road to rich and famous, the people in this town are crazy."

She let out a pent-up sigh, eloquent in its force. "You had me worried for a second."

"There's no way you can't know how good these photographs are," he continued, turning to face her.

"Mondays, Wednesdays and Fridays are my confidence days—you've caught me on a Thursday. You have to remember that photography, like all art forms, is subjective. A painting, a song, a poem, a piece of sculpture...they're only good if the public thinks so. Without other people's acceptance and approval of what I do, I'm nothing."

"I would be the first to admit that I'm not an expert, but from what I've seen tonight, you have a real talent, a special flair for what you do. I can't understand why you don't have the ego to back it up." But he did. She had worked so hard for acceptance and been turned away so often, it was only a matter of time before she began to wonder if the men in their ivory towers were right, after all. Unreasoning anger shot through him, and lacking any other direction in which to vent it, he turned on her. "Why in the hell have you stayed in this town as long as you have, beating your head against a brick wall that you admit you've known all along was there?"

"Because this is my home. I like Phoenix." She was stunned by his attack, and her chin rose defensively.

"Are you sure it isn't that mile-wide stubborn streak of yours that's keeping you here? That old, 'By God, they're going to accept me if I have to kill myself in the effort' syndrome?"

"All my family is—"

"You're a big girl. It's time you made a life of your own."

Her eyes narrowed. "By any chance does that 'life of your own' translate into traipsing around the country with you?"

"No," he said, the word an incredibly painful admission. "It means going somewhere, *anywhere*, your talent will be recognized and appreciated."

She was even more confused, not by his anger this time, but by his answer. Hadn't he said his reason for coming to Phoenix was to try to talk her into seeing him? Was she wrong to think that he still wanted her to accompany him on his wanderings? "I don't understand...."

"You've given these people more chances than they deserve, Kelly. It's time for you to move on."

"That's not true. How can you even suggest I leave when everything is beginning to work out for me here? Once the right people see what I've done with this account, they'll send other business my way."

"What makes you so sure?" he demanded.

"That's the way it is."

"Then why hasn't it worked before now? You've been doing small accounts around here for years. Why hasn't anyone noticed how talented you are after all this time?"

"They're just set in their ways."

"And you really believe that somehow it's all miraculously changed and with the strength of your work on this one job you will be let into their tight little circle?"

"Yes!" She had to believe it was true. What else was there?

Brian rubbed his forehead. There had to be a way to wake her up, to make her see that a close-knit business community didn't change its behavior any more readily than a tiger its stripes. She was so painfully naive. He was convinced that if he could get into the minds of the men who had been closing her out all these years, what he would find there would be fear. Fear of her talent, of the challenge she would give them, of the unruly competition she was sure to create in their ordered little worlds. "This is getting us nowhere," he said with a sigh.

"You're right," she answered, the fight leaving her as quickly as it had come. "Why don't we call it an evening while we're still talking to each other?"

Never once in all the times he had dreamed of seeing her again had Brian imagined that they would wind up as they had. "I'm sorry, I had no right to come on so strong." But he did. Loving her gave him that right.

"Brian, I...." She didn't want the evening to end like this. He had come so far and she had missed him so much.

"It's okay, Kelly. It's been a long day and we're

both tired." They were meaningless words meant to get them through a bad situation. "Come on, I'll take you home."

THE DRIVE BACK to Kelly's apartment seemed impossibly long. With all that had happened that evening, a quiet sense of desperation had started to settle over Brian, making him feel for the first time that it might indeed be impossible for the two of them to build a life together. It was a strange feeling. Years had passed since he had even considered the possibility of defeat.

There had to be a way to make her see how futile it was to stay in Phoenix. And then what, an insistent inner voice demanded. What difference would it make between them if she moved to another city? Was he ready to follow? To settle down again so soon after rediscovering freedom?

When they arrived at the thirty-unit apartment complex where Kelly lived, Brian parked the car on the street and went around to open her door. The day's punishing heat had lingered in the asphalt and concrete and stucco of the city, leaving those who chose to live surrounded by the trappings of civilization without the usual cooling that occurred in the open desert. To Brian it was oppressive, something that robbed him of breath, of energy.

Kelly dug the keys from her purse. "Would you like to come in?" she asked, not wanting the evening to end until they had found a way to part friends again.

He needed time alone to think, but even more he needed to be with her. "Yes," he said softly. "I would like that."

# 11

KELLY OPENED THE DOOR to her apartment, stepped into the tiny foyer and reached for the light switch. Long seconds passed as she hesitated, unwilling to destroy the peacefulness of the dark with the harshness of light. How she wished he would touch her. If he would give her the tiniest message of welcome, she would be in his arms. But their earlier argument lingered like an invisible barrier, one they seemed incapable of either surmounting or setting aside. With a soft sigh she flipped the switch and erased the night. Unable to trust her runaway emotions, she used etiquette to see her through the tense moment when she turned to face him. "Can I get you something to drink?"

In his desperate need to forget everything but how much he loved her, Brian had been on the verge of reaching for her, but the coolness of her voice made him pull back. "Yes, something cold would be nice," he said formally, contributing his part to the social game they played.

"I have some white wine...or there's iced tea."

"Iced tea would be fine."

Kelly nodded once in acknowledgment but made no move toward the kitchen. They were so close—fewer than twenty inches separated them—and yet they were so far away. Why couldn't she be the one to initiate something intimate? When every sensual part of her cried out for the release he could give, what perverse force kept her from going to him? Dropping her purse on the hallway table, she mentally cursed her cowardice. "Spiced or plain?"

Brian saw the terrible inner turmoil reflected in her eyes, and it tormented him to realize that he was unquestionably the cause. "Plain," he automatically answered. Without conscious consideration of the inevitable outcome, he reached out to her, touching her arm. "Kelly, would you rather I left?"

Where his hand made contact with her skin it felt as if an emotional charge had passed between them. A poignant sob caught in her throat. She swallowed, then tried to speak. Her mouth formed the answer, but the words remained unspoken. Finally she just shook her head. She had been so wrong. The magic between them had survived distance and time; it was as strong in a desert city with thousands of people around them as it had been in a meadow in the isolation of the mountains. They had created a portable Shangri-la, one that would follow them wherever they went.

Since visiting Kelly's studio, Brian had felt like a person who had haughtily walked the edge of a cliff and because of his arrogance it had crumbled beneath him. In the ensuing fall, whatever footing he had sought had slipped away, and each handhold had been like sand. He needed time to reconcile the distasteful person he had discovered himself to be with the man who loved Kelly beyond reason.

His fantasy that he would come to Phoenix, sweep her off her feet and take her with him had died a quick, uncompromising death. And yet...he still could not make himself believe they were finished. How could they be so right for each other and still be so wrong? "Kelly." His hand tightened on her arm. Suddenly, passionately, the selfless side of him, the side that loved her beyond what he wanted for himself, demanded once again to be heard. Although he could no longer in good conscience ask her to leave Phoenix with him, he had to make one last attempt to talk her into leaving for herself. "You've got to get out of this place. If you stay here, you'll eventually lose everything that makes your work special."

Kelly blanched. Taking him to her studio had been a terrible mistake. Instead of seeing how close she was to succeeding and how important it was that her success come to her in the place where she had strived so long, he had bypassed her feelings in favor of encouraging her ambitions to aim for the "big time." She covered the hurt caused by his insensitivity with a surge of blinding defensive anger, striking out in a direction that surprised them both.

"I think it's about time you realized it isn't just my work that's separating us." She took a moment to form words for what had up until then only been remote feelings. "From the day I was born—mixed in and served right along with the mashed bananas and rice cereal—I was spoon-fed gigantic doses of the work ethic. The way I was raised, it didn't matter how rich someone was or even how philanthropic. If they didn't do something to earn their keep, they were lumped right in with everyone else who refused to work, hobos, drifters, et cetera."

Brian's eyes narrowed as he thought about her inexplicable attack. Not once had she so much as hinted that she felt this way about him. Why now? "In plain language, because I left a job that was suffocating me, you think I'm behaving like a bum?"

Her anger deserted her as fast as it had come, and she was left in the position of defending something she not only wished she had never said but also didn't really believe. "I wouldn't have used the word, 'bum,'" she tried to hedge.

"Let's not muddy this up with semantics, Kelly," he said far louder than he had intended. "Do correct me, however, if what I'm saying is wrong." He looked down at the floor and ran his hand through his hair, stalling for time to bring his runaway temper back in check. When his gaze swung up to meet hers again, there was still fire in his eyes. "Am I right in thinking that even if I did manage to find a way for us to be together, you still wouldn't have anything to do with me unless I had become *gainfully employed*?" His voice had deceptively softened until it was little more than a whisper.

"You make me sound so mercenary."

"And here I thought I was bending over backward to sound fair."

Her chin rose. "You can't go on 'finding yourself' for the rest of your life. Someday you have to do *something*."

Brian shook his head as if to clear it. "I think we'd better say good-night before this goes any further."

His words punctured her balloon of self-defense, leaving her terribly vulnerable. "Please..." she said, a catch in her voice. "Don't go. Not like this. Surely you didn't come all this way—"

"Just to argue?" He touched her cheek with the back of his hand. "You're right," he said quietly. "Arguing is the last thing on my mind when I see you. I remember our time together...the laughter, the shared meals, how you curl up in a tight ball when you sleep...and how unbelievably exciting it is to make love to you." Longing radiated through him, stealing his breath, destroying common sense, leaving only raw need. He reached for her and she went to him, fitting so perfectly into his welcoming arms that it seemed they had been created for just that purpose. His hands cupped the sides of her face and tilted her head back so that she looked at him. He gazed into her eyes. Tenderly, expressing the gentlest side of his love, he kissed her.

Kelly's arms left his waist to wrap around his neck. She stood on her toes to return the kiss. As their lips parted and tongues met, a soft cry came from the back of her throat to blend with the groan that rose from his chest. His hands combed through the silken length of her hair, grasping the back of her head and pressing her closer still.

Now that she was in his arms she recognized the dream that had come to her night after night, leaving her with a feeling of emptiness each morning. She had imagined herself like this with him—had ached for the feel of him, the smell, the taste. As if seeking reassurance that she was indeed awake this time, she slipped her hands beneath his sports coat and then across his back, remembering the strength of the muscles beneath his shirt, outlining the curve of his shoulder blades and finally spanning the width of his waist.

Brian cradled her against him, wondering at, exalting in the erotic sensation her simple touch aroused. He lightly pressed his lips against her temple, letting the rhythm of her pulse flow into him. Softly he sighed her name, seeking the tone, the quality that would tell her how much he loved her, how bereft he would be if and when they were no longer together. Intellectually he knew that for them to make love now was insanity. It would only make their parting more painful. But he could not pull away.

As if he could ward off the insidious realities of their relationship with the strength of his love, Brian held Kelly against him until they seemed to have melded into one. Soon every thought, every emotion disappeared, save one—their need for each other.

Kelly stepped back and took Brian's hand. "Come with me," she said softly, leading him the short distance to her bedroom.

Light from a full moon shone through a window high on the far wall opposite the door, illuminating the antique brass bed and handmade coverlet and giving the room a muted silver glow. This was Kelly's favorite room, a place she went when she needed to feel comforted. It was her private shelter, an intimately personal expression of her real self.

The bed and quilt had been left to Kelly by her grandmother. The rest of the furnishings had been painstakingly gathered at garage sales, the only place she could afford to do her shopping for more years than she cared to remember. In all ways the room was unabashedly feminine. Lace and ruffles, perfumes and powders bespoke a side of her she usually kept hidden, fearing it would denote weakness and not wanting to expend precious energy fighting mistaken impressions.

Holding her in his arms, Brian slowly looked around the room and then at her. "I like it," he said, knowing she would understand his deeper meaning.

"Not too many people have seen this room."

Unable to keep a twinge of jealousy from flashing through his eyes he looked at her questioningly.

She smiled, somehow pleased by his reaction.

"You're the first man who wasn't related in one way or another."

"I'm honored," he replied, bending to kiss her. "And, I suppose I should add, idiotically pleased."

"As well you should be," she murmured against his mouth.

His hands traveled the length of her back, feeling the smoothness of her skin through the thin jersey. When he reached the curve of her buttocks he gently pulled her to him, fitting her snugly into the receptive planes of his own body, imparting his desire with gentle pressure and movements. She responded with an almost imperceptible rocking motion of her hips.

He buried his face in the softness of her hair. "Ahh, my sweet Kelly. You can't imagine what that does to me."

"You mean this ...." Purposely she snuggled closer. "Or this ...." Her hand moved suggestively along his thigh. "Or perhaps you mean this ...." She traced a moist trail with her tongue around the curve of his ear.

He stopped her teasing by capturing her mouth with his own. His tongue explored and caressed first the smoothness of her teeth and then the softness of her lips. He gloried in her tiny cry of arousal when he welcomed her reciprocal explorations. Bending slightly, he caught the fullness of her skirt in his hands and pulled it up over her hips. She stepped back and raised her arms to help him. The sensuous ritual of lovers continued as she reached for his tie, slowly pulling the tail through the knotted loop. He shrugged from his jacket and then his shirt. She helped with his slacks, seemingly fumbling with the opening, taking far longer than necessary for the simple task.

He pressed his lips to the hollow at the base of her throat and then the line of her collarbone. Catching the straps of her teddy with his fingers he pulled them aside, letting the silken material slip down her arms, uncovering the roundness of the tops of her breasts. With whisper-soft strokes of his fingers he caressed the exposed skin, brushing against the fabric, encouraging it to drop still farther down. When at last her breasts were free, he cupped them with his hands, lightly massaging their fullness with his palms then moving to her back and drawing her to him.

An eloquent sigh escaped his lips as their bare chests met. He felt the thundering of his own heart echoing inside her, the heat of his desire burning in the intensity of her response. Soon the last of their clothing joined the haphazard collection at their feet.

Kelly moved to the bed and turned back the covers. Lying down, she held out her hand to him. "My bedroom isn't as beautiful or as special as our meadow," she said, a teasing twinkle in her eyes. "But at least I can guarantee privacy."

Brian lay down beside her, his hand resting on the arch of her hip, his mouth nuzzling her neck. "Why Ms Stewart, could you possibly be getting prudish in your old age?"

She leaned back so that she could see his face and gave him a wicked grin. Her fingers traced a line down the center of his chest and continued on past his waist. Her smile deepened when she heard him catch his breath in surprise at her boldness. "Did I hear you say something about being prudish?"

"Uncle," he groaned. With a soft growl deep in his throat, he lowered his head to her breast.

Kelly felt an explosive wave of pleasure when he pulled her nipple into his mouth. The touch of his tongue and teeth, the feel of his beard, all combined to create tactile sensations that were more sensual than any she had ever known. With long loving strokes he caressed her, his hands relearning the feel of curves, the excitement of pulse points. Soon his lips replaced his hands as he more intimately discovered the places that brought her pleasure— where the touch of his tongue would elicit a sigh and where it would bring a moan.

Slowly, passionately they made love to each other, lingering, postponing the ultimate coming together as if by so doing they could ward off the devastating reality of their relationship awaiting them on the other side. Finally they could wait no longer; their desire for each other became a force unto itself, destroying all else. Kelly rolled to her back; Brian covered her with his body. Their world focused on one driving need as they neared release from life's sweetest torment. And then it was over.

Brian held her close, listening to her breathing, memorizing the look on her face, absorbing the lightly perfumed smell of her hair, tasting the slight saltiness of her skin. He wanted to carry this moment with him forever, a photograph in his mind's eye, one he could use to get him through the times ahead when he would be alone. He wanted the memory to hurt; it had to be so painful that his life would center on finding a way for them to be together.

Kelly nestled closer, fighting her own version of hell. She kept her eyes tightly closed against the tears she felt hovering. She had never imagined loving someone could bring such pain. Suddenly nothing mattered anymore, not her studio, her work, her hopes, her dreams. Even when they were all put together on one side of a scale, they didn't come close to balancing the cost should she lose Brian. Her talent was portable, as was everything in her studio. It was stubbornness and pride that had created the stumbling blocks. With the tears no longer threatening, she opened her eyes. "Brian, we have to talk."

"Not now, Kelly. It's too soon." There were too many things he had to work out, to understand about himself before he could tackle talking about the two of them. For a man who had always considered himself at the forefront of the sexual revolution, he was shattered to discover he had only been giving lip service to his supposed beliefs. He was not only embarrassed, he was ashamed at how easily, how thoughtlessly, he had expected the woman he loved to become subservient to his whims.

"Too soon?" she repeated, confused.

"Loving you has made me see myself as I really am for the first time in my life." He turned on his back, bringing her with him in the circle of his arm as if afraid to let her go. "I'm not too crazy about what I've seen."

Kelly held her breath, waiting for him to continue.

After a few more seconds had passed, Brian reached up to rub his eyes. He started to speak, then stopped. Finally he began. "Earlier this evening, when we were at the studio and I saw you for the wonderfully talented person you are, I was forced to stand back and look at our relationship and what I've been trying to do with it. I pictured our roles reversed, imagining myself during the exciting years at the bank and how I would have felt if you had come into my life then and demanded that I give up everything to follow you."

"And?" she asked softly.

"Just the idea that you could make such a request infuriated me. It made me feel unimportant as an individual, only consequential insofar as I was an appendage of yours." His voice filled with wonder as he said, "Why didn't you simply tell me to take a flying leap off one of those mountains?"

Kelly propped herself up on her elbow and looked down at him. "If you haven't been able to figure that out by now, you're not nearly as smart as I thought you were."

He caught a strand of her hair and looped it around his finger. "I'm through second-guessing you, Kelly. You're going to have to give me this one."

"All right." Her voice became low and caressing. "Despite my very best efforts not to, I fell in love with you."

For long seconds he simply stared at her, a blank expression on his face. "What did you say?" he finally asked.

She grinned. "Getting a little hard of hearing in your old age?"

"*Yes*...now tell me again." Of course he had known that somewhere beneath the bluster and bravado she really loved him. But he couldn't believe how good it sounded to finally hear her say so.

"I, Kathleen Maureen Stewart, love you, Brian...."

"James."

"Brian James Robertson."

"Hot damn!" he said, his voice filled with awe.

She laughed. "How profound."

Suddenly serious, he reached up to touch the side of her face. "You realize this doesn't solve anything for us."

She leaned her cheek into his hand. "I know. If anything, it makes matters worse. I've tried and tried but every path that seems open to us leads to a dead end."

"This one isn't yours to solve, Kelly. It's mine."

"Why not both of ours?"

"That comes later, sometime after I've figured out just what I want to do with the rest of my life now that I'm finally in touch with who I am again. You were right, you know. Being a bum isn't something I could tolerate for much longer. The mountains brought me the peace I needed, but the time I spent there also made me realize that there's a part of me that thrives on the competition of the marketplace. I have to find a way to be true to both sides of myself."

"And in the meantime?"

"There are still places I have to go, people I have to see." His thumb followed the outline of her lips. "Wait for me...." he said softly.

It was on the tip of her tongue to say she would go with him, but she knew she would forever regret leaving Phoenix now. If and when she walked away from her birthplace, she wanted the journey to be taken as a winner. "How long will you be gone?" she asked, already missing him terribly.

"I don't know. I'm not so sure about things as I once was. Falling in love has complicated things."

"For you, too?" A commiserating smile curved her mouth.

His hand moved from her cheek to the back of her head to draw her down to him. His kiss rekindled fires that had only minutes before been banked. "I wish I knew the words to tell you how much I love you," he whispered, pressing his lips to her eyes, her throat, her breasts. Abruptly he stopped his erotic journey, lifted his head and eyed her. "Privacy?"

It was her turn to look puzzled.

"Unless you keep a fur piece at the foot of your bed, I believe we have a visitor."

She tensed. "Whatever you do, don't make any sudden moves." Charlene's earlier teasing about keeping Andy away from the Beast loomed large in her mind. Despite the cat's truce with Brian, she knew better than to trust him.

Brian slowly lowered his head to rest his cheek on the cushion of her belly. "Don't worry about me," he said. "If need be, I could stay like this all night."

"Beast," she groaned, her frustration almost painful. "I've forgiven you a lot, but I'll never forgive you this one."

Brian started to chuckle, the chuckle became a laugh, the laugh an uncontrolled expression of joy. The Beast lifted his head and stared at the two humans who were now staring at him. He stretched, yawned, lowered his head and started to purr.

Kelly's mouth dropped open. Where was the ferocious, protective creature she had come to know? Could Brian really have won him over so easily?

"Well, I guess that settles it," he remarked. "The cat accepts me, so how could you possibly refuse?"

"Whatever gave you the impression I would refuse you anything?" she asked, her voice low and sultry, full of suggestive meaning.

He lowered his head and began tracing the outline of her navel with his tongue. "You have the most provocative way with words." Slowly he moved lower, leaving a tingling trail of moist kisses across the smoothness of her stomach. "Don't go away, I'll be right back." He scooped the Beast up in his arms. "Sorry, fella," he said, giving the cat's ears a friendly scratch before pushing him out into the hallway. "This room is taken."

Instead of immediately rejoining Kelly, Brian kneeled beside the bed and took her feet in his hands. With the help of the moonlight shining in from the window, he carefully examined first the bottoms and then the tops of her feet. "It doesn't look like there are any scars or permanent damage."

Kelly frantically fought the urge to sit up and tuck her feet safely beneath her. Even after all the times he had already seen her sturdy, too-wide toes and ridiculously low arches, she still cringed at the thought of letting him see them again. "Only to my pride."

Leaning closer he pressed a kiss on the tip of her big toe. She tried to pull away but he was prepared for her defensive maneuver and firmly held her ankles.

"Brian." She gasped. "You shouldn't... you mustn't." His lips touched her arch. She felt a wave of arousal move up her legs and ignite a yearning in her loins. She held her breath as the feeling insistently grew, fueled by his murmured words and slow journey from her feet to her ankles, from her calves to the heat of her inner thighs. Her held breath became a shuddering sigh and then a moan as he gently parted her legs and moved higher still. An experience she had never before been able to concede became something beautiful with Brian. With loving coaxing he gave her a type of fulfillment she had never known.

Later, when she lay quietly in his arms, listening to his sleep-induced rhythmic breathing, she thought about the intimacies they had shared. Instead of the anticipated flush of embarrassment, there was only a warm glow of pleasure. She closed her eyes and snuggled closer, repeating what was rapidly becoming a familiar prayer. *Please, God, let there be a way for us to be together.*

THE NEXT DAY Kelly was taking a shower and Brian was in the kitchen gathering ingredients for an omelet when the telephone rang. He started to answer, then stopped, not wanting to put Kelly in the awkward position of having to explain a man's presence in her apartment at seven-thirty on a Saturday morning. "The hell with it," he muttered, reaching for the receiver. If he had his way, everyone would know about him sooner or later, anyway. "Hello."

There was a long pause before a male voice stammered, "I must have the wrong number."

"Phil?"

"Brian?" The pause was much shorter this time. "What are you—"

"Did you want to speak to Kelly?"

"No," he snapped. "I just thought I'd play with the phone this morning until someone gets up around here to keep me company."

"I'll be sure to tell her you called."

"Don't you *dare* hang up!"

"You couldn't possibly have called to talk to me."

"Cut the comedy, Brian. What are you doing in my sister's apartment—and at this time of the morning?"

Brian tugged on his beard. He should have let the phone ring. "Right now? I'm fixing breakfast."

"Where's Kelly?"

Suddenly it was Brian's turn to hesitate before answering. "In the shower."

"Does this mean what I think it means?" Phil asked, a slyness appearing in his voice.

"If you're asking whether or not my intentions are honorable, it isn't you I have to convince."

"I'll be damned. You're the last person in the world I would have picked for Kelly."

"You two seem to think along the same lines."

Phil laughed. "She's not your run-of-the-mill putty-in-the-hands kind of woman, I take it," he said with a distinct note of pride.

"That's putting it mildly."

"To get back to the real reason I called...I have a copy of next month's Southwest Airlines in-flight and it looks even better than I had hoped. Kelly did a bang-up job, as usual. Tell her the cover will look outstanding in her portfolio. Even better than the ones she's done for *Arizona Highways*."

"I'm on the *cover* of the Southwest Airlines magazine?" Not once had Phil mentioned that he planned to use the piece as a cover story.

"Settle down, Brian, your own mother wouldn't recognize you. The picture is a profile shot that's done in silhouette."

He started to protest Phil's tendency to take a mile when he'd been given a foot, but then realized his quick anger had nothing to do with having his picture on the front page of a magazine. What he was feeling was fury at the intrusion of outsiders into a very special time of his life. He thought of the week Kelly had been with him in the mountains as precious, to be safeguarded and protected and cherished.

In his mind he knew he was being unreasonable. If Kelly hadn't been on the assignment in the first place, they would not have met. He forced himself to take a deep, calming breath before answering. "Should I tell her to drop by or will you send the cover?"

"She's coming to dinner next week. I'll give it to her then. I only called this morning because I know she's been feeling down lately, and I wanted to cheer her up." He chuckled. "It appears I could have waited." When Brian didn't immediately answer, he went on. "Well, I don't want to keep you from whatever it was you said you were doing."

"Fixing breakfast."

"Oh, yeah... I remember."

"Is there anything else, Phil?"

His voice softened. "One more thing. Give Kelly my love."

"I will, right along with mine."

"And Brian—"

"I know, Phil. I'd feel the same way if she were my sister." They said goodbye, and Brian returned the receiver to its cradle just as Kelly came into the room.

"Who was that?" She finished tucking in the end of a towel she had wrapped turban style around her hair.

"Phil...." Brian's heart lurched at the sight of her. Dressed in a caftan of green silk with her skin still flushed from her shower, she looked fresh and clean and incredibly sexy. His body responded as readily as his mind, and he was filled with a physical ache.

A quick grin curved Kelly's mouth. "And was he surprised to find you answering my phone?"

He answered her grin with one of his own. "Actually, once he managed to get past the initial shock, he handled the whole thing quite well. Even down to the mildly veiled threats."

"He didn't!"

Brian crossed the room to take her into his arms. "I assured him I had every intention of doing right by you, if only I could find a way to get you to go along with me."

Kelly stood on her toes to nuzzle her face against his neck. "Did he offer any advice?"

"Uh-huh. But I told him kidnapping was against the law." He tilted his head to the side in response to her lightly placed kisses. The muscles in his groin tightened, his stomach knotted. "Kelly?"

"Mmm?"

"Are you hungry?"

Her hands went to the sash of his robe. "Starved."

"Oh." The single word eloquently expressed his deep disappointment.

"But not for anything that's in the kitchen," she murmured.

He caught her wandering lips with his own then lifted her into his arms. "Did anyone ever tell you that you have a wonderful way with words?"

"Not anyone who counted." Her arms went around his neck. It was sometime after noon before they returned for food.

THE NEXT MORNING Kelly postponed going to the studio in order to accompany Brian to the airport. Their parting was more painful than either of them had anticipated. As their time together disappeared in the rush of last-minute activity, Kelly fought an overwhelming urge to go with him. Finally when Brian could no longer delay boarding the plane, he took her in his arms and kissed her one last time. Holding her face between his hands he stared at her as if memorizing each detail for the lonely times ahead. He pressed his lips to her forehead. "Knock their socks off," he whispered.

She tried to smile. "I will," she answered as softly.

He headed down the ramp, turning once to wave and then disappearing into the plane.

Kelly stood at the terminal window and watched until the 727 banked and disappeared over the building. The drive to her studio was one of the worst half hours she had ever known.

## 12

THE WEEK AND A HALF Brian spent in Alaska with his brother, Tom, and his family only accentuated the deep ache he felt to be with Kelly. His brother's contentment, the love and laughter he shared with his wife and children, the affection they lavished on him, made Brian want the same for himself. Finally the wanting became so powerful he could think of little else. He cut his visit short and made arrangements to fly to Maryland to visit Sally for some sisterly advice.

When Brian arrived, it was a typical August day in Maryland—hot and humid. He felt as if he had stepped into a greenhouse. Sally was at the airport to greet him, her arms open wide.

"I can't believe you're really here," she said, laughing and crying at the same time.

"Neither can I." Brian hugged her so tightly he picked her up off the ground. When he set her back down again, he held her at arm's length. "Let me look at you." She had gained a few pounds in the three years since they had last seen each other, making her once-spare frame slightly more rounded. And while her brown hair had become interspersed with fine lines of gray, her large blue eyes still sparkled with the same intelligence and wit. "You look fantastic," he announced.

"Well, that makes two of you who think so. Martin keeps telling me that the weight I've added has made me the sexiest woman on the East Coast."

"Just the East Coast?"

A laugh bubbled out. "That's exactly what I said." She took his arm and started walking to the luggage area. "How are Tom and Barbara?"

"They're fine...so are the kids. They all send their love and a heartfelt invitation to visit."

"And mom?"

"She's fine, too. At least she was two weeks ago."

"Now how about you? How are you doing?"

The last thing he wanted to do was talk about his problems in the waiting room at the airport. "Couldn't be better."

"No regrets or aftershock from the occupational surgery?"

"Not so far."

"Well, I'll say this for you, when you decide to do something, you sure make the cut clean."

"It was the only way."

"Better than taking a leave of absence?"

A faraway look appeared in Brian's eyes as he stared unseeing at the luggage carousel. "I was desperate at the time—I used desperate measures."

"You used to love banking. What happened?" As usual, Sally had come right to the point.

"The air became too rarefied at the top." Brian spotted his suitcases and stepped over to retrieve them.

Sally insisted that he let her help, so he gave her the overnight bag, knowing it was useless to argue. Purposely he steered the conversation away from himself by asking about Martin and the kids. By the time she had finished filling him in on the trials and tribulations of being the mother of three teenagers, they were parked in front of a massive colonial-style two-story brick house.

"This is it," Sally declared, opening her car door. Brian looked around. He guessed the landscaped portion of the grounds to be at least five acres, the house well over four thousand square feet. Sally and Martin had obviously done very well for themselves.

"I had no idea," he said, motioning toward the house.

"If you had taken me up on just one of my invitations in the past ten years, you wouldn't be surprised to learn that we live in a hotel."

"This is a hotel?"

She laughed. "You used to be a lot quicker on the uptake. I was simply facetiously referring to the size of this barn and to the number of kids who go in and out of here all the time. Mark my word, it won't take you long before you'll be thinking of this place as a hotel, too. But then again, after so many years of living alone, you'll probably think it's a zoo."

Just then he saw the front door open and a beautiful young girl step shyly outside. "Is that Margie?" he asked, incredulous that his niece had grown up so fast.

"Try again," Sally chided.

"Christine?"

"Bingo."

"It can't be, she was just a baby."

"You've obviously not been paying close attention to the pictures I send you every year."

"Not true. I have them on my dresser."

Her voice grew wistful. "They grow up so fast it makes me dizzy to watch. It seems like it was just yesterday that I was yelling at them about stuffing mashed potatoes in their ears, and today I'm worried sick they might be tempted to stuff white powder up their noses."

"They're not—"

"No...thank God, so far we've skipped that problem."

As they neared the porch, Brian stopped. He tried to reconcile the young woman standing in front of him with the mental image he carried. It wasn't until she gave him a hesitant smile that the two merged back into one. Brian dropped his suitcase and opened his arms. It was the gesture she had been waiting for.

After a big hug and a resounding kiss, Brian told her that she was the first woman he had ever had the pleasure of kissing who wore braces. She basked in the "woman" and groaned about the "railroad tracks." By the time they had deposited his suitcases in the guest bedroom, uncle and niece had dealt with the years of separation and reestablished their special bond.

Sally stood at the door watching them. "Come on, Christine, let's give your Uncle Brian some time alone to wash up and relax before supper." She stepped aside to let her daughter pass, ignoring the pleading look to stay. "We eat at seven; if you'd like to take a nap until then, I can have one of the kids wake you in time to get ready."

"Do I look like I need a nap?"

Her eyes narrowed slightly as she critically surveyed him. "I'm not quite sure just what it is that bothers me about the way you look...."

"But I'm sure you'll tell me as soon as you figure it out."

She shrugged, a mischievous twinkle in her eyes.

"What else are big sisters for?" The door closed softly behind her.

DINNER WAS A poignant return to the boisterous family meals Brian remembered as a child: everyone talked at once and laughter served as punctuation. Several hours later, unable to sleep, he made his way downstairs to the kitchen to get a glass of milk and retrieve the piece of cake he had saved from dinner. As he passed the family room he was startled to see Sally sitting on the couch reading a book, dressed in her pajamas and bathrobe.

She closed the book and laid it aside. "I've been waiting for you."

"Me?"

"I could tell you had too much on your mind to fall asleep and knew it was only a matter of time before you came down to get something to eat."

"Old habits die hard."

"You want to get your snack before you tell me what's bothering you, or would you settle for a glass of sherry?"

"I'd rather gargle with gasoline."

She laughed. "I'll be waiting."

When Brian returned a few minutes later, she patiently refrained from questions until the last of the cake and milk had been consumed. Then she launched her attack. "Are you going to tell me straightaway why you have that haunted look in your eyes, or do I have to dig it out piece by piece?"

He studied her for a few seconds, then leaned back in his chair and put his feet up on the leather-covered ottoman. "As simply as I can put it, I'm in love."

Sally momentarily lost her usual aplomb. "Not once did I even consider that as a possibility. Who is she?"

"What makes you think it isn't Paula?"

"You might have married that woman, but love her? Never. At least not enough to put that look in your eyes." She tucked her feet up underneath her, reached for a pillow to hold against her chest, then propped her elbows on her knees. "So tell me about her. I want to hear all the details."

He did, leaving nothing out, not sparing himself or making his behavior sound any better than it was. He also told her how aimless he had begun to feel, how disconnected, and that at thirty-four he was far too old not to know what he wanted to do with the rest of his life, beyond loving Kelly Stewart.

Sally listened carefully, only making occasional comments. She stopped him twice with clarifying questions, but otherwise remained unusually quiet. When at last it seemed he had come to the end of his story, she waited another minute and then said, "I think you've gone a little overboard on this sexist thing about ignoring Kelly's talent. Sure you behaved like a jerk, but at least you're sensitive enough to feel bad about it. No one expects you to go on browbeating yourself or to wear a hair shirt for the rest of your life. The point is to learn from mistakes and to go on." She hesitated, gathering her thoughts. "What did Kelly say when you told her about this?"

"I didn't—at least not everything."

"Oh...I see."

"When we were in the mountains, one of her strongest arguments against loving me was that I didn't know her well enough. After telling her how wrong she was, there was no way I was going to admit something that proved her right."

"Is it possible that she *was* right?" Sally asked softly. "Could it be that you were just exceedingly vulnerable and in need of comfort after leaving Amercoast and she was a handy shoulder for you?"

Brian absently tugged on his beard. "It would sure make my life a hell of a lot less complicated if that were true." An image of Kelly appeared in his mind's eye. He smiled. "Less complicated...and far less worth getting up for each morning."

"You've brought me a tough one to help you with this time, Brian."

He leaned forward, his elbows braced on the arms of the chair. "Are you trying to tell me that you've lost your magic wand? You're not going to wave it and make all the puzzle pieces fit together?"

"My wand disappeared the day you stepped out into the real world; you were just too busy to notice." She reached over to the end table beside her and opened the top drawer. "Here." She handed him a stack of newspaper clippings. "I've been saving these for you for the past two weeks. I thought they might make interesting bedtime reading."

Brian took the papers. His gaze immediately swept the headline. "Connecticut Bank Floundering." He shot her a questioning glance.

"Aren't you interested in reading about the misadventures of one of your college cronies?"

Quickly scanning the first paragraph, Brian found the name Howard Whitten. Somewhere in the back of his mind a bell rang. Fleeting images of an overbearing, obnoxious heavyweight who had lasted less than a year on the wrestling team came to mind. "Thanks," he said with a half grin. "I'm not above a little gossip now and then." He moved the first clipping aside to glance at the second while bending to give her a kiss.

"I couldn't get tomorrow off, so you have the dubious pleasure of having your nieces entertain you for the day." She rose and stretched. "I hope you like rock music. They're convinced they can't function without it."

Brian was only half listening, his mind already consumed with the bits and pieces of information he had picked up in his quick perusal of the clippings. "How did you know I went to school with Whitten?" he asked, effectively letting Sally know that his thoughts were focusing in an entirely different direction, one that was far away from where he was now.

"It was only a lucky guess." She shrugged. "He graduated the same year you did, and his major was business. I thought you might have come across him in some of your classes." She flipped off the light switch and followed him into the hall. "It was simple deduction, my dear Watson."

"Exceptional work, Ms Holmes. As usual I am awestruck by your brilliance." He put his arm around her shoulder and gave her a squeeze.

"You might pass that opinion on to my children. They seem to think I'm nearing dotage."

"Give them a few more years. They'll learn to appreciate you."

"I should live so long." They had arrived at Sally and Martin's bedroom. She quietly opened the door then turned and whispered, "Don't stay up all night reading."

Brian shook his head, an amused grin curving his mouth. "I can't imagine how I've survived all these years without you."

"Frankly, neither can I." She smiled and winked before carefully closing the door.

Walking down the hallway to his bedroom, Brian felt a sense of healing come over him. The time he had spent with Kelly and then alone in the mountains and the visits to his family had been like a dose of sorely needed medicine. A world that had been crazily tilted on its axis had righted itself again, only with a wonderful bonus—Kelly.

HOURS LATER, long after the early-rising summer sun had turned the sky a muted purple, Brian still paced his room. The clippings lay scattered across the bed like confetti. Those containing hard facts about the problems facing First Connecticut Liberty Bank were placed in precise order, while all others had been shunted aside.

Reading carefully, absorbing both what was in type and the more illusive information hidden between the lines, Brian had been able to piece together the scenario of a company in deep financial trouble. True to the personality Howard Whitten had exhibited in college, he had, in fewer than five years, almost destroyed an old institution, one that had managed to survive some of the nation's worst economic disasters.

By offering incredible incentives to employees who brought in new loans, Whitten had encouraged the loosening of credit standards until they had reached the point that a disastrous percentage of the loans were now in default. Without an effective check-and-balance system by management to examine each branch's loan portfolio, all hell had finally broken loose.

Brian had seen this type of thing happen many

times before but rarely had it become the calamitous situation that the Connecticut bank now faced. Normally there would have been a designated period of time for contests like this one—three to six months at the most. The management would have instituted a close watch on each branch's loan portfolio, aware that an atmosphere had been created that could encourage deviation from the usual loan procedure. But at Connecticut Liberty the contest environment had been an ongoing thing, with the prizes getting progressively sweeter. It was inevitable that eventually people who would never have been able to get a loan because of their poor credit ratings were being classified by loan officers as only marginal risks and walking out the door with unsecured loans. It was only a matter of time before payments were coming in late and then not at all.

The curtains moved slightly as a breeze entered the room, drawing Brian's attention to the window. Noticing the fading color of the morning sky, he walked over to watch the outside world respond to the beginning of a new day. He was surprised at his complete lack of fatigue, his surge of energy. But then again, he wasn't surprised at all. Putting Connecticut Liberty back on its feet was going to be a real challenge, one he had waited a long time to experience again. If he had discovered nothing else during the sleepless night just past, it was that challenges were not only what made work interesting for him, they were his lifeblood.

# 13

KELLY STARED INTO the magnifying glass as she fine-focused the lens on the black-and-white enlarger head. She was reprinting—for the eighth time—a photograph of Chuck's Service Center that she had shot a week ago and had to turn in to the newspaper by five o'clock that evening in order to make their advertising deadline. Normally she could whip a job like this one out in an afternoon. But that required concentration, something she had sorely lacked since turning in the Templeton assignment the early part of last week.

The first couple of days hadn't been bad. She knew there was always a procedure work had to follow, and time had to be scheduled to show the client as well as upper- and lower-echelon people at the ad agency. When she hadn't heard anything by Friday, the weekend had become impossibly long. And now here it was almost the end of another week, and still she had heard nothing. Her work, her temper, her peace of mind were suffering terribly. Even the Beast had started giving her a wide berth, choosing to ride in the back seat on their trips to and from the studio instead of up front with her. When he willingly kept clear of the darkroom, the one area of the studio expressly off limits to him, Kelly knew her nerves were showing.

The telephone rang. Her heart thundered in her

chest as she raced to answer it. "Stewart's Studio," she said, sounding composed with great effort.

"I understand the sexiest woman in Phoenix happens to own Stewart's Studio. Could you put her on the phone? I have a proposition to offer her."

She smiled. Brian's voice was like a warm blanket on a cold evening. "I don't know about putting her on," she replied in a sultry voice, "but I'm absolutely positive you could turn her on with minimal effort."

"My God, Kelly. Do you have any idea what it does to me when you say things like that?" He leaned closer to the pay phone, creating a tiny space of privacy in the busy hotel lobby.

"No, tell me."

"I'd rather show you."

"When?" The infinitesimal pause made her hopes sink.

"I'm not sure yet," he said, the frustration almost tangible.

"I wish you'd let me in on what's happening up there that's keeping you so busy."

"I will, as soon as I have something concrete to tell."

"If it's part of your plan to drive me crazy with missing you, you're succeeding."

Kelly's increased openness in expressing her feelings was making their phone calls harder and harder for Brian to get through. For hours afterward he was filled with an ache that precluded everything else. "Have you heard anything from the agency?"

"Not yet. But that's not uncommon," she quickly added. She didn't want him to know how concerned she was. "It's the old 'hurry up and wait' routine. It used to bother me when I first started working with people in this field, but it doesn't anymore."

He let her have her little lie, knowing he had lost all right to become more intimately involved in what she was going through because of his unreasonable behavior in the beginning. He knew—and it hurt more than he cared to admit—that had he been more understanding when she first told him about the project, she would have welcomed the opportunity to share the anxiety she now suffered. Instead she was afraid to expose herself to him again. "Kelly, if you ever decide you want to talk to me about this...."

"You're making far too much out of it." What would he say if she told him that the heady confidence she had felt a week and a half ago when she'd dropped the photographs off had slowly been eroding until she was now left with nagging doubts about the quality of her work?

"I just want you to know that I'm—"

"I do know, Brian. You don't have to tell me."

He couldn't push her any harder. His hand went to his chin to thoughtfully touch a now-absent beard. For an instant he was startled to find himself clean-shaven, and then he remembered. "And do you also know that I lie awake most of the night after we've talked on the phone, just thinking about you and me."

"Only after we've talked? You're lucky." She heard a deep groan.

"Is there any way you could arrange to come up here this weekend?"

"I have to work on some advertising copy for The Toy Store. A shipment of stuffed animals they've been waiting for since last Christmas just arrived, and they're desperate to run an ad to sell them. They want me to figure out a way to get people to come into their store in August to lay away for this year's Christmas. If the owner of the store wasn't so special, I'd put him off a few days, but he's been with me since I first opened the studio."

"What about next weekend?"

She hated saying no; it tore her apart. "More of the same, I'm afraid." She had let her regular clients slip badly toward the end of the Templeton thing and consequntly had wound up putting in twelve- and fourteen-hour days to try to catch up. "I suppose that means you won't be able to get down here, either."

"What for? To watch you work?" Damn! He had no right to make a crack like that. "I'm sorry, Kelly...that was uncalled for."

"It's all right. I haven't exactly been Miss Congeniality lately, either."

"I miss you!"

Her breath caught in her throat. "Are we just playing some sick masochistic game, Brian? Is there really any hope for us?"

The despairing tone in her voice frightened him. "You don't believe what you're saying." She couldn't.

"You're right, I'm just tired. A good night's sleep is all I need."

"Kelly—"

"Really, Brian." She forced a cheerfulness she didn't feel into her voice. "Even the Beast has been on his best behavior lately. He has sense enough to know that when I'm like this, I'm liable to carry out my threats, so he's lying low." Wearily she rubbed her temples with a hand stretched across her eyes. "How's the weather in Maryland?" she said, purposely changing the subject to something safer.

"I would imagine it's pretty much the same as it is here in Connecticut."

"*Connecticut?*" What are you dong there?" He had promised to come back to Phoenix after he left his sister's house.

Brian glanced over to the revolving door at the lobby entrance. The two men he had been waiting for were standing there, surreptitiously glancing in his direction. "I have to go, Kelly. I'll call you back tonight." He started to replace the receiver then brought it back to his ear. "I love you," he said.

"I love you, too." Kelly listened until there was a hum on the line. Slowly she hung up. It was insanity to go on like this. She had been short and moody with Brian when what she wanted more than anything was to sound supportive and understanding.

Tentatively the Beast approached. He gave her foot a quick nudge with his head as if testing her receptiveness. When she didn't immediately scoot him away as she had been doing the past few days, he launched a full-scale assault, wrapping himself around her legs and emitting plaintive, complaining meows. Kelly reached down to pick him up. Cradling him in her arms, she scratched his chin and ears and apologized for her short temper.

She glanced at the phone. Ring, dammit! Unconsciously her arms tightened around the cat. Frantically he fought for escape, leaving long scratch marks on her arms.

"Oh, Beast...." She started after him to apologize but he ran into the studio and disappeared behind the sofa.

"That does it!" She stomped back to the phone, picked it up and before she had a chance to reconsider, dialed the agency's number. When a woman's nasal voice answered, Kelly steeled herself and said, "Mr. Andrews, please."

"May I ask who's calling?"

"Kathleen Stewart."

"And the nature of your business?"

The muscles in her jaw tightened with determination. "Mr. Andrews wishes to talk to me about some work I did for the agency."

"Will you hold?"

"Yes." As the seconds slipped by, so did Kelly's nerve. She was behaving unprofessionally. Andrews would think she was a rank amateur, pulling a stunt like this. The nasal voice returned.

"Mr. Andrews will be with you in a moment— he's on another line. Can you hold?"

"Yes...thank you," Kelly said to the now-empty line. She started pacing back and forth down the hall-way, stretching the coiled cord on the wall phone as far as it would go. She rehearsed answers to a dozen possible questions. Would he believe her if she said she'd been out and that her answering service had given her a garbled message mentioning his name? Surely she could come up with something more creative than that. She paced some more. What was the matter with her? Where was her backbone?

"Mike Andrews here. What can I do for you Ms Stewart?"

Kelly sucked in a large, lung-filling gulp of air. "Uh....." *Oh, come on, Kelly, shape up!* "I'm calling about the photographs I left with you last week."

"What about them?" he said warily.

What about them? She had poured her soul into those photographs, and he had the gall to sit there and say, "What about them?" "I was wondering if you had reached a decision yet?"

"Robert hasn't contacted you?"

"Robert?"

"Yes, Robert Stevens, our accountant."

An accountant? Why would— Kelly felt the blood drain from her face. Accountants paid people off. "No...I've heard nothing from anyone at your office."

"I must apologize. Had I known, I most certainly would have—"

"Let's get straight down to business, Mr. Andrews. Why aren't you going to use my photographs?" Her despair gave her the courage she had lacked before.

After a long, pregnant pause, he said, "I'm afraid you wound up caught in the middle of a rather ticklish situation, Ms Stewart. We started the copy on this particular campaign over a month ago. Even though your photographs are, uh, quite good, they are impossible for us to use. At this late date, we can't pull the copy we've already committed ourselves to run."

"You mean to tell me that you already had the photography assigned when you gave me the job?"

"Yes...."

"I don't understand."

"Your brother can be quite persuasive."

Now everything made sense. She closed her eyes in a weary mental sigh. "You never had any intention of using my work, did you?"

"Frankly, I didn't anticipate anything near the quality of the photographs you turned in."

"If you had bothered to look at my portfolio, you would have seen what I can do, and you wouldn't have been so surprised."

"I figured it was a waste of time. After all, you've

been working here in Phoenix long enough that if you were really any good, you should have earned yourself a reputation by now."

Kelly was too stunned to answer. She didn't know whether to laugh or cry.

"Ms Stewart, are you still there?"

"Yes, Mr. Andrews... I'm still here." Only because she had yet to summon the energy to hang up on him.

"Perhaps we can work something out that will be satisfactory to both of us."

She was hardly listening anymore. "Such as?"

"We have a client, a jeweler, who's rather difficult for our regular photographers to please. He likes the avant-garde kind of thing you seem to have a knack for doing."

"What you mean is that he's joined the twentieth century."

There was a long pause. "What I was about to propose is that you meet him and see if you can come up with some ideas—"

"On speculation, of course."

"Of course. We would, however, pay all receipted expenses."

"Mr. Andrews," she said softly. "You can take your proposition and go straight to hell! I wouldn't work for you again on *my* terms." She hung up before he had a chance to reply.

Despite her best efforts, her anger wasn't strong enough to bury the hurt. Tears burned her eyes and when she refused to let them be shed, they seemed to clutch at her throat. Blindly seeking shelter from the pain she pressed herself into the hallway corner, digging the heels of her hands into her eyes. Slowly she sank to the floor.

How could she have been so stupid? Everyone had been able to see what was happening except her. Both Phil and Brian had tried to warn her, but she had stubbornly refused to listen.

She felt pressure against her knee as the Beast stood on his hind legs and tried to crawl up on her lap. "Get away from me," she raged, venting her anger on the hapless animal.

"Oh, Beast..." she moaned. "I'm sorry. I have no right to take my anger out on you." She reached for him but he backed warily away from her, fear in his eyes.

A buzzer announced that someone had entered the front office. Kelly considered ignoring the summons, figuring that sooner or later whoever it was would go away. Then she heard Charlene's cheery "Hello," and knew her friend would not leave without finding her.

By the time she had reluctantly opened the office door, Charlene had the outer door open, ready to leave. "So there you are," she said. "I had decided you must be elbow deep in chemicals and couldn't hear me."

"I'm just not as fast as I used to be." She forced a smile. "I keep saying I'm going to have an intercom installed but never seem to get past the talking stage." Out of the corner of her eye she saw a streak of orange-and-white fur fly by. "Charlene!" she cried. "The door." But it was too late. The Beast was gone before Charlene had a chance to react.

"Oh my God, Kelly...I forgot."

Kelly ran after the cat but by the time she was outside, he had disappeared.

"He'll be back," Charlene said when Kelly returned. "Won't he?"

"If I were him, I'd just keep running and never give this place a backward glance."

Charlene put her arm around Kelly's shoulder and gave her a hug. "Boy, I haven't seen you this down in the dumps since you accidentally told Sean and Steven that you were the one who hid their Easter eggs, and not the Easter Bunny." She guided her friend back into the studio. "Now how about fixing me a cup of that awful stuff you call coffee and telling me all about what's bothering you."

THREE HOURS LATER as Kelly stood outside on the sidewalk of her studio, calling a still-absent Beast, she mentally acknowledged that sharing her disappointment with Charlene had helped to dull its cutting edge, but had done little to raise her spirits. She had started for the corner for one last look down the other street when the telephone rang. It was Phil.

"I just hung up from talking to Mike Andrews," he said. "He told me what happened. I can't tell you how sorry I am, Kelly."

"It wasn't your fault."

"Yes, it was. I should have warned you what you were getting into."

"You mean you knew they had already hired someone else for the job?"

"No, but I'm aware of how prejudiced they are toward outsiders. It took me two weeks to get them to agree to even look at your work."

Kelly winced. He was right. Had he told her this before, she would have gone into the project with a decidedly different attitude. But it was behind her now—a painful lesson certainly, but a valuable one. A Pollyanna attitude had no business in advertising.

"Forget about it, Phil. We'll chalk it up to experience."

"I sure hope Brian appreciates what he's getting in you."

"If he doesn't, I'm sure you'll tell him."

They talked a few minutes longer and then said goodbye. Before Kelly could replace the receiver, she heard Phil call her name. "Yes?"

"I really am sorry," he said softly.

"I know. Me too." She managed to hang up before tears again welled up in her eyes.

BRIAN SHIFTED in the low-backed chair, seeking a more comfortable position in a piece of furniture he was convinced had been designed for children. He hated conducting business meetings in restaurants and was particularly anxious to see this one come to an end. Explaining what he intended to do to put Connecticut Liberty back on its feet was not something he felt should be worked in between courses of a meal and around the attentions of a waiter. That he was here at all was testimony to the persuasive arguments of the representatives of the three major stockholders who wanted the transition of power to be as amicable as possible.

He glanced around the table at the eight vice-presidents, mentally noting which of them would likely be included in a gathering of this type a year from now and which would be missing. He made his judgment with a practiced eye. He had met these men before in different guises, in different banks, but they were basically the same. There were those who did their work with diligence and little attention to personal glory, who rarely rose above the junior vice-president level. And then there were others who only worked on projects that would bring them acclaim. To have the power to pick and choose between the two types and to have the opportunity to mold a bank into the customer-responsive institution it could and should be had given Brian back the enthusiasm he thought had gone forever. He was concentrating on the man sitting across from him when the senior vice-president, Rob Baxter, tapped his knife against a water glass.

"Gentlemen, if I may have your attention." Forks were returned to plates and wine goblets were tipped one last time as the eyes that were turned to Baxter also found their way to Brian. "As you all know, we are meeting like this in order to let Mr. Robertson get to know everyone on an informal basis. In keeping with that idea, I think a few words of background on our guest might be appropriate." A manicured hand smoothed the side of his sleekly cut hair in a practiced motion that brought attention to the large diamond he wore on his little finger. "I'm sure most of you have heard by now that Brian Robertson comes to us from the boardroom of Amercoast Bank. For those of you who may not be familiar with all the details of his remarkable career, it should be noted that while at Amercoast, Mr. Robertson rose through the ranks in such a phenomenally short time that the media gave him the tag, 'banking's boy genius.'"

Brian leaned back in his chair and crossed his arms over his chest in a display of body language Rob Baxter was too involved to notice.

"When we discovered that Connecticut Liberty had, shall we say, overextended itself and was in need of a dynamic leader who would be able to restore to the people of this state trust in our bank, there was never any doubt who that man should be. Brian Robertson has a reputation for being a conservative and yet an aggressive leader. Precisely the—"

Unable to stomach the gross inaccuracies of what was obviously a speech intended to impress him, Brian held up his hand. "I hardly think my reputation is of concern or interest to anyone here at this late date." Pointedly he looked around the table. "What should be of interest to everyone here, however, is what course of action I plan to pursue should I decide to take this job." He tossed his napkin on the table and leaned forward. "I'll briefly outline those plans. First, all profits will be put into a reserve account to cover possible future unsecured loan defaults. As soon as feasible, there will be a review of the standards that have served this bank for over a hundred years and an accounting made as to why they were deviated from and what the results were in each case." Brian continued describing the course of action he would take, carefully studying each man's reaction. By the time he was finished, he was fairly sure who would work for him and who would work against.

An anticipatory shiver traveled down his spine, much, he imagined, like the feeling a racer would get while waiting for the green flag to drop. It was a sensation he hadn't experienced since his early years at Amercoast. The challenge touched him as intimately and completely as if it were flowing through his veins, reaching every part of him with its lifeblood. Only one thing was capable of destroying the special feeling—if he were to have to go it alone. Without Kelly the victories would not be so sweet, the outcome not as rewarding.

IT WAS MIDNIGHT when Kelly had finally given up her search for the Beast and headed for her apartment. After he had failed to return she had systematically covered the area around the studio block by block, first in the car and then on foot, only giving up when a policeman stopped her to tell her how unwise it was to be walking around alone so late at night. He took her back to her car and promised he would keep an eye out for an orange-and-white male cat while he drove his beat.

When she arrived home her apartment seemed painfully empty. She wandered from room to room, foolishly hoping that by some miracle she would see the familiar orange-and-white bundle of fur curled up and sleeping, as usual, somewhere he wasn't supposed to be. But there were no miracles.

At least she wasn't foolish enough to seek solace in the hope that he might find a new owner, someone who would love and care for him. His personality hadn't improved nearly enough for that.

With a silent chest-heaving sob, she went into the kitchen, took his food out of the cupboard and poured a cupful into two plastic containers. One she left on the porch as she went out again, the other she took to the studio to leave by the front door, in case he should come back in the middle of the night.

ALONE IN HIS HOTEL ROOM and aching with the need to hear Kelly's voice, Brian had his hand on the telephone to call her one last time when he glanced at his watch and quickly calculated Phoenix time. It was well past midnight. If he called now, she would surely be asleep. Reluctantly he released the receiver. Besides, he reasoned, what he wanted to tell her was best said in person where he could watch her eyes and gauge his arguments by their reaction.

Slipping his shoes off, he lay down on the bed, his hands cradling the back of his head. There it was again—an overwhelming, urgent need to get in touch with her, almost as if she were calling out to him. Not fighting it any longer, he rolled over to his side and before he could rationalize what he was doing, dialed her number. When she didn't answer after ten rings, he reached for the phone book to look up the number of United Airlines.

# 14

FOR LONG SECONDS Kelly mentally stumbled out of the depths of sleep. When her eyes opened she looked around in confusion. Why was she sleeping on the couch fully clothed? What had awakened her? A loud knock sounded on the front door. She pushed herself upright into a sitting position. "I'm coming." Another knock. "I'm *coming*," she repeated.

Propping one hand against the wall to brace herself, she opened the front door with the other. "Brian?" Her eyebrows drew together in puzzlement. There was something wrong with the way he looked. She wondered if she was still asleep, deeply enmeshed in a particularly real and comforting dream that was slightly out of kilter.

"My God, Kelly. You look terrible."

Surely she could come up with a better opening line if this really was a dream. "Well, you look a little strange yourself," she mumbled, leaning her head against the door. He looked exhausted, as if he hadn't slept for days. "Would you like to come in?"

A tired laugh greeted her question. "It seems we've had this conversation before."

She rolled her eyes in disgust. "I remember. It sounds as dumb now as it did then." Suddenly, finally realizing that she was not dreaming, that Brian was really in Phoenix, standing in front of her, close enough for her to touch, she let out a tiny delayed cry of welcome and threw her arms around his neck.

"That's more like it," he murmured, holding her close, burying his face in her sweet-smelling hair.

She leaned back to look up at him. "You've shaved off your beard." Her gaze swept his face. "Why? No, first tell me what you're doing here."

"Last night I had this peculiar feeling that you needed me. When I couldn't reach you by phone, I decided I'd better come down."

"You mean you flew all the way down here because you thought—" She couldn't finish. Since she had been old enough to have such dreams she had fantasized that someday there would be a man who would love her beyond reason—an intuitive man, one who would share her sorrows and rejoice in her triumphs as if they were his own. Never once had she allowed herself to believe the dream could become reality.

"What is it, Kelly?" he gently prodded. "What has happened to you?"

She took his hand. "Come inside."

He followed her into the kitchen where she went to the cupboard, took out a coffeepot and began making coffee. "Kelly, why are you doing that? You always drink tea in the morning, and I've already had a gallon of coffee on the plane coming here."

She dropped the scoop she had been using to ladle grounds and covered her face with her hands. "He's gone...and it's all my fault."

There was such anguish in her voice. "Who's gone?"

Her shoulders shook as silent sobs stole her breath. "Beast," she at last managed to say. She took several deep breaths in an unsuccessful attempt to control her hiccupping sobs. While thoughts of Beast spending the night lost and alone had precipitated the outburst, she was no longer sure whether the tears that followed were shed for the cat or herself or both. All she knew was that deep inside there was a place that hurt terribly.

With loving movements Brian brushed stray wisps of hair from her temple and forehead, then tucked a long strand behind her ear. Seeing a box of Kleenex on the counter, he stretched as far as he could and caught one between two fingers. "Here," he said, putting the tissue into her hand.

She blew and sniffed, then swiped at her eyes. "He disappeared yesterday afternoon... from the studio."

"Was he chasing something?" he asked, more to help her with the story than anything else.

"No...."

"Was something chasing him?"

"No...."

"Kelly, I know it hurts to talk about what happened, but you're going to have to be a little less cryptic. Why would he suddenly take off like that when he's willingly followed you to and from your car and the studio every day?"

She took a deep shuddering breath. "Probably because I've never hollered at him when he wasn't doing anything wrong before."

"Why were you hollering?" But as soon as he asked, he knew the answer. There was only one thing that would make Kelly lose control that way. "You heard from the agency." It was a statement, not a question.

She nodded.

"What did they say?"

"Thanks, but no thanks."

"Come on, Kelly...give."

"They never had any intention of using my work. The project had already been assigned to someone else."

"So it didn't matter how good your photographs were—"

"They've been working on the layouts for over a month."

"I'm sorry." It sounded so meaningless. She had worked so hard, had invested not only time and energy but her heart, as well.

She shrugged. "You've earned an, 'I told you so.' Are you sure you don't want to use it?"

For long seconds he stared at her, noting the tears that lingered on her eyelashes, the wounded look in her eyes. "I take it back—I'm not sorry. Maybe you needed something like this to shake you up enough to get you to leave this place. The only thing I'm sorry about is that it had to hurt you so terribly."

"I thought a lot about moving last night while I was waiting in my car outside the studio for Beast to show up. Nothing's really changed. If I left Phoenix, I would be abandoning dozens of clients who have been with me for years. It really wouldn't be fair—"

"Stop right there." Anger suffused his face. "I won't listen to another word of that garbage. You've let some pompous idiot sit in judgment of your talent and you've listened to him. My God, Kelly, how could you do that?"

"You don't understand."

"You're right. How can you react to my pressures like you're made of steel and then listen to someone like that jerk at the agency? What technique did he use that I don't know? Maybe I should take a few lessons." He raked his hand through his hair. His voice dropped back to normal volume when he said, "Why is his opinion more valid than mine?"

"Because you love me."

What possible answer could he come up with for that? "It would be useless to try to convince you that I probably judged your talent with a more critical eye than anyone ever has, so I won't bother. But you can't believe that loving you has blinded me to everything else that's been going on around here."

"No, but that puts us right back to where we started. Loving me could make you see talent where there was nothing but mediocrity and that would put everything in a different light. If I'm so talented, why haven't I succeeded on my own?" She inwardly flinched at her parroting of Andrews's words.

Slowly he shook his head. "Self-effacement was the last thing I ever expected from you."

She felt as if he had hit her. Could he be right? All her life she had run from self-effacing people, considering them pathetically boring. Had she let herself slip that far? She stood and walked across the room then turned to look at him. "Have I...do I...."

Because he loved her, his first instinct was to spare her. But then he realized he loved her too much to lie. "Yes," he said softly, crossing the distance between them to take her into his arms. He pressed a kiss to the top of her head. To pursue this any further now was useless. She needed time to think. "I'm going to see if I can find Beast. You stay here and get some rest."

"Wait a minute. I'll change my clothes and come with you."

"He might be more willing to come out of hiding if I go alone."

Kelly winced. "You're probably right."

He touched her chin with his hand, tilting it up to give her a kiss. "I love you," he said, his eyes saying as much as his words.

She threw her arms around his neck and held him close. "Don't give up on me yet."

"Not a chance." Brian knew the longer he stayed, the harder it would be for him to leave, and still he could not release her. Finally it was the telephone that tore them apart.

Kelly picked up the receiver. "Hello. Yes? You didn't? Well, thank you for calling.... Yes, I will." She hung up and turned to Brian. "That was the policeman I met last night. He told me he would keep an eye out for Beast."

"No luck, I take it?"

She shook her head.

"Then I guess it's my turn."

AFTER BRIAN LEFT KELLY he stopped at a convenience store for change and then headed for a phone booth that was out of the blistering late-morning sun. He had decided to start his search with phone calls to veterinarians and the animal control and felt it was better for Kelly's peace of mind if he didn't make them in front of her. She had already suffered enough without the added trauma of listening to him repeatedly describe Beast and then wait to hear whether or not he had been brought in.

Almost an hour later, after he had given up on those two possibilities, he decided to take a swing by the studio before returning empty-handed to the apartment. Sure enough, there was the cat, patiently sitting by the front door waiting for Kelly to come to work. Brian opened the car door and called to him. After hesitating, he sauntered over and jumped up on the car seat. He looked a little bedraggled but unhurt. Within minutes he was curled into a ball and sound asleep.

KELLY WAS IN THE BATHROOM drying off from a shower when she heard the car door slam and Brian's admonition to Beast to settle down or he was going to hurt himself. Not bothering to finish toweling herself down she put on her slinky silk robe and headed for the front door, tying the sash as she went. A beaming smile on her face, she flung open the door just as Brian reached for the bell.

"You found him!"

Without warning Beast left Brian's loose grip and stretched himself out toward Kelly. As soon as he was securely balanced in her arms, he started meowing, displaying an incredible range of inflections that sounded like everything from garbled profanity, to an apology, to a syrupy, "I love you." He inched up to her neck and licked her chin, all the while "talking" to her. Tears filled Kelly's eyes. She gazed at Brian. "Thank you."

"You're welcome."

She stood on her toes to give him a kiss, an impish look sparkling through the tears of happiness. "You want to come inside?"

"Actually, I spend so much time out here every time I visit, I'm beginning to feel right at home."

"Well, come inside, anyway. I'm not dressed for front-porch visiting. Besides, there's something I want to do with you that we should do alone."

He could tell by the tiny smile that she knew exactly what she had just done to him. "We'll have to make it another time," he said, his voice filled with regret. "My plane leaves in less than an hour."

Her eyes widened in disbelief. "What?"

"If you recall, I told you that I was tied up all weekend. I only flew down because I couldn't reach you by phone and I was worried." He tried but couldn't keep a straight face.

She stared at him, taking several seconds to confirm her suspicion that he was putting her on. "Get in here," she ordered, finally convinced that he was doing just that.

"Right away," he said, enjoying, yet wondering about, her pervasive good cheer. He had expected her to be happy about having Beast back, but there was something more afoot.

Brian followed her into the apartment, answering her rapid-fire questions about how and where he had found the cat. They went into the living room where Kelly made a bed for the cat on the sofa with an old afghan. Within minutes Beast had again fallen asleep.

Brian came up behind her as she stood and looked at the slumbering cat. He slipped his arms around her waist and pressed the side of his face against hers. "I believe you said you had something you wanted to show me...or was it do with me...."

She leaned against his chest, tilting her head back to lay in on his shoulder. He turned her, then held her face cradled between his hands. Slowly they moved toward each other, until their lips met and melded in a kiss that was a homecoming for two passionately independent souls. Without words they communicated their surrender to each other.

Brian broke their kiss and pulled her close, deeply breathing in the sweet smell of her, while branding her body with the feel of him. In such a short time she had become a part of him. "I think it's time for us to talk...to *really* talk to each other," she murmured, breaking in on his reverie.

He took his arms from around her and shoved his hands in his pockets. "If we're going to talk, I think you'd better find something else to wear."

She shook her head and started for the bedroom, giving him a parting shot. "I don't know about you, Robertson. You let the strangest things bother you. First a bit of lace and silk on a backpack and now one skimpy little robe."

Brian watched her disappear, fighting an urge to follow. He decided he'd better look for something to do while he waited and went into the kitchen to make them each a glass of iced tea. He then sat at the table drumming his fingers across the oak.

She was right—it was time they laid everything out in front of them and came to some conclusions together. They had been doing in bits and pieces what needed to be done all at once. He propped his elbows on the table and held his head between his hands. What if she didn't want what he wanted?

She joined him a few minutes later, wearing a pair of white shorts and red halter top. He inwardly laughed at himself for thinking her attire had anything to do with the craving he had whenever she was near. She could have come in wearing a sack and he would have wanted to make love to her with equal intensity.

She sat across from him and held out her hands. "Better?" She smiled softly.

He took her hands in his. "You look beautiful."

"Do you know, I really think that in your eyes I am beautiful."

"It amazes me that you have ever doubted your looks."

She started to answer, to tell him what it does to a young girl's fragile ego to go to a dance and be virtually ignored by every boy there, or to go through high school stick thin and flat chested, but she decided to save it for another time. "As long as you keep lighting up the way you just did whenever I come into a room, I'll never doubt how you feel." She squeezed his hand. "You make me feel good about myself in so many ways. While you were gone, I thought about what you said...and you were right. I've held these people who control advertising in such high esteem for so long that I automatically accepted their opinion on everything— including my talent. What's so incredible is that at the same time, I recognized how old-fashioned the work they turn out is."

Brian held his breath as he waited for her to continue.

"I've been listening to other people's opinions about my work for too long. Somehow I'm going to have to find a way to get back in touch with the part of me that senses when I've turned out a dynamite photograph and learn to stick by that feeling." She gave him a tiny smile. "You may find this hard to believe, but when I was in school, I would argue for hours in defense of one of my photographs."

"And have you decided where this metamorphosis is to take place?"

"Now that I'm confident I could eventually make it happen right here, it's no longer necessary for me to stay."

Had he heard her correctly? "Are you sure?"

"I owe it to myself to go somewhere that's open and receptive to new talent—a place where I can succeed or fall on my face all by myself."

"I'm not sure there is a city anywhere that doesn't have some networking, but I do know of a place where there's enough work to get your foot in the door. Where you go from there will be pretty much up to you."

"It sounds like you've been doing a little investigating for me."

"Some," he admitted. It had only taken a few phone calls to old banking acquaintances to learn whom to contact for answers.

"And?"

"New York was the place recommended the most often."

"I'm not surprised."

"You don't want to go to New York?" he said, responding to the lack of enthusiasm in her voice. His heart felt as if it was in his throat.

"That's not it...." She stared at their clasped hands. Slowly her gaze rose to meet his. "Moving to New York is fine for me, but what about you?"

He closed his eyes and let out a deep sigh. He felt as if he had been walking a tightrope stretched over a rocky canyon and had just reached the landing. When he opened his eyes again, they were mirrors of his happiness. "Let me tell you what I've been doing for the past two and a half weeks. But first—" he reached in his pants pocket "—I have a present for you." He handed her an exposed roll of black-and-white film.

Kelly studied the canister, then turned it over in her hand. Unable to see anything that would set the film apart from any other, she eyed him quizzically. "Did you want me to process this?"

"Yes.

She grinned. "You know you could get a much better deal down the road at the drugstore. My prices are pretty high by comparison."

"Yeah, but would they let me fool around in the darkroom with the lab technician while she was working?"

"Most assuredly not."

"Then hang the cost. I wouldn't dream of passing up a chance like this."

ON THE WAY to the studio Brian finally told Kelly what he had been doing in Connecticut. "I've delayed giving the stockholders my final answer in order to talk to you first."

Kelly's gaze shifted from his face to the road ahead. She no longer doubted Brian's love or how important she was to him, but she had known all along that her love alone would never have been enough to bring him complete happiness. He needed the challenge that work brought him. He was a doer, not a man to spend the rest of his life wandering. Now that she had seen this side of him, she was deeply moved at the patient and loving way he had dealt with her insecurities. For a man who had never experienced self-doubt, he had been unbelievably tolerant toward someone who did.

"Kelly, are you listening?"

She smiled. "Would you like me to repeat your last three words?"

"We'll discuss that later," he said meaningfully. "In the meantime, at least give me a hint of your feelings about the job and New York."

"Do they have any idea how lucky they are at that bank to get you?"

"Actually, I'm getting a little sick of hearing them tell me."

"Then I guess I'd have to say go for it." She looked at him again. "If I had been my usually sharp self this morning, I would have guessed all this before you said anything."

"How—"

"The beard. Why else would you have shaved?"

AFTER THE FILM HAD BEEN PROCESSED Kelly resisted the impulse to view the negatives before they were ready to print, realizing that Brian would never believe she could "read" them as clearly as she could a photograph. When they were ready, she made a contact print—twenty-four 35mm photographs on a sheet of eight-by-ten paper.

Viewing the pictures under a magnifying glass, she realized they were all shots of the same house. She laid the glass aside. "Well? Would you kindly interpret?"

"Do you like it?"

"What's not to like?" The old farmhouse was warm and welcoming and looked as well cared for as the meticulously tended lawn and gardens that surrounded it. Beast would love it there.

"Did you notice the building to the left of the house?"

"Uh-huh."

"Don't you think it would make a perfect studio? Especially since it's only a short train ride into New York City?"

Kelly picked up the contact sheet and looked more closely at the house that would be her new home.

How many days had he spent looking for just the right place, one that would be absolutely perfect for her to set up a darkroom? A wonderful warmth enveloped her. It seemed the fantasy she had secretly harbored all these years had not been a fantasy, after all. There really was a shining knight ready to sweep her off to a castle in a faraway land. She looked up at him, a twinkle in her eyes. "Possibly," she answered.

*"Possibly?"*

"An awful lot would depend on the quality of the water."

He reached for her, pulling her into his arms. "You did that on purpose."

She gave him an indulgent smile filled with love. "Of course I did."

"Why?"

"It's beginning to get through to me that if I don't keep you just a little off balance, you're going to steamroll me with that pushy personality of yours."

He suddenly grew very serious. "You're wrong, Kelly. I've discovered a lot about myself in these past two months—the most important of which is just how empty my life was before you came along. I could never go back to being the man I was. Banking is what I do for a living and it pleases me that I do it well, but it will never control me to the exclusion of everything else the way it once did. Plain and simple—I love you. You are my one and only priority from now on."

Her arms closed around his neck as she pressed her lips to his throat. "What would you have done if I had said no to the house and vetoed New York, too?"

A wicked grin curved his mouth. "I would have moved on to plan B."

"Which was?"

"I was going to make you my captive and ravish you until my charm worked its magic."

"Oh, I see." Long seconds passed before she gave him a coy glance and said, "Do you suppose it would be possible to temporarily withdraw my previous answer?"

Suddenly a picture of the two of them years in the future flashed before him. Their life together was going to be more than he had dared to dream during the lifetime of loneliness he had spent without her. "Not only possible, my love..." he murmured against her mouth. "You can consider it done."

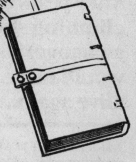

M000018656

# The Big Book of
# BABY
# NAMES

# The Big Book of
# BABY
# NAMES

*Every parent's inspirational
guide to naming their new child*

Marissa Charles

ARCTURUS

**ARCTURUS**

This edition published in 2010 by Arcturus Publishing Limited
26/27 Bickels Yard, 151–153 Bermondsey Street,
London SE1 3HA

ISBN: 978-1-84837-297-9
AD000073EN

Cover design by Alex Ingr
Layout by Metro Media Limited
With thanks to Andrew Adamides, Lee Coventry

Printed in the UK

# Contents

# Introduction

# Introduction

**Naming your newborn can be a daunting task.** With thousands of names to choose from, it is easy to become overwhelmed. Should you opt for the traditional – Victoria, Mary or John – or the 'out-there': Moon Unit or Stardust? Should you choose a name that reflects your religious beliefs or one that has been used in your family for generations?

Does the name of a celebrity or current storybook hero appeal, or do you want to preserve your child's individuality by being creative and inventing something truly original? The options are seemingly endless, but leaf through the pages of this book and you will find answers to these questions which plague all parents. There are handy tips on the best way to choose a name for your child and the pitfalls to avoid.

If you want a name that reflects your ethnic or cultural background, we have separate sections highlighting those that are popular in the African, Celtic, Muslim and Native American communities. You can also read up on naming fashions and trends that have influenced parents through the ages. Having said that, the main aim of this book is dedicated to answering the basic question: what does the name mean and where does it come from?

Obviously, a name is much more than just a label. It is a gift from you to your children, and one that you hope they will love enough to carry with them for the rest of their lives. It is also the first step towards building their unique personal identity.

In years to come your child may be interested to know how you chose his or her name – the story behind it, the history and meaning. What language does the name come from? With which culture is it associated? Which historical figures bore the name and what was their contribution to society?

However, the very thing that makes choosing a name interesting can also make it confusing. A single name may have come from more than one language, each one seemingly unrelated. It is perfectly possible for one name to boast Latin, Old French, Old English and German roots simultaneously. In some cases it is because the exact meaning or origin of the name is unknown and research has thrown up more than one possible

# *Introduction*

source. However, another factor lies in the history of Europe and the development of the English language.

When the Romans first invaded Britain in 54 BC they found a land largely inhabited by Celtic-speaking peoples. The invading forces left their own cultural imprint on the area – Latin – and subsequent armies did the same. West Germanic invaders such as the Jutes, Angles and Saxons all contributed linguistic marks. The result was that, from around AD 500 onwards, Anglo-Saxon – or Old English – became the dominant language in England.

Later, the arrival of the Danish and Norwegian Vikings injected Old Norse elements, and, after the Battle of Hastings in 1066, the Normans brought with them their French dialect, which was also imbued with Old Norse by the way.

These three elements – Anglo-Saxon, Old Norse and Norman French – developed into Middle English and later, Modern English. Add the fact that the Latin the Romans brought with them borrowed from Greek and it is clear that the languages of Europe are multi-layered and interrelated.

The ebb and flow of history, the changing fortunes of different rulers and invaders also explains why some names are popular and others are not, why some survived throughout the centuries but others did not. For example, after William the Conqueror and his followers arrived in England in the mid-11th century, many Anglo-Saxon names were replaced by Norman French ones. It was the Victorians who, fuelled by their fascination with Old English and Medieval names, reintroduced Alfred and Edwin into society. The renewed interest in the legend of King Arthur and his Knights of the Round Table also contributed to the hunger for names associated with early English folklore.

Similarly, as Christianity spread throughout Europe, efforts were made to break ties with the pagan past. Names from the classical world – especially those associated with Greek and Roman mythology – were replaced with ones belonging to characters from the Bible. Adam and Eve, Mary and Sarah, Rebecca and Joseph, the

# Introduction

names of Christ's Apostles, especially Andrew, John and Peter, were all favoured by parents wanting to reflect their faith.

Equally popular were the names of Christian martyrs, saints and missionaries, such as St Francis of Assisi and St Christopher. It was not until the English Renaissance that classical names like Penelope were plucked from the past and bestowed upon children.

This pattern is repeated throughout the annals of history. During the Reformation, English parents shied away from names associated with the Roman Catholic Church. In the 17th century the Puritans sought out obscure Old Testament names such as Malachy, Zillah and Beulah or ordinary words that reflected a quality they would like their child to possess, like Hope, Faith and Patience.

In the modern age no such rules or social mores apply. Of course there are names that parents may avoid because of the current or historical figures associated with them. Adolph conjures up images of the Austrian-born German dictator Adolf Hitler. However, there are also names that mothers and fathers warm to because of a well-known personality. In the last 20 years Kylie, Madonna and Britney have found favour because of the influence of popular culture.

It is this, the influence of the arts (literature, plays, music, film and television), that has guided many of the definitions in this book. While the works of Shakespeare and other classical writers have long been a source of inspiration for parents, it is wrong to underestimate the powerful force of the mass media in today's world. In the golden age of Hollywood, films like *Gone with the Wind* and *High Society* inspired parents to name their children after leading characters like Scarlett and Tracy. But in the 21st century, soap operas, sitcoms, pop music and even the Internet have a role. Parents today truly have a wealth of information at their fingertips.

We have tried to offer some guidance within the pages of this book, as well as provide thousands of suggestions that may appeal to you – see the Index on page 367 for a full listing. Naming your baby should be entertaining, educational and fun. We hope you enjoy the journey. ∎

# How to choose a name

The process of choosing a baby name is a straightforward process for those who are already decided, particularly if there is a favourite name selected years in advance of giving birth. However, there are plenty of parents who are not at all decided and don't even know to start. Here are a few tips to help kickstart the process.

## Meaning
Look at names that have meaning for you and/or your family, perhaps naming the baby after a favourite relative or relatives. Alternatively, if you don't have a preference for your relatives, names, or want the baby to be more individual without being entirely different, look for derivatives or feminine/masculine versions of relatives' names.

## Avoid teasing
Bear in mind the different stages of life your child will go through with their name, and try to avoid picking something which could lead to teasing in the classroom and playground. Look at your baby's physical characteristics (or those that tend to run in your family) and if there are any which generate teasing, avoid names that can exacerbate this.

## Syllables
Look at the length of each name and the number of syllables. Very long names can be difficult to fit on forms, while very short ones may look odd. In terms of syllables, try to vary the number of syllables in the first name and surname, and avoid first names that stress the same syllable as the last name.

## Rhyme and rhythm
Think of the rhythm of the name in combination with your last name. Try and avoid repeated sounds, as in Herman Wyman, for example. Also try and avoid rhyming names like Jane Vane and names that repeat part of the surname (e.g. John Johnson).

**Pronunciation**

Think about pronunciation. Going through life with a name that is difficult to pronounce – or that is pronounced very differently to how it is spelt – can lead to frustration. The same goes for anything spelt in an overly-exotic way.

**Middle names**

Middle names are a means of including relatives who might otherwise feel excluded from the baby-naming process – as long as the names all work together. The syllable rule also applies when picking out a middle name, so do check how all three sound together.

Anne, Lynne and Marie are popular girls names due to the number of syllables they contain. Most first and last names have two syllables and the emphasis is placed on the first, so these names change this and make for a comfortable rhythm. There are, however, plenty of other names accented differently that can be used instead, like Alexandra, Fiona, Evelyn and Valerie.

Middle names for boys can be trickier, as most male names follow the same pattern of having two syllables, with the accent on the first. There are, however, plenty which differ, like Adrian, Anthony and Xavier. ∎

# Top 10 first names

BOYS

| 1800 | | 1900 | | 2000 | |
|---|---|---|---|---|---|
| 1 | William | 1 | William | 1 | Jack |
| 2 | John | 2 | John | 2 | Thomas |
| 3 | Thomas | 3 | George | 3 | James |
| 4 | James | 4 | Thomas | 4 | Joshua |
| 5 | George | 5 | Charles | 5 | Daniel |
| 6 | Joseph | 6 | Frederick | 6 | Harry |
| 7 | Richard | 7 | Arthur | 7 | Samuel |
| 8 | Henry | 8 | James | 8 | Joseph |
| 9 | Robert | 9 | Albert | 9 | Matthew |
| 10 | Charles | 10 | Ernest | 10 | Callum |

| 1850 | | 1950 | |
|---|---|---|---|
| 1 | William | 1 | David |
| 2 | John | 2 | John |
| 3 | George | 3 | Peter |
| 4 | Thomas | 4 | Michael |
| 5 | James | 5 | Alan |
| 6 | Henry | 6 | Robert |
| 7 | Charles | 7 | Stephen |
| 8 | Joseph | 8 | Paul |
| 9 | Robert | 9 | Brian |
| 10 | Samuel | 10 | Graham |

# Top 10 first names

GIRLS

| 1800 | | 1900 | | 2000 | |
|---|---|---|---|---|---|
| 1 | Mary | 1 | Florence | 1 | Chloe |
| 2 | Ann | 2 | Mary | 2 | Emily |
| 3 | Elizabeth | 3 | Alice | 3 | Megan |
| 4 | Sarah | 4 | Annie | 4 | Charlotte |
| 5 | Jane | 5 | Elsie | 5 | Jessica |
| 6 | Hannah | 6 | Edith | 6 | Lauren |
| 7 | Susan | 7 | Elizabeth | 7 | Sophie |
| 8 | Martha | 8 | Doris | 8 | Olivia |
| 9 | Margaret | 9 | Dorothy | 9 | Hannah |
| 10 | Charlotte | 10 | Ethel | 10 | Lucy |

| 1850 | | 1950 | |
|---|---|---|---|
| 1 | Mary | 1 | Susan |
| 2 | Elizabeth | 2 | Linda |
| 3 | Sarah | 3 | Christine |
| 4 | Ann | 4 | Margaret |
| 5 | Eliza | 5 | Carol |
| 6 | Jane | 6 | Jennifer |
| 7 | Emma | 7 | Janet |
| 8 | Hannah | 8 | Patricia |
| 9 | Ellen | 9 | Barbara |
| 10 | Martha | 10 | Ann |

# Top 10 first names

**USA**

BOYS

GIRLS

| 1900 | | 2000 | | 1900 | |
|---|---|---|---|---|---|
| 1 | John | 1 | Jacob | 1 | Mary |
| 2 | William | 2 | Michael | 2 | Ruth |
| 3 | Charles | 3 | Matthew | 3 | Helen |
| 4 | Robert | 4 | Joshua | 4 | Margaret |
| 5 | Joseph | 5 | Christopher | 5 | Elizabeth |
| 6 | James | 6 | Nicholas | 6 | Dorothy |
| 7 | George | 7 | Andrew | 7 | Catherine |
| 8 | Samuel | 8 | Joseph | 8 | Mildred |
| 9 | Thomas | 9 | Daniel | 9 | Frances |
| 10 | Arthur | 10 | Tyler | 10= | Alice |
| | | | | 10= | Marion |

| 1950 | | | 1950 | |
|---|---|---|---|---|
| 1 | Robert | | 1 | Linda |
| 2 | Michael | | 2 | Mary |
| 3 | James | | 3 | Patricia |
| 4 | John | | 4 | Susan |
| 5 | David | | 5 | Deborah |
| 6 | William | | 6 | Kathleen |
| 7 | Thomas | | 7 | Barbara |
| 8 | Richard | | 8 | Nancy |
| 9 | Gary | | 9 | Sharon |
| 10 | Charles | | 10 | Karen |

# Top 10 first names

**AUSTRALIA**

| | BOYS | | | GIRLS | |
|---|---|---|---|---|---|
| **2000** | | **1950** | | **1950** | |
| 1 | Emily | 1 | John | 1 | Susan |
| 2 | Hannah | 2 | Peter | 2 | Margaret |
| 3 | Madison | 3 | Michael | 3 | Ann(e) |
| 4 | Ashley | 4 | David | 4 | Elizabeth |
| 5 | Sarah | 5 | Robert | 5 | Christine |
| 6 | Alexis | 6 | Stephen | 6 | Jennifer |
| 7 | Samantha | 7 | Paul | 7 | Judith |
| 8 | Jessica | 8 | Philip | 8 | Patricia |
| 9 | Taylor | 9 | Christopher | 9 | Catherine |
| 10 | Elizabeth | 10 | Ian | 10 | Helen |

| | | | **2000** | | **2000** | |
|---|---|---|---|---|---|---|
| | | 1 | Joshua | 1 | Jessica | |
| | | 2 | Jack | 2 | Emily | |
| | | 3 | Thomas | 3 | Sarah | |
| | | 4 | Lachlan | 4 | Georgia | |
| | | 5 | Matthew | 5 | Olivia | |
| | | 6 | James | 6 | Emma | |
| | | 7 | Daniel | 7 | Chloe | |
| | | 8 | Nicholas | 8 | Sophie | |
| | | 9 | Benjamin | 9 | Hannah | |
| | | 10 | William | 10 | Isabella | |

# Naming trends

Fads and fashions in names are nothing new – in fact they date way back into history, with favoured names coming in and going out of fashion as easily and as often as clothing styles do. Of late, however, one interesting factor has been noted – girls names tend to be subject to more trends than boys names, with the likes of David and Michael remaining popular, while Rose, Ruby and Emma come and go far more regularly. Here are a few trends from the last thousand years or so!

## Upper Class Names (1066 onwards)

When the Normans invaded England, they became the higher members of society, and Norman names became trendy with the lower, and more aspirational classes. Prior to this, Anglo Saxon names had been altered from generation to generation, while Norman names stayed the same. Norman names include William, Brian, Robert, Alan, Alice, Laura and Emma.

## Biblical Names (Medieval times)

As the Christian church took hold, it became all the rage to name your child after a character from the Bible. Saints' names in particular started to become extremely popular. By the 16th century, 28 per cent of boys were being named John, overtaking William as most popular boy's name somewhere around 1400. Other popular biblical names of the period include Matthew, Luke, Mary, Margaret and Agnes.

## Puritan Names (16th – 17th century)

The Puritans brought with them their own favoured names. Catholic names went out of favour and names denoting qualities the Puritans thought were admirable became popular. Hence, the likes of Patience, Temperance, Mercy, Hope, Charity and Faith came to the fore. In addition to not liking Catholic names, the Puritans also avoided any Biblical names associated with anything less than savoury. Hence Eve, Cain, Bathsheba and Dinah all declined in popularity.

# Naming trends

**Literature and Fame (17th century onwards)**
While it can be argued that naming children after the famous really starts when people took names from the Bible, this is one trend that has continued to this day, with many parents looking to both real-life figures and artistic movements for naming inspiration. The author JM Barrie created the name Wendy for his play *Peter Pan*. The romantic movement popularised romance names like Quentin, Nigel and Amy, and the pre-Raphaelite movement gave renewed popularity to medieval names like Mabel, Lancelot and Edith. In Victorian times, those who weren't too enamoured of the flower-name trend turned to the Gothic revival and picked Norman and Anglo-Saxon names from this, including Alfred, Emma and Matilda.

**Flowers and Jewels (19th century)**
From the 1850s onwards, flowers became hugely popular as names for girls, with Lily, Ivy, Hyacinth, Poppy, Rose and Daisy all cutting huge swathes into the public consciousness. Gemstones also started appearing as first names for the first time, such as: pearl, ruby, amber, jade and amethyst.

**Flower Power (1960s)**
The psychedelic 1960s saw a major breakout in the number of 'out-there' names chosen for children, with the rise of flower power, free love and the hippy movement. Names like Sun, Moon and Sky briefly became popular.

**Unisex Names (1970s)**
Unisex names became fashionable in the 1970s due to the influence of women's lib and the desire to erase the lines between the sexes. Girls' names such as Georgie, Nicola and Philippa all became popular during this time.

**Welsh Names (20th century)**
A recent trend has pushed Welsh names to the fore. Rhys, Rees, Lewis, Sian and Evan have all become popular. ■

# Naming traditions

**While most westerners simply pick a name they like for their child, or choose the name of a favourite friend or relative, other parts of the world have rather more rigid and unusual traditions for naming babies.** Even other parts of Europe have customs and traditions which seem rather unusual by British standards.

### France
In France, theoretically, a law passed in 1803 limits parents' choices to the names of saints or historical figures. While the law has been relaxed over the years, there have still been recent court cases where parents demanded the right to give their babies rather more unusual names.

### Spain
In Spain, the child gets two last names – first the father's name, then the mother's maiden name. Hence, if Juan Perez Castillo marries Carmen Ramirez Polo, their child Ramon would be named Ramon Perez Ramirez.

### Italy
Italian first names are never unisex. Boys' names generally end with the letter O, as in Enrico, Paulo, etc, while girls' names generally end with the letter A, as in Valeria, Anna, etc. Families often use both the male and female derivatives of names, so it is quite common to have a brother and sister called, for example, Ilario and Ilaria.

### Austria and Germany
In Germany and Austria, the names of historical kings and other royals are extremely popular, with the likes of Wilhelm and Ludwig being used frequently.

### India
Indians enjoy many different naming methods, with many citizens having several names; a first name, a name derived from

# Naming traditions

their father, a village name, a caste name etc. In different parts of the country these are used in different orders.

Hindu families will often call their children after one of their ancestors, as the Hindu religion believes in reincarnation and in this way the ancestor can be 'reborn' in the child.

Parents also often use words as names, choosing words which mean qualities they would like the children to possess. Kaushal, for example, means clever or skilled.

Another popular source of names are the Hindu gods, including Siva, Lakshmi, etc.

**Israel**
Israelis usually pick first names from the old testament of the bible. Even quite obscure Biblical names, like Eldad and Medad are popular. Many names end in the suffix 'el' as in Hebrew this refers to God. Israelis do not have middle names.

**China and Japan**
Due to the different way they use language the Chinese naming system is wholly different. All the characters in the Chinese alphabet can be used as first names, and as there are thousands of these, there is plenty of choice! The most common include Wen (culture, writing), Zhi (will, intention, emotions), Yi (cheerful), Ya (elegant), Ming (bright), Hui (smart, wise), Hong (great, wide). Boys' names are picked from a set of around 20 characters used in rotation by generations of the same family. Girls' names are far less rigidly governed – parents can pick anything they like.

Similarly, in Japan, Chinese characters are used as first names. Boys are often given names which indicate the order in which they were born. Neither use middle names. ■

# Popular culture and names

**Since popular culture took over from – well, from pretty much everything else as the dominant force in peoples' lives, its no coincidence that more and more children have found themselves being named after TV and film characters, celebrities and, in a few cases, even the children of celebrities.** In fact, numerous internet baby-naming sites now tell you what TV show character/famous person shares which particular name, along the lines of 'Daphne – featured character in *Frasier* and *Scooby Doo.*'

Probably the best-remembered case of TV-related naming obsession occurred in the late 1980s, when the proliferation of children named Kylie and Jason in the UK was attributed to the huge popularity of Australian TV soap *Neighbours* and its then-stars Kylie Minogue and Jason Donovan.

However, as far back as the thirties, parents were turning to celebs for name inspiration. A quick look at the statistics shows Greta (as in Garbo) peaked in popularity in the 1930s, while Marilyn (as in Monroe) held its popularity throughout the 1950s and 1960s, declining thereafter. Boys' names tend not to be quite so trend-driven, however, although Clark (as in Gable) was slightly more popular in the 1930s and 1940s than it is today. This may well be due to the fact that trends tend to affect female names more than male, as standards like James, which have been particularly popular in the 1950s and 1960s thanks to James Dean and James Bond, have stayed at an almost constant level of popularity for the past hundred years.

TV chef Jamie Oliver's use of the name Poppy for his daughter has been credited with the resurgence in popularity of a name last popular in the Victorian era. Elsewhere, the Beckhams' choice of Romeo as a name for their second son was also copied by numerous other parents. *Amelie* became more popular after the French film of the same name hit it big recently.

When considering a pop-culture name, however, do beware. TV shows date quickly, and while Kylie and Jason were everyone's favourites yesterday, the names swiftly went out of fashion. ■

# Making up a name

**The quest for a name that is unique is becoming increasingly difficult.** Where once unusual names have now become commonplace, an option is to make up your own name for baby. Here are a few guidelines that can be used when making up a name.

Try combining names to come up with something new. You can try putting the baby's parents' names together, hence John and Eileen might have Joneen, or with the names of two or more relatives (this also dodges arguments about who the baby gets named after!). Alternately, it's a great way, if you are undecided between two names, just to try putting them together. Since most made-up names are combinations of some sort, try combining words you like either the sounds or the meanings of. This can apply to choosing names to combine as well, since you can create a new name with a combination meaning.

Try spelling another name or word or last name backwards, which can create a nice effect by giving the baby a 'mirror' effect name. For example, the last name Allen becomes a first name Nella.

Anagrams can also be very effective. Try re-arranging the letters in one or both parents' names. This can be a good option if you like the idea of combining the two names into one, but have names that don't work for this. This usually works better with longer names.

Alternately, you can combine any or all of the above or try random name generators, of which there are plenty online. ■

# Embarrassing names – beware!

**It is up to you to make sure whatever name is chosen is not going to cause embarrassment to your son or daughter.**

Considerations include; initials, how does your first name combine with your surname, and how it could potentially be broken down into a diminutive or nickname.

When it comes to initials, write down the initials and make sure you don't end up with something like Roland Andrew Taylor, or Penelope Irene Grainger.

As for checking how names work together, just try saying the names out loud, and you will soon notice if there is something not quite right. Most of the following are urban legends, but you will want to avoid the likes of Paige Turner, Crystal Waters, Theresa Greene, Jay Walker and Ima Hogg. (Ms. Hogg actually existed – she was the daughter of a prominent Texas politician in the early 20th century).

Children can be incredibly cruel when it comes to nicknames as well, so try and think of these in advance. Richard can often be turned into Dick, so if your last name is Head, you may want to avoid using that as a first name. So probably best to jot down all options before making your final decision. ■

# Named for greatness?

**Many cultures do believe that your name affects your life-path, and giving a child the right name can influence what he/she does in life.** Certainly, Hindu cultures choose names based on what qualities parents hope a child will possess as an adult.

Historically speaking, there are certain names which have been associated with those in positions of power, although it should be borne in mind that royalty and other powerful families tend to use the same names, but already have the connections and status in place to push their children on to success, so it is not really a coincidence that Henry and Elizabeth are popular.

Nevertheless, US academics have identified several names – including Anne, Joseph, Samuel, Henry and William – as being 'successful' names, based mostly on the track records of individuals with those names throughout US history (i.e. William Clinton being an example of success, having been US President for eight years.)

Numerology can also be applied to naming. Numbers are assigned to each letter of the alphabet (i.e. A is one, B is two etc), and all the letters in a first and last name are added together until one final number is found. This is then used to determine numerous things about the subject's life. There are many variations on how this is calculated, however, and the eventual meaning of this number. It should also be noted that in some cases numerology does also take into account nicknames and diminutives, which may not be known when the baby is named. Hence, you may name your baby Christopher, with no intention of referring to him as Chris, but he may then become known as such by his own demand or through interaction with peers. As this is his own chosen name, numerology would use that, rather than his full name.

So there are many facts that can be played around with in order to try and ensure success for your child. However, no amount of slaving over a numerology chart or the history books in search of a name guaranteeing fame will replace good parenting in terms of increasing your child's chances of success in life. ■

# Celebrity name changes

**Celebrities change their names for a variety of reasons, most commonly because their birth names just don't trip off the tongue easily enough.** In a business where names have to be short, sharp, instantly recognisable, and project the right sort of image, it's doubtful whether Thomas Cruise Mapother IV would have got nearly as far had he not dropped the Mapother and shortened Thomas to Tom. In music, a single name makes even more of an impact, hence Madonna Ciccone dropping her last name all together, and Gordon Sumner opting to be called Sting.

In the early days of Hollywood, the studio system dictated stars' name changes, often running fan contests to come up with new names for up-and-coming actors. That was how Lucille LeSueur became Joan Crawford, a name she hated, in 1925. There was also often the question of ethnicity in rather less free-thinking times and this lead to many casting off their more exotic-sounding names. Besides which, foreign names were often harder to pronounce and hence easier to forget. Although in a few cases, performers have gone for more ethnic-sounding names, Lou Diamond Phillips, for example, was born Lou Upchurch.

In just as many cases, however, actors' union rules dictate that names must be changed because two performers can't have names that are too similar. In many name-change cases, whatever the reason, many have altered their original first/last name and swapped them around, Tammy Wynette, for example, was born Wynette Pugh, while veteran actor Karl Malden was born Mladen Sekulovich.

In some cases, celebs have changed names for religious reasons, most notably Cassius Clay who became Muhammad Ali. Others, meanwhile, have deliberately chosen a different name to avoid being accused of using family connections – hence the actor Nicholas Coppola became Nicholas Cage. Charlie Sheen, meanwhile, adopted for his father Martin's self-chosen last name (Martin was born Ramon Estevez, Charlie Carlos Estevez) while brother Emilio stuck with the family's original name. ■

Celebrity name changes – a few of the best:

Woody Allen — **Allen Stewart Konigsberg**
Lauren Bacall — **Betty Joan Perske**
Anne Bancroft — **Anna Maria Louisa Italiano**
David Bowie — **David Robert Hayward-Jones**
Richard Burton — **Richard Jenkins**
Nicholas Cage — **Nicholas Coppola**
Michael Caine — **Maurice J. Micklewhite**
Chevy Chase — **Cornelius Crane Chase**
Eric Clapton — **Eric Clapp**
Alice Cooper — **Vincent Damon Furnier**
Elvis Costello — **Declan Patrick McManus**
Bo Derek — **Mary Cathleen Collins**
Kirk Douglas — **Issur Danielovitch Demsky**
Jodie Foster — **Alicia Christian Foster**
Cary Grant — **Archibald Alexander Leach**
Jean Harlow — **Harlean Carpentier**
Rita Hayworth — **Margarita Cansino**
Hulk Hogan — **Terry Jean Bollette**
Bob Hope — **Leslie Townes Hope**
Rock Hudson — **Roy Scherer**
Engelbert Humperdinck — **Arnold Gerry Dorsey**
Michael Keaton — **Michael Douglas**
Ben Kingsley — **Krishna Bhanji**
Stan Laurel — **Arthur Stanley Jefferson**
Spike Lee — **Shelton Lee**
Sophia Loren — **Sophia Scicoloni**
Meat Loaf — **Marvin Lee Adair**
George Michael — **Georgios Panayiotou**
Joan Rivers — **Joan Sandra Molinsky**
Mickey Rooney — **Joe Yule, Jr.**
Dusty Springfield — **Mary Isobel Catherine O'Brien**
Donna Summer — **La Donna Andrea Gaines**
John Wayne — **Marion Michael Morrison**
Stevie Wonder — **Steveland Judkins**

# Girls

## Aaliyah

Both Arabic and Hebrew in origin, this name means 'to ascend', 'highly exalted' and 'tall or towering'. Aaliyah may have also been derived from the Biblical Aliya, which means 'defender'.

## Abigail

In the Bible Abigail was one of King David's wives. In Hebrew the name Avigayil means 'father rejoiced', 'source of joy'. In Britain Abigail has been in use since the 16th century, but in the 17th century the name was used as a term for 'lady's maid' and fell out of favour. It regained its popularity in the 19th century and again in the 20th century.
*Variants: Abbie, Abby, Abagael, Abigael, Abigayle*

## Abira

This Hebrew name means 'strong' and 'heroic'.
*Variants: Adira, Amiza*

## Abra

A female form of the Biblical name Abraham, Abra means 'mother of multitudes' and 'mother of the earth'. It was a popular name in the 17th century.

## Ada

There are two main theories about the origin of this name. One belief suggests Ada is the Latin version of the Biblical name Adah, which means 'lovely ornament' in Hebrew. In the Old Testament Adah was the wife of Lamech, a direct descendant of Adam and Eve.

But another theory suggests Ada comes from the Old English for 'happy' and the Old German for 'noble and kind'. Either way it has been used in English-speaking countries since the 16th century and, in 1815, the poet Lord Byron gave the name to his daughter.
*Variants: Adah, Adda, Addie, Addy, Aeda, Aida, Eada, Eda, Etta*

### Adelaide

Of Germanic origin, Adelaide is the French form of the Old German for 'noble' and 'sort'. At the beginning of the 10th century the name held some currency because of the wife of the Holy Roman Emperor, Otto the Great. She bore the name and was known for her beauty and goodness.

In Britain Queen Adelaide, the wife of William IV, increased its popularity in the 19th century. In 1836, an Australian city was named in her honour.

*Variants: Ada, Adalhaide, Adalia, Adda, Addi, Addison, Adélaïde, Adelina, Heidi*

### Adelpha

This name comes from the feminine form of the Greek for 'brother' or 'brotherhood'. Therefore, it means 'sisterly' or 'sister to mankind'.

### Adesina

Families from the Yoruba tribe in West Africa give this name to the first baby of a previously childless couple. It means 'my arrival opens the way for more'.

### Adiel

In Hebrew this name means 'ornament of the Lord'.

*Variants: Adie, Adiell, Adiella*

### Aditi

'Free abundance' or 'unbounded creativity' is what this name stands for in Sanskrit. Aditi was the mother of the Hindu deities.

### Adrienne

The origin of Adrienne and its male counterpart Adrian could be the place name, Adria – a city and port in northern Italy close to the Adriatic Sea. Distinctive because of its dark water and sand, it may explain the eventual Latin meaning of the name – 'dark one' or 'black, mysterious one'. In Greek, Adrienne means 'rich'.

Adria is also the family name of the Roman Emperor Hadrian.
*Variants: Adrea, Adria, Adriana, Adrianna, Adriane, Adrien, Adrienne, Hadria, Riana*

**Afina**
Romanian in origin, this name means 'blueberry'.

**Agatha**
This name is the feminine form of the Greek word agathos, which means 'good' and 'honourable'. It can also mean 'good, kind woman'.

In the 3rd century the veil of St Agatha was supposed to have saved her from the lava of Mount Etna. Hence, she is the patron saint of fire fighters.

The name was first introduced to Britain by a Norman conqueror who bestowed it upon his daughter. Its popularity increased in the 19th century.
*Variants: Ag, Aga, Agathe, Agg, Aggi, Aggie, Atka*

**Agnes**
Another name of Greek origin, the adjective hagnos ('pure' and 'holy') led to the name Hagne, the Latin form of which is Agnes. The first saint to bear this name was a child who, refusing to marry, offered herself for martyrdom in 3rd century Rome. Her story made the name popular during the Middle Ages and the Old English forms – Annis, Annes and Annot – reflect the pronunciation of the time. It is especially popular in Scotland.
*Variants: Aggie, Aggy, Annais, Annice, Anis, Ina, Inez, Nesta*

**Aida**
Aida is the feminine form of Aidan and the title of Giuseppe Verdi's 1871 opera. The heroine, who bears the name, is an Ethiopian princess who is enslaved in Egypt.

But the origins of this name do not lie in Africa. In Latin and Old French Aida comes from words meaning 'to help, assist'. When taken from Greek it means 'modesty', and in

Arabic it means 'reward' and the Old English interpretation is 'happy'.
*Variants: Aidan, Iraida, Zaida, Zenaida, Zoraida*

## Aine
According to Irish mythology Aine was the queen of the fairies. The name is of Irish Gaelic origin and means 'little fire' or 'brightness, splendour and delight'.

## Aisha
The favourite wife of the Prophet Mohammed was called Aisha. It was also the name of Pharaoh's wife, who Aisha drowned in the Red Sea when the Children of Israel fled Egypt. In Arabic the name means 'woman', 'prospering' or 'alive and well'.
*Variants: Aesha, Asha, Ayasha, Ayesha, Aysha, Aishali, Asia*

## Alberta
The 19th century trend of calling girls Alberta may have something to do with Queen Victoria's husband, Prince Albert, and their daughter, Princess (Louise) Alberta.

Like Albert, this name is of Germanic origin. It stems from the elements: adal 'noble' and bertht which means 'bright and famous'. Brought to England by the Normans, the name died out until its Victorian revival.
*Variants: Albertha, Albertina*

## Alcina
Alcina, the feminine version of Alcander, was the name of King Arthur's half sister. The origin of the name stems from Greek meaning 'strong-willed' and 'determined'.
*Variants: Alcie, Alcine, Alzina, Elsie*

## Alexandra
Like Albert, Elizabeth and Victoria this name has long been associated with royalty. According to Greek mythology the first

person to be called Alexander – the male version – was the Trojan, Paris, Helen of Troy's lover. A group of shepherds gave him the nickname Alexander because he protected their flock from thieves. Hence the name means 'defender'.

The female variant, Alexandra, has been popular among European royalty for many generations. It was the name of the last Tsarina of Russia. The Danish princess who married Edward VII, and went on to become Queen Alexandra, revived its use in 19th century Britain.

*Variants: Alexandria, Alexandrina, Alexandrine, Alexia, Alessandra, Lexie, Xandra*

### Alice

An independent name in its own right, Alice started life as a pet form of the German name Adelaide, which means 'noble'. It first appeared in England – via the French shortened variant Adaliz – as Aliz and Alys.

The popularity of the name in English-speaking countries grew in the 19th century following the success of Lewis Carroll's children's books – *Alice's Adventures in Wonderland (1865)* and *Through the Looking Glass (1872)*.

*Variants: Alicia, Allie, Alli, Allis, Alix, Alys*

### Alicia

A variant of Alice, this name is a modern Latinate form of the same name.

*Variants: Alissa, Alyssa*

### Alison

This name, like Alicia, is a pet form of Alice that is now an independent name in its own right. Although it was popular in the 20th century it has long had currency in Europe. It was a common medieval name that died out in England in the 15th century, only surviving in the UK in Scotland.

Like Alice and Adelaide, Alison means 'noble'.

*Variants: Allie, Allison, Ally*

**Alma**

The name Alma has several roots. In Hebrew it comes from the word for 'maiden'. In Italian it means 'soul' and in Spanish, 'warm-hearted'. 'Apple' is the Turkish interpretation and to the Celts it is 'all good'.

But in Latin it comes from the word almus, which means 'nourishing, kind'. From this is derived the term for one's university – 'alma mater' or 'fostering mother'.

When Britain and her allies defeated the Russians in the Crimean War at the Battle of Alma in the mid-19th century, the name grew in popularity in the UK.
*Variants: Aluma, Alumit, Elma*

**Almita**

Of Latin origin, this name means 'benign' or 'kindly behaviour'.

**Alvina**

The roots of this name are firmly entrenched in Old English. It is derived from words that mean 'noble', 'sharp' and 'friend'. Thus the name Alvina has been interpreted to mean 'strong, wise woman'.
*Variants: Alvinia, Vina, Vinni, Vinnie, Vinny*

**Amalia**

A variant of the name Amelia, Amalia comes from the Latin for 'toil' and 'hard work'. It is also derived from the Hebrew for 'God's labour'.
*Variants: Amalie, Amaliah, Amalthea, Amelia*

**Amanda**

British dramatist John Vanbrugh may have invented the name Amanda for his 1697 work *The Relapse*, where it was the name of his heroine. However, if he did, he derived it from the Latin for 'worthy of love' or 'loveable'. He may have also devised it as a feminine equivalent of Amandus, which was borne by a number of saints from the 4th to the 7th century.
*Variants: Amandine, Amata, Manda, Mandi, Mandie, Mandy*

## Amarinda

Of Greek origin, Amarinda means 'long-lived'.
*Variants: Amara, Amargo, Mara*

## Amaryllis

A favourite of the poets Theocritus, Virgil and Ovid, who often used it in their works, Amaryllis comes from the Greek word amarullis meaning 'refreshing' and 'sparkling' and refers to eyes that were either sparkling or giving quick glances.

Milton also used the name in his poem *Lycidas*.

## Amber

Both a colour and a gemstone Amber was a fashionable name for girls in the 1960s. It comes from the Arabic ambar, which means 'jewel' and obviously refers to the precious stone that is used to make jewellery and ornaments.

First used as a given name in the late 19th century its popularity grew in North America during the 1980s and 1990s.
*Variants: Amberlea, Amberlee, Amberline, Amberly, Ambur, Amby*

## Ambrosia

The Greek word ambrosios means 'immortality' and 'elixir of life' and was often used in reference to the food of the gods. Thus it came to be associated with delicious foods and smells.
*Variants: Ambrosina, Ambrosine*

## Amelia

The Latin meaning of Amelia is 'industrious'. In the 20th century Amelia Earhart, the American aviator, was the embodiment of the qualities of her first name. She toiled and worked hard for her success.

But the name Amelia may have come from another Latin word, aemilia, which meant 'persuasive and flattering'. This version of the name, Aemilia, was used by Shakespeare in his 16th century play *The Comedy of Errors*.
*Variants: Amalea, Amalia, Amalie, Ameline, Emelita, Emil, Emilia, Emily*

**Amethyst**
Also the name of a violet-coloured gemstone, Amethyst comes from the Greek word for 'intoxicated'. This jewel was thought to prevent intoxication from alcohol. Leonardo Da Vinci wrote that amethyst was able to dissipate evil thoughts and quicken the intelligence.

**Amina**
The female form of Amin, Amina, has its roots in both Arabic and Hebrew. It means 'truth, certainty' and 'affirmation'.

**Aminta**
The origin of this name is uncertain but it is thought to come from the Latin word amintas, which means 'protector'. One theory suggests that Aminta is a derivative of the Greek masculine name Amyntas, which was used by the country's royal family from the 4th century onwards.

But another theory puts the creation of Aminta in the 17th century during the Restoration, when it was often used by the poets of the day.
*Variants: Amynta, Arminta, Minty*

**Amorette**
Amorette comes from the Latin for 'beloved, sweetheart' and 'little dear'. It may have been an invention of the poet Spenser who used it for a character in *Faerie Queene* in 1590.
*Variant: Amorita*

**Amy**
Amor is Latin for 'love'. Aimée is the French interpretation of this word as a girl's name and Amy is the Anglicised version. A direct descendant of Esmée – the early French form of this name – is Esme, the Scottish variant.

The name enjoyed popularity during the 1600s and was revived in the 19th century.
*Variants: Aimee, Aimée, Amata, Ame, Ami, Esme, Esmee, Ismay*

**Anaïs**
This is a French name, taken from the Greek for 'fruitful'.

**Anastasia**
The Russian name Anastasia comes from the Greek for 'resurrection' or 'one who will rise again'.
*Variants: Ana, Anastas, Anstis, Annestas, Anstes, Nastia, Stasa, Tansy, Tasya*

**Andrea**
Andrea is thought to be the feminine form of the name Andrew, which comes from the Greek word 'andreia' ('manliness' or 'virility').
   An Italian variant of this name is Andreana, while in France it becomes Andrée.
   Scotland has produced numerous variants of this name including Andrina, Andrene, Andreena, Dreena and Rena.
   Andrea has been in use since the 17th century.
*Variants: Andreana, Andrée, Andreena, Andrene, Andrina, Dreena, Rena*

**Anemone**
According to Greek mythology this is the name of a nymph who was transformed into a flower by the wind. Hence, it comes from the Greek for 'wind flower'.
   Another Grecian tale suggests that the anemone flower is so named because it sprang from the blood of the god Adonis who was killed while out hunting.

**Angel**
The word angel comes from the Greek for 'a messenger from God'. It is more frequently given to children as a name in Spanish-speaking countries and then mostly to boys. However, it is sometimes given to girls born on the festival of St Michael and the Angels which falls on 29 September.
   As a girl's name it is popular among African-Americans.
*Variants: Angela, Angeles, Angelica, Angelina, Angelique*

### Angela

Like Angel this name comes from the Greek word for 'messenger'. But it is also the female version of the Latin name Angelus. It has been in use in America and Britain since the 18th century.

It is also the name of the 16th century saint from northern Italy, who founded the first teaching order of nuns.

*Variants: Ange, Angeles, Angelica, Angelina, Angelique, Angy*

### Angelique

This is another member of the Angel/Angela family of names. Angelique comes from the Latin (via French) angelicus, which means 'like an angel'.

*Variants: Angeliki, Angelita*

### Annabel

Common in Scotland since the 12th century, Annabel is thought to be an elaborate form of the name Anna, which itself is derived from the Biblical name Hannah. According to that theory Annabel is a compound of Anna (Hebrew for 'God has favoured me') and bel ('beautiful' in French and Italian).

However, the name may have been derived from the Old French name Amabel which comes from the Latin for 'lovable'.

*Variants: Annabella, Annabelle*

### Anne

The Biblical name Hannah was thought to be the name of the mother of the Virgin Mary. Anna is the Greek form and Anne, its French equivalent. In Hebrew the name means 'God has favoured me'.

The popularity of this name has led to many variants and independent names. The pet forms Nan and Nanna have led to Nancy and Nanette. Anneka and Anika are Scandinavian versions while, in Russia it becomes Anushka.

*Variants: Anita, Ann, Anna, Annalise, Annette, Annias, Nanette, Nansi, Nina, Ninette*

### Anoushka

This is the Russian form of Anne, which has become an independent name.
*Variant: Anushka*

### Anthea

Although this name has been known since the classical period and has appeared in literature since the 4th century it did not become a popular first name until the 1960s.

Anthea comes from the Greek word for 'flowery'. It was the ancient title of Hera, the Greek queen of the Gods.
*Variant: Anthia*

### Antoinette

Perhaps the most famous bearer of this name is Marie Antoinette, the wife of Louise XVI who was beheaded during the French Revolution in 1793. The young queen was famous for her extravagance, intelligence and wit.

Her name, Antoinette, is the French feminine version of Anthony. Ultimately it comes from the Roman family name Antonius and in Latin means 'without price'. In Greek it means 'flourishing'.
*Variants: Anonetta, Antonette, Antonia, Toinette, Toni, Tonneli*

### Aphrodite

According to Greek mythology Aphrodite was the goddess of love, fertility and beauty. She was also the daughter of Zeus, the supreme god.

Her name is said to mean 'foam born' because she came to life by rising from the sea.

### April

The month of April is traditionally associated with spring and for good reason. It comes from the Latin word 'to open' or 'to open to the sun'. Hence its association with growth, renewal and blooming buds.

Girls born during this month are usually given this name or its French equivalent, Avril.
*Variants: Aprilette, Averyl, Avril*

### Arabella
This is a Scottish name of Latin origin, which means 'moved by prayer'. It is also thought to be either another variant of Annabel or to have come from a word that means 'Arab'.
*Variants: Ara, Arabel, Arabela, Arabelle, Arable, Arbel, Orabell, Orable*

### Aria
In opera an aria is sung by one voice. Unsurprisingly the name comes from the Latin for 'melody', 'air' and 'tune'.

### Ariana
Ariana has both Greek and Welsh roots. It means 'holy', 'holy one' and 'silver'.

### Ashanti
The Ashanti are a West African tribe that once ruled a great empire. The name is traditionally given to African-American girls in celebration of their cultural roots.
*Variants: Asante, Shante*

### Ashley
Originally a surname, Ashley became a popular name for both boys and girls in Australia and North America during the 20th century. The name was originally derived from the Old English for 'ash' and 'wood'.

Ashley is also the name of a pivotal character in Margaret Mitchell's *Gone with the Wind*. Following the success of the novel and the film in the 1930s the name became popular with American parents. That trend continued during the 1980s and 1990s when Ashley was among the top 10 names given to baby girls in North America.
*Variants: Ashlea, Ashleigh, Ashlee, Ashlie, Ashly, Ashlynn, Ashton*

### Atlanta

According to Greek mythology Atlas was a giant who held the sky up on his shoulders. It is from him that the Atlantic Ocean gets its name. Atalanta is the female form of Atlas and Atlanta is its variant.

However, Atlanta is also a city in Georgia, North America and its modern day usage may be attributed to this association and not Greek mythology.

*Variant: Atalanta*

### Audrey

The popularity of the name can be attributed to a 6th century saint called Etheldreda. She was an East Anglian princess who died because of a tumour in her neck, believed by her to be divine retribution for her love of fine necklaces. Etheldreda's name comes from the Old English for 'noble strength', but in Britain she was also known as Audrey. The name was especially popular during the 17th century.

*Variants: Atheldreda, Addie, Addy, Aude, Audey, Audra, Audrie, Awdrie, Ethel, Etheldreda*

### Aura

Of Greek origin, this name means 'gentle breeze'.

*Variant: Awal*

### Aurora

The Romans believed that Aurora was the goddess of dawn, and that the morning dew were the tears that she shed following the death of her son. The name comes from the Latin for 'dawn'.

*Variants: Alola, Aurore, Ora, Rora, Rori, Rorie, Rory*

### Ava

The name Ava resembles Eva and can be taken to be a variant of the name Eve, which means 'living'. Alternatively it could come from the Latin word 'avis' ('bird').

During the early Middle Ages Ava was also considered to be

a pet form of names beginning with those three letters. In fact, in the 9th century an abbess and member of the Frankish royal family bore the name. She was later canonised.
*Variants: Eva, Eve*

### Avalon

According to Arthurian legend Avalon was the island to which King Arthur was taken after his death. The name comes from the Latin for 'island', but also from the Old Welsh for 'apple'.
*Variant: Avallon*

### Avis

The exact meaning of the Germanic name Avis is uncertain. It is believed that it comes from the German name Hedewig, which means 'combat' or 'refuge in war'. But it is also said to have come from the Latin for 'bird'.

The name was brought to England by the Normans as Havoise.
*Variants: Amice, Aveis, Aves, Avice, Havoise*

### Bailey

Used for both boys and girls, Bailey is the transferred use of a surname. Its exact meaning is unclear. It could come from the Old English for 'berry' and 'wood'. It could equally be an old occupational name given to someone who was a bailiff. Alternatively the surname Bailey may have referred to someone who lived near a city fortification.
*Variants: Bailee, Baileigh, Bailie, Baily, Bayleigh, Baylee, Baylie*

### Barbara

The name Barbara comes from the same root as the word barbarian. Of Greek origin, it means 'foreign' or 'strange'.

Babs, Barbie and Bobbi are all short forms of this name. Babette is the French interpretation. Meanwhile the singer and actress Barbra Streisand gave the world a variant spelling of the popular 20th century name.
*Variants: Bab, Babette, Babs, Barbra, Baubie, Bobbi, Bobbie*

**Bathsheba**
In the Bible Bathsheba was the married woman King David saw taking a bath. He later married her himself after bringing about the death of her husband, Uriah. Bathsheba then went on to become the mother of King Solomon.

This Biblical name has various meanings in Hebrew – 'seventh daughter', 'daughter of an oath' and 'voluptuous'.
*Variants: Sheba, Sheva*

**Bea**
An independent name in its own right Bea is also the short form of Beatrice. Beatrice comes from the Latin beatrix which means 'bearer of happiness' and 'blessings'.
*Variant: Bee*

**Beatrice**
Occasionally used in England during the Middle Ages the name Beatrice was later used by both Dante and Shakespeare in their works. As mentioned above, it derives its meaning from the Latin for 'blessed' or 'blessings'. But it is also believed that the earliest Latin form of the name was Viatrix, which means 'voyager'.
*Variants: Bea, Beah, Beate, Beatrise, Beatrix, Bebe, Bee, Trixie, Trixy*

**Belle**
In French the word belle means 'beautiful'. The Italian word for beautiful is bella. An independent name, Belle is also a short form of Isabelle, just as Bella is a pet form of names such as Arabella and Isabella.
*Variants: Bel, Bela, Bell, Bill, Billi, Billie*

**Belinda**
The first part of Belinda, 'bel', comes from the Latin for 'beautiful' while the second part, 'linda', comes from the Old German for 'a snake or serpent'. The serpent is a symbol of wisdom.
*Variants: Bel, Bell, Bellalinda, Bindy, Blenda, Linda, Lindi, Line, Lynda, Lynde*

**Bena**
This name comes from the Hebrew for 'wise'.
*Variants: Bina, Buna, Bunie*

**Bernadette**
St Bernadette was the French teenager who saw visions of the
Virgin Mary at Lourdes in the 19th century.
  Her name is the French feminine form of Bernard – a German
name that means 'strong, brave as a bear'.
*Variants: Berna, Bernarda, Bernadina, Bernette, Bernita*

**Bernice**
Bernice is a variant of the Biblical name Berenice which comes
from the Greek for 'bringer of victory'. Well known during both
Greek and Roman times, in the New Testament it was the name
of the sister of King Herod Agrippa II.
*Variants: Berenice, Bernelle, Bernine, Bernita, Bunni, Bunnie,
Pherenice, Vernice*

**Bertha**
Bertha is the Latinised version of the Germanic name that has
been in England, in some form, since Anglo-Saxon times. The
name comes from the Old High German for 'bright, illustrious'.
  In Medieval Europe the name was made famous by the
mother of the Emperor Charlemagne.
*Variants: Berta, Berte, Berthe, Bertie, Bertina*

**Bess**
Elizabeth I of England was known as Good Queen Bess and the
name Bess has been long considered a short form of Elizabeth.
However, it is also given as an independent name. Bess shares
the same Hebrew meaning as Elizabeth – 'God is perfection'.
*Variants: Bessie, Bessy*

**Bethany**
In the Bible Bethany was the village outside Jerusalem where

Jesus stayed during Holy Week before his crucifixion. It was also used in reference to one of his disciples – Mary of Bethany.

In Hebrew the name means 'house of figs'. In Aramaic the meaning is 'house of poverty'.

**Betsy**
This name is another pet form of Elizabeth, which has been used independently. It may have been created by blending Betty with Bessie.
*Variant: Betsie*

**Bette**
In the 20th century the most famous bearer of this name was the American actress Bette Davis. The Hollywood legend pronounced her name as *'bet-te'*, but it can also be pronounced as *'bet'*.

Like Betsy and Bess, Bette is a short form of Elizabeth, which means 'God is perfection', 'God is satisfaction' or 'dedicated to God' in Hebrew.
*Variants: Betsie, Betsy, Bettie, Bettina, Betty*

**Bettula**
Of Persian origin, this name means 'maiden, young girl'.
*Variant: Betula*

**Beulah**
This Biblical name was popular among the Puritans in the 17th century. In the Bible the prophet Isaiah referred to Israel as the 'land of Beulah'. The name is of Hebrew origin and means 'she who is to be married, ruled over'.

**Beverley**
At one time this name was given to both boys and girls in North America. This transferred surname was originally a place name. It comes from the Old English for 'beaver's meadow' or 'beaver's stream'.
*Variants: Beverlee, Beverly, Buffy*

**Bharati**
This Hindu name is associated with the goddess of speech and learning. It is said to mean 'India'.

**Bianca**
In Shakespeare's play *The Taming of the Shrew* Bianca is Katherina's more subdued sister. The name comes from the Italian for 'white' or 'pure'. Shakespeare used the name again for a character in *Othello*.
*Variants: Biancha, Blanche*

**Bibi**
Bibi comes from the French beubelot, which means 'toy' or 'bauble'. It is also a short form of Bianca, which means 'white'.

**Bijou**
Another name derived from the French language. Bijou comes from French for 'jewel'. It also has Old English roots and may stem from a word meaning 'ring'.

**Billie**
Traditionally a short form of the boy's name William, Billie has also been given to girls. William comes from the Old English for 'resolution' and 'determination'. Legendary blues singer Eleanora Fagan is more famously known by her stage name, Billie Holiday.
*Variants: Bill, Billy*

**Blair**
Given to both boys and girls, Blair is more commonly found as a Scottish surname. Fittingly it has Celtic roots and means 'place', 'field' or 'battle'.
*Variants: Blaire, Blayre*

**Blaise**
Blaise comes from the Old English for 'torch' or 'shining' and the Middle English for 'proclaim' and 'to blow'.

In the tales of King Arthur Blaise was the name of Merlin's secretary. The name is occasionally given to boys.
*Variant: Blaze*

### Blanche
Like Bianca, Blanche means 'white'. This name comes from the Old French version of this word and was often given to girls who were blonde or fair-haired.

The name was brought to England by the Normans. One famous, early bearer of the name was Blanche of Artois who married Edmund, the Earl of Lancaster in the 13th century.
*Variants: Balaniki, Bellanca, Bianca, Blanca, Blanch*

### Bleu
Of French origin, in English this name simply refers to the colour blue.

### Bliss
This girl's name has the same meaning in modern English that it did in Old English – 'happiness' and 'joy'.

### Blossom
Blossom comes from the Old English for 'flower'. The name was first given to girls in the 19th century.
*Variants: Blom, Bloom, Blum, Bluma*

### Blythe
In Old English blithe means 'mild', 'gentle' and 'kind'. In old verses it was linked with the name, and affectionate Scottish term, Bonnie. It can also be given to boys.
*Variants: Bliss, Blisse*

### Bo
This name comes from the Chinese for 'precious' and also has the Old Norse meaning 'house-owner'.
*Variant: Bonita*

B

*Girls*

### Bobbie

Girls called Barbara and Roberta share the pet name Bobbie. However, this name has become an independent name and one that is used in conjunction with others to produce a double-barrelled first name such as Bobby-Anne.
*Variants: Bobbi, Bobby*

### Bonita

Although this is not a common name in Spanish-speaking countries it comes from the Spanish for 'pretty'. It was popular in North America in the 1940s, but can be directly traced back to the Latin for 'good'.
*Variants: Boni, Bonie, Bonnie, Bonny, Nita*

### Bonnie

In Margaret Mitchell's novel *Gone with the Wind* Bonnie was the name of the daughter of Scarlett O'Hara and Rhett Butler. The popularity of this book and film may account for the use of the name in the 20th century.
But the name has long been an affectionate term in Scotland and before that, like Bonita, was associated with the Latin and Middle English for 'good'.
*Variants: Bonita, Bonnee, Bonni, Bonny*

### Brady

This surname is usually found as a boy's name. It is mainly used in North America but it has Irish roots. It is thought to come from a Gaelic word that means 'broad or large chested'

### Brandy

The word Brandy comes from the Dutch word brandewijn ('burnt wine'). It arrived in Northern Europe from Southern France and Spain in the 16th century and described wine that had been 'burnt', or boiled, in order to distill it. As a girl's name it is thought to be a feminine form of Brandon. It is popular in North America.
*Variants: Brandi, Brandee, Brandie*

# Girls

### Breanna

This is a name of recent coinage. One theory suggests it is a blend of the names Bree (a short form of Bridget) and Anna. But it is also believed to be the feminine equivalent of the name Brian, which is of Celtic origin and means 'strong'.
*Variants: Breanne, Breeanna, Brenna, Bria, Brianna*

### Brenda

Logic would suggest that this name is the female version of Brendon – a Celtic name that means 'stinking hair'. But it has also been suggested that Brenda may be of Scandinavian origin, being a short form of the Old Norse word 'brand', meaning 'sword'.

While the name was popular in English-speaking countries during the 1950s and 1960s before the 20th century it was mainly found in Ireland and Scotland.
*Variants: Bren, Brenna*

### Bria

Brianna, the feminine version of Brian, can be shortened into the pet form Bria, which in North America is also used as an independent name. Like Brianna and Brian it means 'strong'.

### Bridget

Bridget is the name of the ancient Celtic goddess of fire, light and poetry. It is also the name of two saints – St Brigid of Kildare, the patron saint of Ireland and St Bridget of Sweden, the patron saint of healers.

The Celtic meaning of the name is 'strength' and 'high one', while the Scandinavian interpretation is 'protection'.

Brigitte is the continental form of the name that was popularised by French actress Brigitte Bardot.

Meanwhile, the short form Britt comes from the Swedish forms Birgit and Birgita and is born by the Swedish actress Britt Ekland.
*Variants: Biddie, Biddy, Birgit, Bridie, Brigette, Brigid, Brigitte, Britt*

**B**

**Britney**
Mainly found in North America, this name means 'from Britain'.
*Variants: Britany, Brittany, Brittanie, Brittnee, Brittney, Brittni*

**Bronwyn**
Of Welsh origin, Bronwyn means 'fair bosomed'. In Middle English the name means 'a robust or well-built friend'.

The name is popular in Wales where, according to legend, the name was borne by the daughter of the god of the sea.
*Variants: Bron, Bronnie, Bronny, Bronwen*

**Brook**
As a surname Brook was originally the name of someone who lived near a brook or a stream. Hence in Old English it meant 'stream'. But there is another Old English meaning of the word – 'to enjoy, be rewarded by'.

This name has been given to both boys and girls, along with the place name Brooklyn.
*Variants: Brooke, Brooklynn, Brooklynne*

**Bryony**
Bryony is often thought to be the feminine equivalent of the boy's name Brian, which means 'strong'. But it is also a variant of the Greek name for a wild climbing plant which, when translated into English, means 'to grow luxuriantly'.

It was first used as a girl's name in the 20th century.
*Variants: Briony*

**Bunty**
In the English language bunty has long been a term of endearment and, in the early 20th century, the nickname was used in reference to pets or lambs. It may have been derived from the verb 'to bunt', which means 'to butt gently'.

The pet name for a rabbit, Bunny, can also be given to girls.
*Variant: Bunny, Buntie*

### Caitlín

Pronounced 'kat-leen', Caitlín is the Irish Gaelic version of Catherine, which was brought to Ireland by the Anglo-Norman conquerors. An Anglicised version of the name, Kathleen, later became popular. So too did Caitlin, without the accent, which is pronounced 'kate-lin'.

The above versions all stem from Catherine, which comes from the Greek for 'pure'.

*Variants: Caitlin, Katelyn, Katelynn, Kaitlyn, Kaitlynn*

### Calista

Calista comes from the Greek meaning 'most beautiful'.

*Variants: Calesta, Calisto, Calla, Calli, Callie*

### Calpurnia

In Shakespeare's play *Julius Caesar*, Calpurnia is Ceasar's wife. The name comes from the Greek for 'beauty' and 'prostitute'.

### Camilla

The name Camilla is derived from the Roman family name Camillus, which means 'messenger'. In Roman times a camillus was also an attendant at a religious rite. Boy attendants were known as Camilli and girls were known as Camillae.

According to the Roman poet Virgil the woman who bore the name Camilla was a female warrior known for her speed. Legend has it that she could run so fast that if she ran over the sea her feet would not get wet. Roman mythology also names Camilla as a huntress and attendant to the goddess Diana.

Although the name was used in Europe during the Middle Ages, it was reintroduced during the 18th century. Its popularity was aided by the 1796 novel *Camilla*, which was written by Madame D'Arblay.

*Variants: Cam, Camala, Camel, Camila, Camille, Cammie, Milli, Millie, Milly*

### Caprice

With meanings from Latin, Italian and French, Caprice is thought to mean 'head with hair standing on end' or 'hedgehog-like head'. It could also mean 'fanciful'.

### Carlene

A variant of Carla and Karla this name is another feminine form of the name Charles, which comes from the Old German for 'man'. (See also Carol and Karla.)
*Variants: Carla, Carleen, Carly, Carlyn, Carol, Karla*

### Carmel

Carmel is the name of a mountain in Israel that was mentioned in the Bible. It is also the name attached to one title for the Virgin Mary, Our Lady of Carmel.

It comes from the Hebrew for 'garden' or 'orchard'.
*Variants: Carmela, Carmelina*

### Carmen

The famous title of Bizet's opera, *Carmen,* is ultimately the Spanish form of Carmel, which comes from the Hebrew for 'garden'.

The Latin meaning of this name is 'to sing, praise' and 'be lyrical'.
*Variants: Carmia, Carmine, Charmione, Charmaine*

### Carrie

Sometimes thought to be a variant of Carol – the feminine form of Charles – Carrie may also come from the Welsh word for love. As such it would belong to the Carys, Cerys and Ceri family of names. As another form of Carol its roots lie in the Germanic word for 'man'.
*Variants: Cari, Carin, Carine, Carol, Carole, Caryn, Carys, Ceri, Cerys*

### Carol

Though common today the name Carol was not popular as a child's name before the late 19th century. It drew its roots from the Latin 'carolus' and from the Old German for 'free man' or 'man' as the feminine form of Charles.

However, its cultural roots are varied. It is also linked to the Welsh for 'brave in battle' and the Old French for 'round dance'. Sometimes a short form of the longer name, Caroline, it is also given to girls born at Christmas time.

*Variants: Carey, Carrie, Carola, Carolee, Carole, Carroll, Caroline, Carolyn, Cary, Caryl*

### Catherine

The history books are littered with notable, powerful women who bore this name. The 4th century saint Catherine of Alexandria escaped death on a spiked wheel and in her honour the Catherine-wheel (a firework) was named. It was also the name of Catherine of Aragon, the first wife of Henry VIII of England, whom the king divorced to marry Anne Boleyn.

Whether spelt with a 'k' or a 'c' the meaning is the same. It comes from the Greek word for 'pure'.

*Variants: Caitlin, Carina, Cathleen, Cathy, Katerina, Katherine, Katharine, Kate, Kathryn, Katie*

### Cecilia

This female version of Cecil was first introduced to England by William the Conqueror's daughter who bore the name. During the early Middle Ages Cecily was the preferred version.

The name was also well known because of the fame of St Cecilia – a Christian martyr who is the patron saint of music.

Cecilia comes from the Welsh for 'sixth' and the Latin for 'blind'.

*Variants: Cacilia, Cacile, Celia, Cecile, Cecily, Sissy, Cissie, Cissy*

### Celena

Celena is a variant of the name Selena or Selene who, according to Greek mythology, was the goddess of the moon. The name is also thought to have a French meaning – 'always smiling'.

*Variants: Celene, Selena, Selene, Selina*

### Ceres

According to Roman mythology Ceres was the goddess of corn who was also responsible for the growth of fruits. Because of this association this name is often given to girls born in springtime.
*Variants: Cerelia, Corella*

### Cerys

This name, like Carys, comes from the Welsh word for 'love'. As such it is the equivalent of the English name Amy, which becomes Aimee in French.

Boys are sometimes given the masculine form of the name, Ceri.
*Variants: Cari, Caryl, Carys*

### Chandra

Chandra comes from the Sanskrit for 'illustrious' or 'like the moon'.
*Variants: Chan, Chandah, Shan, Shandra*

### Chanel

As a first name for baby girls this name has been popular among African-Americans since the 1980s. French in origin it means either 'channel' or 'canal'.
*Variants: Chanelle, Shanell, Shannel*

### Chantelle

Another French name, Chantelle either means 'to sing clearly' or 'stone'. The name was associated with the 17th century saint, St Jeanne de Chantal.
*Variants; Chantal, Chantel, Shantal, Shantel, Shantell, Shantelle*

### Charity

Together with faith and hope, charity is one of the three great Christian virtues. In a letter to the Corinthians in the New Testament St Paul declared charity – Christian love – as the greatest of the three.

The word, and the name, comes from the Greek for 'grace', hence Charis the goddess of beauty and grace. Charity also

comes from the Latin for 'kindness' or 'brotherly love'.
*Variants: Charito, Karis*

**Charlotte**
Introduced to England in the 12th century by the Earl of Derby's wife, the name Charlotte was especially popular in the UK in the1970s.

It is the French form of the name Charles which comes from the Old German for 'man'.
*Variants: Cara, Charlayne, Charleen, Charlie, Lottie*

**Charmaine**
The origin of this name has been disputed as it did not seem to exist before 1920. It is believed that Charmaine was derived from the older name Charmian – used by Shakespeare for the name of a character in his play *Antony and Cleopatra*. If that is the case Charmaine comes from the Greek for 'joy'. Alternatively it may have come from the Latin for 'song'.
*Variants: Carman, Charmain, Charmian, Charmayne, Sharmaine, Sharmayne*

**Chastity**
Another Christian virtue, the word chastity comes from the Latin for 'pure, virtuous, decent' and 'undefiled'.

After it was chosen by pop star couple Cher and Sonny Bono for the name of their daughter in 1969, its popularity increased.

**Chelsea**
In Old English it means 'chalk landing place' but in England the name Chelsea is usually used in reference either to an affluent part of London or a football club. However, since the 1950s Chelsea has been increasingly used as a girl's name.
*Variants: Chelsi, Chelsie*

**Chenoa**
This Native American name means 'white dove'.

**Chere**
Chere comes from the French word for 'dear' or 'beloved'. Another related name, Cherami, means 'dear friend'.
*Variants: Cher, Cherami, Cherri, Cherie, Cherrie, Cherry, Cheryl, Cherylie*

**Cherie**
As above, Cherie comes from the French for 'dear' or 'beloved'.
*Variants: Ceri, Cher, Cherami, Chérie, Cherry, Sheree, Sherry*

**Cheera**
Of Greek origin, Cheera is derived for the word for 'face' and probably implies a cheery, warm expression.

**Cherry**
A pet form of Charity, Cherry has become an independent name in its own right. It was used by the 19th century novelist Charles Dickens as a nickname for his character Charity in *Martin Chuzzlewit*.

It also refers to the fruit and, in Middle English, may have appeared as Cherie.

**Cheryl**
Another name not found before the 1920s, Cheryl may have started life as a blend of Cherry and the popular German name Beryl.

The name may mean 'love' if Cherry is taken to be a short form of charity. Alternatively, if the name came from the French Cherie then it also means 'dear, beloved'.
*Variants: Chère, Sheryl, Sherrell, Sheralyn*

**China**
Like India and Kenya this is the name of a country that is now being used as a girl's name. The name originally comes from the word Qin, which is the name of the dynasty that ruled China from 221 BC.
*Variants: Chynna*

# Girls

### Chloë

Chloë comes from the Greek word for 'green' or a 'young green shoot'. Hence Chloë was the name of the goddess of young crops.

The name is mentioned in both the Bible and the 19th century anti-slavery novel *Uncle Tom's Cabin*.

*Variant: Chloe*

### Christabel

The English poet Samuel Taylor Coleridge is thought to be the creator of the name Christabel, which was the title of his 1816 poem. The name is a combination of the first syllable of Christine and the feminine suffix 'bel'. Thus it means 'beautiful Christian'.

The suffragette Christabel Pankhurst is one famous bearer of the name.

*Variants: Christa, Christabell, Christabella, Christable, Christabelle, Christie, Christobella, Bell, Bel*

### Christina

The boy's name Christian means exactly what it implies – follower of Christ. Christina is a simplified form of Christiana, the Latin feminine version of this name. Like Christine it has lead to a number of variants from around the world and the independent name Tina.

*Variants: Chris, Chrissie, Christiana, Kirstie, Kirsty, Krista, Kristen, Kristine, Krystyna, Tina, Xena*

### Christine

Christine comes from the Old English word for Christian – in other words a follower of Christ and a member of the Christian faith. The name has been in use, for both boys and girls, in various forms since the 11th century.

Christian is the masculine form. Kirsty and Kirstie are the Scottish variants. Kirsten and Kersten are the Scandinavian forms.

*Variants: Chris, Chrissie, Kersten, Kirsten, Kirstie, Kirsty, Krista, Kristen, Kristine*

C

### Cicely

A variant of the name Cecilia, Cicely is an independent name in its own right. Like Cecilia it is a feminine form of Cecile and is derived from an ancient Roman family name that means 'blind'.
*Variants: Cecily, Cecilia, Celia*

### Cillian

Of Irish origin this name may have one of two meanings. It either comes from the Gaelic word for 'strife' ('ceallach') or from 'ceall' – another Gaelic word meaning 'monastery' or 'church'. Cillian has been borne by a number of Irish saints. While Cillian is the Irish spelling, Killian is the Anglicised version.
*Variants: Keelan, Killian, Killie*

### Cindy

In the 19th century this name may have been a pet form of the popular name Cynthia. In the classical world Cynthia was an alternative name for Diana, the Greek moon goddess.

Cindy is also the pet form of the names Lucinda and Cinderella. Lucinda comes from the Latin word for 'light', while Cinderella comes from the French for 'ashes'. It is also the name of the fairytale heroine who, once bullied by her stepmother and sisters, went on to marry Prince Charming.

Cindy is now used independently as a girl's name, especially in North America.
*Variants: Cindi, Cyndi, Sindy, Syndi*

### Claire

This name was derived from the Latin word 'clarus', which means 'bright, clear' and 'famous'. It was brought to England by the Normans and has appeared in various forms ever since.

In 1975 it was the most popular name given to girls.
*Variants: Clair, Clare, Claribel, Clarrie*

### Clara

Like Claire the name Clara comes from the Latin word for

'bright, clear' and 'famous'. The name was borne by a 1920s silent film actress, Clara Bow. She was the original 'it' girl and an early Hollywood celebrity.

It is ironic that the name is associated with a woman made famous by the medium of film, for the patron saint of television is St Clare of Assisi who witnessed a mass being celebrated far away. Clara is the Latinised form of Claire.
*Variants: Claribelle, Clarinda, Clara-Mae*

## Claudette

Claudette is the French feminine form of Claudius, which started life as a Roman family name. The Claudii believed their name came from the Latin word 'claudus', which means 'lame'. It may have been a nickname given to one of their ancestors.

Claudii became Claudius, the feminine of which is Claudia. Claudette is a variant of that girl's name.
*Variant: Claudia*

## Cleo

The name Cleopatra was borne by many women in the Ptolemaic royal family who ruled ancient Egypt. The most famous bearer of this name was the final member of this dynasty Cleopatra VII, who was born in either 70 or 69 BC. She had affairs with the Roman leaders Julius Caesar and Mark Antony. Cleo is the pet form of Cleopatra and thus shares its Greek roots and meaning – 'glory of her father'.
*Variants: Cleopatra, Clio*

## Clove

Cloves are dried flower buds that are often used to add flavour to food and drinks. They are also prized for their aromatic and medicinal qualities. The name comes from the Latin for 'nail'.

## Clover

Usually clover has three leaves on each stem and flowers. However, according to tradition a four-leaved clover is supposed to bring good luck.

The name is derived from the Old English word for the plant.

### Coco

The exact meaning of this name is unclear beyond the fact that it is a French pet name. Its most famous bearer was Coco Chanel, the fashion designer whose given name was Gabrielle.

The variant of Coco, Koko, has both Japanese and Native American roots. The Japanese meaning is 'stork'. The Native American interpretation is 'night'.
*Variant: Koko*

### Colleen

Little used in Ireland but popular in North America and Australia, Colleen comes from the Irish Gaelic word for 'girl'. It may also be a feminine form of the boy's name Colin.
*Variants: Coleen, Colena, Colene, Collice, Coline, Collene*

### Colette

The boy's name Nicholas comes from the Greek for 'victory of the people'. Colette is a French feminine variant of this name. It was popular in the 1920s because of the French novelist Sidonie Gabrielle Colette, the author of *Gigi*.
*Variants: Colet, Collette, Cosette, Cosetta, Kalotte*

### Comfort

To strengthen, give solace to or ease someone's pain is to 'comfort' them. During the 17th century this name was given to both boys and girls by the Puritans. It comes from the Latin word 'confortare'.

### Connie

Constance was another name that was popular with the 17th century Puritans primarily because it had an association with Christianity. The Roman emperor Constantine is considered to be the first Christian emperor, and steadfastness, or constancy, is celebrated as a virtue of that faith.

The name was first brought to England by the Normans. One of William the Conqueror's daughters was called Constance. Its popularity declined after the 17th century but was revived by the Victorians. The short form, Connie, is now given as an independent name.

*Variants: Conetta, Constance, Constanza*

### Consuela

Another Puritan favourite, Consuela comes from the Latin meaning 'to free from sadness'.

*Variants: Consolata, Consuelo*

### Cora

The origin of this name is uncertain. It may have been coined by the American writer James Fennimore Cooper, who used it for one of his characters in the 19th-century novel *The Last of the Mohicans*.

The name may have been a derivative of the Greek word 'kore', which means 'maiden'.

*Variants: Corabelle, Coretta, Corette, Corinna, Corinne, Kora*

### Coral

This colourful hard substance that is found at the bottom of the sea is often turned into ornaments and jewellery. Its association with gemstones may have led to its adoption as a girl's name during the 19th century, when names such as Ruby were in vogue. Its meaning is derived from the Greek word for 'pebble'. However, the French name Coralie existed some 100 years before Coral.

*Variants: Coralie, Coraline*

### Cordelia

Cordelia was the name of the youngest of King Lear's three daughters in the 1606 play of the same name. It comes from the Latin for 'from her heart', while its Celtic meaning is 'harmony' or

'daughter of the sea'. The saint of that name was a martyred virgin.
*Variants: Delia, Della, Neila, Nellie, Nell, Nelly*

### Cori
Usually given to boys, especially in North America, Cori began life as a surname. It is derived from an Old English word for 'helmet'. It is especially popular among the African-American community.
*Variants: Corey, Corie, Cory, Korey, Kori, Korie, Kory*

### Corina
Like Cora, the name Corina was derived from the Greek word 'kore', which means 'maiden'. It was also the name of a poetess in ancient Greece.

The Roman poet Ovid called the object of his affection Corina in his work *The Amores*.
*Variants: Cora, Corene, Cori, Corinna*

### Courtney
Once an aristocratic surname Courtney has become popular in North America where it is given to both boys and girls. It was also once the name of a Norman village and refers to a place that still exists in France.

Its French connection implies that the name comes from a phrase which, in French, means 'short nose'. But it is also thought to be an English name that means 'from the court' of 'member of the court'.
*Variants: Cortney, Courteney, Kortney, Korteney*

### Crystal
The name Crystal is derived from the Greek word 'krystallos', which means 'ice'. This probably refers to the clear quality of the gemstone often used to make jewellery and ornaments.

Like Ruby, Emerald and Coral, Crystal was bestowed upon girls as a name from the 19th century onwards.
*Variants: Christel, Chrystal, Krystal, Krystle*

**Cynthia**

In Greek mythology to say someone was 'of Cynthus' was to say that they were born on Mount Cynthus on the island of Delos. This applied to Artemis (also known as Diana) the goddess of the moon.

Her epithet became a name in England during the classical revival of the 17th and 18th centuries, but did not enjoy popularity until the 1800s.

*Variants: Cynth, Cindi, Sindi, Cindy, Sindy*

**Cyr**

The boy's name Cyril comes from the Greek word for 'lord'. Cyr is its feminine form.

*Variants: Ciri, Cirilla, Cyra, Cyrilla*

**Daffodil**

This bright yellow flower is so closely associated with springtime that it is known as the Lent Lily. Its name is taken from the Dutch for asphodel – the Greek name for the lily family of flowers that include daffodils and narcissus.

*Variants: Daff, Daffie, Daffy, Dilly*

**Dahlia**

The 18th century Swedish botanist Anders Dahl lent his name to this family of Mexican and Central American plants that produce large, brightly coloured flowers. The root of the name comes from the Old Norse for 'from the valley'.

*Variants: Dahla, Dalia, Daliah*

**Daisy**

This name may owe its popularity to the 19th century trend to name baby girls after flowers. The daisy, a European plant, derived its name from the Old English for 'day's eye', which was a reference to the yellow discs of the flower opening their petals to the morning sunlight and closing them at night.

The name is also a pet form of Margaret because of its

association with a saint. The daisy was a symbol of St Margherita of Italy.

### Dakota
North and South Dakota are two states in North America. They got there name from the Dakota division of the Sioux tribe of Native Americans, who lived on the plains before the Europeans arrived. Unsurprisingly Dakota is a popular choice for children in the United States where it is given to both boys and girls. It means 'friend'.

### Dallas
This Texan city may have been named after George M Dallas, the American vice president from 1845 to 1849. His surname comes from the English and Scottish for place names, meaning 'house or dwelling in the valley'.

In North America this name is given to both boys and girls as a first name.

### Damaris
In the Bible Damaris was the name of an Athenian woman who was converted to Christianity by St Paul's preaching. Although the origin of her name is unclear it is believed to come from the Greek for 'calf' or to mean 'gentle'.
*Variants: Damara, Damaras, Damaress, Damiris, Mara, Mari, Maris*

### Dana
Several theories exist to explain the origin of the name Dana. As a female variant of the boy's name Daniel, it has the Hebrew meaning 'God has judged' or 'God is my judge'. But it could also come from the Old English for 'a Dane'.

Again, the name could come from the Irish Gaelic for 'bold' or 'courageous'. In fact, according to Irish mythology, Dana was the goddess of fertility.
*Variants: Daina, Danae, Dane, Dania, Danice, Danita, Danna, Danni*

### Danielle

In the Bible Daniel was an Israelite slave who could interpret dreams. His enemies conspired against him and he was thrown into a den of lions. But it was his faith in God that saved him.

In Hebrew the name Daniel means 'God is my judge'. Danielle is the French, feminine form of this name. Daniella is the Italian equivalent.

*Variants: Dani, Danii, Daniella*

### Daphne

In Greek mythology Daphne was a nymph with whom the god Apollo fell in love. Unfortunately the feeling was not reciprocal and she was turned into a laurel tree to escape his advances. Henceforth, Apollo declared that plant as being sacred to him. The name comes from the Greek for 'laurel, bay tree'.

Used in England from the late 19th century, it was especially popular in the early 1900s.

*Variants: Daff, Daffie, Daffy, Dafna, Dafnee, Daphna, Daphnee*

### Daria

This name is thought to have Persian, Greek and English roots. As the feminine form of the Persian name Darius it means 'protector' or 'royalty'. Its Greek meaning is 'wealthy, rich'. Meanwhile, as a variant of Dara, it comes from the Middle English for 'compassion' and 'to have courage, daring'.

*Variant: Dara, Darice, Darya*

### Darcie

Given to both boys and girls Darcie began life as a Norman baronial name. It was borne by a family who came from Arcy in northern France – hence, d'Arcy ('of, from Arcy').

Darcy also appears as an Irish surname via the Anglicisation of an Irish name that meant 'descendent of the dark one'.

The most famous Darcy in English literature is the hero, Mr Darcy, in Jane Austen's classic novel *Pride and Prejudice.*

*Variants: Dar, Darce, Darci, Darcy, D'Arcy, Darsey*

# D

*Girls*

**Darleen**
Common in North America and Australia, the name Darleen comes from the Old English for 'darling', 'beloved', 'highly valued, worthy, favourite'.
*Variants: Darlene, Darilyn, Darilynn, Darlin, Darline*

**Daron**
Daron is a feminine form of the boy's name Darren, which is a variant of the Persian name Darius ('protector').

**Daryl**
The name of the Norman village Airel was derived from the Latin for 'an open space'. A family from Airel would have been given the surname de Airel, which later became Daryl.

It was in 19th-century North America that this French surname was given to babies of both sexes as a first name. This trend became especially popular towards the end of the 20th century.
*Variants: Darrel, Darrell, Darryl*

**Davina**
This Latinate feminine form of the name David originated in Scotland, but ultimately is Hebrew for 'beloved, friend'.
*Variants: Davene, Davi, Davida, Davinia, Davita, Devina*

**Dawn**
This name comes from the Old English word for 'daybreak'. It was first used as a given name in the late 19th century. Until then the Latin form Aurora was more commonly used.

In Greek mythology Aurora was the 'goddess of dawn'.
*Variants: Aurora, Dawne, Dawnelle, Orrie, Rora*

**Dayle**
In Old English the word 'dael' meant valley. Thus, the surname Dale originally referred to where a person lived and meant 'dweller in the dale'.
*Varients: Dael, Dale, Daile*

**Deborah**

Deborah was the name of more than one Biblical character. In Genesis Deborah was Rebecca's nurse. Later on, in another Old Testament book, it was the name of a prophetess and female judge of the people who helped the Israelites to defeat the Canaanites.

The name, which was favoured by the Puritans in the 17th century, comes from the Hebrew for 'bee'.

*Variants: Deb, Debbi, Debra, Debs, Debora, Debbie, Debby*

**Dee**

As a nickname Dee is given to girls whose first names begin with the letter 'D'. However, it is also an independent name in its own right. Welsh in origin, it comes from the word for 'dark' or 'black' and could be given to children – boys and girls – with a dark complexion.

*Variants: DeeDee, DD, Dede, Didi*

**Delwyn**

Welsh and of modern origin, this name is a compound of two words. It is derived from the Welsh words 'del' ('pretty, neat') and '(g)wyn', which means 'white, fair' or 'blessed and holy'.

*Variant: Del*

**Delwyth**

This is another Welsh name which comes from the word for 'pretty' and 'neat'. The suffix 'yth' gives it the added meaning 'lovely'.

*Variant: Del*

**Deirdre**

The tale of Deirdre of the Sorrows is a tragic one. According to Celtic legend this beauty was to be wed to Conchobhar, the king of Ulster, but she rejected him and eloped with his younger brother Naoise instead. Hurt and angry, the king murdered his brother and Deirdre subsequently died of a broken heart. Hence the name Deirdre is taken to mean 'the broken-hearted', but it

could also mean 'the raging one' or 'fear'. This legend was cherished and honoured by Irish authors W B Yeats and J M Synge, who both produced acclaimed works based on this story in the early 1900s.
*Variants: Dede, Dee, Deerdre, Diedra, Dierdra*

**Delia**
The originally meaning of the name Delia was 'girl from Delos' – the Greek island that was sacred to Apollo and Artemis in ancient times.

As a first name it has been popular with poets since the 1<sup>st</sup> century BC. It was the favourite of the Latin poet Tibullus who wrote about Delia in his love poems. In 16<sup>th</sup>-century England Samuel Daniel produced his own sonnets dedicated to a beloved of the same name.
*Variants: Dede, Dee, Dehlia, Delinda, Della, Didi*

**Delilah**
One of the most tragic tales in the Bible is that of Samson and Delilah. Samson was a judge who, famed for his strength and his might, was a great protector of Israel. Delilah was his Philistine mistress who was persuaded to betray him. Discovering that the source of his strength lay in his long hair, she cut it off as he slept. Unable to defend himself Samson was captured by his enemies who blinded him and forced him to work for them.

Despite the negative portrayal of this temptress in the Bible, Delilah was a popular name among 17<sup>th</sup>-century Puritans. However, perhaps due to its Biblical connotations, its popularity began to wane in the 18<sup>th</sup> century.

In Hebrew the name means 'full of desire' and also comes from the Arabic for 'guide, leader'.

**Delma**
This name was derived from the Spanish for 'of the sea'. It also has a German meaning 'noble' and 'defender'.
*Variants: Delmar, Delmi, Delmira*

**Denna**
When taken as a feminine form of the name Dean, Denna coincidently shares the Old English and Native American meaning 'valley'.

However, it is also considered to be a variant of the name Diana who in both Greek and Roman mythology was the goddess of the moon.
*Variants: Dea, Deana, Deanna, Deanne, Diana*

**Delta**
The term for the Greek letter 'D' also gave its name to the mouth of a river which, like the upper-case letter delta, is triangular in shape.

**Dervla**
This Anglicised version of the Gaelic name Deirbhile is rarely found outside Ireland. It is a compound of the words 'der' ('daughter') and 'file' ('poet'). Thus the name means 'daughter of the poet'.
*Variants: Dearbhla, Derval, Dervilia*

**Desdemona**
In Shakespeare's tragic play *Othello* Desdemona was murdered by her jealous husband Othello, who was led to believe by the cunning Iago (wrongly, as it happened) that she had been unfaithful. Fittingly the name comes from the Greek for 'woman of bad fortune' or 'bad luck'.

**Desiree**
Desiree, the name of the mistress of Napoleon Bonaparte, is an appropriate one, for it comes from the Latin and French for 'to long for, crave, wish or desire'.

'Desiderata' was the Latin form of the name. Early Christians gave this name to a longed-for child.
*Variants: Desarae, Desaree, Desi, Desideria, Desire, Désirée, Deziree*

**Destiny**
This alternative word for 'fate' has found popularity as a given name in North America.
*Variants: Destinee, Destiney, Destinie*

**Deva**
Depending on the source Deva can have more than one meaning. According to Hinduism it is the name of the goddess of the moon. Indeed, in Sanskrit Deva means 'god, divine' and the variant 'Devi' is the name of the supreme goddess. However, Celtic mythology suggests Deva was the goddess of the River Dee in Scotland.
*Variants: Devaki, Devanee, Devi, Devika, Dewi*

**Devon**
Beyond being the name of an English county it is not certain where Devon comes from. It may derive from the Celtic people who inhabited the south western peninsula of Britain at the time of the Roman invasion, the Dumnoni. Equally it is said to mean 'protector' and 'poet'.
*Variants: Davon, Devan, Deven, Devonne*

**Dextra**
This name comes from the Latin for 'right-hand side', the implication being that the bearer is skilful with their hands.

**Diamond**
This name is more popular in North America than it is in the United Kingdom. Until the 15th century only kings wore diamonds as a symbol of strength, courage and invincibility. The clear, precious stone was given this name that comes from the Greek for 'hardest' or 'unconquerable'.
*Variant: Diamanta*

**Diana**
The name was first brought to Britain in the 16th century and has

been a common English first name since the 1700s. Of Latin origin it means 'god-like', 'divine' and 'the bright one'.

Perhaps the most famous bearer of this name in recent times is the late Diana, Princess of Wales who died in 1997. However, the name has been well-known since ancient times.

Diana is another name for Artemis, the Greek goddess of the moon. Meanwhile, according to Roman mythology, Diana was also the goddess of hunting and the protector of wild animals. Beautiful and chaste, disinterested in men, she was also associated with fertility.

*Variants: Deanna, Deeanna, Dian, Diandra, Diane, Dianne, Dinah, Dyanna*

### Diandra

This variant of Diana (see above) has become an independent name in its own right. It is also thought to be a blend of two names – Diana and Andrea ('manly').

*Variant: Diandrea*

### Diantha

Of Greek origin this name means 'heavenly flower'. According to Greek mythology it was the flower of Zeus, the supreme god.

*Variant: Dianthe*

### Dilys

This Welsh name means 'genuine', 'perfect' and 'true'. It is also thought to mean 'steadfast' and 'certain'.

*Variant: Dilly*

### Dinah

Dinah was the Biblical name of Jacob and Leah's beautiful daughter. She was raped but her brothers Simeon and Levi sought revenge for the attack. The Hebrew meaning of Dinah, therefore, is 'vindication', 'judgement' or 'revenged'. It is also believed to be a modern variant of Diana.

*Variants: Deanna, Deanne, Deena, Dena, Diana, Dina*

### Dixie

The Mason-Dixon line (surveyed by Charles Mason and Jeremiah Dixon in 1763 to 1767) is said to divide northern and southern states of North America. The term Dixieland will forever be inextricably linked to the American South and is often used as a wistful reference to that region.

Dixie could have also been been inspired by the French word for 'ten', 'dix'. Thus Dixie was derived from an American-English pronunciation of the word for a ten-dollar bill.

However, it is also thought that Dixie may come from the Old Norse word 'diss', which means 'active sprite'. And the name may originally have been that of a Nordic fairy guardian.
*Variants: Dis, Disa, Dix*

### Dolcila

This name comes from the Latin word 'dolcilis', which means 'gentle' and 'amenable'.
*Variants: Docila, Docilla*

### Dolly

Before this name became used for a child's toy it was the pet form of Dorothy which means 'God's gift'. It is now an independent name.
*Variant: Doll*

### Dolores

Santa Maria de los Dolores is a name given to the Virgin Mary by the Spanish. It means St Mary of the Sorrows or Lady of the Sorrows. Hence the name Dolores comes from the Spanish word for 'sorrows'.

In 1423 the feast day of St Mary of the Sorrows was established on 15 September and henceforth it was common to name girls born on that day Dolores. Often it was a way of naming a child after the Virgin Mary, if the parents felt that the name 'Mary' was too sacred to use.

During the 1930s Dolores was popular in North America.

*Variants: Dalores, Dela, Delora, Delores, Deloris, Delorita, Dola, Dolore, Lola, Lolita*

## Dominique

This French name is the feminine form of Dominic, which comes from the Latin for 'of the Lord'. Traditionally, those born on a Sunday were given this name because they were born on the Sabbath – the day of the Lord.

The name is also thought to mean 'servant of God'.

## Donna

Of Italian, and ultimately Latin origin, this name means 'lady, woman worthy of respect' or 'mistress of a household'. It is also thought to be a short form of Madonna and a feminine form of Donald, which comes from the Celtic for 'proud ruler'.

The name has been in use since the beginning of the 20th century. *Variants: Donalie, Donnis, Donny, Dona, Donella, Donelle, Donica, Ladonna*

## Dora

Charles Dickens used this name for one of his characters in his 1850 novel *David Copperfield*. Although it is now considered to be an independent name, it began life as a diminutive of the names Theodora and Dorothy, both of which mean 'God's gift'.
*Variants: Dorah, Doralyn, Doreen, Dorrie, Dorit, Dorita, Dorothy, Theodora*

## Doreen

The name Doreen is thought to be a combination of Dora – a diminuitive of Dorothy and Theodora meaning 'God's gift' - and the suffix 'een'.

However, Doreen is also associated with the Irish name Dorean, which may come from the Gaelic word 'der' meaning 'daughter' and Finn, the name of a legendary Irish hero which means 'white, fair'.

Whatever its origin Doreen was first introduced to Britain at

the beginning of the 20th century and it has become more widespread since that time. (See also Dora and Dorothy.)
*Variants: Dora, Doraleen, Dorean, Dorene, Dorine, Dorletta, Dorothea, Dorothy*

**Dorit**
This is another short form of Dorothy that is associated with Charles Dickens. *Little Dorrit* was the title of one of his novels. Like Dora, Dorothy and Theodora it means 'God's gift'.
*Variants: Dora, Dorrit, Dorothy*

**Doris**
In Ancient Greece a person coming from the Doris region was known as a Dorian. However, the name was also associated with a character from Greek mythology who was the daughter of Oceanus, the god of the sea. Doris went on to marry Nereus and bore him 50 daughters who became sea nymphs that were also known as the Nereids.

The name Doris also means 'bountiful sea' and 'sacrificial knife'. It was especially popular during the late 19th century and the early 1900s.
*Variants: Dorea, Dori, Doria, Dorice, Dorie, Dorisa, Dorit, Dorrit, Dory*

**Dorothy**
In Greek 'doron' means 'gift' and 'theos' means 'God'. Thus the name Dorothea means 'gift of God'. Dorothy is the English version of this name, which has led to a variety of pet forms including Dolly, Dora and Dorrit.

**Dove**
This white bird is a symbol of peace and gentleness.
*Variant: Dova*

**Drew**
This short form of the name Andrew ('manly') is also a girl's name.

### Dulcie
This 19th century girl's name is little used today. It was derived from the Latin word 'dulcis' which means 'sweet'. It is also a variant of the medieval name Dowse.
*Variants: Dowsabel, Dulce, Dulcee, Dulcia, Dulcy*

### Dymphna
The Irish Gaelic meaning of this name is 'eligible', 'one fit to be' or 'little fawn'.
*Variants: Damhnait, Dympna*

### Eartha
The name Eartha means exactly what it implies – 'earth', 'the ground'.
*Variants: Ertha, Erthel*

### Easter
Though the name Easter is associated with the Christian festival the word actually comes from the Middle English for 'ester', which means 'where the sun rises'. It is also thought to be related to the Old High German word 'ostarun' – 'eastern'.

Easter is also thought to be a variant of Esther, which comes from the German for 'radiant dawn' and means 'bride' in Hebrew or 'star' in Persian.
*Variant: Esther*

### Ebony
This name comes from the word for the black, hard wood of a tropical tree.
*Variants: Ebbony, Eboney, Eboni, Ebonie*

### Echo
Greek in origin, the name means 'nymph, repeated voice'. In Greek mythology, Echo was a nymph who had the unfortunate task of talking non-stop to the queen of the gods so she would not notice her husband's infidelity. When her motive was

discovered the queen placed a curse on her and thereafter she could only say what others had just said.

Echo was later the victim of unrequited love. She pined away for Narcissus until nothing was left of her but her voice, which could only repeat the words of others.

### Edwina

Edwina, the feminine form of Edwin, was coined in the 19th century but it is derived from far older stock. Edwin is an Old English name that was borne by the 7th century king of Northumbria who was an early convert to Christianity. It means 'fortunate friend', 'happiness' and 'riches'.
*Variants: Edina, Edna, Edweena, Edwene, Edwyna*

### Eileen

Eileen is the Anglicised form of the Irish Gaelic name Aibhilin, which in turn was derived from the Norman French name Aveline. The differences in pronunciation account for the variant spellings of the same name. In Gaelic 'bh' is pronounced as a 'v', but sometimes it is silent – hence, Eileen.

Like Evelyn, Eileen comes from Aveline. So both names are related and mean 'hazelnut'. However, Eileen is also thought to be an Irish variant of the name Helen, which comes from the Greek for 'bright'.
*Variants: Aibhilin, Aileen, Eilleen, Elly, Evelyn, Helen, Ileen, Ileene*

### Elaine

This name is thought to have both French and Welsh roots. While some believe it comes from the Old French form of the name Helen ('bright'), others suggest that it was derived from the Welsh for 'fawn'.

The fact that it was the name of the woman who fell in love with Lancelot in the Arthurian legend gives credence to this theory, as many of the names from those tales are of Welsh origin.

Elaine is also considered to be a short from of Eleanor.
*Variants: Elain, Elaina, Elane, Elayne, Eleanor, Ellaine, Helen*

### Eleanor

As an Old French variant of Helen, Eleanor is thought to mean 'bright'. However, it may also be a derivative of the Old Provencal name, Alienor – which comes from the German for 'foreign'. Brought to England by the French, Eleanor may just be a different spelling of this Gallic name. Another theory suggests it is derived from the Arabic for 'god is my light'.
*Variants: Ella, Elenora, Elenor, Elle, Ellie, Elyn, Helen, Nell, Nora, Norah*

### Electra

Of Greek origin, this name is derived from the word 'elektron', which means 'amber one that shines brightly'. It is from this Grecian element that the word 'electricity' was born.
*Variants: Electre, Elektra*

### Elisha

This name can be viewed in one of two ways. Sometimes it is thought to be a combination of the names Elise (a short form of Elizabeth) and Alicia (a derivative of Alice). When these two names are its source it means 'God's oath' and 'noble'.

However, Elisha is also a derivative of the Biblical name Eli. In the Old Testament Eli was a high priest who raised Samuel from infancy. Eli comes from the Hebrew for 'high, elevated' and Elisha, which is sometimes given to boys, means 'God saves'.
*Variants: Alicia, Elise, Elisa*

### Elizabeth

In the Bible, Elisabeth was the Virgin Mary's cousin and the elderly mother of John the Baptist. In England the name is usually spelt with a 'z', but the meaning is still the same. Elizabeth comes from the Hebrew name Elisheva, which means 'God's oath' or the 'fullness of God'.

The name first appeared in England towards the end of the 15th century and its popularity grew during the reign of the Tudor queen, Elizabeth I, who was also known as Good Queen Bess. The name continued to be fashionable in the 20th century,

especially in the United Kingdom where it was borne by both Queen Elizabeth II – whose accession to the throne was in 1952 – and her mother. The name has spawned numerous short forms and independent names including Bet, Libby, Lilibet, Lisbeth, Liesel and Liza.
*Variants: Bess, Bessie, Beth, Betsy, Betty, Elise, Elisa, Elsa, Eliza, Lisa*

### Ella
Of both Old English and Old German origin, Ella means either 'fairy maiden' or 'all'. It was introduced to Britain by the Normans and was particularly popular with the Victorians.
It is also considered to be a pet form of the names Eleanor and Isabella.
*Variants: Ala, Eleanor, Ellen, Isabella*

### Ellie
Now widely considered to be an independent name Ellie is also the short form of a wide variety of names. It is the perfect pet form for any name beginning with El, such as Elizabeth and Eleanor. However, it is also believed to be a short form of Alice, Adelaide and Alicia. Thus this name could have a variety of meanings from 'noble' and 'God's oath' to 'bright' and 'God is my light'.
*Variants: Adelaide, Alice, Alicia, Ella, Elle, Eleanor, Elizabeth*

### Elma
Both Turkish and Greek in origin this name means 'apple' and 'amiable' respectively.

### Elsa
As the Scottish short form of the Biblical name Elizabeth, Elsa means 'God's oath'. However, the name may have been derived from another independent source. It is possible that it comes from the Anglo-Saxon word for 'swan' or the Old German for 'noble maiden'. It is even thought to be related to the Greek for 'truthful'.
*Variants: Aliza, Elizabeth, Else, Elsie, Elza*

### Elsie

Now considered an independent name in its own right Elsie is also a variant of Elsa, the Scottish short form of the name Elizabeth. Like Elizabeth and Elsa, Elsie means 'God's oath'. But it has a variety of other meanings.

Elsie also comes from the Greek for 'truthful' and the Germanic for 'noble' or 'nobility'. Like Elsa it also comes from the Anglo-Saxon for 'swan'.

*Variants: Elsa, Elisabeth, Elizabeth, Elspeth, Elspie*

### Emma

The name Emma was originally the short form of names containing the German element 'ermin', which means 'universal' and 'entire'. Thus, like Em or Emmie, it was the short-form of Ermintrude ('universal strength').

Queen Emma brought the name to England from Normandy when she married King Ethelred the Unready in the 11th century. She later went on to marry his successor, Cnut.

In the 19th century the name appeared in a classic piece of literature, Jane Austen's *Emma*.

*Variants: Em, Ema, Emily, Emm, Emmie, Emmy, Irma*

### Emerald

In his novel *The Hunchback of Notre Dame,* Victor Hugo christened the object of Quasimodo's affections Esmeralda. Her name comes from the Spanish word for the precious, green stone which is called emerald in English.

*Variants: Emeralda, Emeraldine, Esmeralda*

### Emily

The name was popular in the 19th century and is derived from the medieval form of the Latin name Aemilia. Aemilia, in turn, came from the name of a Roman family, Æmeli.

Emily is also related to the Germanic name Amelia and, as such, also means 'industrious' and 'hard working'.

*Variants: Amelie, Amelia, Em, Emma, Emmie, Emilie*

### Enya
This Irish name means 'small fire'. It is also a variant of the name Eithne, which means 'kernel'.
*Variant: Ena, Eithne*

### Erica
Coined in the 18th century, Erica is the feminine form of the Viking name Eric, which means 'eternal', 'honourable', 'alone' and 'ruler'. In addition to this Old Norse meaning it also comes from the Latin word for 'heather'.
*Variants: Ericka, Erika, Rica, Ricki*

### Erin
This poetic name for Ireland has often appeared in sentimental text about the Emerald Isle. First used as a name in North America, its popularity as a first name has grown since the 1970s. It also means 'peace'.
*Variant: Errin*

### Esmé
Esmé comes from the French for 'esteemed'. However, in the past that word was mistakenly translated as 'aimer' ('to love'), so Esmé is also a variant of the French version of Amy, Aimée.
*Variants: Aimee, Aimée, Esme, Esmee, Esma*

### Essence
Of English origin this name is thought to mean 'beginning'. As a word it means 'the essential characteristic of something'.

### Estelle
The name, and its variant Estella, is derived from the Old French for 'star'.
*Variants: Essie, Estella, Esther, Stella*

### Eternity
To say something will survive for eternity is to say that it will be

'everlasting'. The use of this word as a girl's name began in North America.

### Etta
This name is the short form of both Henrietta ('home rule') and Rosetta ('rose').

### Eugenie
Eugenie is the French feminine form of the name Eugene, which comes from the Greek for 'excellent', 'well-born' and 'fortunate'. It was the name of several saints, one of whom was a fallen woman who became an abbot of a monastery, which she entered disguised as a man.

While the name was well-known during the Middle Ages, in Britain it came back into fashion because of Empress Eugenie – the wife of Napoleon III – who fled to England in 1870 and lived there until her death in 1920.
*Variants: Eugenia, Gene, Genie, Ina*

### Eunice
In the Bible Eunice was the mother of Timothy who introduced him to the Christian faith. Her name comes from the Greek for 'well, good' and 'victory'.
*Variants: Niki, Nikki, Unice*

### Eve
The name of the first woman in the Bible comes from the Hebrew for 'breath of life'. It is also believed to mean 'living', 'lively' and 'mother of all living'.

First found in Britain in the 12th century, it was believed that girls bearing the name would be blessed with longevity. The name has produced many derivatives including Eva, Evie and Evita.

The Greek form of Eve is Zoe. Efa is the Welsh version and Eveleen is the Irish interpretation.
*Variants: Eva, Evadne, Eveleen, Evie, Evita, Zoe*

**Evelyn**

Like the Irish name Eileen, Evelyn comes from the Germanic and Old French name Aveline, which means 'hazelnut'. The hazelnut is the Celtic fruit of wisdom.

Evelyn, which is sometimes given to boys, is also believed to come from the Latin for 'bird'.
*Variants: Aibhilin, Aileen, Eileen, Eveline, Evelyne*

**Fabia**

This is the Latin feminine form of the old Roman family name Fabianus, which was derived from the word for 'bean'.

Quintus Fabius Maximus, who defeated the renowned general Hannibal Barca and his forces, was a member of the house of the Fabii. The British socialist movement, the Fabian Society, was founded in 1884 and named in his honour.

**Faith**

One of the three major Christian virtues Faith comes from the Latin word 'fides', which means 'trust', 'devotion' and 'loyalty'. The name was popular with the 17th century Puritans and in the 20th century produced the shortened version Fay.

The Spanish boy's name Fidel has the same meaning.
*Variants: Fay, Faye, Fayth, Faythe, Fidelity*

**Faline**

'Feles' means 'cat' in Latin hence the English word 'feline'. Faline, a girl's name, comes from the same root.
*Variant: Feline*

**Fallon**

Fallon is an English form of an Irish surname that means 'leader' or 'descendant of the leader'.

**Fancy**

To fantasise about something is to visualise it or wish that it would come true. Similarly, someone with a 'fancy' has a 'whim'

or a dream that they want realised. So fancy, the word and the name, comes from the Greek for 'to make visible'.
*Variant: Fancie*

**Fanny**
This name was especially popular in the 18th and 19th centuries. Originally it was a short form of Frances ('Frenchman') and the Welsh name Myfanwy ('my treasure'). But it is now considered to be an independent name in its own right.

**Farrah**
Farrah has both Arabic and English roots so consequently this name has numerous meanings.

It comes from the Arabic for 'happiness', 'joy' and 'cheerfulness', but also comes from the Middle English for 'lovely', 'beautiful' and 'pleasant'.
*Variants: Fara, Farah, Farra*

**Fatima**
The name Fatima has links to both Islam and Christianity. It is the name of the Portuguese village where, in 1917, the Virgin Mary was said to have appeared to three peasant children.

However, the name is also popular among Muslims because Fatima was the favourite daughter of the Prophet Mohammed.

In Arabic the name means 'chaste', 'motherly' and 'abstainer'.
*Variants: Fatimah, Fatma*

**Faustine**
Of Italian and Spanish origin this name means 'fortunate'.

**Fawn**
In English a 'fawn' is a 'young deer'. It is related to the French word 'feon', which means 'off-spring of an animal' and the Latin word 'fetus' ('offspring').
*Variants: Fauna, Fawna, Fawnah, Fawniah*

**Faye**
This name started life as a short form of the name Faith, which means 'trust' and 'devotion'. However, Faye was also derived from the Old French word for 'fairy'.

According to legend the name was also borne by King Arthur's half-sister Morgan le Fay. She was also known as the Lady of the Lake.
*Variants: Fae, Faith, Fay, Fayette*

**Fayme**
The Latin for 'reputation', 'public esteem' and 'acclaim' is 'fama'. Fayme is the Anglicised feminine form of the word.
*Variant: Faym*

**Felicia**
Felicia is a variant of Felicity, which comes from the Roman name Felicitas. Felicitas was the Roman goddess of happiness and good fortune. Hence the name and its derivatives share that meaning.
*Variants: Falice, Falicia, Felice, Felicity*

**Felicity**
As mentioned above Felicity comes from the Latin word for 'happiness'. It is also the feminine form of the boy's name Felix. A number of early saints bore the name.
*Variants: Falice, Falicia, Felicie, Felicite*

**Fenella**
This name is the Anglicised version of the Gaelic name Fionnghuala which is made up of the words for 'white, fair' and 'shouldered'.

The use of Fenella increased in Britain following its inclusion by Sir Walter Scott in the 19th century work *Peveril of the Peak*.

Fiona is believed to have been derived from the same root.
*Variants: Finella, Fionola, Fionnuala, Nuala*

### Ferelith

A Scottish name Ferelith comes from the Old Irish words for 'true, very' and 'lady or princess'. Thus the meaning of this name is believed to be 'perfect princess'.

In 8th century Ireland Ferelith took the form of Forbflaith, while in 13th century Scotland it was Forreleth.

### Fern

Taken from the Old English for 'leaf' the name Fern comes from the word for the flowerless, feathery plant. Its use as a given name began during the late 19th century and its popularity increased during the 1900s.
*Variant: Fearne, Ferne*

### Ffion

In medieval love poetry this Welsh name was used to describe the colour and/or softness of a girl's cheek. But Ffion also comes from the old Welsh word for foxglove.
*Variants: Fionn, Ffiona*

### Fifi

Of Hebrew origin the Biblical name Joseph means 'God shall add another'. In the Old Testament it was borne by Jacob's favourite son whose jealous brothers sold him into slavery. In the New Testament it was the name of Mary's husband and the stepfather of Jesus.

Fifi is associated with this name and its rich history because it is the pet form of the French female equivalent, Josephine.
*Variant: Josephine*

### Filma

This name comes from the Old English for 'misty veil'.

### Filomena

Two Greek words are believed to be the source of this name – 'philos' ('beloved') and 'armonia' ('harmony'). Filomena is

believed to be the feminine form of the Latin name Philomenus. It was popular during the 19th century, especially in Ireland, because it was borne by St Philomena – the patron saint of impossible causes.
*Variants: Phil, Philly, Philomena*

**Fiona**

According to Irish mythology Fionnuala was a woman who was transformed into a swan and cursed to wander the lakes and rivers until Christianity came to Ireland. The name comes from the Celtic word for 'white, fair' and it is from this that Fenella gets its meaning (see above).

While the name Fiona shares the same Gaelic root, it is also believed to be a creation of the writer William Sharp who penned his romantic works under the pseudonym Fiona Macleod. It is this use that popularised the name from the 19th century onwards.
*Variants: Fenella, Finella, Fionola, Fionnuala*

**Flavia**

Flavia is an appropriate name to give a blonde or fair-haired daughter, because it comes from the Latin for 'golden' or 'yellow'. The name Flavius is an old Roman family name, which may have begun life as a nickname for a flaxen-haired person. Flavia is the feminine form of that dynastic name.

**Fleur**

Like Flower and Flora this name means 'flower' or 'blossom'.

Occasionally used in the Middle Ages, it has Old French roots.
*Variants: Ffleur, Fflur, Fleurette, Flora, Flower*

**Floella**

This name is believed to be a compound of two short forms – Flo (a diminutive of Florence) and Ella (an independent name and pet form of Eleanor and Isabella). It is a modern creation.

### Flora

Flora Macdonald is the name of the woman who helped Bonnie Prince Charlie to escape the Scottish mainland in 1746 following his defeat at the Battle of Culloden. The name is closely associated with Scotland and was not found in England before the 18th century.

But the history of the name stretches back into Roman times as Flora comes from the Latin for 'flower' or 'blossom'. According to the mythology of that time the goddess of fertility, flowers and spring was called Flora. Florrie is the short form.
*Variants: Fflur, Fleur, Fleurette, Flo, Flor, Flores, Florrie, Flossie*

### Florence

During the Crimean War, in the latter half of the 19th century, the name Florence became associated with the founder of modern nursing, Florence Nightingale. It was the fame of 'the lady with the lamp' that popularised this name throughout the world. She, in turn, had been christened after her birthplace, the town of Florence in Italy.

But the name was popular long before the 19th century. During the Middle Ages it was given to both boys and girls. Florence comes from the Latin for 'blossoming' or 'flourishing'. The name Flo is the pet form.
*Variants: Flo, Flora, Florance, Floreen, Florrie, Flossie, Flossy*

### Flower

This is the English version of the French name Fleur. It is also used as a term of endearment. (See Flora.)
*Variants: Fleur, Flora*

### Fonda

Of Spanish origin this name means 'profound'. It can be used as a first name for both boys and girls and is also a surname.
*Variants: Fon, Fondea*

### France
This short form of the name Frances is sometimes bestowed on boys and girls in honour of the European country.
*Variant: Frances*

### Frances
The Old Middle Latin word 'franciscus' meant 'a free man' and it is from this word that the name Frances is derived. The male version of this name is Francis.
*Variants: Fran, France, Francesca, Frankie*

### Francesca
This is the Italian version of the name Frances (see above) which is now common in the English-speaking world.
*Variants: Fran, France, Frances, Frankie*

### Frankie
The names Frank, Francis, Frances and Francesca are all associated with freedom because of their namesake – the Franks. They were a German tribe who, having won their liberty from the Romans, settled in Gaul, which later became known as France.
*Variants: Fran, France, Francis, Francesca*

### Frayda
Frayda is taken from the Yiddish word for 'joy'.
*Variants: Frayde, Fraydyne, Freida*

### Frederica
Of Old French and German origin, this name is made from the elements 'fred' ('peace') and ric ('power, ruler'). Thus it means 'peaceful ruler'.

The name Frederick was originally brought to England by the Normans. It was reintroduced to Britain during the reign of George I and it experienced another wave of popularity during the Victorian age. Frederica is its feminine form.

*Variants: Federica, Fredda, Freddi, Freddie, Ricki, Rica*

**Freya**
According to Norse mythology Freya was the goddess of
fertility, love and beauty. The name means 'noble lady' or
'mistress'. Her male counterpart, Frey, was the god of peace
and prosperity.
*Variants: Freja, Freyja, Froja*

**Fulvia**
The name comes from the Roman family name Fulvius, which
was derived from the Latin word for 'dusky' and 'tawny'.

**Gabrielle**
The archangel Gabriel makes more than one appearance in the
Bible, bringing with him messages from God. It is fitting, therefore,
that his name comes from the Hebrew meaning 'messenger of
God' or 'my strength is God'.

Gabriel makes his first appearance in the Old Testament
where he is seen by David as a vision (see Gabriel in boys' names).

Gabrielle and its variant Gabriella are just two feminine
forms of this name.
*Variants: Gabbie, Gabi, Gabriella, Gaby, Gigi, Gaye*

**Gae**
Little used as a first name before the 20th century Gae was
derived from the English word meaning 'cheerful' and
'merry'.

However, the name fell out of favour from the 1960s
onwards when the word 'gay' became synonymous with
homosexuality.

In Ireland it is a pet form of Gabriel and Gabrielle. It is also a
diminutive of Gaynor. As an independent name it can be given
to both boys and girls.
*Variants: Gabriella, Gabrielle, Gaenor, Gaye, Gaynor*

**Gaenor**

This name is a diminutive of the Guinevere who according to popular legend was King Arthur's queen and Sir Lancelot's lover. As a short form of this Arthurian name, Gaenor comes from the Welsh for 'beautiful maiden'.
*Variants: Gae, Gainer, Gayner, Gay*

**Gaia**

In Greek mythology Gaia was the goddess of the earth and, as Mother Earth, she embodied its richness and fertility. This name is of symbolic importance to environmentalists and feminists.
*Variants: Ge, Gaea*

**Gardenia**

The gardenia – sweet-smelling flower – was named after the 18th century American botanist Dr Alexander Garden. The white gardenia also became associated with blues singer Billie Holiday, who would often wear one in her hair when performing in the 1930s.

**Gayle**

This short form of the Biblical name Abigail is now used independently as a Christian name. It comes from the Hebrew for 'my father rejoices' and 'source of joy'. It is not found before the 20th century.
*Variants: Abigail, Abigayle, Gail, Gale*

**Gazelle**

A gazelle is a small, graceful antelope. Thus as a given name it implies 'delicacy' and 'grace'.
*Variant: Gazella*

**Gemma**

Popular in 1980s Britain this name implies that the bearer is 'precious' for it is derived from the Latin for 'precious stone' or 'gem'.

The poet Dante, who was born in 1265, was married to a woman called Gemma.

The name was also borne by Gemma Galgani an orphaned Italian girl who had visions of the Virgin Mary. She died in 1903 and was canonised in 1940. Thereafter the name grew in popularity.

*Variants: Gem, Germaine, Jemma*

**Genette**

Genette is a variant of Jeanette, Janet and Jean. The afore-mentioned girls' names are all derived from the Biblical name John, which means 'God has favoured', 'God is gracious' and 'God is merciful'.

*Variants: Gene, Genie, Genna, Ginette, Ginetta, Jane, Janet, Jean, Jeanne, Jeanette*

**Geneva**

As well as being the name of a city in Switzerland, Geneva is a short form of Geneviève – a French name that comes from the German for 'womankind'.

The name Geneva is also derived from the French, and ultimately the Latin, for 'juniper' which is a bush that does not lose its leaves in winter.

*Variants: Gena, Genevia, Genevieve, Geneviève, Genna, Janeva*

**Geneviève**

As mentioned above this French name comes from the German for 'womankind'. Its Gallic connection is further entrenched because St Geneviève is the patron saint of Paris, France's capital city.

This 5th century Gallo-Roman nun devoted her life to prayer and emboldened the city at a crucial hour – when it was threatened by Attila the Hun. Parisians followed her example, stood firm, and the attack failed to materialise. It was believed that her prayers saved the city.

*Variants: Geneva, Genevieve, Genny, Genovera, Genoveva, Gina*

**Georgette**
Georgette, like other feminine versions of George, was especially popular in Britain during the reign of the Hanoverian kings which began with the ascendancy of George I in 1714.

It is the French feminine form of George, which means 'farmer'.
*Variants: Georgett, Georgia, Georgi, Georgie, Gigi*

**Georgia**
Georgia is also the name of an American southern state that was so-called in honour of King George II. This is not to be confused with the country that was once a part of the former USSR.
*Variants: Georgett, Georgette, Georgiana, Georgina, Georgi, Georgie, Gigi*

**Geraldine**
The name Geraldine owes its existence to a poem and the adoration of one man. In 1540 Henry Howard, the Earl of Surrey, professed his love for Lady Elizabeth Fitzgerald in a poem calling her the 'fair Geraldine'. It was a name that he alone invented.

'Fitzgerald' means 'sons of Gerald'. 'Gerald' is derived from a Germanic name that means 'spear' and 'rule'. 'Geraldine' is another, romantic, way of saying 'one of the Fitzgeralds'.
*Variants: Deena, Dina, Geralda, Geraldene, Geraldina, Gerrie*

**Germaine**
In the 20th century the feminist writer Germaine Greer was a famous bearer of this name. In the 19th century it was associated with Germaine Cousin, who was canonised in 1867.

The name comes from the Old French for 'German' and from the Latin for 'brother'.
*Variants: Gem, Gemma, Germain, Germana, Germane*

**Gertrude**
The name of Hamlet's mother comes from the Old High German for 'spear' and 'strength', 'wizard'.

In Norse mythology Gertrude was a goddess who helped to escort slain heroes to the palace of bliss.

It appeared in England during the late Middle Ages and may have been introduced by migrants from the Low Countries where the name was associated with a mystic saint. Its use increased during the 19th century when Germanic names were in vogue in Britain.
*Variants: Gerda, Gert, Gerte, Gertie, Trudie, Trudi, Trudy*

**Gigi**
This French name will forever be connected with the novel and the 1958 Hollywood film *Gigi*. The book was written by Colette who bestowed the name upon her heroine.

In France Gigi is a diminutive of Gilberte and Giselle. Gilberte is a feminine form of the name Gilbert, which is derived from the Old German for 'bright' and 'pledge'. Giselle means 'pledge' and 'hostage'. It too is derived from the Old German language.
*Variants: Gilbert, Giselle*

**Gila**
Gila comes from the Hebrew for 'joy'.
*Variant: Ghila*

**Gilda**
The origin of the name is uncertain but it is thought to have been derived from the Old English for 'to gild' or 'to gloss over'.
*Variants: Gilde, Gildi, Gill, Jill*

**Gillian**
This name is the English form of Juliana, which is the feminine variant of Julian. Julian comes from the Greek for 'soft-haired' or 'fair complexioned'. It was also the name of the first Roman emperor – Gaius Julius Caesar. He belonged to the ancient Roman family, the Julii who traced their descent to Aphrodite, the goddess of love.
*Variants: Gill, Gillaine, Gilly, Jill, Jillian, Jilly, Juliana*

*Girls*

### Gina

Gina began life as a pet form of the names Georgina ('farmer'), Eugena ('well-born, fortunate') and Regina ('queen'), but is now an independent name in its own right. In Japanese Gina means silvery.

*Variants: Eugena, Geena, Gena, Georgina, Jeanna, Regina*

### Ginger

This nickname for someone with red hair is also the pet form of Virginia. The Hollywood actress Ginger Rogers, for example, was born Virginia McMath in 1911.

*Variant: Virginia*

### Giselle

The meaning of this name may have come from a medieval European practice. It was common during those times to leave children to be raised in a foreign court to symbolise an alliance between two states. This was an agreement between two bodies hence the name Giselle comes from the German word for 'pledge'.

The name Gigi is the pet form of Giselle.

*Variants: Ghislaine, Gigi, Gisela, Giselda, Gisèle*

### Gita

As the short form of the Spanish version of Margaret, Margarita, Gita means 'pearl' or 'daisy'. It could also stem from the Sanskrit for 'song'.

*Variants: Ghita, Greta, Gretchen, Gretel, Margaret, Margarita, Rita*

### Gladys

Although it was well known in England since the 1870s, a mystery surrounds the origin of the name Gladys. It may have been derived from the Latin for either 'small sword' or 'lame'.

Its association with the Latin for 'lame' is concurrent with the theory that Gladys comes from the Roman family name

Claduii, which also has the same meaning. This theory is further strengthened by the belief that Gladys comes from the Welsh form of Claudia.

However, Gladys may have been derived from the Welsh for 'ruler' and 'princess'.
*Variants: Glad, Gladi, Gladis, Gwladys*

### Glenda
Glenda is a modern name that was first found in North America and Australia. It is sometimes thought to be a feminine form of the name Glen, which is a Celtic name meaning 'valley'.

Glenda is orginally derived from the Welsh for 'clean, pure, holy' and 'good'.
*Variants: Glen, Glennie, Glenny, Glinda*

### Glenna
Like Glenda and Glen, Glenna is derived from the Scottish Gaelic word 'gleann' which means 'valley'. It is also considered to be a feminine form of the name Glen.
*Variants: Glen, Glena, Gleneen, Glenesha, Glenni, Glenice*

### Glenys
This modern Welsh name is derived from 'glân' which means 'pure' and 'holy'.
*Variants: Glen, Glenis, Glennis, Glennys, Glynis*

### Gloria
Gloria comes from the Latin for 'fame, renown, praise' and 'honour'. It has been a popular name for girls since the late 19th century but appeared in both literature and public life in another form long before that.

During the reign of Elizabeth I in England the poet Edmund Spenser wrote *The Faerie Queen*. In that work the queen of the fairies was known as Gloriana, which itself was a title sometimes given to Elizabeth.
*Variants: Glora, Gloriana, Glorianna, Glory*

### Goldie

Originally a nickname for someone with blonde or fair hair, Goldie is derived from the word for 'gold'. The Hollywood actress Goldie Hawn is perhaps the most famous bearer of this name.

However, Golda stems from the same source. It was the name of former Israeli Prime Minister Golda Meir who led the country from 1969 to 1974.

*Variants: Golda, Goldia, Goldina*

### Gozala

Of Hebrew origin, this name means 'young bird'.

### Grace

Favoured by the 17th century Puritans, 'grace' is another quality that has been bestowed upon girls as a first name. It comes from the Latin 'gratus', which means 'pleasing', 'attractive' and 'charming'. To say someone is 'graceful' is to say that they possess beauty, elegance and a certain poise.

In Greek mythology the Three Graces were nature goddesses who brought joy to the world.

In the 20th century the film star Grace Kelly seemed to possess all those qualities associated with her name.

*Variants: Gracia, Gracie, Gráinne, Grayce, Grazielle, Grata*

### Grainne

In English this Irish name is sometimes translated as Grace (see above). For example, Irish heroine Gráinne Ui Mnáille is also known as Grace O'Malley, a female pirate who fought the English during Elizabethan times.

Nevertheless the name Grainne may have been derived from the word for 'love' or the Irish Gaelic for 'grain'. According to legend it was borne by an Irish princess who was betrothed to the warrior Finn, but eloped with his nephew Diarmait (Dermot) instead.

*Variants: Grace, Gráine, Gráinne, Granya*

### Greer

The late actress Greer Garson was given her mother's maiden name when she was born in London in 1904. This example clearly shows how the Scottish surname Greer went on to become a woman's first name.

It comes from the Greek for 'the watchful mother' and is believed to be a contracted form of Gregor that was coined in the Middle Ages.
*Variant: Grier*

### Greta

The name Greta is a short form of Margarita – a Spanish version of the name Margaret. Margaret is of Greek origin and means 'pearl'. However, the French form Marguerite means 'daisy'.
*Variants: Daisy, Ghita, Gita, Gretchen, Gretel, Margaret, Margarita, Marguerite, Maggie, Rita*

### Gretchen

Like Gita and Greta, Gretchen is a derivative of Margaret, which means 'pearl' or 'daisy'. It comes from Germany.
*Variants: Ghita, Gita, Greta, Gretel, Margaret, Margarita, Marguerite, Rita*

### Guinevere

Like many of the names that featured in the legend that surrounds King Arthur, Guinevere is believed to be of Welsh origin. It is thought to be a compound of two words – 'gwyn' ('fair, white', 'blessed, holy') and 'hwyfar' ('smooth, soft' or 'phantom').

Legend has it that, not only was Guinevere King Arthur's queen, she was also Sir Lancelot's lover. The name Jennifer is a Cornish form of Guinevere.
*Variants: Gaenor, Gaynor, Guenevere, Jennifer*

### Gwendelon

Like Guinevere the name Gwendolina (a variant of Gwendelon)

featured in the story of King Arthur. According to the legend Gwendolina was the wife of Merlin the wizard.

Of Welsh origin, the name Gwendelon was derived from the words 'gwen' ('white, fair') and 'dolen' meaning 'ring or bow'. Hence it means 'white ring'.

According to Welsh legend it was the name of King Locrine's wife. He left her for a German princess and she took her revenge by drowning his daughter Sabrina in the River Severn.

*Variants: Gwen, Gwenda, Gwendolina, Gwendolyn*

### Gwenllian
Another member of the family of Welsh names that begin with 'Gwen', Gwenllian means 'white flood' or 'fair flow'. The name has been in use since the 12th century and probably referred to the pale or fair complexion of the bearer's skin.

*Variant: Gwen, Gwenlian*

### Gwyneth
Popular since the late 19th century Gwyneth may be a variant of the Welsh county name – Gwynedd. Gwynedd comes from the Celtic for 'blessed' or 'happy'. Like Gwendelon and Gwenllian, Gwyneth shares the short form Gwen.

*Variants: Gwen, Gwenda, Gwenith, Gwenn, Venetia, Wendi, Winnie*

### Habiba
Habiba comes from the Arabic for 'lover' and 'beloved'. It is the feminine version of the name Habib.

*Variant: Haviva*

### Haidee
Used by Lord Byron in his 1819 poem *Don Juan*, Haidee is a variant of the Greek name Haido, which means 'to caress'. In the poem the characters Juan and Haidee fall in love.

The name is also a variant of Heidi, which is a Swiss pet form of the German name Adelaide ('noble').

*Variant: Heidi*

### Halina
Halina comes from the Hawaiian for 'likeness' or 'resemblance'.

### Halle
Halle is a variant of the name Hayley, meaning 'hay field' in Old English. However, Halle is also thought to come from the Irish Gaelic for 'ingenious' and the Norse for 'hero'.
As well as being a Belgian place name it is borne by the Oscar-winning actress Halle Berry.
*Variants: Hayley*

### Hana
Although it looks as if it could be related to the Hebrew name Hannah, Hana is of Arabic origin. It means 'bliss' or 'happiness'. The same name means 'flower' or 'blossom' in Japanese. It also comes from the Arapaho tribe of Native Americans. In that culture it means 'sky' or 'dark cloud'.
*Variants: Hanae, Hanako*

### Hannah
In the Old Testament Hannah is the mother of the prophet Samuel. The name is also traditionally believed to belong to the mother of the Virgin Mary. It is this latter belief that ensured the popularity of the name Hannah throughout Europe. It was especially beloved by the Puritans in the 16th and 17th centuries.
   The name comes from the Hebrew for 'God has favoured me'. The Greek translation of Hannah is Anna and hence names such as Anne, Annabel, Anoushka and its derivatives all share the same meaning.
*Variants: Ann, Anna, Annabel, Anne, Annette, Anoushka, Nanette*

### Harmony
According to Greek mythology Harmonia was the daughter of Aphrodite, the goddess of sex, love and beauty. Her name – and the variant Harmony – means 'concord' or 'in agreement'.
*Variants: Harmonia, Harmonie, Harmonee, Harmoni*

### Harper

Mainly found in North America, the name Harper is given to both boys and girls. It is a surname that originally described the bearer's occupation as a harpist.

In the 20th century the novelist Harper Lee bore the name. In 1961 she won a Pulitzer Prize for her novel *To Kill a Mockingbird*.

### Harriett

The name Henry comes from the Old German for 'home rule'. It was brought to England by the Normans as Henri – the French form. In England that name was later translated as Harry and it is from this that the feminine form Harriett was born.

Hat and Hattie are short forms of this name, which is also related to Henrietta.

*Variants: Harrie, Harriet, Hat, Hattie, Henrietta, Hetta*

### Hayley

The name is also a surname that was probably derived from the description of a place as it comes from the Old English words for 'hay field'.

Like Halle (see page 101) it is also associated with the Norse for 'hero' and the Irish Gaelic for 'ingenious'.

*Variants: Hailey, Haley, Hali, Halle, Hallie, Haleigh*

### Hazel

Derived from the Old English word for 'hazelnut', the word 'hazel' also refers to two separate colours. It could be used to describe something that, like the nut, is reddish-brown. Alternatively it may also describe eyes that are greeny-brown in colour.

As a girl's name Hazel became popular in the late 19th century.

*Variants: Hasse, Hazelle*

### Heather

Heather is another name that grew in popularity as a girl's name towards the end of the 19th century. During that period flower names were especially popular with Victorian parents. The name

Heather was particularly favoured by the Scottish because the brightly coloured plant adorned the moors of Scotland.

In recent times the name has become popular in North America. Heath is the male variant.

**Heaven**
Heaven is the use of the English word for 'the place where God lives'.

**Hebe**
In Greek mythology Hebe was the goddess of youth and the daughter of Zeus. Before she married Heracles she was also the cupbearer for the gods and goddesses on Mount Olympus. Fittingly her name comes from the Greek for 'young'.

Hebe is also the name of a flowering shrub.

**Hedda**
This name was derived from the German for 'combat' or 'war'. It comes from the Germanic names Hedewig and Hedwige.
*Variants: Hedy*

**Heidi**
The children's book *Heidi*, written by Johanna Spyri, was about a little orphan girl who lived with her grandfather in the Alps in Switzerland. The heroine's name is a Swiss pet form of the German name Adelaide.

Heidi is also thought to be a German form of the name Hilde, a variant of the English name Hilda ('battle').
*Variants: Adelaide, Adeleid, Heide, Heidie, Hilde*

**Helen**
Once described as 'the face that launched a thousand ships', Helen was the great beauty of Greek mythology. The daughter of Zeus, she was married to Menelaus of Sparta but she left him for Paris, the Trojan prince. It was this event, described by Homer in the poem the *Iliad*, which sparked the 10-year Trojan War.

The name Helen comes from the Greek for 'ray', 'bright' and 'light'.
*Variants: Elaine, Eleanor, Elena, Ellen, Helena, Helene, Lena, Leonora*

### Helianthe
This name comes from the Greek for 'bright flower'.

### Helga
Brought to Britain by the Normans the name Helga comes from the Old Norse for 'prosperous', 'successful' and 'pious'.

Despite its early introduction Helga was not a popular in Britain and the name was only re-introduced into the English-speaking world in the 20th century.
*Variant: Olga*

### Heloise
Although the name Heloise has been used in England since the 13th century its exact origin is disputed. It may have come from the Old German name Helewise. Alternatively it is thought to be of French origin, meaning 'famous fighter'.
*Variants: Eloisa, Eloïse, Eloise*

### Henrietta
The name Henrietta is the feminine form of the Germanic name Henry, which means 'home rule'. Although the name Henri had been brought to England by the Normans, Henrietta was not used until the marriage of Charles I to the French princess Henrietta Maria de Bourbon in 1625.

As explained above the Anglicised form of Henrietta is Harriett. (See Harriett.)
*Variants: Enrica, Harrie, Harriet, Harriett, Hat, Hattie, Henni*

### Herma
Milestones were often made from a square stone pillar, which in Latin was called 'herma'. Like the stone pillar it is hoped that girls blessed with this name will be strong.

**Hermione**
With her Harry Potter series of children's novels J K Rowling has thrust the name Hermione back into the limelight. However, centuries ago Shakespeare used the name for one of his characters in *The Winter's Tale*. And, long before that, Hermione featured in Greek mythology. She was the daughter of Helen and Menelaus.

The name, a feminine form of Hermes, means 'stone' or 'support'. According to legend Hermes was the messenger god who protected travellers.
*Variants: Erma, Hermia, Hermina, Hermine, Herminia, Mina*

**Hertha**
Hertha is an English name that means 'of the earth'.

**Hesper**
Of Greek origin, Hesper means 'evening' or 'evening star'. It comes from the word 'hesperos'.
*Variants: Hespera*

**Hester**
Used since the Middle Ages, Hester is a variant of the Biblical name Esther. In the Old Testament Esther was the Queen of Persia who saved her people from slaughter.

The name Esther comes from the Hebrew for 'bride'. It is also believed to come from the word for 'myrtle', which is a bush. Alternatively Esther, and Hester, also comes from the Persian for 'star'.
*Variants: Esther, Hettie, Hetty*

**Heulwen**
This Welsh girl's name means 'sunshine'.

**Hilary**
During the Middle Ages Hilary was a common boy's name. Its popularity may be associated with the 4th century theologian

St Hilary of Poitiers whose feast day falls in mid-January. It is because of him that the English law courts, and some universities, call their second term in the academic calendar the Hilary Term.

Although the name became less popular from the 1500s onwards it was revived in the 19th century and was given to both boys and girls.

Hilary comes from the Greek word 'hilaros', which means 'jovial', 'lively', 'cheerful' and 'boisterous'.
*Variants: Hilarie, Hillary*

### Hilda
Popular with parents both before and after the Norman Conquest, the currency of this name dipped during Tudor times but rose again in the 19th century. Hilda, believed to be of Germanic origin, also comes from the Old English for 'battle'.

In Anglo-Saxon England the name was borne by St Hilda, a Northumbrian princess who founded the abbey at Whitby.
*Variants: Hildie, Hylda*

### Hina
This Hindu name means 'henna' – the red or black dye that is used to colour hair and decorate the skin and fingernails.

### Holly
Like Carol, Noel and Robin, Holly is associated with the Christmas season. It comes from the Old English word 'holen', which means 'holly tree'. This evergreen tree with red berries is traditionally used to decorate homes during Christmas.

First used as a name at the beginning of the 20th century, its popularity grew during the 1960s.
*Variants: Holli, Hollie, Hollye*

### Honor
To honour someone is to give them recognition and respect. Naturally the name Honor has the same meaning.

The Roman emperor Theodosius the Great was given the title 'Honorius' and his niece was given the name Honoria.
*Variants: Honora, Honoria, Honour*

**Honey**
Both a sweet substance made by bees from nectar and a term of endearment, Honey is also a name given to girls. The word is of Germanic origin and is related to the Dutch 'honig' and German 'Honig'.

**Honesty**
Like Charity, Chastity and Honour, Honesty is another quality that has given birth to a girl's name. It comes from the Latin word 'honestās'.

**Hope**
Hope is one third of the triumvirate of Christian virtues, which stands alongside charity and faith. It comes from the Old English word 'hopa' and means 'to desire or wish something to happen'. The name was another Puritan favourite.

But a second Old English meaning has been identified, that is unrelated to the Bible. Hope may have also been derived from the word for 'little valley'.
*Variants: Hopi, Hopie*

**Hortense**
Widely used in France, the name Hortense comes from the Latin for 'garden' or 'gardener'. Its use in the English-speaking world increased during the 19th century.

The name was borne by Hortense de Beauharnais – the wife of Louis Bonaparte and the mother of Napoleon III.
*Variants: Hortensia, Ortense, Ortensia*

**Hoshi**
This Japanese name means 'star'.
*Variants: Hoshie, Hoshiko, Hoshiyo*

### Hula

Hula comes from the Hebrew for 'to make music'.

### Hulda

This Biblical name is also of Old Norse and Germanic origin. In the Old Testament Hulda was a female prophet who predicted the destruction of Jerusalem. According to Teutonic mythology, the name was also borne by a goddess.

The Hebrew meaning of the name is 'weasel'. The Old Norse meaning is 'muffled' or 'covered', while it can also come from the German for 'beloved' or 'gracious'.
*Variants: Huldah, Huldi, Huldy*

### Hyacinth

In Greek mythology a young man called Hyacinthus was accidentally killed by the god Apollo, his lover. A purple flower – the hyacinth – sprang from his blood by way of memory of him.

Although the name was associated with a legendary Greek man it is now commonly given to girls. It was particularly fashionable during the late 19th century.
*Variants: Ciancinta, Hyacinthe, Jacinda, Jacinta*

### Ianthe

This poetic name was used by both Byron and Shelley in their works. It originates in Greek mythology. According to legend Ianthe was a nymph and daughter of Oceanus who was supreme god of the seas. She was also the granddaughter of Uranus and Ge, who ruled the sky and the earth.

The name comes from the Greek for 'violet' and 'dawn cloud'.
*Variants: Iantha, Iola, Iolanthe, Iole, Ione*

### Ida

Mount Ida on the Greek island of Crete was associated with the king of the gods, Zeus. However the name Ida is thought to have more than one source. It is believed to be derived from the Old

Norse words for 'work' and 'woman'. It is also linked to the Old English for 'protection' and 'possession'.
*Variants: Idane, Idina, Ita*

### Ignatia
Taken from the Latin for 'fiery' and 'ardour', Ignatia is also derived from the Old Roman family name Egnatius.

The male form of this name is associated with St Ignatius who, in the 16th century, founded the Jesuit order. The youngest of 13 children, Ignatius was a soldier who devoted his life to Christianity.
*Variant: Ignacia*

### Ilka
Ilka is a Scottish name that comes from the Middle English for 'of that same standing'. It also has a Slavic meaning – 'striving' and 'flattering'.

### Ilona
This is the Hungarian version of the Greek name Helen, which means 'bright'. In Hungarian it means 'beautiful' and 'sunshine'.
*Variants: Eleanor, Helen, Helena, Ili, Ilonka, Lanci*

### Iman
Of African and Arabic origin, it means 'faith in God'. In the 1970s and 1980s this name became well known because of the Somali-born model Iman.

### Imelda
Imelda comes from the Latin for 'wishful'. It also the Italian form of the Germanic name Irmhild, which means 'universal battle'. During the 20th century the name became associated with Imelda Marcos, the First Lady of the Philippines.

### Imogen
This name is of disputed origin. It may be derived from the Latin

word 'imago' ('image, likeness') or it could mean 'innocent'.

However, it is also believed that Imogen could be a misprint of Innogen, a Celtic name that means 'girl' or 'daughter'.
*Variants: Emogene, Imagina, Immie, Immy, Imogene, Imogine, Innogen, Inogen*

## Ina

As a variant of Agnes, Ina comes from the Greek for 'pure' and 'chaste'. It is also used as a short form of names such as Christina and Georgina, which end in 'ina'.
*Variants: Agnes, Ena*

## India

This Sanskrit word for 'river' is also the name of a country. In her 1936 novel about the American Civil War and its aftermath, *Gone with the Wind*, Margaret Mitchell used the name for one of her characters.

## Indigo

Indigo is a dark blue colour. But the name comes from the Greek for 'from India'.
*Variants: Indie, Indy*

## Indira

Born in 1917 Indira Gandhi was the daughter of the first Prime Minister of India, Jawaharlal Nehru, who went on to assume the office herself. She was assassinated in 1984.

Her name means 'splendid' in Hindi. It is associated with Lakshmi, the goddess of wealth who was the consort of the god Vishnu.
*Variants: Indie, Indy*

## Inés

Inés is the Spanish form of the name Agnes, which is derived from the Greek for 'pure' and 'chaste'. It is also used without an accent.
*Variants: Agnes, Ines, Inez*

# *Girls*

**Inge**

In Norse mythology Ing was the god of fertility, who was also associated with peace and plenty. The feminine name Inge comes from the Old Norse for 'meadow', but because it was also known to the Anglo-Saxons the name has an Old English meaning 'to be descended from'.

Inge comes from the same source as the girl's name Ingrid.
*Variants: Inga, Ingaberg, Inger, Ingrid*

**Ingrid**

Like Inge the name Ingrid is linked to the Scandinavian god of peace, fertility and plenty, Ing. He was associated with a sacred golden boar and it is from this association that the name Ingrid is thought to stem for it means 'Ing's ride or steed'. Ingrid is also thought to mean 'beautiful under the protection of Ing'.

The Swedish actress Ingrid Bergman, born in 1915 helped to introduce the name to the English-speaking world.
*Variants: Inga, Ingaberg, Inge, Inger*

**Inoke**

Hawaiian in origin, Inoke means 'devoted'.

**Iola**

A variant of the name Ianthe, Iola comes from the Greek for 'violet' and 'dawn cloud'. One version of this name, Iole, appears in Greek mythology. Iole was the daughter of Eurytus who was abducted by Heracles.
*Variants: Ianthe, Iole, Yolanda, Yolande*

**Iona**

It was on this Scottish island that St Columba settled and founded his monastery in 563. From that site he spread Christianity throughout Scotland and the north of England.

The name is also believed to come from the Greek for 'violet', 'dawn cloud' or possibly 'purple jewel'.
*Variants: Ione, Ionia*

# I

**Iora**

This name comes from the Latin for 'gold'.

**Ireland**

Like the name Shannon, Ireland is often bestowed upon girls as a tribute to the Emerald Isle.

**Iris**

In Greek mythology Iris was the goddess who passed messages between the gods and earth using the rainbow as her link. Thus the name Iris comes from the Greek for 'messenger of light' or 'rainbow'.

It is also the name of a flower as well as the term used for the coloured part of the eye.

*Variants: Irisa, Irita, Irys, Irisha, Irissa, Risa, Risha, Rissa*

**Irma**

Irmintrude and Irmgard are two examples of German names that begin with the element 'irm(en)', which means 'whole' or 'universal'. Irma is a pet form of names that begin with this element, used independently.

It was first introduced to the English-speaking world in the late 19th century.

*Variants: Emma, Erma, Irmina, Irmgrad, Irmintrude*

**Isabel**

The name Isabel is the Spanish equivalent of Elizabeth, which means 'God's oath' in Hebrew. It was first introduced to England in the Middle Ages and henceforth it became a name associated with royalty. The wives of three kings of England bore the name.

*Variants: Bel, Bella, Bell, Ezabel, Isabella, Isabelle, Isbel, Isobel, Izzie, Izzy*

**Isadora**

Isadora comes from the Greek for 'gift of Isis'. Isis was the

Egyptian goddess of the moon and fertility who was worshipped during classical times.

In the 20th century the name was borne by Isadora Duncan, an American dancer who was considered to be the mother of modern dance. She died in 1927.

*Variants: Dora, Issy, Izzy*

**Isha**

Isha is a variant of the name Aisha which comes from the Arabic for 'prospering'.

*Variant: Aisha*

**Isis**

In Ancient Egypt Isis was the goddess of fertility.

**Isla**

Pronounced 'eye-la', Isla is a Scottish name that means 'swiftly' and 'flowing'. Islay, a Hebridean island, is a variant of Isla.

*Variant: Islay*

**Ismaela**

Ismaela comes from the Hebrew for 'God listens'.

**Isra**

This Turkish name means 'freedom'.

**Ita**

As a variant of Ida, Ita has a variety of meanings. It could come from the Old English for 'possession' and 'protection' or the Old Norse for 'work' or 'woman'.

But, as an independent name, it is derived from the Italian and Irish for 'thirsty'.

*Variant: Ida*

**Italia**

The girl's name Italia means 'Italian' or 'woman from Italy'.

# I-J

**Ivory**

Ivory is a precious bone-like substance that forms the tusks of a certain breed of elephant. White in colour, it is used to make carvings and jewellery.

The girl's name Ivory also comes from the Welsh for 'highborn lady'.

**Ivy**

Introduced as a girl's name in the 19th century, Ivy was especially popular during the 1920s. It comes from the Old English for ivy – the clinging plant.
*Variants: Iva, Ivi, Ivie*

**Jacqueline**

The name Jacqueline was brought to England by the sister-in-law of Henry V, who reigned from 1413 until his death in 1422.

Jacqueline is of French, but ultimately Hebrew, origin. It is the French feminine form of the Biblical name James, which is a variant of Jacob ('follower', 'supplanter').

Jacquetta, another version of the name, has been known in England since the 15th century, while Shakespeare used the name Jacquenetta in *Love's Labour's Lost*. But the popularity of the name Jacqueline increased during the 1960s because it was borne by the glamorous First Lady of America – Jacqueline Kennedy, who went on to marry the shipping magnet Aristotle Onassis.
*Variants: Jacki, Jackie, Jacklyn, Jacquelyn, Jacquelynne, Jacquetta, Jacqui*

**Jade**

Jade is a precious green stone that is used to make carvings and jewellery. In Spain it was sometimes referred to as the 'stone of the bowels' because it was believed to protect the body from intestinal disorders. When Mick Jagger, the lead singer of the Rolling Stones, named his second daughter Jade in the early 1970s the popularity of this name grew.
*Variant: Jayde*

**Jaime**

In French 'j'aime' means 'I like' or 'I love' and the name Jaime shares this meaning. A unisex name, in Spain it is a form of the boy's name James.

However in North America the name is mostly given to girls where it is also considered to be a variant spelling of Jamie. As a feminine form of James, like Jacqueline, it shares the meaning for James and Jacob – 'supplanter'.

*Variants: Jaimi, Jaimie, Jamie, Jaymee*

**Jamelia**

In Arabic this name means 'beautiful'. It is the feminine form of Jamil and is a variant of the North African name Djamila.

*Variants: Jameela, Jameelah, Jamilah, Jamillah, Jamillia*

**Jane**

Like Janine, Joan and Jean the name Jane is a feminine form of John, which comes from the Hebrew for 'God has favoured' and 'God is gracious'. It also comes from the Old French name Jehane.

During the Middle Ages Joan was the favoured form of John – a timeless favourite. However, in Tudor England, Jane became the popular choice. It was the name of Henry VIII's favourite wife – Jane Seymour.

Like Anne, Jane has been used in compounds to produce other names such as Sarah Jane and Mary Jane.

*Variants: Janelle, Janet, Janette, Janie, Janine, Janice, Janis, Jayne, Jean, Joan*

**Janelle**

In 1989 in North America this variant of Jane was more common than the original. Janelle enjoys more popularity in this region than it does in Europe.

Like Jane, Janet, Jean, Joan and Joanne, Janelle ultimately stems from the Hebrew for 'God is gracious'.

*Variants: Jane, Janet, Janette, Janie, Janine, Janice, Janis, Jean, Joan, Jonelle*

# J

**Janet**

Ultimately derived from the Biblical name John ('God has favoured', 'God is gracious') Janet comes from the French variant of Jane – Jeannette. Popular in Scotland, the name Janet was not widely used until the late 19th century.

*Variants: Janette, Janie, Janice, Janis, Jeanette, Jeannette, Jennie, Netta, Nettie, Jessie*

**Janine**

Janine is another feminine variant of the name John ('God is gracious'). Of French origin, it is an alternative spelling of Jeannine.

*Variants: Jane, Janina, Janice, Janis, Jeanette, Jeannette, Jeanine, Jeannine*

**Jasmine**

This fragrant flower is used to make tea, scented oil and perfume. Of Persian and Arabic origin, the name means 'an olive flower'. Yasmin is the Arabic version of the name.

*Variants: Jasmin, Yasmina, Yasmin, Yasmine*

**Jean**

Like Janet, Jean is a Scottish form of the name Jane, which is derived from the French variant Jehane. In the 18th century the name was borne by the mistress of Louise XV, Jeanne Antoinette Poison, who was more commonly known as Madame de Pompadour.

As a feminine variant of John, Jean means 'God is gracious'.

*Variants: Gene, Genna, Jane, Janina, Janine, Jeanette, Jeannette, Jeanine, Jeannine, Jeanne*

**Jemima**

In the Old Testament Jemima was the daughter of Job. In Hebrew and Arabic the name means 'dove'.

Favoured by the Puritans, the name was especially popular in the early 19th century. It is also associated with the feminine form of Benjamin, Jemina.

*Variants: Jem, Jemimah, Jemma, Jemina, Jona, Jonati, Mima*

### Jenna

The name Jenna was derived from Jennifer, the Cornish form of
Guinevere. Hence, it is ultimately of Welsh origin and means
'fair ghost'.

*Variants: Guinevere, Jen, Jenni, Jennie, Jennifer, Jenny*

### Jennifer

Jennifer is the Cornish version of the Welsh name Guinevere. In
Arthurian legend Guinevere was the name of King Arthur's wife
and Sir Lancelot's lover. It means 'fair ghost'.

In 1905 the Irish playwright George Bernard Shaw gave the
name to one of his characters in *The Doctor's Dilemma*. Jennifer
was especially popular in the 1930s. The name has come to the
fore again due to the popularity of singer/actress Jennifer Lopez
and actress Jennifer Aniston.

*Variants: Gaenor, Gaynor, Guinevere, Jen, Jenna, Jenni, Jennie, Jenny*

### Jessie

The name Jessie may have been derived from a number of roots.
In Scotland it is the pet form of the names Janet and Jean, which
are feminine variants of John. The Hebrew meaning of John is
'God is gracious', 'God has favoured'.

Jessie is also a short form of the feminine variant of Jesse. In
the Bible Jesse was the father of King David. His name was
derived from the Hebrew for 'riches, wealthy' or 'a gift'.

*Variants: Jane, Janet, Jean, Jess, Jessica*

### Jessica

In the 1980s Jessica was a popular name for girls born in North
America and the United Kingdom. However centuries before
Shakespeare had given the name to one of his many characters.
In his play *The Merchant of Venice*, Jessica was the daughter of
Shylock the moneylender.

Many believe that the name was a Shakespearian creation as
a feminine form of the Biblical name Jesse. In the Old Testament
Jesse was the father of King David and his name was derived

from the Jewish word 'yisha', which means 'riches', 'a gift'.
*Variants: Jess, Jessie*

## Jewel

During the 19th century it became fashionable to name baby girls after precious stones such as ruby, coral and crystal. In the 1920s this trend was continued when the name Jewel came into use. The name comes from the word jewel and from the Old French for 'plaything'.
*Variants: Jewell, Jewelle*

## Jill

According to the well known nursery rhyme Jack and Jill went up the hill to fetch a pail of water. After Jack fell down, breaking his crown, Jill came tumbling after.

However, the history of the name Jill stems back further than the nursery rhyme. It is derived from the ancient Roman clan of the Julii. Their family name came from the Greek for 'soft-haired' or 'fair complexioned'. Julius Caesar was a descendant of that lineage.
*Variants: Gill, Gillian, Julia, Juliana, Julie*

## Joan

Joan of Arc was the French heroine who led the French army against the English during the 1429 siege of Orleans. As a teenager she said that she heard the voices of St Michael, St Mary and St Margaret telling her to free France from the rule of England and return the Dauphin to the throne. Despite her heroic efforts Joan was captured, sold to the English and burnt at the stake in 1431. She was canonised in 1920.

The popular story of Joan of Arc may have increased the popularity of the name, which comes from the French feminine form of John ('God is gracious').

In Old French the name appears as Jehane, Johanne and sometimes Jeanne.
*Variants: Jane, Janet, Jayne, Jean, Jeanne, Jo, Joanna, Joanne, Johanna*

**Joanne**

A derivative of Joan, Joanne is sometimes thought to be a combination of the names Jo and Anne. While that theory is true, the name also stems from the Old French feminine forms of John – Jhone and Johanne. Thus they are related to other feminine variants of that name – Jane, Janet, Jean and Joan. All mean the same thing 'God is gracious' in Hebrew. Siobhan is the Irish version of Joanne.
*Variants: Giovanna, Jane, Janis, Jayne, Jean, Jeanne, Joan, Joanna, Joann, Johanna*

**Jocelin**

Brought to England by the Normans, Jocelin has a number of meanings and is thought to have been derived from various sources. It may have come from the Latin for 'sportive' or 'just'. Equally it may have been derived from the Old German for 'descendent of the Goths'. But as a German feminine form of Jacob it shares the same meaning as Jacqueline – 'follower', 'supplanter'.

Jocelin also appears in society as a surname and was once a boy's name before being given to girls in the 19th century.
*Variants: Jocelyn, Josceline, Josette, Josie, Joss*

**Jodi**

Jodi began life as a short form of the Biblical name Judith ('Jewish woman'). However, it is also an elaboration of the pet name Jo, which is short for Joan, Joanne or Josephine. As the feminine form of Jude, Jodi means 'praise'. (See Jude.)
*Variants: Jo, Joan, Joanne, Jody, Josephine, Jodie, Jody, Judi, Judith*

**Joleen**

Like Josephine, Joleen is a feminine form of the Biblical name Joseph, which in Hebrew means 'God will increase'. It also comes from the French and Middle English word 'joli' ('high spirited').
*Variants: Jolene, Jolie, Joline, Josepha, Josephine*

# J

**Jolie**

Derived from the French for 'pretty one', Jolie also comes from the Middle English for 'jolly' or 'high spirited'.

*Variants: Jolene, Joleen, Joli, Jolly*

**Jonelle**

Jonelle belongs to the family of girls' names that stem from John. Consequently, like Jane, Jean, Joan, Joanne and Janelle it means 'God is gracious'. Mostly found in North America it is a modern elaboration of Jane.

*Variants: Jane, Janelle, Jo, Joan, Joanne, Jean*

**Jonquil**

Like Rose, Daisy and Daffodil, Jonquil is a flower name given to baby girls. Introduced in the 20th century, it is less common than other flower names.

Jonquil comes from the Latin for 'reed'.

**Jordan**

Jordan is the name of a country and a river in the Middle East. Given to both boys and girls, it means 'flowing down'.

In the Bible Jesus was baptised in the River Jordan by his cousin, John the Baptist. Christian pilgrims used to bottle water from the river to use later to baptise their children.

Jordan is also a surname.

*Variants: Jourdan, Jordin, Jordyn*

**Josephine**

The Biblical name Joseph comes from the Hebrew 'God will increase'. In the Old Testament it was borne by one of the 12 sons of Jacob, while in the New Testament it belonged to the Virgin Mary's husband.

Josephine is the French feminine form of this name. It was borne by the wife of Napoleon Bonaparte, Empress Josephine, who died in 1814.

*Variants: Fifi, Jo, Jojo, Josie, Josey, Josefina, Josephina*

**Joss**

Given to both sexes, Joss is a short form of the name Jocelin that is used independently. Like its source it has a number of meanings. It comes from the Latin for 'sportive' and 'just', as well as the Old German for 'descendent of the Goths'.

Meanwhile the Celtic word 'josse' means 'champion'. As a derivative of the German form of Jacob, Joss also means 'supplanter'.

*Variants: Jacqueline, Jocelin, Jocelyn, Josse*

**Joy**

Derived from the Old French word 'joie', Joy means to be 'merry' or 'happy'. It was first found as a name in the 12th century, but its use was revived by the Puritans perhaps because it was connected to the Christian instruction to be 'joyful in the Lord'. It was also favoured by the Victorians in the 19th century.

*Variants: Joi, Joyce, Joye*

**Joyce**

Borne by some of William the Conqueror's followers, the Norman name Josce was customarily given to men. However, by the 14th century this practice had died out and it was established as a feminine name.

Modern use of Joyce can be explained by the twin influence of culture and literature. It may have derived its popularity from the transferred use of the Irish surname. Its use in two 19th century works, In the *Golden Days* (1885) and *East Lynne* (1861) could have proved influential to Victorian parents.

The exact meaning of the name is unknown. It may have been derived from the Breton for 'Lord' or, equally, it could be a variant of Joy.

*Variants: Joice, Jossi, Jossie, Jossy*

**Jubilee**

Used as a girl's name Jubilee comes from the Latin 'jubilaeus', which means 'a joyful time of celebration'.

**Judith**
In the Bible Judith was the Old Testament heroine who saved her people by beheading their enemy Holofernes. Judith was also the name of Esau's wife.

The name, which means 'a Jewish woman', was popular in both the 18th and 20th centuries.
*Variants: Jodi, Jodie, Jody, Judite, Judithe, Judi, Judy*

**Julia**
Julia is another feminine form of the Old Roman family name Julius, which means 'fair skinned'. A woman bearing that name appears in St Paul's Epistles to the Romans. Juliet and Juliana are both related to this name.
*Variants: Gill, Gillian, Gillie, Jill, Jillian, Juliana, Julie, Juliet*

**Juliana**
Popular in England during the 18th century, Juliana is a variant of the Latin name Julianus. Its male equivalent is Julian and like, Jill and Julia it means 'fair skinned'.
*Variants: Gill, Gillian, Gillie, Jill, Jillian, Julia, Julie, Juliet*

**Julie**
This French form of the name Julia was first found in English-speaking countries in the 1920s. Like Juliana and Julia it belongs to the family of names derived from the Roman clan of the Julii, who traced their descent to Aphrodite, the goddess of love.
*Variants: Gill, Gillian, Gillie, Jill, Jillian, Julia, Julie, Juliet*

**Juliet**
Like Julia, Julie and Juliana, Juliet ultimately stems from the Old Roman name Julius. The form Juliet is an Anglicised version of the French Juliette and the Italian Giuliette. They all share the meaning 'fair-skinned'. The name continues to be well-known to this day because of the influence of the Shakespeare's tragic love story *Romeo and Juliet*.
*Variants: Guiletta, Giulletta, Jules, Julia, Juliana, Juliette*

**June**
In the 20th century it became fashionable to name girls born in June after the month of their birth. It was the Roman supreme goddess Juno who gave her name to that month. According to folklore she joined with a magical flower to produce Mars, the god of war.

June also comes from the Latin for 'young' or 'younger'.
*Variant: Juno*

**Juniper**
This is another plant used as a girl's name. Berries from the juniper plant are used to flavour gin and foods such as meats and sauces.

**Juno**
The Roman goddess Juno was also known as 'she who brings children into the light'. In ancient Greece she was worshipped as the goddess Hera.

Not only is the name a variant of June it is also connected to Una, which is Latin for 'one, unity'. Juno is the Irish form of Una.
*Variant: June, Una*

**Justine**
Popular in 1960s Britain Justine is a feminine form of Justin, which comes from the Latin for 'just'. The name was derived from the French version Justina. Its popularity may be due to the 1957 Lawrence Durrell novel, *Justine.*
*Variants: Justina*

**Kalila**
Kalila comes from the Arabic for 'beloved' and 'sweetheart'.

**Kamala**
Kamala is derived from the word meaning 'lotus', and is an appellation of Lakshmi, the Hindu god of wealth.

**Kamila**

This name comes from the Arabic for 'complete', 'perfect' and 'perfect one'.
*Variant: Kamilah*

**Kanani**

In Hawaiian the name Kanani means 'beautiful'.
*Variants: Ani, Nani*

**Kara**

In Italian the word 'cara' means 'beloved', and like 'dear' in English or 'chéri' in French, is a term of endearment. 'Cara' is also the Irish Gaelic word for 'friend'. It was coined as a name in the 20th century.
*Variant: Cara*

**Karen**

Although it is widely held as an independent name in its own right, Karen is actually the Scandinavian form of Catherine, which comes from the Greek for 'pure'. It was brought to North America by Scandinavian settlers, but has been popular in Britain only since the 1950s.
*Variants: Caren, Caron, Caryn, Catherine, Karan, Kari, Karina, Karin, Karyn, Katherine*

**Kari**

Used independently, Kari was originally a pet form of the names Karol and Karoline ('free man'). It is also a variant of Karen which stems from Katherine ('pure') and is of Scandinavian and Greek origin.
*Variants: Cari, Carol, Caroline, Catherine, Karan, Karin, Karol, Karoline, Karyn, Katherine*

**Karima**

The feminine variant of Karim, Karima comes from 'karam' the Arabic for 'noble' and 'generous'. In the Koran it is also one of

the 99 names of Allah and one of his 99 qualities.
*Variants: Kareema, Karimah, Kharim*

**Karis**
Karis is derived from the Greek for 'graceful'.

**Karla**
As the feminine form of the boy's names Carl and Karl, Karla
stems from the Germanic name Charles, which means 'man'. Like
Carol and Caroline it can be spelt with either with a 'C' or a 'K'.
*Variants: Carrie, Carla, Carol, Caroline, Kari, Karleen, Karlene, Karol,
Karoline*

**Katarina**
The Greek name Katherine has spawned a number of derivatives
with different countries producing their own variants that are
eventually accepted as independent names. Katarina is the
Swedish form of Katherine ('pure'). It is sometimes used in the
English-speaking world.
*Variants: Catherine, Katharina, Katerina, Katherine*

**Kate**
Like the name Katie, Kate is a short form of Katherine which
has become a name in its own right. Kate is also a short form of
Katerina.
*Variants: Catherine, Katarina, Kate, Katerina, Katharine, Katie, Katy*

**Katherine**
The popularity of the name Katherine can probably be measured
by the many different forms it has taken throughout the world.
In English-speaking countries alone the name can be spelt in at
least five ways – Catherine, Catharine, Katharine, Katherine or
Kathryn. However it is spelt, Katherine is derived from the
Greek word 'katharos', which means 'pure'.

Caterina is the Italian form of the name, while in Sweden
Katerina or Katarina are preferred. Kathleen is a well known

Irish variant. (See also Catherine.)

*Variants: Catharine, Catherine, Katarina, Katerina, Katharine, Katherine, Katie, Kathlyn, Kathryn, Karen*

## Kay

At first glance Kay appears to simply be a short form or pet name for names beginning with the letter 'K'. And so it is. But Kay is also an independent name in its own right that is bestowed upon babies of both sexes. Indeed Sir Kay was a knight in Arthurian legend, whose name was believed to be a Celtic form of the Roman name Gaius, the origin of which is unknown.

What is known is that Kay boasts multiple roots. As a short form of Katherine it takes the Greek meaning 'pure' but it could also mean 'rejoice'. There is also a link to the Old Breton word for 'fence' and the Old French for 'quay'. There is a possibility that Kay derives its meaning from the Middle Low German for 'spear' or, equally, from the Old English for 'key'.

*Variants: Kai, Kaye, Kayla, Kaylee, Kaylynn*

## Kayla

More popular in North America than it is in the United Kingdom Kayla is an elaboration of the name Kay (see above). It is also a variant of the Kayleigh – a modern name which is a transferred use of the Irish surname.

*Variants: Kay, Kaylah, Kayleigh, Kayley*

## Kayley

Kayley is a transferred use of the Irish surname Kayleigh, which in Gaelic appears as Ó Caollaidhe ('descendent of Caollaidhe'). Kayley is also derived from the Irish Gaelic word 'caol', which means 'slim'.

*Variants: Caileigh, Kailey, Kay, Kaylee, Kayleigh, Kayly*

## Keeleigh

Keeleigh is another Irish surname that is now being used as a Christian name for baby girls. It stems from the Irish Gaelic for 'beautiful girl' and is also rooted in the word 'cadhla', which means 'graceful'.

It is sometimes used as a variant of Kayley or Kelly.
*Variants: Kayleigh, Kayley, Keelie, Keely, Keighley, Kelly*

### Keira

The Irish word for black, 'ciar' has given birth to a number of Celtic names that mean 'little dark one' or 'dark-haired'. Keira and Kieran, which is a boy's name, are among them.

Like Katherine, Keira can be spelt in a variety of ways but the meaning remains the same.
*Variants: Ciara, Ciaragh, Kiara, Kiera*

### Keisha

Two theories exist about the origin of this name. One theory suggests that Keisha is derived from a Central African language called Bobangi. Taken from the word 'nkisa', Keisha means 'favourite'.

However, another theory suggests that Keisha is a modern blending of the name Aisha with the letter 'K'.
*Variants: Aisha, Keesha, Kiesha, LaKeisha*

### Kelila

This Hebrew name means 'crowned with laurel'. It is also a feminine form of Kyle.
*Variants: Kaila, Kaile, Kayle, Kelilah, Kelula, Kyla, Kylene*

### Kelly

When translated into English the Irish surname Ó Cellaigh means 'descendent of Ceallach' or simply 'Kelly'.

Throughout Western Europe the Celtic warriors were known as warriors or 'keltoi' in Greek. This corresponds with the meaning of Kelly as 'warrior' and its association with the words 'war' and 'strife'. However, the name is also derived from the Gaelic for 'church goer'.
*Variants: Kaley, Keeley, Keli, Kellee, Keeleigh, Kelli*

### Kemba

The name Kemba is derived from the Old English word
'cymaere', which means 'Saxon lord'.
*Variants: Kem, Kemp, Kemps*

### Kendra

The exact origin of Kendra is unknown. It is thought that the
name stems from the Old English word for 'knowledge'
meaning either the 'know how' or 'ability'. It could also be a
blend of the male and female names Ken and Sandra.
*Variants: Ken, Kendis*

### Kenya

Like China, India and Ireland, Kenya is the name of a country
bestowed upon girls as a first name. It is sometimes chosen by
parents of African descent as a celebration of their cultural heritage.

### Keren

According to the Bible the prophet Job had three beautiful
daughters – Jemima, Keziah and Kerenhappuch. Keren is a short
form of the name Kerenhappuch, which comes from the Hebrew
for 'animal horn' or 'horn of eye-shadow'. The name refers to the
material from which boxes, which contained kohl to decorate the
eyes, were made.

Keren is another Biblical name that was favoured by the
Puritans in the 17th century. It is sometimes used as a variant
of Karen.
*Variants: Kaaren, Kareen, Karen, Karin, Karon, Karyn, Kerryn, Kyran*

### Kerry

Like Kelly, Kerry has strong links to Ireland and the Irish people
around the world. Not only is it the name of an Irish county but
it is derived from 'ciar', a Gaelic word meaning 'dark one'.

As a boy's name Kerry's popularity grew in Australia during
the 1940s. However, among the Irish in Boston, Massachusetts
the name has also been used as a pet form of Katherine. Kerry

is now also common in Britain, while in Wales it assumes the form of Ceri.
*Variants: Ceri, Keree, Keri, Kerrey*

**Keshisha**
Keshisha is derived from the Aramaic for 'elder'.

**Ketifa**
This Arabic name means 'to pluck a flower'.

**Keturah**
This Biblical name was not very popular during the 20th century but it found favour among the Puritans. For it was the name of the woman Abraham married after Sarah's death. It comes from the Hebrew for 'fragrance, incense'.

**Keziah**
In the Bible Keziah was the name of Job's second daughter. Her name comes from the Hebrew for 'cassia', a type of fragrant shrub. Thus the meaning of the name ranges from 'cassia tree' to 'bark like cinnamon'.
    Keziah is a popular name among African-American parents.
*Variants: Kasia, Kerzia, Kesia, Kesiah, Ketzi, Kez, Ketzia, Kizzie*

**Khadija**
Not only was Khadija the first wife of the Prophet Mohammad, she was also the first person that he converted to Islam. So important was she to him and so acutely did he grieve for her, that the year of her death was named 'The Year of Grief'.
    The name comes from the Arabic for 'premature baby'.
*Variants: Khadeejah, Khadijah, Khadiya*

**Kiara**
Like Kiera and Ciara, Kiara is a feminine form of the Celtic name Kieran, which means 'dark one' or 'dark haired'. However, it is also a variant of Chiara – the Italian form of Clare. Thus it also

means 'bright' and 'clear'.

This is another name that is popular among African-Americans.
*Variants: Chiara, Ciara, Clare, Keira, Kiera*

### Kiki
Like Kay, Kiki is a short form of names beginning with the letter 'K'. It is of Spanish origin.

It is also of African derivation and can mean 'funny girl'.

### Kimberly
The name Kimberly became popular with British soldiers during the turn of the last century who were involved in the 1899 to 1902 Boer War – which meant they were stationed in South Africa. It was customary for soldiers to name their offspring after the garrison where they were placed, hence the rise of the name Kimberly in honour of Kimberley, the South African town.

Initially the name was given to boys, but it is now more commonly seen as a girl's name. It is especially popular in North America.
*Variants: Kim, Kimberlee, Kimberley, Kimberlie, Kimmi, Kimmie, Kym*

### Kimi
This Japanese name means 'sovereign', 'best' and 'without equal'.
*Variants: Kimie, Kimiko, Kimiyo*

### Kira
Although Kira looks and sounds like the Celtic name Keira ('little dark one') it is also a Persian name that means 'sun', 'throne' and 'shepherd'.

It is a feminine form of the name Cyrus, which once belonged to a powerful king of Persia who died in 529 BC. Famed for his military prowess and mercy Cyrus was also the founder of the Persian Empire. It was this reputation that earned him the name Cyrus the Great.
*Variants: Ciara, Kiara, Keira, Kiera*

### Kirsten

As a Scandinavian variant of Christine, Kirsten means 'Christian' or 'follower of Christ'. However, the name is also derived from the Old English for 'church' and the Greek for 'of the Lord'.

It is now also popular in the English-speaking world.

*Variants: Christine, Kersten, Kiersten, Kirby, Kirstie, Kirsty*

### Kirstie

Kirstin is yet another variant of the name Christine ('Christian') but this version hails from Scotland. It produced the short-form Kirstie, which is now considered a name in its own right.

*Variants: Christine, Kirsten, Kirstin, Kirsty, Kristen, Kristin*

### Koko

This Japanese name is supposed to symbolise longevity. It means 'stork'.

### Kristen

Bestowed upon boys and girls, Kristen is another Scandinavian form of the name Christine, which means 'Christian'.

*Variants: Christine, Kirsten, Krista, Kristeen, Kristina, Krysta, Krystina*

### Kylie

Kylie is sometimes considered to be a feminine variant of the Gaelic name Kyle ('narrow strait'). However, it actually comes from an Aboriginal word that means 'boomerang' – the wooden toy, which when thrown returns to the thrower. Unsurprisingly it is a popular Australian name which, since the success of actress and singer Kylie Minogue from the late 1980s, has spread throughout the rest of the world.

*Variants: Kyley, Kylee, Kyleigh*

### Kyna

Another Celtic name, Kyna comes from the Irish Gaelic for 'wisdom' and 'intelligence'.

# L

## Laila

Although this name is of Arabic origin it was well known in 19th century Britain thanks to the work of two authors. The poet Lord Byron used the variant Leila in two of his works *The Giaour* (1813) and *Don Juan* (1819-24). In *Don Juan* the name was given to a Turkish orphan brought to England by the central character. In *The Giaour* Leila is the name of an Oriental beauty who is the heroine of the romantic poem. Later in the century Lord Lytton used the name again for the heroine of his 1838 novel *Leila*.

However the name is spelt – Laila, Layla or Leila – the meaning of this name is same. It means 'night', 'dark haired' or 'dark complexioned'. In the 20th century the popularity of the name was further emboldened by Eric Clapton's 1972 hit song *Layla*.
*Variants: Laili, Laleh, Layla, Leala, Lee, Leigh, Leila, Leyla, Lila, Lilah*

## Lakshmi

Lakshmi, the Hindu goddess of wealth, beauty, fertility and luck, was married to Vishnu. She is known by more than one name. Kamala is another name for this goddess and Indira is also associated with Lakshmi. (See both Indira and Kamala.)
The name comes from the Sanskrit for 'mark' or 'birthmark'.

## Lalita

This Indian term of endearment is derived from the Sanskrit for 'charming', 'honest' and 'straightforward'.
*Variants: Lal, Lalie, Lita*

## Lana

Lana is a short form of the name Alana, which is a feminine version of the boy's name Alan. Although the latter name is of unknown origin it is believed to be derived from the Celtic for 'harmony'.

However the name Lana seems to have no shortage of possible sources. It may come from the Latin word 'lanatus', which means 'woolly' or 'downy'. Similarly the Hawaiian word for 'buoyant' is thought to be a source as is the Breton for 'rock'. Another possible Hawaiian meaning is 'offering' or 'light'.

But the name Lana may equally have been derived from the Irish term 'alannah' which itself comes from the Irish Gaelic 'a lenbh', which means 'o child'. The Irish Gaelic for 'good looking', 'cheerful' and 'darling' are all thought to be connected with the name as well.

*Variants: Alana, Alanna, Alanah, Alannah, Lanna, Lane, Lanne, Lanette, Lannie, Lanny*

## Lara

For millions of film enthusiasts around the world the name Lara will forever be associated with the classic 1965 epic *Doctor Zhivago*, which was a dramatisation of Boris Pasternak's 1957 novel. Like the film the name has a Russian backdrop, for Lara is the Russian short form of Larissa (see below).

In Roman mythology Lara was the daughter of the river Almon who could not help revealing secrets. For betraying Jupiter's trust and revealing one of his affairs she had her tongue cut out.

The name is also sometimes found as a variant of Laura. (See also Laura and Larissa.)

*Variants: Larissa, Laura*

## Larissa

Larissa appears in Greek mythology. It was the name of the daughter of Pelasgus. It is also the name of an ancient Thessalian town, a moon and an asteroid.

Although little is known about the origin of the name it is thought that it means 'citadel' in Greek and 'playful' or 'merry' in Latin. Lara is a short form of Larissa, which is also sometimes used as a variant of Laura. (See also Lara and Laura.)

*Variants: Lara, Larisa, Laura*

## Lark

A lark is a small bird notable for its sweet voice, hence the phrase 'to sing like a lark'. But the word 'lark' also means something else in the English language. As well as being associated with 'early rising' it also means to have 'fun' or be 'cheery'.

### Laura

In Ancient Greece those who triumphed in the arts, sports or war were crowned with a wreath of laurel. And it is from the Latin for this evergreen shrub that the girl's name Laura is derived. Daphne is of similar origin – it comes from the Greek for 'laurel'.

Although the Romans did not use the name, Laura has appeared throughout history. It was the name of a 9th century nun who died in a cauldron of molten lead and was later canonised. For the Italian poet Petrarch the name was also a source of inspiration. Although he did not meet her, Laura was the name of the woman he loved from afar and many of his sonnets, written in the 14th century, were about her.

Lowri is the Welsh form of the name.

*Variants: Lara, Larissa, Lauren, Lauryn, Lola, Loren, Lorraine, Loretta, Lorrie, Lowri*

### Lauren

A variant of Laura (see above), Lauren is now a name in its own right. Like Laura and Daphne it means 'laurel'. It is also considered to be a feminine equivalent of Laurence.

The film actress Lauren Bacall, who rose to prominence in the 1940s, brought the name to world attention.

*Variants: Lara, Larissa, Laura, Lauryn, Loraine, Loren*

### Lavender

This sweet-smelling plant has clusters of small mauve flowers. Thus the name Lavender is associated with the light purple shade, the herb and the fragrance that is derived from this plant. The name is of Latin origin and means 'to wash'.

### Lavern

In Roman mythology Laverna was the goddess of thieves and conmen but her name has a loftier meaning. It comes from the Old French for 'the green one' and the Latin for 'springtime'.

*Variants: Laverna, Laverne, La Verne, Luvern*

### Lavinia

Lavinia is another name that is found in Roman mythology. According to legend she was the daughter of the king of Latinus and the wife of Aeneas, the Trojan and founder of the Roman people. Her son Silvius was said to have named the town Lavinium in her honour.

Although the name was not used by the Romans it was taken up in Europe during the Renaissance. In the 18th century it received attention again when James Thomson wrote the poem *Lavinia and Palemon*.

The name is said to mean 'Latin woman' or 'woman of Rome'.

*Variants: Lavena, Lavina, Lavinie, Vin, Vina, Vinia, Vinnie, Vinny*

### Leah

In the Bible Jacob fell in love with the beautiful Rachel and served her father for seven years in an attempt to win her hand in marriage. However, on the wedding night his beloved was substituted by her less attractive older sister, Leah. Although Rachel was later given to Jacob as a co-wife, Jacob did not like Leah.

Leah, which means 'languid' or 'weary', was a favourite among the 17th century Puritans.

*Variants: Lea, Lee, Leigh, Lia, Liah*

### Leigh

Leigh derives its meaning from other names. As a variant of the English surname Lee it means 'meadow'. As an alternative form of the Biblical Leah it comes from the Hebrew for 'weary' (see above). And as a variant of the Arabic name Laila, Leigh means 'night' or 'dark complexion'. (See also Laila.)

*Variants: Laila, Leah, Lee, Leila*

### Leilani

This Hawaiian name means 'heavenly child' or 'heavenly flower'.

*Variants: Lei, Lelani*

**Leoma**
Leoma is derived from the Old English for 'light' and 'brightness'.

**Leona**
Leona is believed to be the feminine elaboration of the name Leo, which means 'lion' in Latin. However, it is equally regarded as a variant of the name Eleanor via Leonora. As a derivative of this name it means 'bright', 'God is my light' and 'foreign'. (See also Eleanor and Helen.)
*Variants: Eleanor, Helen, Leonie, Leonora*

**Lesley**
Lesley belongs to the group of names that are unisex and can be comfortably given to both girls and boys. Leslie is the male form of the name which is Scottish in origin.

Indeed the name Leslie originally belonged to a noble family who rose to prominence in Scotland during the 15th century. Closely associated with the Stewart royal dynasty, the Leslies hailed from Aberdeenshire.

The name Lesley stems from the Scottish Gaelic meaning 'low-lying meadow' and 'garden of hollies'.
*Variants: Lea, Lesli, Leslie, Lesly, Lezlie*

**Letifa**
The name Allatif was one of the 99 names and qualities given to Allah in the Koran. Like Letifa it stems from the Arabic word 'latif', which means 'gentle'.
*Variants: Latifah, Letipha*

**Letitia**
Letitia comes from the Latin for 'joyful' or 'unrestrained joy'. During the 12th century it was found in England as Lettice, but Letitia and Letisha are the modern variants. It is a favourite among African-American parents.
*Variants: Laetitia, Lece, Lecia, Leta, Lettice, Lettie, Letisha, Tisha, Titia*

### Levanna

In Roman mythology Levanna was the goddess of newborn babies who lifted the babies up from the ground. Hence her name comes from the Latin for 'lifting up' and 'rising sun'.
*Variants: Levana, Levona, Livana, Livona*

### Levina

Levina comes from the Middle English for 'lightning'.

### Lianne

The exact origin of the name Lianne is uncertain. It is thought to be the French equivalent of either Juliana or Elaine. As a variant of Juliana, Lianne means 'fair skinned' and ultimately comes from the Roman family name Julius (see Julia and Julie.) But as a variant of Elaine it is connected to the Greek name Helen which means 'bright'.

Lianne may also have been derived from the French for 'to bind' or it could be a compound of Lee ('meadow') and Anne ('God has favoured me'). This blend is English and Hebrew in origin.
*Variants: Ann, Anne, Elaine, Helen, Leana, Leann, Leanne, Lee, Lianna*

### Libby

Like Bess, Betty, Betsy and Liz, the name Libby began as a pet form of Elizabeth. Thus it shares the Biblical meaning 'God is perfection', 'God is satisfaction', 'dedicated to God' and 'God's oath'. It is thought to have been derived from a child's mispronunciation of Elizabeth or one of its short forms.
*Variants: Bess, Bessie, Bet, Betty, Elizabeth, Lib, Libbie, Liberty, Lisa, Liz, Lizzie*

### Liberty

Of Latin origin Liberty is another way of saying 'freedom'. It comes from the word 'libertas'. Libby is also a short form of this name.
*Variants: Lib, Libbie, Libby*

**Lilac**
Like lavender, lilac is both a colour and a plant. The lilac shrub boasts sprays of fragrant purple and white flowers. As a colour it is a shade of light purple. The word and name also come from the Persian and Arabic for 'indigo' and 'blue'.

**Lillian**
As a variant of Elizabeth, Lillian shares the Hebrew meaning 'God is perfection'. However, it is also a derivative of the flower name 'lily'. (See also Elizabeth and Lily.)
*Variants: Elizabeth, Liliana, Lilibet, Lily, Lilly*

**Lilith**
According to Assyro-Babylonian tradition Lilith was a female demon who roamed the wilderness on stormy nights and was a threat to newborn babies and little children. She is also said to have been the first wife of Adam who refused to submit to him and was banished from the Garden of Eden as a result. Lilith later became an evil spirit, an ugly demon.

The name is also associated with a serpent, screech-owl and a vampire. Given these dark connotations the name was rarely given to children but it has become symbolic within the feminist movement.
*Variants: Lilis, Lilita, Lillith, Lillus, Lily*

**Lily**
In the Sermon on the Mount Jesus asked his followers to 'Consider the lilies of the field, how they grow; they toil not, neither do they spin. And yet I say unto you that even Solomon in all his glory was not arrayed like one of these.'

The lily – the trumpet-shaped genus of flower – is connected with Christianity on another level. It has been portrayed in art as the symbol of purity. Of the 80 types of this flower one is called the Madonna lily, which is associated with the Virgin Mary.

Although this name was first recorded in the late 16th century it was not widely used as a name in England until the

1800s. Lily is also considered to be a short form of Elizabeth ('God is perfection').
*Variants: Elizabeth, Lilith, Lilibet, Lillian, Lilly*

### Lindsey

Like Leslie, Lindsey is an aristocratic Scottish surname which is now given to boys and girls as a first name. It was thought to have been originally borne by Sir Walter de Lindesay who was associated with King David I of Scotland.

In England Lindsey is a name connected with a family from the Lincolnshire district. Indeed Lindsey may stem from the Old English for a place name in Lincoln, meaning 'wetland' or 'waterside linden trees'.
*Variant: Lindsay*

### Linnea

Linnaea is a type of flower named after the 18th century Swedish botanist Carolus Linnaeus. It is the national flower of Sweden.
*Variants: Linea, Linna, Linnae, Linnaea, Lynea, Lynnea*

### Lisa

Widely regarded as a name in its own right, Lisa actually originated as a pet form of the name Elizabeth ('God is perfection'). It is a another form of Liza, which is a variant of Eliza. (See also Elizabeth.)
*Variants: Elisa, Elisabeth, Eliza, Elizabeth, Liza*

### Lois

During the 20th century through comic books, and later television and film, this name became synonymous with Superman. Lois Lane was the love interest of both the superhuman hero and his alter-ego Clark Kent.

But the name has a much longer history. It is actually Biblical and can be found in the New Testament as the name of Timothy's grandmother whose faith was praised by St Paul. This association with Christianity made Lois a favourite among the

Puritans who took the name with them to North America.

Its popularity was reinforced by the French names Heloise and Eloise, as Lois is a contracted form of both. (See also Heloise.) Equally it is a variant of the Germanic name Louise, which means 'famed' and 'warrior'.

Lois, which can be pronounced as either 'Lo-is' or 'Loy' may also be derived from the Greek for 'desirable' and 'good'.

*Variants: Eloise, Heloise, Louise*

## Lola

The 19th century Spanish dancer Lola Montez was neither from Spain nor called Lola. She was Eliza Gilbert who was born in Ireland in 1821. However the plucky performer adopted the stage name Lola and courted fame throughout Europe. French novelist Alexander Dumas was among her lovers before she caught the attention of Ludwig I of Bavaria. But he made the mistake of making his mistress the virtual ruler of his country. His people revolted, Ludwig I abdicated and Lola Montez ended her days in North America where she died in 1861.

Before Lola Montez the name was mostly found in Spanish-speaking countries as a short form of Dolores ('sorrows'). (See also Dolores.)

*Variants: Delores, Dolores, Lita, Lo, Lolita*

## Lolita

Since the publication of Vladimir Nabokov's 1955 controversial novel *Lolita* the name has been associated with underage sex. In the book Dolores Haze is the pre-teen object of the narrator's obsession. Thus the name has become associated with the pejorative term for a pubescent 'sex kitten'.

However, like Lola, Lolita is the short form of Dolores and thus means 'sorrows'. Before the book changed its perception in society Lolita was a popular name.

*Variants: Delores, Dolores, Lita, Lo, Lola, Loleta*

**Lonnie**
An independent name in its own right, Lonnie derives its meaning from Leona, which means 'lion' or 'bright'. (See also Leona)
*Variants: Eleanor, Elenora, Leona*

**Lora**
Laura comes from the Latin for 'laurel' and Lora is the German form of that name. However, Lora is also derived from the Latin for 'a thin wine made from grape husks'.
*Variants: Lara, Laura, Lauren, Lauryn, Lolly, Lori*

**Lorelei**
Lorelei is the name of a cliff near the River Rhine. According to German legend it was from this point that a siren would call luring sailors away from the rocks. As a name Lorelei is believed to mean 'song' or 'melody'.
*Variants: Lorelie, Lorilee, Lura, Lurette, Lurleen, Lurlene, Lurline*

**Lori**
Lori is a pet form of the names Lora, Laura and Lorraine. Thus it means 'laurel'.
*Variants: Laura, Laurie, Lora, Lorraine*

**Lorraine**
Although it stems from the French place name, Lorraine. It is little used as a first name in France. It has been favoured in England and North America since the 19th century.
*Variants: Laraine, Lauraine, Loraine, Lori*

**Lotus**
To be called a 'lotus eater' is to be described as someone who is a work-shy pleasure-seeker. The meaning of this term is connected to Homer's *Odyssey*, written in the 8th century BC. In the poem lotus is the fruit eaten by an imaginary African tribe that makes them drugged and lethargic.
   In China and India the fragrant lotus flower has a more

positive connotation. The aquatic bloom that is native to both Asia and Africa is powerful religious symbol of the past, present and future.

### Louise

It was the invading Germanic tribe the Franks who brought the name Clodowig with them when they conquered Gaul in the Dark Ages. Clovis, a variant of that name, which means 'famous battle', was the name of the first French king. Clovis eventually became Louis and Louise is its female equivalent. Louise was especially popular in 17th and 18th century Europe.

The variant Louisa was borne by Louisa May Alcott, the American author of the children's classic *Little Women*.
*Variants: Aloise, Eloise, Heloise, Louisa, Louisetta*

### Lourdes

Although the name is of uncertain origin, it is highly regarded within the Roman Catholic Church as the place in southern France where St Bernadette saw a vision of the Virgin Mary in February 1858.

In that same spot a healing spring was uncovered that is believed to cure the illnesses and physical handicaps of the faithful. Lourdes has been a place of pilgrimage ever since. The place name is now also a girl's name.
*Variant: Lola*

### Lowri

An independent name in its own right, Lowri is the Welsh form of Laura which comes from the Latin for 'laurel'.
*Variant: Laura*

### Loveday

This Old English name stems from a quaint tradition. The day of love was the day dedicated to reconciliation and children born on that date were given this name. Although Loveday was originally a unisex name it is now only given to girls.

## Lucinda

The Latin word 'lucere' means 'to shine, glitter or be light'. This was at the root of the name Lucia, which predated Lucinda. This longer variant first started making an appearance in the literary works of the 17th century. It was given to a character in *Don Quixote*, the 1605 novel by the Spanish author Miquel de Cervantes. By the 18th century the name was popular in England.
*Variants: Cindi, Cindy, Lucia, Lucy, Sindy*

## Lucretia

The name Lucretia is closely connected to the foundation of the Roman Republic. Lucretia was a Roman noblewoman who was raped by Sextus, the son of Tarquin, the despotic king. Devastated by what happened Lucretia gathered together the men in her family to tell them what Sextus did to her. She then committed suicide. Her husband and father led an uprising, which resulted in the kings being driven out of Rome. In their place a new republic was born.

Although the origin of the name is uncertain it is associated with the twin virtues of purity and chastity.
*Variants: Lucrece, Lucrecia, Lucretzia*

## Lucy

Although Lucy looks like a short form of Lucinda, the latter was actually derived from the former, via Lucia. Like Lucia, Lucy comes from the Latin for 'light' or 'bringer of light'. Lucille is another variant of this popular name.
*Variants: Luci, Lucia, Lucille, Lucinda*

## Lulie

Taken from the Middle English word 'lullen', Lulie means to 'soothe', 'cause sleep' or 'dispel fears'.

## Lulu

This pet form of Louise is now widely known as an independent name. Its Germanic interpretation is 'famed warrior' or

L

'famous battle', but it may also come from a Native American name that means 'rabbit'. As a diminutive of Lucy it borrows the meaning 'light'.
*Variants: Lleulu, Louise, Leu, Lucy*

**Luna**
According to Roman mythology Luna was the goddess of the moon. It is fitting, therefore, that her name means 'moon' or 'crescent'. The Latin name 'luna' is the root of many words associated with the moon such as 'lunacy', believed to the acute when the moon is full.
*Variant: Lunette*

**Lynne**
The exact origin of Lynne is uncertain. It may have been derived from the Welsh name Eluned, which means 'idol' or 'icon'. Equally it may have come from the short form of various names ending in 'line' such as Caroline.
   Another possible root is the Old English word 'hylynna' which means 'brook'.
*Variants: Eiluned, Eluned, Lin, Linn, Lynn*

**Lys**
Lys comes from the medieval French for 'lily'. It is also a variant of Lizi which stems from Elizabeth ('God is perfection').
*Variants: Elizabeth, Liz, Lizi, Lizzie*

**Lysandra**
Lysander was a Spartan general who lived during the 5th century BC. His name was derived from the Greek for 'free' and thus Lysander means 'freer of men'. Lysandra is the feminine equivalent.
*Variants: Sandie, Sandra, Sandy*

**Lyzelle**
The exact origin of this name is unknown but it is believed to mean 'beautiful'.

**Mabel**

The name Mabel is thought to stem from another source. It may be a derivation of the Latin word 'amabilis' or 'worthy of love' which developed into the name Amabel and Amabella. Sometime during the 12th century the 'A' was dropped from this name and Mabel was born.

*Variants: Amabel, Amabella, Mab, Mabell, Mabella, Mabelle, Mable, May, Maybell, Maybelle*

**Macy**

Although this name is popular in North America it is not derived from the well known department store, Macy's. Instead it is the transferred use of a surname that ultimately came from a French place name. Originally Macy meant 'Maccius' estate'.

*Variants: Macey, Maci, Macie*

**Madeline**

In the Bible Mary Magdalene was the reformed sinner who became a devoted follower of Christ. Her second name was not just another way of distinguishing her from the other Biblical Marys, it also told the reader where she came from. Magdala was a village by the Sea of Galilee.

Madeline is the French version of this Biblical place name.

*Variants: Madalain, Madaline, Madaliene, Madeleine, Magdalen, Magdalene, Magda*

**Madison**

Throughout the world this name is probably best known as a street name – Madison Avenue, New York City. However, before it became associated with a place in Manhattan, Madison was a surname. Madison means 'Matthew's son', 'Maud's son' or 'Madde's son' – Madde being a pet form of the name Madeline (see above).

As a first name it is given to both boys and girls in North America.

*Variants: Maddison, Maddy, Maddie*

**Madra**
Madra comes from the Spanish, and ultimately Latin, for 'mother'.
*Variant: Madre*

**Magdalene**
Mary Magdalene was the reformed sinner who bathed Christ's feet with her tears and dried them with her hair at the Last Supper. She was a constant and faithful follower of Jesus. In the Bible Mary can be found at the foot of the cross during Christ's crucifixion and she was one of the few people who discovered his empty tomb on Easter Sunday.

Mary's second name indicated where she was from. Magdala was a village located by the Sea of Galilee.

It is no surprise that the name of this well-known saint has been given to girls throughout history. While Madeleine was the variant used during the Middle Ages, Magdalene has had its place. Sometimes pronounced as 'Maud-e-lin' it has led to variants such as Maudlin and its short form Maude.

Whatever the pronunciation Magdalene is also thought to come from the Hebrew for 'high tower'. (See also Madeline.)
*Variants: Madalena, Madelena, Madeline, Madeleine, Magdalen, Magdalena, Maude, Maudlin*

**Mahalia**
Found to have Hebrew and Native American origins, Mahalia sometimes appeared in 17th century Britain. As a variant of the Biblical name Mahala, Mahalia comes from the Hebrew for 'barren' or 'tenderness'. In the Native American culture Mahalia means 'woman'.
*Variants: Mahala, Mahelia, Mahila, Mehala, Mehalah, Mehalia*

**Mahira**
Mahira has been found to have a number of meanings. It comes from the Hebrew and Italian for 'energetic' and 'quick' and from the Arabic for 'young' and 'horse'.
*Variant: Mehira*

### Maia

According to Greek mythology Maia was the daughter of Atlas and mistress of Zeus. A fair-haired woman she bore him his blond son Hermes. Her name comes from the Greek for 'nurse' or 'mother'.

In Roman mythology Maia was the goddess of springtime and growth. She was the Earth Mother after whom the month of May is named. Mercury and Jupiter were her children.
*Variants: Mae, Mai, May, Maya*

### Mairin

Mairin is the Irish form of Mary, which means 'dew of the sea'.
*Variants: Mary, Maureen*

### Majesta

Majesty is a word that means 'greatness' and 'grandeur', which is usually used when addressing royalty. Majesta comes from the Latin for majesty.

### Makani

Makani is a Hawaiian name that is given to both boys and girls. It means 'wind'.

### Malu

The Hawaiian name Malulani means 'beneath peaceful skies'. As a short form of this name Malu simply means 'peace'.
*Variant: Malulani*

### Manuela

This Spanish name is ultimately derived from the Biblical Emmanuel, which means 'God is with us'. The feminine equivalent of Emmanuel is Emmanuella and Manuela is the Spanish version.
*Variants: Emanuella, Emmanuela*

### Marcella

Marcella is the feminine form of Marcel which comes from the

Roman name Marcellus. In Roman mythology Mars was the god of war and it is this meaning that seams to be at the root of Marcellus and the names derived from it.

A 4th century saint who was a Roman noblewoman bore this name, which has been found in Britain since the 1600s.
*Variants: Marcela, Marcelle, Marcellina, Marcille, Marcelyn*

### Mardell
Mardell comes from the Old English for 'meadow near the sea'.

### Margaret
The various forms that Margaret has taken across the world throughout the ages demonstrate its enduring popularity. The same name is known as Marguerite in France, Margarita in Spanish-speaking countries and has produced the pet forms such as Maggie and Rita.

All stem from the same source – the Latin for 'pearl'. The French form Marguerite is the exception as here it means 'daisy' because that flower is associated with a saint bearing the name.

In Scotland, where the name was borne by the saint and queen Margaret I, it is especially popular.
*Variants: Greta, Maggie, Majorie, Margarita, Margaux, Margherita, Margot, Marguerite, Meg, Rita*

### Margot
The name Margot is of French origin. Usually pronounced without sounding the 't' Margot is a pet form of Marguerite – the French form of Margaret. Hence it means 'daisy' and 'pearl' (see above).
*Variants: Margaux, Margaret, Margo, Marguerite*

### Marigold
The marigold is a yellow and orange flower that was named after its gold hue. Originally it was simply called 'a gold', however, in the 14th century it became associated with the Virgin Mary. Thus the name stems from the Old English for 'Mary's gold'. At the turn of the last century this flower name

was especially popular with parents.
*Variants: Goldie, Goldy, Mari, Marie, Mary, Marygold*

**Maria**
A variant of the Biblical name Mary, Maria is also related to the earlier name Miriam. It comes from the Hebrew for 'longed for child' and 'rebellion'.
*Variants: Mariah, Mariam, Mary, Maryam, Miriam*

**Mariah**
Mariah is a variant of the name Maria (see above) which has now become a first name in its own right. Although it shares the Hebrew meaning for Mary and Maria ('longed for child', 'rebellion'), Mariah is also said to come from the Latin for 'bitter' and 'God is my teacher'.
*Variants: Maria, Mariam, Mary, Maryam, Miriam*

**Marilyn**
Marilyn is yet another elaboration of Mary and is indeed a combination of two names – Mary ('longed for child') and Lyn ('brook' or 'idol'). (See also Mary and Lynne.)

In the second half of the 20th century the name Marilyn became inextricably linked to the screen goddess Marilyn Monroe.
*Variants: Lyn, Lynne, Mari, Marilynn, Mary, Marylyn, Marylynn*

**Marina**
A marina is a harbour specially designed to accommodate yachts and small boats. Unsurprisingly the word comes from the Latin 'marinus', meaning 'belong to the sea' or 'produced by the sea'. It is from this word that the girl's name Marina is derived.

In 20th century Britain the popularity of the name soared thanks to the marriage between Princess Marina of Greece and Prince George, the Duke of Kent. The couple married in 1934 and such was her popularity that a shade of blue-green was named marina blue in her honour.
*Variants: Mare, Maren, Marena, Maris, Marissa, Marna, Marne, Rina*

**Marini**

Of African origin, this name comes from the Swahili for 'healthy', 'fresh' and 'pretty'.

**Marissa**

Like Mariah and Marilyn, Marissa is an elaboration of the Biblical name Mary. Consequently it comes from the Hebrew for 'longed for child' and 'rebellion'. Marissa, which is sometimes spelt with one 's', also comes from the Latin for 'of the sea'.
*Variants: Mareesa, Mari, Maria, Mariah, Marie, Marina, Marisa, Mary, Risa, Rissa*

**Marquita**

A marquee is a large tent that is used as a venue for social occasions. The name Marquita comes from the French for this word.
*Variant: Marquite*

**Martha**

For centuries the name Martha has been associated with hard work and the roots of this link can be found in the Bible. In the New Testament Martha was the sister of Lazarus, the young man who Jesus raised from the dead. She was also the sister of Mary. But while Mary sat and listened to Christ's stories during his visit to their house, Martha diligently attended to the housework, complaining to Jesus about her sister as she did so.

The name comes from the Aramaic for 'lady'. It was borne by Martha Washington, the wife of the first American president, George Washington.
*Variants: Mardi, Marta, Marthe, Martie, Mat, Mattie, Matty, Pattie, Patty*

**Marva**

Marva is taken from the Hebrew word for the fragrant herb, 'sage'.

**Mary**

One of the most popular Biblical names of all time belongs to the mother of Jesus, the Virgin Mary. According to the Christmas story Mary was betrothed to the carpenter Joseph when the Archangel Gabriel appeared to her. He told the teenager that she would give birth to the Son of God and the conception would be brought about by the Holy Spirit, not through intercourse with a man.

Though the mother of Jesus is the most well known Mary in the Bible the name is borne by others in the New Testament including Mary of Magdalene and Mary the sister of Martha and Lazarus. In the Old Testament the name appears as Miriam and comes from the Hebrew for 'sea of bitterness' or 'child of our wishes'.

The popularity of the name Mary has led to a plethora of variants and short forms, some of which have gone on to be independent names in their own right. They include Maria, Mariah, Marissa, Moira and Maureen. Mary has also been used in numerous compounds including Marilyn, Marianne and Marylou.

The name was especially popular in North America where it was consistently the first choice for baby girls in the 19th, and well into the 20th, century. In England and Wales Mary was also the favourite of parents during the 18th and 19th centuries.
*Variants: Maria, Mariah, Marianne, Marie, Marilyn, Marissa, Marylou, Maureen, Moira, Molly*

**Marylou**
The names Mary ('bitterness' and 'longed for child') and Louise ('famed battle') were joined together to form this name.
*Variant: Lou, Louise, Marie, Marilou, Mary, Miriam*

**Matilda**
The Normans brought the name Matilda to English shores. This distinctly Germanic name was borne by the wife of William the Conqueror. It is made up of two elements – 'maht', or in English 'might', and 'hild', which means 'battle'. The name Hilda shares the same Germanic root.

The French translated Mahthilda into Maheud, which the English transformed into Maude – now an independent name.

The granddaughter of William the Conqueror, Empress Maud, was also called Matilda. The name is also associated with the popular Australian song *Waltzing Matilda*.
*Variants: Matelda, Mathilda, Matildis, Matti, Maud, Maude, Maudie, Mawde, Tilda, Tillie*

## May

The name May is commonly associated with the springtime month, which was named after the Roman goddess Maia. However, the popularity of May was strengthened by its use as a pet form to other well known names. As a short form of Mary it assumes the Hebrew meaning of 'longed for child' and as a diminutive of Margaret it becomes 'pearl'.

During the month of May the Romans celebrated the festival of spring, fertility and birth. That tradition continues in some form today as many calendars around the world recognise May Day, 1 May, as a public holiday. However the link between the festival and springtime has not always been maintained.

In Wales May took the form of Mai and in America it is often spelt with an 'e' instead of a 'y'. (See also Maia.)
*Variants: Mai, Maia, Mae, Margaret, Mary, Maya, Maybelle, Mei*

## Mavis

Little used as a given name before the 19th century, Mavis is derived from the Old French 'mauvis', which means 'song thrush'.
*Variants: Mave, Maeve,*

## Meave

Taken from the Irish word 'meadhbh', Meave means 'joy'. However, as a variant of Maeve it also means 'intoxicating'.
*Variants: Maeve, Meaveen*

## Meera

This Indian name means 'saintly woman'. But it also has the meaning 'radiant' and 'light' in Hebrew.

### Megan

In Scotland and Wales Meg is a pet form of Margaret, which means 'pearl'. Megan is the Welsh elaboration of Meg.
*Variants: Maegan, Maygen, Meag(h)an*

### Melanie

In Greek mythology Melanion won the hand of Atalanta by beating her in a race. Legend has it that the speedy Atalanta successfully competed against all but one of her suitors. To win her hand Melanion knew he had to win the race so he asked the goddess Aphrodite for a solution. She gave him three golden apples which he threw down as he ran. He won the competition because Atalanta, distracted by the apples, slowed down long enough to pick them up. Melanion's name was derived from the Greek for 'black' or 'dark complexion'.

In the 5th century two saints bore the female version of that name, Melania. Although it was re-introduced to England in the early 1900s it was first imported from France during the Middle Ages.
*Variants: Melany, Melony*

### Mercy

This Christian quality was used by Charles Dickens as a name for one of his characters in his 1843 novel *Martin Chuzzlewit*. To have 'mercy' on someone is to be 'compassionate' and to 'pity' them. The phrase 'God's mercy' also demonstrates his forgiveness of sinners, hence the popularity of the name among the 17th century Puritans.

Mercedes is the Spanish equivalent of this name. Another version, Mercia, was an Anglo-Saxon kingdom.
*Variants: Mercedes, Merica, Mercille, Merry*

### Merit

Of Latin origin, Merit comes from the word 'meritus', which means 'earned' and 'deserved'.
*Variant: Merritt*

### Merle

Though often thought of as a girl's name, in North America Merle is also given to boys. Country music veteran Merle Haggard, who was born in 1937, is a perfect example of its use as a man's name. However in Britain Merle, or the variant Merlene, is traditionally given to baby girls.

The name comes from the Latin for 'blackbird'. As a variant of Muriel, Merle comes from the Irish Gaelic for 'sea' and 'bright'.

In the 1930s the popularity of the name increased thanks to the fame of the actress Merle Oberon.

*Variants: Merla, Merlene, Merlina, Muriel, Myrl, Myrle*

### Merrie

In Charles Dickens' novel *Martin Chuzzlewit* Merry was used as a pet name. The sisters Charity and Mercy were also known as Cherry and Merry.

The word 'merry' comes from the Old English for 'pleasant', 'festive' and 'jolly' and from the Hebrew for 'rebellious'. But as the pet form of other names Merry has taken on more than one meaning. When it is used as a variant of Mercy (as Dickens did) it means 'compassion', 'pity' or 'clemency'. As a short form of the Welsh name Meredith it means 'magnificent chief'.

*Variants: Mercy, Meredith, Merry*

### Mia

The Italian name Mia can be pronounced in one of two ways, either as 'Me-ah' or as 'My-ah'. Its meaning is derived from the Latin for 'mine'.

### Michaela

This feminine form of Michael comes from the Hebrew for 'who is like God'.

*Variants: Miia, Mica, Michael, Michaelle, Michelle, Mikelina*

### Michelle

Like Michaela, Michelle is a feminine form of the Biblical name

Michael, which means 'who is like God' It is of French origin.
During the 1960s interest in this name soared thanks to the
popularity of The Beatles' hit song *Michelle*.
*Variants: Chelle, Michael, Michaela, Michaelle, Shell*

### Milly

Although it is widely considered to be an independent name in
its own right Milly began life as a short form of a number of
names. They include Amelia ('toil'), Camilla ('one who helps at
sacrifices'), Mildred ('gentle stength') and Millicent ('strong
worker', 'determined'). As a short form of all these names Milly
has adopted these meanings. However, it also comes from the
Israeli for 'who is for me?'.
*Variants: Amelia, Camilla, Mildred, Millicent, Millie*

### Mina

Mina has a number of meanings from the Old German word for
'love', the Japanese for 'south' and the Persian for 'daisy'. It is
also a short form of the German name Wilhelmina, which means
'will' and 'protection'.
*Variants: Minella, Minna, Minnie, Wilhelmina, Willa, Wilma*

### Mirabel

Although Mirabel was used by the Victorians it was actually
common in Europe during the Middle Ages. The name is derived
from the Latin word 'mirabilis', which means 'marvellous',
'admirable' and 'lovely'. It is also related to the Spanish for
'beautiful'. Mirabella is the Italian version.
*Virants: Bella, Belle, Mira, Mirabella, Mirabelle, Mirella*

### Miranda

Like Mirabel, Miranda is derived from the Latin for 'wonderful'
and 'admirable'. But it also comes from the Latin word
'mirandus', which means 'to be wondered at'.

The name has also been used by playwrights and authors:
Shakespeare in his play *The Tempest* whilst D H Lawrence

featured a character called Miranda in his novel *Sons and Lovers*.
*Variants: Maranda, Marenda, Meranda, Mina, Mira, Mirabel, Mirinda, Myranda, Randi, Randy*

**Miriam**
In the Bible Miriam was the sister of Moses and Aaron who led the rejoicing after the Israelites crossed the Red Sea. In Hebrew it means 'longed for child' and 'rebellion' and it is from this source that Mary is derived. An earlier form of the name is Maryam.
*Variants: Maria, Marian, Marianne, Mary, Maryam, Meryem, Mimi, Minnie, Mitzi*

**Misty**
Misty comes from the Old English for 'clouded' and 'obscure'. As a girl's name it is popular in North America.
*Variants: Misti, Mistie, Mystee, Mysti, Mystie, Mystique*

**Moira**
In Ireland the Biblical name Mary was transformed into the Gaelic name Maire which, when Anglicised, became Moira. Hence, Moira comes from the Hebrew for 'longed for child' and 'rebellion'.

Aside from the Biblical origin of his name, in Greek mythology the Moirae were the Three Fates who were the embodiment of destiny. Clotho spun the thread of life, Lachesis was the drawer of lots or the goddess of luck and Atropos represented the inevitable or inescapable fate, cutting the thread.
*Variants: Maire, Mary, Maura, Maureen, Miriam, Moirae, Moreen, Moyra*

**Molly**
Molly is another short form of Mary. Thus it shares the Hebrew meaning 'longed for child' and 'rebellion'. Originally the pet form of Mary was Mally, which eventually became Molly.
*Variant: Mary*

**Mona**

In 1503 the Italian painter Leonardo da Vinci started painting the portrait that would henceforth become known as the Mona Lisa. The exact origin of this name is unknown, but there has been no shortage of theories about its meaning. One possibility is that Mona stems from the Greek for 'alone' or 'just'. In Ireland Mona is thought to have been derived from three different Gaelic words 'noble', 'nun' and 'angel', but in Arabic there is only one meaning 'wish'. The Old English interpretation is 'month'. Another equally legitimate possibility is that Mona came from the Latin name for the Welsh island, Anglesea.

Mona also appears as a short form of Monica, which means 'to advise'.

*Variants: Madonna, Monica, Monique, Monna, Moyna, Muna*

**Monica**

St Monica is recognised by the Roman Catholic Church as the mother of St Augustine. She was born in Algeria in 322 and was frequently mentioned in the writings of her famous son.

Monica's name comes from the Latin 'monire', which means 'to warn'. It is also derived from the Latin for 'to counsel' and 'to advise'.

*Variants: Mona, Monique*

**Morag**

This Irish Gaelic name was popular in Scotland during the 20th century. It means 'great', 'sun' and 'young one'. But, as the Scottish version of Sarah, it also shares the Hebrew meaning 'princess'.

*Variants: Marion, Moirin, Moreen, Sarah*

**Morgan**

According to Arhurian legend Morgan Le Fay was the half-sister of King Arthur. Her name comes from the Welsh for 'sea' and 'bright' or 'great' and 'born'. In North America Morgan is given to both boys and girls. In Britain it is frequently found as a surname.

*Variant: Morgana*

## Morwenna

Borne by a little known 5th century saint, the Welsh name Morwenna was especially popular during the Middle Ages. It is derived from the word 'morwyn', which means 'a maiden'.

In the 20th century Morwenna was favoured by Welsh parents as a symbol of their nationalism. It is also thought to be related to Maureen, an Irish version of Mary ('longed for child').

*Variants: Maureen, Morwen, Morwyn, Wenna, Wennie, Wenny*

## Muriel

Muriel was brought to the British Isles by William the Conqueror's Celts from Brittany. Thus the name comes from the Irish words 'muir' ('sea') and 'geal' ('bright').

*Variants: Marial, Meriel, Merril, Merrill, Meryl, Muriell, Murielle*

## Myfanwy

First found in medieval times this Welsh name means 'rare one' or 'my treasure'. It was revived during the 19th century and spawned the short form Fanny.

*Variants: Fanni, Fannie, Fanny, Myf, Myfi, Myfina*

## Myrna

According to the Christmas story the Three Wise Men brought the baby Jesus gifts of gold, frankincense and myrrh. It is from this reddish brown material that the Arabic name Myrna is derived. Considered to be valuable in ancient times, myrrh was frequently used in perfumes and incense.

Myrna also has roots in Ireland and is thought to be a variant of the Irish name Muirne, which means 'blood'.

*Variants: Merna, Mirna, Morna, Muirna, Muirne*

## Naama

Naama comes from the Hebrew for 'beautiful' and 'pleasant' and the Arabic for 'good fortune'.

*Variants: Naamah, Naava*

### Nadia

Nadia is the pet form of the Russian name Nadezhda, which means 'hope'. The French variant of this name is Nadine. Nadia is also believed to come from the Spanish for 'nothing' and from the Arabic word 'nazir' or 'opposite to zenith'.

In the English-speaking world Nadia grew in popularity during the 20th century.

*Variants: Nada, Nadeen, Nadie, Nadina, Nadine, Nadja, Nadka*

### Naia

In Greek mythology the Naiads were water nymphs who dwelled in rivers, brooks, streams, fountains, ponds and lakes. Blessed with the gift of prophecy, they had the ability to heal the sick and were associated with fertility. Though they lived for thousands of years they were destined always to look young. Fittingly the name Naia comes from the Greek for 'to flow'.

*Variants: Naiad, Naida, Naiia, Nalda*

### Nancy

The name Nancy has a long history that stretches back to the Biblical name Hannah. Hannah comes from the Hebrew for 'God has favoured me'. It is from Hannah that the name Anne was derived and Nancy was a pet form of Anne as far back as the 18th century.

Nancy may also be related to the name Agnes which comes from the Greek 'hagnos' meaning 'pure' or 'holy'. (See also Agnes, Anne and Hannah.)

*Variants: Agnes, Ann, Anna, Anne, Hannah, Nance, Nancie, Nanette*

### Nanette

Nanette is the French version of the name Nancy, which is a pet form of Anne, itself a derivative of Hannah ('God has favoured me').

It is now considered independently of Nancy, Anne or Hannah.

*Variants: Ann, Anna, Anne, Hannah, Nance, Nancie, Nancy, Nannie, Nanny*

### Naomi

Naomi is another Biblical name that proved popular with the Puritans of the 17th century. It comes from the Hebrew for 'delightful', 'pleasant' and 'charming' and for good reason. In the Old Testament Naomi and her family were Israelites living in the land of Maob. When her husband and sons died Naomi decided to return to her homeland, but her daughter-in-law Ruth, a Maobite refused to leave her side. She loved her mother-in-law so much that she determined to leave her birthplace and go to Israel with her.

*Variants: Nae, Naome, Noemi, Nomi*


### Natalie

The Latin word 'natalis' means 'anniversary', 'birthday' or 'festival' and traditionally it is associated with the birth of Christ. Thus like Noel, which is the French for Christmas, the name Natalie is linked to the festive season.

Natalia, Natalya and Talia are the Russian forms of the name. Nathalie is the French spelling.

*Variants: Natalia, Natalya, Natasha, Natassia, Nathalie, Talia*


### Natasha

Natasha is sometimes given to girls as the feminine version of Nathan, which comes from the Hebrew for 'gift'. However, it is more commonly seen as the Russian pet form of the name Natalie.

As mentioned above, Natalie is derived from the Latin for 'birthday' or 'anniversary'. But the Russian pet form Natasha was given prominence in Leo Tolstoy's classic novel *War and Peace*, published from 1865 to 1868. In the English-speaking world the name proved popular from the 1960s onwards.

*Variants: Natacha, Natalia, Natalie, Natalya, Nathalie, Natasja, Natassia, Tasha*


### Nayer

Nayer is taken from the Persian for 'sunshine'.

### Nebula
This name comes from the Latin for 'mist', 'smoke' and 'darkness'.

### Nell
Eleanor Gwyn, the English actress who died in 1687, was the most famous mistress of King Charles II. The name she was given at birth betrays the origin of her pet name, the one that she is more commonly known by – Nell.

Now an independent name, Nell is also a pet form of Ellen and Helen. Ellen and Eleanor share the Greek meaning of Helen – 'bright'.
*Variants: Eleanor, Ellen, Helen, Nellie, Nelly*

### Neoma
Neoma comes from the Greek word 'neomenia', which means 'new moon'.

### Nerissa
The exact origin of Nerissa is unknown but the name was used by Shakespeare in his play *The Merchant of Venice*. Nerissa was maid to the wealthy heiress Portia.

In Greek mythology the Nereids were the daughters of Nereus, the god of the sea. Thus the name Nerissa is believed to mean 'sea nymphs'.
*Variants: Nerida, Nerina*

### Nerys
Nerys derives its meaning from the Welsh word 'ner', which stands for 'lord'. Although it has long been in the Welsh vocabulary it has only come into use as a girl's name within recent times.

### Ngaire
This Antipodean name comes from the Maori word, 'ngaio' which means 'clever'.
*Variant: Ngaio*

### Niamh

Irish mythology holds that Niamh was a goddess who fell in love with Oisin, and took him back with her to Tir na n'Og – the land of youth where there was no sadness, dying or ageing.

Pronounced as 'Neev' Niamh means 'bright'. In Wales the name is shortened to Nia, which as a first name comes from the Swahili word for 'purpose'.

*Variants: Nia, Niar*

### Nicole

The boy's name Nicholas comes from the Greek for 'people's victory'. Nicola is the Italian feminine form of the name and Nicole and Nicolette are popular in France. Nicole has enjoyed great popularity in North America.

*Variants: Nichole, Nicola, Nicolette, Nicci*

### Nikita

Although Nikita is currently perceived as a girl's name, it was originally a boy's name in Russia that came from the Greek for 'unconquered'. But it is also an Indian name that means 'the earth'. Like Nicole, Nikita is popular among North American parents.

### Nissa

Nissa has meanings in both Hebrew and African. Its Hebrew meaning is 'sign', 'emblem' or 'to test'. But it also comes from the Hausa for 'never forgotten loved one'.

*Variants: Nissie, Nissy*

### Nokomis

This Native American name means 'daughter of the moon'.

### Nola

As the feminine version of the Irish name Nolan, Nola means 'son of the noble one'. However, it is also derived from the Celtic name Fionnuala, which means 'fair-shouldered'.

*Variants: Fiona, Fionnuala, Nolana, Noleen, Nolene, Nuala*

## Nona

In Victorian England, when big families were common, Nona was bestowed upon the ninth child if she were a baby girl for the name comes from the Latin for 'ninth'. Nona could also be given to babies born in September, the ninth month in the calendar, or to those born on the ninth day of any month.

The name is also associated with the Roman goddess of foetal development.
*Variants: Noni, Nonie*

## Norah

Eleanor, Leonora and Honoria are all shortened to form the name Norah. As a variant of Eleanor and Leonora this short form assumes the Greek meaning for Helen 'bright' or 'light'. Honoria provides Norah with the meaning 'honour'.

In Ireland, where it is especially popular, Norah is sometimes adopted as a derivative of Nuala and ultimately Fionnuala ('fair-shouldered').
*Variants: Eleanor, Fionnuala, Helen, Honoria, Honor, Nora*

## Nova

In astronomy a nova is a star that burns brightly for a time but eventually returns to its normal state in a few weeks, months or years. Both the word and the name come from the Latin 'novus', which means 'new', 'newcomer'.
*Variant: Novia*

## Nuala

Nuala is another popular Irish name that is derived from the Celtic name Fionnuala ('fair-shouldered'). It is pronounced 'New-la'.
*Variants: Fenella, Fionnghuala, Fionnuala, Nola, Nora*

## Octavia

Octavia comes from the Latin for 'eighth', thus traditionally the name was given to the eighth child in a family.

Octavia may have also been derived from the Ancient Roman

family name, Octavius. The first Roman emperor, Augustus Gaius Julius Octavius, was born in 63 BC. His sister, Octavia, married Mark Antony.
*Variants: Octavio, Octtavia, Tave, Tavia, Tavy*

**Odessa**
Written by the Greek poet Homer, *The Odyssey* recounts the story of Odysseus, the king of Ithaca, who spent 10 years trying to return home after the fall of Troy. His name, and the female equivalent Odessa, means 'extended wandering' or 'epic voyage'.

**Olga**
The first Russian state was established by Scandinavian settlers in the 9th century and with them they brought the name Olga. Olga comes from an Old Norse adjective that means 'prosperous' and 'successful'.

Although it was not introduced into the English-speaking world until the late 19th century it was born by a saint, Olga of Kiev, who died in 969. This Russian saint, who was baptised in Constantinople (Istanbul), helped the spread of Christianity.
*Variants: Helga, Ola, Olenka, Olia, Olina, Olli, Ollie*

**Olive**
Olives are the fruit of the evergreen tree that is grown in the Mediterranean. They can be eaten alone, used in food or pressed into oil, but traditionally the branches of that tree have been offered as symbol of peace. Consequently the name Olive is taken from the Latin word 'oliva' and is associated with peace. In Greece brides traditionally carry an olive garland and the wreath is seen as a mark of success.
*Variant: Olivia*

**Olivia**
Like Olive the name Olivia is associated with the olive tree and the symbol of peace. It is also considered to be the female equivalent of Oliver, which shares the same Latin root 'oliva'.

However, Oliver may have also been derived from the Old Norse for 'ancestor, remains'.

Olivia has been in currency in Britain since the Middle Ages and Shakespeare used the name for the heroine of his 1599 play *Twelfth Night*. Although Livia is a pet form of Olivia it also comes from the Roman family name Livius and was borne by the wife of the Emperor Augustus.
*Variants: Livia, Livvy, Oliva, Olive*

## Olwyn

In Celtic mythology Olwyn was the daughter of the giant Ysbadden, who would die if he were separated from his offspring. Prince Culhwch wanted to win Olwyn's hand in marriage and to do so he had to perform a series of difficult tasks.

According to Welsh legend Olwyn was so-called because her footprints were covered in white clover. Her name is made from the word 'ôl', 'footprint' and '(g)wen', which means 'white' or 'fair'.
*Variants: Olwen, Olwin*

## Olympia

It is the tallest mountain in Greece but, according to the mythology of that country, Mount Olympus was also the heavenly abode of the gods and goddesses. It is from this place that the Olympic Games derived their name, for they were held every four years in honour of the great Olympian, the supreme god Zeus.

The girl's name Olympias was later borne by the mother of Alexander the Great, the king of Macedon who conquered Persia and Egypt. She died in 316 BC, but the 4th century St Olympia helped the name to become popular throughout Europe.
*Variants: Olimpia, Olimpie, Olympias*

## Omega

In the Greek language omega stands for 'O', the last letter of the Greek alphabet. Traditionally it was given to the last child in the family.
*Variant: Mega*

**Opal**
The Sanskrit word 'upalas' means 'precious stone' and like Diamond, Emerald, Ruby and Crystal, Opal is a gemstone that is now used as a girl's name. Opals are pale in colour and are said to bring luck.

**Ophelia**
Ophelia is thought to be a name created by Shakespeare and derived from the Greek word 'ophelos', which means 'help'. In his play *Hamlet* Ophelia is the tragic girlfriend of the lead character and the daughter of Polonius, an advisor to King Claudius. When Hamlet kills her father accidentally Ophelia goes mad and drowns herself.

Although the name featured in a Shakespearian play it did not become popular until the 19th century.
*Variants: Ofelia, Ofilia, Ophelie*

**Orchid**
Like Daisy, Orchid is a girl's name derived from a flower. The flower is considered to be exotic, rare and is generally associated with luxury.

**Orla**
The name Orla comes from the Irish for 'golden lady' or 'golden princess'.
*Variants: Orfhlaith, Orlagh*

**Paige**
In medieval times a 'page' was a young boy who attended a knight as the first step in becoming a knight himself. The occupational title became a surname and in modern times has become a girl's first name. It was especially popular in 1980s North America.

The name comes from the Greek for 'child' and the Italian for 'page boy'.
*Variant: Page*

## Palma

Christian crusaders who went to the Holy Land were known as Palmers because they returned from their journey with crosses made from palm leaves. But the name Palma is probably derived from the Latin word 'palmus' which means 'the palm of the hand'.

Traditionally a large palm is associated with victory, success and happiness.

*Variants: Palmeda, Palmer, Palmyra, Pelmira*

## Pamela

The name Pamela was the creation of the English poet Sir Philip Sidney who used it in his 1580 work *Arcadia*. The Greek words 'pau' ('all') and 'meli', ('honey') were believed to be the source of his inspiration.

However, the name only became popular once it was used by another English writer, Samuel Richardson in *Pamela: or Virtue Rewarded* (1740).

*Variants: Pam, Pamelia, Pamelina, Pamella, Pammi, Pammy*

## Pandora

Pandora was the first woman, created by Zeus for the confusion of men. She was given a box that she was forbidden to open, but her curiousity got the better of her and out spilled all the evils of the world. The only positive present to be released from the box was hope.

Pandora's name comes from the Greek for 'all gifts' or 'gift in everything'. The phrase 'Pandora's box' stems from this story.

*Variant: Panda*

## Paris

The capital city of France is associated with elegance, sophistication and romance. But as a given name Paris was originally bestowed upon boys. Indeed Paris was the name of the Trojan prince who instigated the 10-year Trojan War by stealing Helen, the wife of Menelaus and queen of Sparta.

Paris is now a common first name for girls.

## Patience

Early Christians associated the virtue of patience with those who suffered persecution because of their faith without complaint or loss of devotion. The word comes from the Latin word 'pati', which means 'to suffer'.

As a given name Patience was popular with the Puritans of the 17th century.

*Variants: Pat, Pattie, Patty*

## Patricia

The feminine form of Patrick. The origins stem from the Latin for 'noble one'.

*Variants: Patrice, Patrizia, Patsy, Patty, Pattie, Pat, Tricia, Trish, Tish, Rickie, Ricky*

## Paula

Paula is the feminine form of the boy's name Paul. St Paul was originally known as Saul, a man who persecuted Christians during Biblical times. However, after seeing Christ in a vision on the road to Damascus he changed his belief and subsequently his name. Paul comes from the Latin for 'small'.

The girl's name Paula was carried across Europe by a saint of the same name. Born in 347, she was the founder of a number of convents in Bethlehem. Paulette is the French version of the name and Paola is the Italian equivalent. (See also Paul.)

*Variants: Paola, Pauletta, Paulette, Paulina, Pauline, Paulita*

## Peace

The name is taken from the Latin 'pax', which means 'peace'.

*Variants: Paz*

## Pearl

Pearl is sometimes used as a pet form of the name Margaret, and for good reason. The Greek word for 'pearl' is 'margaretes'. As a name in its own right Pearl became popular among parents during the late 19th century when it was extremely fashionable to bestow gemstone names on girls.

However the name Pearl boasts a much longer history. The variant Perle is an Anglicised version of the Yiddish name Penninah, which means 'coral'. The name was borne by the co-wife of Elkanah, the father of Samuel.

*Variants: Margaret, Pearlie, Pearline, Peninnah, Pennina, Perla, Perle*

**Penelope**

In Homer's *The Odyssey* Penelope is the faithful wife of Odysseus who, for 20 years, faithfully waits for his return. During that time she is approached by a string of suitors, all who want to marry her so that they can control the kingdom. She promises to remarry, but only after she has woven a shroud for her father-in-law. Cunningly Penelope weaves all day and unpicks her work at night, thus she never completes her task and her devotion to her husband remains unbroken. Thus Penelope means 'weaver'.

*Variants: Penelopa, Pennie, Penny, Popi*

**Peta**

This Scandinavian feminine version of the name Peter was little used before the 1930s. In the Bible Saint Peter was one of Christ's apostles and his name comes from the Latin and Greek for 'stone' or 'rock'. (See also Peter.)

*Variant: Pet, Petra*

**Petra**

In Latin and Greek the word 'petra' means 'stone'. Thus, Petra, like Peta, is a female equivalent of Peter. (See also Peta and Peter.)

*Variants: Pet, Peta, Petie*

**Petula**

The exact origin of Petula is uncertain but it is thought to come from the Latin for 'forward', 'saucy' and 'impudent'. Another possibility is that it came from the Latin word 'petulare' meaning 'to ask'.

There is a theory that Petula is connected to the plant name 'petunia' or that it is an elaboration of 'pet' – an English term of endearment.

## Phoebe

Phoebe is also a Biblical name and was mentioned by Paul who associated it with a Corinthian woman in the New Testament. The name comes from the Greek and the Latin for 'bright' and 'shining'. The name Phoebe was borne by more than one person in Greek mythology. It was the alternative name for Artemis, the goddess of the moon and sister of Apollo who was known as Diana to the Romans. It was also the name of her grandmother, one of the original Titans.
*Variant: Phebe*

## Phoenix

In Ancient Egypt the phoenix was regarded as a sacred bird that was said to live for 500 years. At the end of its life it would set itself and its nest alight and from the ashes a new bird would arise.

The Greeks also had a myth surrounding the phoenix. To them it was a bird that dwelled in Arabia and bathed in the water of a well each morning. Apollo, the sun god, always stopped to listen.

Phoenix comes from the Greek word 'phyllidis', which means 'leafy branch'. The name Phillis shares the same root.
*Variants: Phillis, Phyllida, Phylis, Phyllis*

## Philippa

The Biblical name Philip is a combination of the Greek words 'philos', 'loving' and 'hippos', 'horse'. Thus Philip and its feminine equivalent Philippa mean 'someone who loves horses'.
*Variants: Felipa, Filipa, Phillipa, Philly, Pippa*

## Pippa

This pet form of Philippa is now independently given as a name. In England the name became more popular following the

publication of Robert Browning's 1841 poem, *Pippa Pauses*.
*Variants: Felipa, Filipa, Philippa, Phillipa, Philly, Pip*

**Poppy**
In the United Kingdom red poppies are worn during the month
of November to commemorate the soldiers who died in the two
World Wars and subsequent conflicts. This emblem was chosen
because red poppies littered the battlefields of Flanders during
the Great War of 1914 to 1918.

The word was derived from the Old English 'popaeg'. As a
girl's name it has been in use since the turn of the last century
and it was especially popular during the 1920s.
*Variants: Poppi, Poppie*

**Portia**
William Shakespeare used the name Portia for characters in
two of his plays. In the historically-based *Julius Caesar* Portia
was the wife of Brutus, the man who played a pivotal role in
the plot to assassinate the Roman emperor. In *The Merchant of
Venice* Portia was the cross-dressing heroine who disguised
herself as a man.

As a girl's name Portia is derived from the old Roman
family name Porcius, which comes from the Latin for 'pig'.
*Variants: Porsha, Porsche, Porchia, Porshia*

**Precious**
To say something or someone is 'precious' is to suggest they are
'invaluable', 'priceless' and 'treasured'. Often used as a term of
endearment, it is now also given to baby girls.

**Primrose**
Like Daisy and Rose, Primrose is a flower name that became
popular with parents during the turn of the last century. The
plant, with its pale yellow flowers, derives its name from the
Latin 'prima rosa' meaning 'first rose'.
*Variant: Rose*

**Priscilla**

The Biblical Priscilla was a follower and supporter of St Paul. Her name was derived from the Latin word 'priscus', which meant 'ancient', 'old-fashioned' and 'antique'. The Roman family name Priscus came from the same root.

*Variants: Cilla, Precilla, Prescilla, Pricilla, Pris, Prissy, Silla*

**Quintana**

This name derives its meaning from the Latin word for 'fifth', traditionally given to the fifth child, or to a baby born in May, or on the fifth day of a month.

*Variants: Quinn, Quinta, Quintilla, Quintina*

**Quinn**

Like Quintana, Quinn is associated with the Latin word for 'fifth'. However it is also a variant of the name Queenie, which comes from the Old English and Old Norse for 'wife', 'companion' and 'woman'. Queenie also means 'ruler' or 'queen'.

During the Middle Ages the name was associated with the Queen of Heaven, the Virgin Mary, but during the 19th century it was often used in reference to Queen Victoria.

*Variants: Queenie, Quintana, Quinta, Quintilla, Quintina*

**Rachel**

The name Rachel comes from the Hebrew for 'ewe', a female sheep. In the Bible it was borne by the beautiful second wife of Jacob. She was the mother of his last two sons – Joseph and Benjamin.

Upon meeting Rachel, Jacob laboured seven years to win her hand, but on the wedding night he realised that his father-in-law had tricked him into marrying her older sister Leah. Although Jacob later took Rachel as a second wife, she died in childbirth. (See also Leah.)

*Variants: Rachael, Rachele, Racheli, Raquel, Ray, Raye, Rochell, Shell, Shelley*

**Raquel**

Although this name is considered to be an independent name in its own right, it is actually the Spanish form of Rachel. As mentioned above Rachel is derived from the Hebrew for 'ewe'. In the 1960s the name was popularised by the actress Raquel Welch who was born Raquel Tejada in 1940.

*Variants: Rachael, Rachel, Rachelle, Raquelle*

**Rashida**

In Sanskrit and Arabic Rashida means 'follower of the correct path'. It is the feminine equivalent of Rashid.

*Variants: Rasheeda, Rashi*

**Reba**

This modern name is believed to be a short form of Rebecca. In the Bible Rebecca is the wife of Isaac and her name comes from the Hebrew and Aramaic for 'knotted cord'.

*Variants: Bec, Becca, Becky, Rebecca, Rebekah*

**Rebecca**

In the Bible, Rebecca was the wife of Isaac and the mother of Esau and Jacob. She conspired with Jacob to trick her blind and elderly husband into bestowing the older son's blessing and inheritance on to him. Rebecca dressed the younger twin in Esau's clothes and adorned him in goatskin so that he would smell and feel like his hairy, hunter brother. The deception worked.

The Old Testament spelling of Rebecca (Rebekah) closely resembles the Hebrew and Aramaic word that the name was taken from. 'Ribkah' means 'knotted cord' and implies a faithful wife.

Rebecca was one of the many Biblical names favoured by the Puritans in the 1600s. In 1938 the name was the title of Daphne Du Maurier's classic novel, which went on to become an Oscar-winning film directed by Alfred Hitchcock.

*Variants: Bec, Becca, Beck, Beckie, Becky, Bekky, Bex, Reba, Rebe, Rebekah*

*Girls*

### Reese

This Welsh name was once borne by a 12th century warrior, Rhys.
His name meant 'ardour' or 'rashness'. He earned his place in
history by fighting against the English invaders of Wales. Reese
is the feminine equivalent of his name.
*Variants: Reece, Rees*

### Rhea

In Greek mythology Rhea was the mother of Zeus, the supreme
god, but the exact origin and meaning of her name is unknown.
It may come from the Greek for 'flowing' or 'protector'.

According to Roman legend Rhea was a Vestal Virgin raped
by the god Mars, who gave birth to twin boys, Romulus and
Remus, the founders of Rome.
*Variants: Rea, Reanna, Ria*

### Ria

Ria comes from the Spanish for 'small river' or 'river mouth'. It
is also a variant of Rhea, which is thought to mean 'flowing' or
'protector' (see above). But it can also be used as a pet form of
names ending in 'ria', such as Maria ('longed for child') and
Victoria ('victory').
*Variants: Maria, Rhea, Victoria*

### Rita

Margarita is the Spanish version of the name Margaret, which
comes from the Latin and Greek for 'pearl'. Rita is the short form
of this Spanish variant.

However, as an independent name it also boasts Hindu
roots. Rita is an Indian name that means 'brave', 'strong' or
'proper'.

Famous Ritas include the actress Rita Hayworth and
St Rita of Cascia, the patron saint of desperate causes and
unhappy marriages.
*Variants: Daisy, Margaret, Margarita, Margherita, Marguerita,
Marguerite, Reda, Reeta, Reida*

**Robyn**

The boy's name Robin is sometimes used as a pet form of Robert, a name of Germanic origin that means 'fame' and 'bright'. But children are also named Robin after the red-breasted bird associated with Christmas. Thus, like Carol, Noel, Nicholas and Nicola, Robin is often given to children born during this time. Robyn is the feminine equivalent.

**Rose**

Throughout history roses have been associated with love and beauty. In the ancient world this flower was sacred to several goddesses and later it became a symbol of the Virgin Mary. The red rose is the national flower of England and is also represents love and romance.

While the girl's name Rose may be derived from the flower it may also stem from the German word for 'horse'. It could equally have been derived from the Germanic word 'hrad', which means 'fame'.

*Variants: Rosa, Rosanna, Rosabella, Rosalie, Rosalind, Rosemary, Rosetta, Rosie, Rosina, Rosita*

**Rosanna**

This popular North American name was derived by combining the names Rose and Anna. As mentioned above the name Rose may either be associated with the flower or may be derived from the German words for 'horse' and 'fame'. Anna ultimately comes from the Biblical name Hannah, which means 'God has favoured me'.

*Variants: Anna, Hannah, Rosa, Rosanne, Rose, Roseanna, Roseanne*

**Roxanne**

Roxana was the name of a beautiful Asian princess who married Alexander the Great in 327 BC. The name was later used by Daniel Defoe in his 1724 novel *Roxana, The Fortunate Mistress*.

However, the variant Roxanne is best known as the heroine in Edmond Rostand's 1897 play *Cyrano de Bergerac*, which is

based on the life of a writer of the same name.

The exact meaning of Roxanne is unclear but it is thought to come from the Persian for 'dawn'.

*Variants: Roxana, Roxane, Roxy*

### Ruby

Ruby was a popular gemstone name for baby girls born during the late 19th century and early 1900s. It comes from the Latin word 'rubeus', which means red.

*Variants: Rubetta, Rubette, Rubi, Rubia, Rubina*

### Ruth

In the Old Testament Ruth was the devoted daughter-in-law of Naomi. Following the death of her husband and father-in-law, Ruth left her homeland to return to Israel, the birth place of Naomi.

Although the exact meaning of the name is unknown it is associated with companionship and friendship and is also of Hebrew origin.

*Variant: Ruthie*

### Sabrina

In England, in ancient times, the River Severn was known as Sabrina. According to Celtic legend its name was derived from the illegitimate daughter of a Welsh king whose stepmother ordered that she be drowned in its waters. In his writings the Roman historian Tacitus refers to the river by its ancient name.

*Variant: Zabrina*

### Saffron

As a girl's name Saffron was little used (if at all) before the 1960s. It comes from the crocus that produces yellow dye and spice that adds flavour to food.

The name is derived from the Arabic word 'zafaron', which means 'crocus'.

*Variants: Saffie, Safflower, Saffrey, Saffy*

### Sage
The herbal plant sage is used to flavour food and is as also used as a tea. In English the word means an old, wise man. Today it is given to both boys and girls as a first name.

### Sahara
Situated in North Africa, and covering 9,065,000 sq km, the Sahara Desert is the largest desert in the world. It sprawls between the Atlantic Ocean on the west and the Red Sea of Egypt in the east. To its north lay the Atlas Mountains and the Mediterranean. Its southern boundary is the valley of the Niger River.

Fittingly the name comes from the Arabic word 'sahra', which means 'desert'.
*Variant: Zahara*

### Salena
The name Salena comes from the Latin word 'sal', meaning 'salt' and 'salt water'. To say someone is the 'salt of the earth' is to say they are genuine, selfless and blessed with common sense.

The similar-sounding name Selena, comes from the Greek for 'moon'.
*Variant: Salina*

### Sally
Today Sally is considered to be an independent name, but originally it was a pet form of Sarah, a Hebrew name meaning 'princess'. It is sometimes combined with Ann to produce the separate name Sally-Ann.
*Variants: Sal, Sallie, Sally-Ann, Sarah*

### Salome
Although this name comes from the Hebrew word for 'peace' ('shalom') in the Bible it was not borne by a peaceful woman. In the New Testament Salome was the stepdaughter of King Herod who was asked to dance for him at a banquet. In return he promised to give her anything her heart desired. Prompted by

her mother she asked for the head of John the Baptist, the preacher and cousin of Jesus.

In 1893 the Irish playwright Oscar Wilde wrote a play about Salome, which Richard Strauss later developed into an opera.
*Variants: Sal, Salama, Saolma, Salomi, Shulamit*

### Samantha

The exact origin of Samantha is unknown. It could be the feminine equivalent of the Biblical name Samuel, which comes from the Hebrew for 'heard by God'. Alternatively it may have been derived from the Aramaic for 'one who listens'.

Whatever its origin, the name first came into use in the 18th century when it was especially popular with parents in the southern states of North America.
*Variants: Sam, Sammie, Sammy*

### Samira

This name derives its meaning from the Arabic for 'entertainer' and 'companion in night talk'.
*Variants: Mira, Sam, Sami, Sammie, Sammy*

### Sarah

Sarah was the wife of Abraham – who, to Christians, Jews and Muslims is the patriach of their faiths. Sarah, at 90 bore him a son, Isaac, who went on to father Esau and Jacob.

In the Old Testament God changed Abraham's name from Abram ('exalted father') to Abraham ('father of many'). Although he changed his wife's name from Sarai to Sarah, the meaning in Hebrew remained the same – 'princess'.

The popularity of this name increased throughout the English-speaking world after the Reformation. The Scottish Gaelic version of Sarah is Morag.
*Variants: Morag, Sara, Sarai, Saran, Sarann*

### Saskia

The 17th century Dutch artist Rembrandt first brought this name to England. He was married to a woman called Saskia von Uylenburg who modelled for many of his paintings.

The exact origin of the name is unknown but it is thought to stem from the Germanic word 'sachs', which means 'Saxon'.

**Selma**
Selma is of both Celtic and Scandinavian origin. Its Celtic meaning is 'fair' but it is also derived from the Old Norse for 'divinely protected'.

Scandinavian immigrants brought the name with them to the shores of North America, ensuring its spread throughout the English-speaking world.

Previously the name Selma had grown in stature in Sweden thanks to the works of the poet Frans Mikael Franzen who used it in his work. He died in 1849. Later the Swedish novelist Selma Lagerlöf brought the name further public attention. In 1909 she became the first female writer to win the Nobel Prize for Literature.
*Variants: Aselma, Zelma*

**Shannon**
Located in Ireland and stretching over 200 miles the River Shannon is the longest river in both Ireland and Britain. As a surname Shannon means 'descendent of Sean' in Gaelic.
Despite its connections Shannon is little used as a first name for babies born in Ireland. It is generally given to girls whose parents are of Irish descent but live abroad. Shannon is sometimes used as a boy's name as well.
*Variants: Shanna, Shannagh*

**Siân**
Siân is the Celtic version of the name Jane, which is the feminine equivalent of John ('God is gracious'). Like the boy's name Sean it is pronounced 'Shaw-an'.
*Variants: Jane, Janet, Jayne, Jeanette, Sian, Siani, Shani*

### Sierra
The name Sierra is derived from the Spanish for 'mountain range'. It is especially popular in North America.

### Sinéad
The Irish name Sinéad is the Gaelic version of Jane and Janet, both of which are feminine versions of the Biblical name John. John comes from the Hebrew for 'God has favoured', 'God is gracious' and 'God is merciful'. Sinéad is pronounced as 'shin-aid' or 'sin-aid'.
*Variants: Jane, Janet, Jayne, Jeanette, Sinead*

### Skye
During the hippy flower-power age of the 1960s it became popular to choose children names from the world of nature. The Phoenix family – an American acting clan – are a perfect example of this trend. The family boasted the names Rain, River and Summer. The popularity of the name Skye is indicative of this movement. However this name is sometimes given to children in honour of the Scottish island of Skye.
*Variant: Sky*

### Sophie
The Greek word 'sophia' means 'wisdom' and throughout history it has been used in connection with the holy wisdom of God. In 6th century Constantinople (Istanbul, Turkey) a large cathedral was built as part of the Christian Orthodox Church. It was called Hagia Sophia, meaning 'Sacred Wisdom'. Although it was torn down in 532 it was rebuilt over the next few years and still stands in the city today.
*Variants: Sofi, Sofia, Sofya, Sonia, Sondya, Sonja, Sonni, Sophia*

### Stella
In Latin 'stella' means 'star' and the Virgin Mary is sometimes known as 'Stella Maris' or 'star of the sea'.

The Elizabethan poet Sir Philip Sidney was said to be the first

person to use this Latin word as a girl's name in his sonnets and songs called *Astrophel and Stella*. But the French name Estelle, which was popular in the 19th century, was derived from the same root. (See also Estelle.)

### Susan

Popular in the 20th century, Susan is a short form of the name Susannah. The 1616 painting by Ludovico Carracci depicts the Biblical story of Susannah and the Elders, the beautiful woman who was seen bathing in her garden. Lusting after her, the men tried to blackmail Susannah into sleeping with them by threatening to say they had seen her having sex. Susannah refused, the elders carried out their threat, and the young woman faced the punishment of stoning. However she was exonerated when the judge Daniel interviewed the two men separately. Their stories did not match and Susannah was saved.

Her name comes from the Hebrew word 'shoshana' meaning 'lily'. Although it was not common until the 1700s, Shakespeare gave the name to one of his daughters.
*Variants: Chana, Shoshan, Siusan, Suki, Susana, Susannah, Susanne*

### Tabitha

According to the Bible Tabitha is the name of a follower of Jesus who was raised from the dead by St Peter. Her name comes from the Aramaic for 'gazelle'.

Although Tabitha was favoured by the 17th century Puritans it was not popular with the Victorians.
*Variants: Tab, Tabatha, Tabbi, Tabbie, Tabbitha, Tabby*

### Tamara

Tamar was the name of a 12th century queen of Georgia, a region that was once part of Russia. Her name comes from the Arabic and Hebrew for 'date palm tree'.

There were two Tamars in the Bible. One was the daughter-in-law of Judah. The other was the daughter of King David who

was raped by her half-brother Amnon. Tamar's other brother Absalom, another son of David, took revenge by killing their mutual sibling. Tamara is an elaboration of Tamar.
*Variants: Mara, Tam, Tamah, Tamar, Tamarah, Tammi, Tammy, Timi*

## Tammy

The name Tammy was first used as a pet form of Tamara and Tamsin. As a short form of Tamara it assumes the meaning 'date palm tree'. As a variant of Tamsin, which is the feminine equivalent of Thomas, it means 'twin'.

Today Tammy is given to girls as an independent name, especially in North America where it was borne by the Country music singer, Tammy Wynette. She was given the name Virginia Wynette Pugh when she was born in 1942 but adopted Tammy when she became a singer.
*Variants: Tami, Tammi, Tammie*

## Tamsin

There are a number of feminine versions of the Biblical name Thomas. They include Thomasina and Tomasina, but Tamsin is the Cornish form. Like Thomas it comes from the Arabic for 'twin'.
*Variants: Tamasin, Tamasine, Tami, Tammie, Tammy, Tamzin, Thomasina, Thomasine*

## Tania

In Russia the name Tatiana is associated with royalty. Not only was it associated with a fairy queen it also belonged to a daughter of Nicholas II, the country's last Tsar. Tatiana was also borne by an early Christian martyr who died in 228.

Tania is the pet form of Tatiana, which is now used as an independent name.
*Variants: Tatiana, Tanya, Titania, Tita.*

## Tara

In Margaret Mitchell's novel *Gone with the Wind*, Tara was the name of the fictional home of the O'Hara family. In Ireland Tara was the name of the hill in County Meath, which was the seat of the country's ancient kings.

Now used as a girl's name, Tara also comes from the Aramaic 'to throw' or 'carry'. It was little used in Britain before the 1960s.
*Variants: Tarrah, Taryn, Tatiana*

**Tatum**
The exact origin of this modern-day girl's name is unknown. It may be a feminine version of Tate, which comes from the Middle English for 'cheerful' and 'spirited'. Tate is also believed to stem from the Old English for a variety of other words and phrases. They include 'dear', 'dice', 'hilltop', 'tress of hair' and 'treat'.

Tatum is also believed to come from the Native American for 'windy' or 'garrulous'.
*Variants: Tata, Tait, Tayte*

**Taylor**
The word 'tailor' is derived from the Anglo-Norman word 'taillier', meaning 'to cut'. Thus the surname Taylor was originally a tag for someone who was a tailor by profession. However, in modern times Taylor has been given to babies of both sexes as a first name. It is especially popular in North America.

**Tempest**
Used by William Shakespeare as the title of one his plays, Tempest is also bestowed on girls as a first name. It comes from the Old French for 'storm'.
*Variant: Tempestt*

**Terri**
As the feminine variant of the boy's name Terence, Terri ultimately comes from the Old Roman name Terentius. It is also used as a pet form of Theresa, which may come from the Greek for 'to reap'. (See also Theresa.)

In North America it is used as an independent given name.
*Variants: Teresa, Teri, Theresa*

## Thalia

Thalia comes from the Greek word 'thallein' which means 'to flourish', 'to prosper' or 'to bloom'. According to Greek mythology she was one of the Three Graces (also known as the Charites) – the daughters of Zeus who were associated with charm, beauty, creativity, fertility and nature. Thalia was also the name of one of the nine Muses who were goddesses of the Greek arts and sciences. Thalia presided over comedy.
*Variants: Talia, Talya*

## Theresa

The exact origin of the name Theresa is unknown, but it is thought to come from the Greek for 'harvest' or 'to reap'.

The name was first brought to England via Roman Catholicism but it fell out of favour once the country became Protestant. In the 20th century Mother Theresa was perhaps the most famous bearer of the name. Born in 1910 she died in September 1997 after a life devoted to caring for the poor and sick in Calcutta, India. A Roman Catholic nun and the founder of her own order, the Missionaries of Charity, she was awarded the Nobel Peace Prize in 1979.
*Variants: Teresa, Thérèse, Theresia, Terri, Tess, Tessa, Tracy, Tracey*

## Tia

This short name derives its meaning from others. As a pet form of Christina it means 'Christian', but as a variant of Tatiana it means 'fairy queen'.
*Variants: Christina, Christine, Tatiana, Tania, Tanya, Tina*

## Tina

Although Tina is now used as an independent name in its own right it was first used as a pet form of Christina, which means 'Christian'. It is also used as a short form for other names ending in 'tina', such as Valentina.
*Variants: Christina, Christine, Tatiana, Tiana, Tia, Tyna*

### Toni

The boy's name Anthony was derived from the Old Roman family name Antonius, which may have come from the Greek for 'flourishing' or 'flower'. Antonia is the feminine equivalent of that name and Toni is its short form.

Toni is now given to girls as an independent name.
*Variants: Antonia, Tonie, Tonya*

### Tonya

Like Toni, Tonya is an independent name that derives its meaning from Antonia, the feminine form of Anthony. Thus it assumes the Greek meaning 'flourishing'.
*Variants: Antonia, Toni, Tonie, Tonia*

### Tracy

While the exact meaning of Tracy is unclear the source of its popularity is not. The name became more widespread following the 1940 film *The Philadelphia Story* and the 1956 musical *High Society*. Katharine Hepburn played the central character, Tracy Lord, in the first film and Grace Kelly assumed the role in the second.

The name is sometimes used as a pet form of Theresa, which comes from the Greek for 'to reap'. However, it may also derive its meaning from the Latin word 'tractare', which means 'to manage, handle or lead'.

Another possibility is that Tracy was taken from the Gallo-Roman personal name meaning 'inhabitant of Thrace'.
*Variants: Teresa, Terese, Theresa, Thérèse, Trace, Tracie, Tracey*

### Troy

Troy derives its meaning from two surnames and one place name. According to Greek legend Troy was an ancient city located in the Asia Minor and the scene of the 10-year Trojan War.

As a surname Troy was given to those who lived in the French town of Troyes. But as an Irish last name it comes from the Gaelic for 'a foot soldier'.

**Tuesday**

According to Teutonic mythology Tiw was the god of war and the brother of Thor. The second day of the week, Tuesday or 'Tiwesdaeg', was named after him. The fourth day 'Thor's day' or Thursday, was named after his brother.

**Tyler**

In North America this surname is popular as a first name for both boys and girls. It comes from the Old English for 'tile' and was used as an occupational name for someone who was a tiler. Its popularity in North America may be due to the 10th president of the United States, John Tyler.

**Uma**

Uma is the name of the Hindu goddess of beauty and sunlight. Her name is derived from the Sanskrit word for 'flax' and 'turmeric'.

R L Stevenson used the name in his 1893 novella *The Beach of Falesa*.

**Unity**

The girl's name Unity is derived from the Latin 'unitas', which comes from 'unus' meaning 'one' or 'together'.

The name Unity is also a variant of Una, which is taken from the Irish word for 'lamb'. In Latin 'una' also means 'together'. In 1930s and 1940s Britain the name was borne by Unity Mitford, one of the glamorous Mitford sisters.

*Variants: Una, Unique*

**Ursula**

Ursula is derived from the Latin for 'little bear' or 'female bear'. In the 5th century it was borne by a saint who, according to legend, was martyred in Cologne with 11,000 martyrs as they returned from a pilgrimage to Rome. Ursula was a popular saint during the Middle Ages.

It is also the feminine equivalent of the name Orson ('bear').

*Variants: Orsa, Orsola, Ursala, Urse, Ursel, Ursie, Ursola*

### Valentina

Valentina is the feminine version of Valentine, the name of the saint whose feast day is celebrated on 14 February. Valentine was a 3rd century Roman martyr and his name is derived from the Latin word 'valens' which means 'healthy', 'strong', 'vigorous' and 'powerful'.

Both Valentine and the feminine equivalent Valentina are traditionally bestowed upon children born on St Valentine's Day – a day associated with love and romance.

*Variants: Valeria, Valerie*

### Valerie

Like Valentina and Valentine, Valerie is derived from the Latin for 'healthy' and 'vigorous'. It is the feminine form of the Old Roman family name.

The variant Valeria was borne by Valeria Messalina, the granddaughter of Mark Antony. Valeria became the third wife of the Roman emperor Claudius and bore him two children. But she conspired with her lover to kill him and suffered the fate of execution.

*Variants: Val, Valaree, Valari, Valeria, Valery, Valentina*

### Vanessa

The name Vanessa is thought to be the invention of the Anglo-Irish 18th century writer Jonathan Swift who used it as a nickname for his friend Esther Vanhomrigh. He appears to have combined the first part of her surname, 'Van', with the suffix 'essa'. Swift used the nickname in the title of his poem *Cadenus and Vanessa*.

The name may also be associated with the Greek word for 'butterflies'.

*Variants: Nessa, Nessie, Van, Vania, Vannie, Vanny*

### Vashti

Vashti was the name of a Biblical woman who was married to the King of Persia. However, she was later replaced by Esther, when she refused to place herself at her husband's feet.

Vashti comes from the Persian for 'beautiful'.

### Venus

Venus was an Italian goddess who became associated with Aphrodite, the Greek goddess of love. It is also the name given to the second planet from the sun.
*Variants: Venita, Vinita, Vin, Vinnie*

### Verdi

The name Verdi is usually associated with the Italian composer Giuseppe Verdi. However, it can also be given to girls as a first name.

Verdi comes from the Latin word 'vivere', which means 'to be green'. It is associated with lush vegetation and springtime.
*Variants: Vera, Veradis, Vere, Verene, Verina, Verine, Verita*

### Verity

Verity is another name favoured by the Puritans of the 17th century because of its value as a Christian virtue. It is derived from the Old French and Latin words for 'truth'.
*Variants: Vera, Verena*

### Veronica

St Veronica was the woman from Jerusalem who was said to have taken pity on Christ as he carried his cross on the road to Calgary. She offered him a cloth to wipe the sweat from his face and, when it was returned to her, it bore the imprint of his image.

Thus the name Veronica is derived from the Latin for 'true image' and, fittingly, Veronica is the patron saint of photographers.

The French variant Veronique, was carried to Scotland in the 17th century, but the name was not popular in England until the 1800s.
*Variants: Berenice, Bernice, Nika, Ron, Roni, Verenice, Verona, Veronika, Veronique, Vonni*

### Victoria

Queen Victoria, the Empress of India, died in January 1901 after reigning over Britain and its Empire for over 63 years. But when she was born in 1819, the name that would lend itself to an era was little used in the nation she went on to rule.

Queen Victoria was named after her German mother Mary Louise Victoria of Saxe-Coburg. Their shared name came from the Latin for 'victorious' and during Victoria's reign it was bestowed upon both a Canadian city and an Australian state in her honour.

More than a century after Victoria's death the name continues to be used as a girl's name. However, it was especially popular in 1970s Britain.

*Variants: Tora, Tori, Tory, Vic, Vicci, Vicki, Vicky, Victoire, Victoriana, Victorina*

### Violet

Violet is both a colour – bluish-purple – and a flower. Although it was a popular girl's name during the 19th century a variant of the name was used by Shakespeare in *Twelfth Night*. Viola is the name of his heroine who disguises herself as a man when she is shipwrecked in a hostile country.

*Variants: Viola, Violetta*

### Virginia

The American state of Virginia was christened by the explorer Sir Walter Raleigh who named it in honour of Elizabeth I, the Virgin Queen. The name was derived from the Latin for 'virgin' or 'maiden', but it was also the feminine version of the Old Roman family name, Virginius. Virginia is also associated with the Latin for 'manly race'.

In Ancient Rome the name was borne by a young girl who received the unwelcome sexual attention of a corrupt ruler. She was killed by her father to save her virtue.

Although the name Virginia enjoyed great popularity in 18th century France, it was not as widespread in Britain until the late 1900s.

(See also Ginger.)

*Variants: Gina, Ginger, Ginia, Ginni, Ginny, Virgie, Virginie*

# V - W

## Vivian

Although this name was originally given to baby boys it is now more frequently associated with girls. Vivian comes from the Old French, and ultimately Latin, word for 'alive'. To say someone is vivacious is to say they are bubbly and full of life.

The name existed in England as far back as the Middle Ages. In the 20th century it was associated with the British actress Vivien Leigh who won an Academy Award for her portrayal of Scarlett O'Hara in the film adaptation of *Gone with the Wind*.

*Variants: Vivi, Vivien, Vivienne, Vyvian, Vyvyan*

## Wallis

The origin of the name Wallis is disputed. One theory suggests that it is derived from the Old French for members of the Celtic race, 'waleis'. Another possible theory points to the Old Norse word 'val', meaning 'choice' or 'selection'. It could also come from the Old English for 'defence' or 'fortification'.

Wallis Simpson was the twice-married American divorcee who created a constitiutional crisis in Britain in 1936. It was for the love of Mrs Simpson that Edward VIII abdicated the British throne in favour of his younger brother Prince Albert, the Duke of York. Albert became King George VI and was succeeded by his daughter, Elizabeth II.

In Scotland the surname Wallace is associated with the patriotic hero William Wallace who led an army against the English. Wallis may be a transferred use of this surname or it could equally be derived from the Latin for 'Welshman'.

*Variants: Wallace, Wallie, Wally*

## Wednesday

Wednesday is the name given to babies of either sex who are born on that day of the week. The practice is more common in North America than in the United Kingdom.

In England the name comes from the Old English for 'Woden's Day'. Woden was a one-eyed Anglo-Saxon god.

### Wendy

Wendy is another name that was a literary invention. The Scottish writer J M Barrie created the name for a character in his play *Peter Pan*. The inspiration for the name was a child called Margaret Henley who called Barrie 'my friendy', 'friendy-wendy' or 'fwendy-wendy'.

The popularity of the children's story about Peter Pan, the boy who refused to grow up, helped to spread the use of Wendy.
*Variants: Wanda, Wenda, Wendi, Wendie*

### Whitney

Situated in California, Mount Whitney is the highest point in North America outside of Alaska. It was named after Josiah Whitney who was a professor of geology at Harvard University during the 19th century.

Although Whitney was associated with a surname in North America it came from the Middle English for 'by the white island'. Thus it was originally a place name.
*Variants: Whitnee, Whitni, Whitnie, Whitny, Witney*

### Willow

The willow is pliant and graceful and it is from this tree that the girl's name is derived.

### Wilma

Wilma is the short form of the German name Wilhelmina, which is the feminine form of William. William comes from the Old German for 'resolute protection'.
*Variants: Wilhelmina, Mina, Minnie*

### Winona

Winona comes from the Old High German and Old English for 'blissfully happy' and 'joy'. It also has a Native American meaning – 'firstborn daughter'.

In North America Winona is also known as a place name. For example, in the Midwestern state of Minnesota there is a county

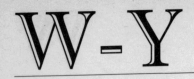

bearing the name. It is a popular first name in North America.
*Variants: Wenona, Wenonah, Winnie, Wynona*

**Winter**
The name of the season is sometimes used as a girl's name.

**Yasmin**
Yasmin is a variant of the name Jasmine, which is also used as an independent name. The two names share the same meaning. They are both derived from the jasmine flower, the sweet-smelling plant from which oil is made. Yasmin is the Arabic form of this name.
*Variants: Jasmine, Yasmina, Yasmine*

**Yoko**
Yoko comes from the Japanese for 'positive' and 'female'. In the Western world the most famous bearer of this name is Yoko Ono, the widow of former Beatles' member John Lennon. Yoko's name is rooted in Japanese philosophy, which says that 'Yo' and 'In' lay still in an egg until they are split to form heaven and earth.

**Yolanda**
This name stems from the Greek word 'ion', which means 'violet'. Thus it is closely related to the name Iolanthe, which means 'violet flower'. In France Iolanthe became Yolande and Yolanda is its variant. The Latin meaning of Yolanda is 'modest'.
*Variants: Iolanthe, Violet, Yolande*

**Yoshiko**
Yoshiko is a Japanese name that is given to boys and girls. It means 'good' and 'respectful'.
*Variant: Yoshi*

**Yvette**
Yvette is of both French, German and Hebrew origin. Its Germanic meaning is 'yew' and 'small archer'. But in France it is held as the feminine version of Yves, the French form of the

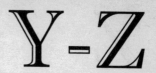
Biblical name John. John comes from the Hebrew for 'God has favoured', 'God is gracious' and 'God is merciful'.
*Variants: Ivetta, Yevette, Yve, Yvonne*

### Yvonne

Like Yvette, Yvonne borrows its meaning from the French and ultimately Germanic word for 'yew'. It is also associated with 'small archer' because the yew tree was used to make long bows. As the feminine form of Yves, the French for John, Yvonne also means 'God has favoured', 'God is gracious' and 'God is merciful'. It has produced a plethora of variants and is not confined to the French-speaking world.
*Variants: Evona, Evonne, Ivetta, Yevette, Yve, Yvette*

### Zara

A granddaughter of Queen Elizabeth II, Zara Phillips, bears this name. It is taken from the Arabic word 'zahr', which means 'flower'. It is also thought to come from the Arabic for 'brightness' and 'splendour of the dawn'. Sometimes it also appears as a variant of Sarah, which comes from the Hebrew for 'princess'.
*Variants: Sara, Sarah, Zahra, Zarah*

### Zita

Zita comes from the Italian for 'child'. It was borne by a 13th century Tuscan saint who was canonised in 1696. St Zita is the patron saint of domestic servants because that was once her profession. A bunch of keys are her emblem. St Zita also represents bakers, home-makers and those who have misplaced their keys. The last empress of Austria also bore this name.

As a short form of the Spanish name Rosita, Zita means 'little rose'.
*Variants: Citha, Rosita, Sitha, Zeta*

### Zoe

The name Zoe was popular with early Christians because of its association with eternal life. The name is the Greek translation of the Hebrew word 'hawwah', which means 'life'.

Zoe was borne by martyrs in the 2nd and 3rd centuries and was popular among British parents during the 1800s. It is also a variant of the name Eve, which shares the same meaning.

*Variants: Eva, Eve, Evita, Vita, Zoë, Zoey, Zowie*

**Zola**

Zola may be a combination of the name Zoe ('life') with the ending 'la'. However, it is more likely that it is the transferred use of a surname made famous by the French novelist Emile Zola who died in 1902.

Whether used as first name or surname Zola comes from the German word 'zoll', which means 'toll', 'tax' and 'price'.

*Variant: Zoe*

# Unisex names

**The concept of unisex names is steeped in history.** Back in medieval times, names were translated between languages, and most children were named after religious figures. But while most Romance languages distinguished between masculine and feminine in the way names ended – Alexander and Alexandra, for example, the English didn't. Hence, Alexander would be Alexandra in French, but when translated into English, it remained as Alexander. Medieval names used for girls and boys include Alexander, and also names like Patrick, Basil, Nicholas and Simon.

When French and Latin influences started to creep into English during the following centuries, the feminine endings for these names were adopted, and girls stopped being called Philip, as the daughters of the educated classes served as beacons of their parents' educated status by being given the original Latin/French versions of names, hence Patricia, Juliana, Philippa, etc.

By the 19th century, many new girls ' names were created by adding 'a' or 'ina' suffixes to boys' names, creating the likes of Roberta and Edwina. But in the late 19th and early 20th centuries, a fashion started in the US for shortening girls' names, and making them sound masculine in the process – Jimmie, Jamie, Eddie, etc. By the 1960s, and the arrival of feminism, names like Ashley, Cameron and Alexis were given to girls. Pop culture has further spread this habit, and below are some of the more popular names considered to be gender–free. ∎

# Unisex names

Addison
Aden
Ainsley
Alex
Alexis
Andy
Angel
Asa
Asher
Ashley

Bailey
Beau
Berkeley
Beverly
Billie
Blair
Bobby
Brady
Brooke

Cade
Cameron
Carol
Casey
Charlie
Christy
Cody
Connor
Corey

Darcey
Dale
Dallas
Dana
Drew

Dusty

Eddie
Elisha
Emmanuel
Evelyn

Fletcher
Flynn
Frankie
Freddie
Francis

Gabriel
Gale
Gerry
Grady
Greer

Haley
Harley
Hillary
Hunter
Hyatt

Indiana
Ireland

Jackie
Jan
Jean
Jermain
Jocelyn
Jody
Jordan
Jordy

Judd
Kasey
Kelly
Kendall
Kennedy
Kingsley

Lacey
Lane
Lee
Leslie
Lindsay
Lorne
Lynn

Mackenzie
Misha
Murphy

Nat
Nevada
Nicky
Nikita

Ocean

Palmer
Paris
Pat

Quinn

Rae
Randy
Ray
Regan

Riley
Robbie
Ronnie
Rowan
Ryan

Sacha
Sage
Sam
Sandy
Sawyer
Sean
Shae
Sheridan

Tara
Tate
Tatum
Tegan
Terry
Toby
Tracy
Tristan
Tyler

Val
Valentine

Wallis
Warner
Wynne

Xerxes

Yancy
Young

# Surnames as first names

Using surnames as first names dates back to 17th century Scotland, when Protestants, newly freed from having to call their offspring after various saints, started to give sons their mother's maiden name as a first name. The idea soon caught on, spreading throughout families, and by the 19th century, parents were looking outside the family circle, using the last names of various notaries and heroes as their children's first names. Military heroes and, for those with more pious inclinations, religious figures, all had children named after them.

In keeping with those male-dominated times, most children named in this fashion were boys, but by the 20th century, the practice had spread to girls. However, even now the vast majority of surnames-used-as-first names are boys: Barry, Clifford, Milton and Zane, for example, are all most definitely boys' names. There are some which can now be considered unisex: Ashley, Casey, Lindsay and Mackenzie.

Others that might formerly have been thought of as boys' names are now being used for girls as well, with the likes of Hunter and Dylan popping up on the birth certificates of female children. There are also a few which are specifically female, including Audrey, Kimberly, Shelby and Tiffany. The following are a list of common last names found as first names. ■

# Surnames as first names

Addison
Ainsley
Allen
Alison
Anderson
Avery
Alton
Ashley
Aubrey
Audrey
Austin

Bailey
Baron
Barrie
Barrington
Barry
Bentley
Beverly
Beverley
Blake
Bradley
Brady
Brandon
Brent
Brewster
Bria
Bryan
Bronson
Brooke
Bruce
Bryson
Byron

Cade
Calvin

Cambell
Cameron
Carlton
Carson
Carter
Casey
Cassidy
Chance
Chandler
Chase
Chauncey
Chester
Clark
Clayton
Clifford
Clifton
Clinton
Clive
Cody
Colby
Cole
Colton
Cooper
Corey
Cory
Courtney
Craig
Curtis

Dale
Dallas
Dalton
Dana
Darby
Darcy
Darrell

Darryl
Dawson
Dean
Delaney
Denzil
Desmond
Dewitt
Dexter
Dillon
Dylan
Douglas
Drake
Dudley

Earl
Elmer
Emerson
Everard
Everett

Forrest
Franklin

Garnet
Garrett
Garrison
Gary
Gerard
Glanville
Glenn
Gordon
Graham
Grant
Grayson
Greyson
Grover

Hadley
Hailey
Haley
Hayley
Harley
Harrison
Hartley
Hogan
Howard
Hudson
Hunter

Irving

Jamison
Jameson
Jackson
Jefferson
Jensen
Jenson
Johnson
Jordan

Kayley
Keith
Kelly
Kelsey
Kendall
Kennedy
Kent
Kenton
Kerry
Kimberly
Kirk
Kyle

# Surnames as first names

Porter
Preston

Quentin

Ramsay
Randall
Riley
Rodney
Roosevelt
Ross
Roy
Royston
Russell
Rutherford
Ryan

Sawyer
Scott
Shane
Shawn
Shelby
Sheldon
Sheridan
Sherman
Shirley
Shannon
Skylar
Spencer
Stacey
Stanley
Stuart
Sullivan

Tanner
Tate

Taylor
Todd
Tiffany
Tracey
Travis
Trevor
Troy
Truman
Tucker
Turner
Tyler
Tyson

Van
Vance
Vaughan
Vernon

Wade
Walker
Wallace
Warren
Wayne
Wendell
Wesley
Whitney
Wilbur
Willard
Willis
Wilson
Winston
Woodrow
Wyatt
Wynne

Zane

Lacey
Lance
Lane
Laurence/
Lawrence
Lawson
Lee
Leigh
Leland
Leslie
Lesley
Lester
Lindsay
Linsey
Logan
Lucas
Luther
Lyle

Mackenzie
McKenzie
Macy
Madison
Marshall

Mason
Maxwell
McKinley
Meredith
Michael
Millard
Milton
Mitchell
Morgan
Morris
Mortimer
Morton
Nelson
Neville

Odell
Otis

Page/
Paige
Parker
Percival
Perry
Peyton

# *Place names as first names*

Place names can make excellent first names, especially if the name chosen will have some meaning to the child, i.e. being the place their parents met, where they were born, or, in extreme cases, where they were conceived. It may be a country, county, town, river, desert or mountain range.

Not all place names work, however, as a child named Scunthorpe or Bognor is less likely to take to the name than one named Atlanta or Paris.

The following are a list of names inspired by places, most are unisex, although some may suit boys better than girls, or vice versa.

| | | | |
|---|---|---|---|
| Adelaide | China | Iona | Nile |
| Africa | Clyde | Ireland | |
| Alabama | | Israel | |
| Albi | Dakota | | Odessa |
| Arabia | Dallas | | Olympia |
| Arizona | Derry | Jamaica | Ohio |
| Asia | Denver | Jordan | |
| Aspen | Devon | | Paris |
| Atlanta | | Kelly | Persia |
| Austin | | Kent | Phoenix |
| Avalon | Eden | Kenya | |
| | | Kerry | Sahara |
| | Florence | Kingston | Savannah |
| Brazil | Florida | Korea | Shannon |
| Brittany | | | Sienna |
| Brooklyn | Geneva | Lincoln | Sierra |
| | Georgia | London | Sydney |
| Cairo | | Loiusiana | |
| Caledonia | Hamilton | Lourdes | Texas |
| Camden | Houston | | |
| Carolina | Hudson | Manchester | Valencia |
| Catalina | | Memphis | Venetia |
| Chelsea | Idaho | Milan | Verona |
| Chester | India | | Vienna |
| Cheyenne | Indiana | Nevada | Virginia |

# Boys

### Aaron

Although the exact meaning of the name is unknown it is believed to come from the Hebrew for 'mountain of strength' or 'brightness'. Its Arabic meaning is 'messenger'.

In the Old Testament Aaron was the older brother of Moses who became the founder the Jewish priesthood. As well as being the first high priest of the Israelites, Aaron was also his brother's spokesman.

*Variants: Aharon, Ahron, Ari, Arnie, Aron, Arron, Haroun, Ron, Ronnie*

### Abdul

Although Abdul is considered to be an independent name in its own right, it is actually a short form of Abdullah, which means 'servant of Allah' in Arabic.

*Variants: Ab, Abdal, Abdel, Abdullah*

### Abel

Abel is another well-known Biblical name that is of uncertain origin. Two Hebrew meanings have been suggested as possible interpretations – 'son' or 'source of God'. It is also thought to mean 'herdsman'.

In the Bible Abel is the second son of Adam and Eve who is murdered by his older brother Cain. Abel is also significant to the Muslim faith because in the Koran it is his non-violent attitude – his refusal to defend himself – which is emphasized.

*Variants: Abelard, Abeles, Abell, Able*

### Abir

In Hebrew this short name has a significant meaning – 'strong' and 'heroic'.

*Variants: Abira, Amoz, Amzi, Azaz, Aziz, Aziza*

### Abner

In the Old Testament Abner was King Saul's cousin and the commander of his army. In Hebrew his name means 'father of

light' or 'my father is light'. In Britain the name was popular after the Reformation.
*Variants: Ab, Abbey, Abby*

### Abraham

In the Christian, Jewish and Islamic faiths Abraham is the spiritual father who connects the three religions. In the Old Testament Abraham was originally known by the name Abram, which in Hebrew meant 'exalted father'. He and his elderly wife longed for a child. Unable to give her husband what he desired most, Sara suggested that he conceive a child with her Egyptian attendant, Hagar. The result was Ishmael, who went on to become the forefather of the Arab race.

To signify that Abram would indeed have a child with his wife Sara, God changed Abram's name to Abraham, 'father of many' or 'father of a multitude'. Sara became Sarah. Both names mean 'prince'. The couple went on to have a son, Isaac, who fathered the twins Esau and Jacob. The latter's children later gave birth to the 12 tribes of Israel.

This popular Jewish name was also favoured by Christians in 17th century England. In North America the name is associated with the twice-elected President Abraham Lincoln, who fought to preserve the Union during the Civil War. The Islamic version of Abraham is Ibrahim.
*Variants: Ab, Abe, Abi, Abie, Abrahan, Bram, Ham, Ibrahim*

### Absalom

Absalom was a popular name in the Middle Ages. Taken from the Old Testament, it was the name of one of King David's sons who fell out of favour with his father after he brought about the murder of his brother Amnon. Absalom took revenge on Amnon for raping their sister Tamar.

The name was later used by the 17th century British poet and playwright John Dryden in his poem *Absalom and Achitophel* (1681). The name means 'father of peace' in Hebrew.
*Variants: Absolun, Axel*

### Ackley

This name is taken from the Middle English words for 'acorn' and 'meadow'. Thus Ackley means 'acorn meadow' or 'meadow of oak trees'.
*Variant: Ackerley*

### Adam

The name Adam has long been a favourite with Christians and Jews alike. According to the Book of Genesis in the Bible, it was the name of the first man created by God. It is appropriate that the Hebrew meaning of Adam is 'earth', for this holy text says that God created him from a handful of dirt. The name also comes from the Hebrew for 'mankind' and 'red earth'.

Adam has been used as a name by early Christians from the 7th century. Widespread in Celtic areas such as Wales and Ireland, the name has been popular throughout the English-speaking world since the 1960s.
*Variants: Ad, Adamo, Adamson, Addie, Adom, Edom*

### Adolph

The Old Germanic name Aethelwulf was used in England from the 11th century onwards. It was formed from the elements 'athal', meaning 'noble', and 'wolfa', which means 'wolf'. The implication was that the bearer would be like a 'noble wolf' guarding the home and family.

It was the House of Hanover – whose period of British rule began with the reign of King George I in 1714 – that brought the Latin form of Aethelwulf, Adolph, with them.

The popularity of the name in Britain plummeted during the 1930s with the rise of the Austrian-born German dictator Adolf Hitler. The name has been associated with the Nazi leader ever since.
*Variants: Ad, Adolf, Adolfo, Adolphe, Adolpho, Aethelwulf, Dolf, Dolph, Dolphus*

### Adrian

The Adriatic Sea and the neighbouring northern Italian town of Adria are believed to be the sources of the name Adrian. Both place names derive their meaning from the Latin word 'ater' or 'black' in English – a direct reference to the black sand of the beaches in that area. In the days of the Roman Empire a man from Adria or Hadria was known as Adrianus or Hadrianus.

The name Hadrian was born by the Roman Emperor Publius Aelius Hadrianus who ruled from 117 to 138. During that time the defensive border Hadrian's Wall was built in the north of England to separate that province from Scotland. Hadrian was also the adopted name of the only Englishman to head the Roman Catholic Church. Born Nicholas Breakspear in the 12th century, Hadrian IV – also known as Adrian IV – was Pope from 1154 until 1159. (See also Adrienne.)

*Variants: Ade, Adriano, Adrien, Hadrian*

### Adriel

In Hebrew this name means 'God's majesty' or 'one of God's congregation'.

*Variants: Adri, Adrial*

### Aelwyn

More than one theory exists to explain the origin of this name. It may have been derived from two Old English first names – Athelwine, 'noble friend', and Alfwine 'elf friend'. After the Norman Conquest both names became Alwin, which can also be spelt with a 'y' replacing the 'i'. In Wales Alwen and Alwyn also mean 'great', 'child' or 'brow' and 'white, fair'. An alternative Old English interpretation is 'friend of all'.

*Variants: Alvan, Alvy, Alvyn, Alwen, Alwin, Alwyn*

### Ahmed

This Arabic name means 'greatly adored' or 'praised the most'. The character Prince Ahmed appears in the classic tale *Arabian Nights*.

*Variants: Ahmad*

### Aidan

In the 7th century, St Aidan was a missionary from Ireland who helped to convert the north of England. His name comes from the Irish Gaelic for 'little fiery one', but it also has Latin roots, which give it the meaning 'to help'.

The use of Aidan as a given name was revived during the 20th century. It was primarily bestowed upon boys but has also been given to girls.

*Variants: Aiden, Aden, Aodán, Aodham, Edan, Eden*

### Ainsley

Today Ainsley is considered to be a boy's name, but during the 12th century it was given to children of both sexes. It is a Scottish name that was once a surname associated with a powerful family. They derived it from a place name – possibly Annesley in Nottinghamshire or Ansley in Warwickshire. Ainsley, therefore, comes from the Old English word 'ān' – 'one', 'only' or 'own' – and 'lēah', which means 'wood', 'clearing' or 'field'. Thus the name means 'my meadow or land'.

*Variants: Ainie, Ainslee, Ainslie*

### Alan

The exact meaning of this name is unclear. It is a known Old Celtic name that appeared in early Welsh records and means 'harmony'. It may also come from the Irish Gaelic for 'good looking' and 'cheerful'.

The use of the name in Britain died out only to be reintroduced by the Normans shortly after their conquest of England. Indeed, two members of William the Conqueror's court bore the name – the Count of Brittany and the Earl of Richmond. The Breton meaning of Alan is 'rock'.

*Variants: Al, Allan, Allen, Alleyn, Alyn*

### Alban

Although this name was borne by the first British martyr its use as a given name was not widespread until the 19th century. Alban was the name of a 3rd century Roman soldier who was born a pagan, but offered shelter to a priest during a time of Christian persecution. Under the priest's instructions he converted to Christianity and when his fellow Roman soldiers came to seize his house guest, he swapped clothes with the priest and allowed them to take him instead. Alban was executed in the priest's place. The town where he lived, Verulamium, is now known as St Albans in his honour.

Alban's name means 'white', 'man from the town of Alba' or 'from Alba Longa' in Latin. Alba Longa was a Roman city.
*Variants: Al, Alba, Albany, Alben, Albin, Albion*

### Albert
When Prince Albert of Saxe-Coburg-Gotha married his cousin Queen Victoria in 1840, he not only had a major influence on her rule but on the popularity of the name Albert in Britain. Its use became more widespread once it was associated with the Queen's consort.

Albert comes from the Old High German name Adelbrecht, which consists of the elements 'adal' and 'beraht' meaning 'noble' and 'bright' or 'noble' and 'illustrious'.
*Variants: Adalbert, Adel, Adelbert, Al, Albe, Alberto, Bert, Berty, Burt*

### Aldous
This rare name comes from the Old German for 'old' and may have been a short form of various Norman names including Aldebrand, Aldemund and Alderan. All were formed using the German element 'ald' – 'old'. It was borne by the British novelist Aldous Huxley, who wrote *Brave New World* in 1932.
*Variants: Aldan, Alden, Aldin, Aldis, Aldo, Aldos, Aldus*

### Aled
Aled is the name of a river in Wales. It means 'offspring' or 'noble brow' in Welsh.
*Variants: Al*

### Alexander

According to Greek mythology the first bearer of this name was the Trojan prince Paris – the man who caused the 10-year Trojan War by abducting Helen, the Queen of Sparta. He was given the nickname Alexander because he helped to defend the flock of some shepherds. They called him Alexandros, which means 'defender of men'. The name has been popular ever since.

It appeared in the Bible, was borne by a number of early saints and belonged to Alexander the Great, the King of Macedon who lived from 356 to 323 BC. He is credited with spreading the name throughout the world because he conquered Persia, Egypt and his realm touched the borders of India.

The name is especially popular in Scotland where it is associated with Scottish royalty. Three kings of Scotland bore the name Alexander. It was also bestowed upon more than one Tsar of Russia. In that region, Sacha is a pet form of Alexander.
*Variants: Al, Alec, Aleksander, Alex, Alexei, Alexis, Ali, Alistair, Sacha, Sandy*

### Alfred

The name Alfred was frequently used in Britain before the arrival of the Normans in 1066. Until that time its most famous bearer was Alfred the Great the celebrated king of Wessex – a kingdom that stretched from Sussex to Devon. It was this 9th century king who was credited with building Britain's first navy and forcing the Danes out of southern England.

Although the name Alfred was adopted by the Normans, who used it in the form of Avery, it fell out of favour during the 16th century. It was the Victorians – fascinated by Anglo-Saxon and medieval culture, history and folklore – who revived the name.

Alfred comes from the Old English for 'good counsel' or 'elf counsel'.
*Variants: Alf, Alfie, Fred, Freddie*

### Algernon

It was William de Percy, a companion of William the Conqueror,

who brought the name Algernon to British shores at the time of the Norman Conquest. Most of the Normans were clean-shaven, but Percy had a moustache. Algernon was his nickname, which came from the Old French for 'with whiskers' or 'with a moustache'.
*Variants: Alger, Algie, Algy*

**Alistair**
The name Alistair has enjoyed popularity in Scotland for many centuries. It is an alternative spelling of the Gaelic name Alasdair, which is a version of the Greek name Alexandros – more commonly known as Alexander. Like Alexander, Alistair means 'defender of men' or 'warrior'.
*Variants: Alasdair, Alastair, Alexander, Alister*

**Alphonse**
Alphonse comes from the Old High German for 'noble' and 'ready' or 'apt'. In Spain the name is associated with royalty as it was borne by more than one king of Castile – a former Spanish kingdom.
*Variants: Al, Alfonso, Alphonso, Alphonsine, Fons, Fonsie, Fonz*

**Ambrose**
In Greek the name Ambrose means 'divine' or 'immortal'. It comes from the same root as the word 'ambrosia', the food of the gods and goddesses according to Greek mythology.
*Variants: Ambie, Ambros, Ambrosio, Ambrosius, Brose*

**Amir**
This Arabic name means 'prince'.
*Variant: Emir*

**Amos**
Amos was the Old Testament prophet who predicted that Judah and Israel would be destroyed if the people did not change their ways. The Hebrew meaning of his name is 'to carry', 'bearer of a burden' or 'troubled'.

### Andrew

Andrew is a name that has been borne by more than one saint, including the patron saint of Scotland and Russia. In the Bible the Galilean fisherman Andrew was the first of Christ's Apostles to be called to join him. He was accompanied by his brother, Simon Peter. The name is of Greek origin and means 'manly'.
*Variants: Anders, Anderson, André, Andreas, Andrei, Andres, Andy*

### Angus

Angus is another name that has a special place in the hearts of the Scots for it belonged to one of the Irish founders of their nation. Angus is a form of the Gaelic name Aonghus, which means 'one choice'.
*Variants: Aengus, Ennis, Gus*

### Anthony

Anthony comes from the Old Roman family name Antonius. The most famous bearer of the surname was Marcus Antonius, better known as Mark Antony. A soldier and statesmen, he was a follower of Julius Caesar who went on to co-rule the Republic following Caesar's assassination.

The exact origin of the name is unclear but is thought to have been derived from the Greek for 'flourishing'. The Romans believed that it meant 'inestimable' or 'priceless'.

The name has since been borne by a number of saints and early Christians, including St Antony, the patron saint of lost property. The 'h' was added to the name in the 16th century.
*Variants: Antoine, Anton, Antonio, Antony, Toni, Tonio, Tony*

### Anton

Anton is the French form of the name Anthony, which, during Roman times, was known as Antonius. Like its source the exact meaning of Anton is unknown. It may come from the Greek for 'flourishing' or has the Roman meaning of 'priceless'.

Anton is now commonly used in the English-speaking world.
*Variants: Anthony, Antoine, Antonio, Antony, Toni, Tonio, Tony*

### Archibald

This name comes from the Germanic for 'noble' and 'bold'. In England a similar name, Ercanbald ('very bold'), was used. It was James VI of Scotland who brought the Scottish variant to England when he ascended the English throne in 1603. He brought with him his jester Archie Armstrong.
*Variants: Archie, Archy, Baldie*

### Ardal

Ardal is an Irish name that stems from the words for 'high valour'. It may also mean 'bear'.
*Variants: Ardgal, Ardghal*

### Arden

The name Arden comes from the Latin for 'to be on fire', 'ablaze', 'sparkle', 'glitter' and 'dazzle'. It was used by Shakespeare as a place name – the Forest of Arden – in his comedy *As You Like It* (1599).
*Variants: Ard, Arda, Ardie, Ardin, Ardy*

### Argus

According to Greek mythology Argus was a giant who had 100 eyes and was the servant of Hera, wife of Zeus. Jealous of his affair with the nymph Io, she sent Argus to watch over Io, but her plan was foiled when Zeus instructed Hermes to kill the giant. After his death Hera decorated the tail of a peacock with his eyes.

Unsurprisingly, the Greek meaning of Argus is 'highly observant' or 'bright-eyed'.

### Arnold

Arnold is a Germanic name that was adopted by the Normans and brought to England as Arnaud. This name, which means 'eagle' and 'rule', was a popular surname in Britain during the Middle Ages before it died out, only to re-emerge as the first name Arnold in the 19th century.
*Variants: Armand, Armant, Arn, Arnald, Arnaud, Arnie, Arny*

### Arthur

More than one theory exists to explain the origin of the name Arthur. It is thought to stem from the Greek for 'bear-keeper' or the Celtic for 'bear'. Equally it could mean 'stone' or 'rock' in Irish Gaelic, 'noble' in Welsh or 'follower of Thor' in Norse. A link between Arthur and the Roman family name Artorius has also been suggested.

During the reign of Queen Victoria, Arthur became the name of choice for many parents. Another reason for its popularity is that it was the first name of the first Duke of Wellington, Arthur Wellesley, who defeated Napoleon in 1815 at the Battle of Waterloo. The Duke's name was later bestowed upon his godson, Prince Arthur, whose mother was Queen Victoria herself.

However, another Arthur had also captured the imagination of Victorian parents – King Arthur, the mythical 6th century British figure who, according to legend had a court at Camelot, and presided over the Knights of the Round Table.
*Variants: Art, Arth, Artie, Arty*

### Asher

In the Bible Asher was one of Jacob's 12 sons and one of the children that he had with his first wife Leah. His mother gave him the name Asher, which means 'happy' in Hebrew. It is also thought to mean 'martial', while the Swahili interpretation is 'born during Asher (a Muslim month)'.

### Ashley

This unisex name has enjoyed popularity in North America and Australia. Its growing use from the 1940s onwards may be explained by the success of Margaret Mitchell's 1936 novel, *Gone with the Wind*, and the Hollywood epic made of the book in 1939. Ashley Wilkes was the object of Scarlett O'Hara's affection, if not obsession. His name comes from the Old English for 'ash' and 'wood'. Hence originally it may have been given to someone who lived either in or near an ash wood.
*Variants: Ashlie, Ashly*

### Ashton
Like Ashley, Ashton is a name with Old English roots that can be given to children of either sex. It is derived from the words 'æsc', meaning 'ash-tree', and 'tūn' ('enclosure' or 'settlement'). Hence the name means 'settlement where ash trees grow' or 'dweller on the ash tree farm'.

### Auberon
This Old French name is believed to be of Germanic (Frankish) origin. It means 'noble' and 'like a bear'. It is also a pet form of Aubrey, which is related to Alberic – the name of the Scandinavian king of the elves.
*Variants: Alberic, Aubery, Oberon*

### Aubrey
The Norman-French name Aubrey comes from the Germanic name Alberic, which means 'elf-ruler'. The name enjoyed some popularity during the Middle Ages but its use subsequently declined only to be revived during the 19th century.
*Variants: Alberic, Alberich, Aubary, Auberon, Aubri, Aubry*

### Augustus
Augustus was the name of the first emperor of Rome – Gaius Julius Caesar Octavianus. Emperor Augustus, who was the grandnephew and adopted son of Julius Caesar, acquired the name in 27 BC. His successors also bore the title and Augustus eventually came to mean 'majesty'. It also means 'great' and 'magnificent'.

Augustine, a variant of Augustus, was borne by the great Saint Augustine of Hippo and also by another early saint St Augustine who converted King Ethelbert of Kent to Christianity and became the first Archbishop of Canterbury.
*Variants: August, Augustine, Austen, Austyn, Gus, Gussie*

### Aurelius
The Roman family name Aurelius comes from the Latin for

'golden'. It was adopted by the Roman Emperor and philosopher Marcus Aurelius who ruled the empire from 161 to 180 AD. The name was also borne by several early saints.
*Variants: Aurea, Aurek, Aurel, Aurelio, Aurelo, Aury*

**Avi**

This name comes from the Hebrew for 'my father'. It is traditionally used in reference to 'God'. Thus the name Avidan means 'God of wisdom and justice', Avidor stands for 'father of a generation' and Aviel is interpreted as 'God is my father'.
*Variants: Abi, Av, Avodal*

**Axel**

The name Axel has two meanings. In German it stands for 'oak' or 'small oak tree'. But it may also come from the Scandinavian for 'divine reward'. It is also a variant of the Biblical name Absalom.
*Variants: Absalom, Aksel*

**Azaria**

The name Azaria was another favourite of the 17th century Puritans probably because it was the name of a Biblical prophet. In Hebrew the name means 'God is my help'.
*Variants: Azariah, Azriel*

**Bailey**
See Bailey in the Girls' section.

**Baldwin**

This Old German name was adopted by the Normans who brought it to England. It is the combination of two words 'balda', meaning 'bold', and 'wini', 'friend'. Thus, Baldwin means 'courageous friend'.
*Variants: Baldawin, Baudoin, Bawden, Boden, Bodkin, Bowden*

**Balthazar**
Balthazar is said to be the name of one of the three wise men

who came to visit baby Jesus bringing him gifts of gold, frankincense and myrrh.

In Hebrew Balthazar means 'may Bel (God) protect the king'. It was popular in Britain during the Middle Ages.

*Variants: Balthasar, Belshazzer*

**Bancroft**

The Middle English meaning of this name is 'bean' and 'small field' or 'small holding'. Thus, Bancroft means 'bean field'.

**Barclay**

Barclay comes from Berkeley, a place in Gloucestershire. In Old English it means 'birch-tree' and 'wood' or 'clearing'. It is also the name of a powerful Scottish family.

**Barnabas**

This Biblical name has been used in Britain since the 13th century. In the New Testament Barnabas was an early Christian who assisted St Paul in spreading the tenets of the faith through Asia Minor. The two men also took Christianity to Cyprus.

The Aramaic meaning of this name is 'son of consolation' or 'son of exhortation'. Barnaby is a popular short form.

*Variants: Barn, Barnabe, Barnaby, Barnie*

**Barry**

In the 20th century this name became well-known and was widely used, especially in Australia. However, until the 1800s use of the name Barry was largely confined to Ireland. It is from Ireland – and Wales – that the name derives its meaning.

There are four theories of the origin of Barry. One suggests that it comes from the Gaelic name Bearrach, which means 'spear' or 'good marksman'. Another theory is that Barry comes from the Welsh for 'son of Harry'. Alternatively it could be a short form of the Irish name Finbar, which means 'fair head'. Finally, Barry may have been taken from a Welsh place name – Barry Island – 'bar' meaning 'dune' or 'mound'.

*Variants: Bari, Barnard, Barnett, Barra, Barrie, Barrington, Barrymore, Baz, Bazza, Finbar*

## Bartholomew

In Hebrew Bartholomew simply means 'son of Talmai'. Talmai is the surname of Nathanial, one of Christ's Apostles, and it means 'abounding in furrows'.

*Variants: Bart, Bartel, Bartholomieu, Bartlett, Bartley, Bate, Tolly, Tolomieu, Tolomey*

## Basil

Widely associated with the green herb, 'basil' it also comes from the Greek for 'royal' or 'kingly'. It also has an Irish Gaelic meaning – 'war'.

An early Christian bore the name in the 4th century. The bishop and theologian St Basil the Great was not the only member of his family to be canonised. Six of his relatives also received sainthood – his grandmother, his parents, elder sister and two younger brothers.

*Variants: Bas, Basie, Basile, Baz, Bazza, Brasil, Vas, Vasil*

## Baxter

Originally used as a surname, Baxter comes from the Old English for 'baker'. A feminine equivalent of this name existed during the Middle Ages, but today Baxter is usually given to boys.

## Beasley

This name comes from the Old English for 'field of peas'.
*Variants: Peasley*

## Beau

The French meaning of the name Beau is 'handsome', making it the male equivalent of the girl's name Belle, which means 'beautiful'. A young woman's suitor is also traditionally known as her 'beau'.

However in Hanoverian Britain the name Beau became associated with a one-time friend of the Prince Regent. George Bryan Brummell was a fashionable man, well known for his outrageous style of dress. Beau was his nickname and eventually it was used in reference to any 'dandyish' young man obsessed with beautiful clothes. In 1816, after his friendship with the Prince of Wales ended and he had run up a number of gambling debts, Brummell fled England. He died penniless on the Continent in 1840.

Beau is also the short form of the name Beauregard, which means 'handsome look'. This name was borne by the Confederate general Pierre Gustave Toutant Beauregard who successfully defended the southern city of Charleston during the American Civil War. In the south Beauregard was bestowed upon children in his honour.

*Variants: Beauregard*

## Bede

In 1899 the Venerable Bede was canonized and named a doctor of the Catholic Church by Pope Leo XIII. It is a title that underscores the importance of the work of this gentle Benedictine monk and priest.

St Bede, who lived from 673 until 735, was an author, historian, theologian and one of the most influential writers of his time. In particular *The Ecclesiastical History of the English People*, is one of the most valuable historical works.

His name comes from the Middle English for 'prayer'.

*Variant: Bedivere*

## Benedict

The Latin meaning of Benedict is 'blessed'. The name comes from the word 'benedicere', which means 'to bless', 'speak well of' or 'praise'.

Fifteen popes and a number of saints bore this name, which could explain its widespread use throughout the ages. One such bearer was an Italian monk and hermit who founded the first

Benedictine monastery in Monte Cassino, Italy in 529.
*Variants: Ben, Benedicto, Benes, Beniton, Bennett, Benny, Dick, Dixie*

## Bentley

Today this name is widely associated with the expensive type of car. However it was originally a surname that was derived from a number of place names throughout England. Bentley comes from the Old English words 'beonet', 'bent grass', and 'leah', which means 'wood' or 'clearing'. Thus the name means 'place where there is bent grass'. Another Old English meaning of the name has been suggested – 'to exist' or 'to become'.

Charles Dickens used the name for a character in his novel *Great Expectations* (1860-61).
*Variants: Ben, Benny, Bently*

## Bernard

Bernard is an Old French name that is of Germanic origin. It is derived from two words meaning 'bear' and 'hardy, brave or strong'. Hence Bernard means 'to be as bold or brave as a bear'. An Old English form of the name existed in Britain before the Normans arrived bringing their variant that became Bernard.

The popularity of the name may have been influenced by two holy men who lived in medieval Europe. St Bernard of Clairvaux was a French abbot, theologian and monastic reformer who criticised the luxurious lifestyle of his contemporaries. Another St Bernard, of Montjoux, founded hospices on each of the Alpine passes that bear his name. He died in 1008 and later become the patron saint of mountaineers and skiers. The breed of Alpine rescue dogs is named after him.
*Variants: Barnard, Barnet, Barney, Bernardo, Bernhard, Bernhardt, Bernie, Björn*

## Björn

Björn is the Scandinavian version of Bernard, which has the Germanic meaning of 'bear' and 'strength'.
*Variants: Bernard, Bjorn*

### Blain

Blain comes from the Gaelic word for 'yellow', thus the name Blain may have originated as a nickname for someone with blond hair. Another Irish Gaelic meaning of the name is 'narrow' or 'servant of St Blane' – an early Celtic saint who lived during the 6th century. The name is given to children of both sexes.

*Variants: Blaine, Blane, Blayne*

### Blair

This Scottish surname was originally a place name. It comes from the Gaelic for 'plain', 'field' or 'battle' and is taken to mean 'marshy plain'.

Although Blair can be given to children of either sex, in North America it is frequently given to girls.

*Variants: Blaire, Blayre*

### Blake

Blake comes from the Old English for two words that are directly opposed to each other – 'black' and 'white'. In that language the word 'blæc' means 'black' and 'blāc' means 'pale' or 'white'. Thus Blake was originally a nickname for someone with fair hair and pale skin and also for someone who had a dark complexion.

*Variants: Blanchard, Blanco*

### Benjamin

In the Bible Benjamin was the youngest and favourite son of Jacob. His mother, Jacob's second wife Rachel, died giving birth to him. Like his brothers he went on to head one of the 12 tribes of Israel.

This popular Jewish name means 'son of my right hand' and 'son of the south' in Hebrew. During the 16th century – a time when giving children Old Testament names was in vogue – Benjamin became a favourite among Christian parents.

*Variants: Ben, Benjy, Bennie, Benny*

### Bodi
This Hungarian name means 'may God protect the king'.

### Bonamy
Bonamy comes from the French for 'good friend'.
*Variants: Bonaro, Boni, Bunn*

### Boris
The name comes from the Slavonic for 'battle' or 'stranger'. It also has the Tartar meaning of 'small'.

The patron saint of Moscow is called Boris, which is also the short form of the Russian name Borislav meaning 'battle' and 'glory'.
*Variants: Borislav*

### Boyd
Boyd is the name of a clan in Scotland. It comes from the Gaelic for 'yellow hair'.
*Variants: Bow, Bowen, Bowie*

### Brad
Brad shares the Irish meaning of Bradley – 'descendant of Brádach'. The Old English interpretation of the name is 'wide meadow'.

Brad is also the pet form of Braden, which comes from the Old English for 'to broaden', 'make spacious' or 'plain spoken'. It also means 'to be broad minded'. (See also Brady.)
*Variants: Bradd, Bradford, Bradleigh, Braden, Bradley, Brady*

### Brady
Like Bradley, the name Brady comes from the Gaelic for 'descendant of Brádach'. The exact meaning of Brádach is unknown although it is thought to come from the word for 'large-chested'. Brady also comes from the Old English for 'to broaden'.
*Variants: Brad, Bradd, Bradleigh, Bradley*

### Brandon

As a variant of the Irish name Brendan, Brandon has a rather inauspicious meaning – 'stinking hair'. Nevertheless the name was borne by two 6th-century Irish saints, one of whom was said to have sailed to America long before Christopher Columbus.

The name Brandon has more than one meaning. It comes from the Old English for 'broom' and 'hill'. However the Middle English meaning is 'torch', 'fire' or 'sword'.

*Variants: Branden, Brandt, Brant, Brendan, Brent*

### Brian

This Celtic name was borne by a High King of Ireland who reigned during the 11th century. Known as Brian Boru, he successfully drove the Viking invaders out of his homeland. His name comes from the Old Celtic for 'high' or 'noble' and the Irish Gaelic for 'strong', 'hill' and 'elevated'.

The name Brian was brought to England during the Middle Ages by the Celtic-speaking Bretons, but it is also linked to the classical world. It comes from the Greek for 'strong' and, according to legend, the name Briareos was borne by one of the offspring of Uranus and the earth goddess Gaea.

*Variants: Briant, Briar, Bryan, Bryant*

### Brent

During the 1970s and 1980s the name Brent enjoyed popularity among parents in Britain and North America. Both a surname and a first name, it was originally a place name in England.

Its Celtic meaning is 'high place' or 'hill' but the Old English interpretation is 'burned'.

*Variants: Brendt, Brenten, Brenton*

### Brett

This name comes from the Old French for 'a Breton or Briton' and was originally used in England following the Norman Conquest as a way of identifying the newly-arrived Bretons.

*Variants: Bret, Brit, Briton, Britton, Bretton*

# B

### Brice

The name Brice has more than one meaning. It comes from the German for 'rich' and 'wealthy', but it also means 'powerful ruler'. The Welsh interpretation of the name is 'dappled'.

A 5th century bearer of the name was St Brice who became the bishop of Tours. His fame may have helped to encourage the use of the name, which today enjoys popularity in North America where it is given to children of either sex.
*Variants: Bryce, Bryson, Bryston*

### Brock

The Old English meaning of the name Brock is 'badger'. In children's stories the character of a badger is traditionally called Brock.
*Variants: Badger, Braxton, Brook*

### Bruce

Although popular in modern-day Australia its roots stretch back to the time of the Normans. Its exact meaning is uncertain, but Bruce may come from the French for 'wood' or 'copse'. It was the name of a Norman feudal lord, a relative of whom came to Britain with William the Conqueror.

Robert the Bruce was a descendant of this Norman feudal lord but his fame is connected with Scotland, not France. In 1306 Robert the Bruce, also known as Robert I, secured Scotland's independence from England.
*Variants: Brucey, Brucie, Bruis, Brus*

### Bruno

Like Brock the name Bruno is traditionally used in children's stories as a Christian name for a particular animal – a bear. This is fitting because the German meaning of the name is 'bear' or 'brown like a bear'. Bruno became popular throughout the English-speaking world when German immigrants took the name to North America with them.
*Variants: Bronson, Bruin, Bruna, Bruns*

### Brynn

A unisex name, Brynn comes from the Welsh for 'hill'. It is also a short form of the name Brynmor – a place name in Gwynedd, Wales which means 'big hill'.
*Variants: Brin, Brinn, Bryne, Brynmor, Bryn, Brynne*

### Bryson

Bryson is a variant of the name Brice which means 'rich, wealthy' and 'powerful ruler' in German. It also shares the Welsh meaning of the name, 'dappled'. (See also Brice.)

However, Bryson derives its meaning from another root, the Irish Gaelic language. It is the Anglicised version of the surname Ó Briosáin, which itself was another form of Ó Muirgheasán – 'descendant of Muirgheasán'. The personal name Muirgheasán means 'sea' and 'vigour'.
*Variants: Brice, Bryce*

### Buck

In English the word 'buck' has taken on numerous meanings. It still has the Old English meaning of 'stag', 'male deer' and 'he-goat'. It is also used in North America as a slang term for 'dollar'. Furthermore, to say that a man has the qualities of a young 'buck' is to say that he possesses the robust spiritedness of an animal. This word is also now used as a boy's name.

### Bud

The name Bud comes from 'buddy', the English for 'friend' or 'brother'. Like Buck, this vocabulary word is given to boys as a nickname and is sometimes bestowed upon them as a first name.

The American comedian and actor Bud Abbott was one half of the popular screen pairing Abbott and Costello. He was born William Alexander Abbott in 1895. His countryman, the musician Buddy Holly, born Charles Hardin Holly in 1936, also took this name.
*Variants: Budd, Buddy*

**Burgess**
This name comes from the Late Latin for 'fortified place'. In Old French it was used to describe a free man in a borough or town. It was also once the name for a member of parliament who represented his local area.
*Variants: Burgiss*

**Burr**
The Middle English meaning of this name is 'rough edge', but the Scandinavian interpretation is 'youth'.
*Variants: Burbank, Burrell, Burris, Burton*

**Burt**
Burt is a variant of Bert, which is the short form of a variety of names ranging from Albert and Bertram to Gilbert and Robert. It comes from the Old English for 'bright'.
*Variants: Albert, Bert, Bertram, Cuthbert, Egbert, Gilbert, Herbert, Lambert, Osbert, Robert*

**Burton**
Burton comes from the Old English words 'burh' and 'tūn' and means 'fortress' and 'enclosure' or 'fortified place' and 'settlement'. It is both a surname and the name of various places in England.

**Buster**
In the early days of Hollywood Buster was the screen name of silent movie actor Joseph Francis Keaton. In North America the nickname means 'smasher' or 'breaker'. It comes from the verb 'to bust'.

**Byron**
In Old English the word 'byre' means 'stall', 'hut' or 'cottage'. Thus Byron comes from the Old English for 'cow shed' or 'cattle herder'.

In Britain the first Lord Byron was the 17th-century supporter of

Charles I who received the title in recognition of his loyalty during the Civil War. His descendent, George Gordon Byron, inherited the baronetcy at the age of 10 although he was best known for his poetry and was one of the standard-bearers of the British Romantic Movement. Nineteenth century boys may have been given the name Byron in his honour.

*Variants: Biron, Byram, Byrom*

### Caesar

Caesar is a Roman family name that became associated with leadership and eventually became a title by which Roman emperors were addressed.

The most famous bearer of this name was the Roman political and military leader Gaius (or Caius) Julius Caesar who was born in 100 BC. It was this Caesar who romanced Cleopatra and made her Queen of Egypt. He invaded Britain in 55 BC.

Several theories exist to explain the meaning of his name. It is thought to come from the Latin for 'to cut', 'blue-grey', 'dark hair', 'long hair' and 'head of hair'.

*Variants: Casar, Cesar, César, Cesare, Cesareo, Cezar, Czar, Tsar*

### Cahil

This Turkish name means 'young' and 'naïve'.

### Caleb

In the Bible this name belonged to the man who led the Israelites into the Promised Land alongside Joshua following the death of Moses. Its Hebrew meaning is 'bold' or 'without fear'. The Arabic interpretation is similar – 'brave in victory'.

Caleb also has another Hebrew meaning, 'dog', which apparently symbolises devotion to the Almighty.

*Variants: Cal, Cale, Kalb, Kale, Kaleb, Kalev*

### Callum

Although the two names may not look the same, Callum comes from Columba, a Late Latin personal name that means 'dove'. It is through Columba that Callum derives its association with Scotland, for it was the Irish saint of that name that used the Scottish isle of Iona as a base for the conversion of that nation. From Columba we also get the name Malcolm, which means 'follower of St Columba'.

*Variants: Calum, Colm, Colum, Kallum, Kalum, Malcolm*

### Calvin

John Calvin was the French-Swiss Protestant theologian whose doctrines were the foundation of Presbyterianism. His beliefs centred upon learning, the belief that God was all powerful and the adherence to a strict moral code. It was from this man that the Calvinist movement derived its name. Religious Nonconformists also bestowed his surname upon their children in his honour.

Its meaning is derived from the French for 'bald' or 'little bald one'.

*Variants: Cal, Vin, Vinny*

### Cameron

This Scottish surname was borne by one of the great Highland clans. Its meaning comes from the Gaelic for 'crooked nose', which may suggest that it was once a nickname given to an ancestor. Today it is bestowed upon children of both sexes.

*Variants: Cam, Camaron, Camron, Kam, Kamaron, Kameron, Kamron*

### Carl

This Old German name is a German and Scandinavian form of Charles, which means 'man'. It can also be spelt with a 'K' as demonstrated in Karl Marx.

*Variants: Carlo, Carlos, Karl*

### Carlton

Carlton is an Old English surname and place name that refers to numerous locations in England. It is derived from two words 'carl', meaning 'free man or peasant', and 'tūn', 'town'

or 'settlement'. Thus Carlton means 'settlement of free men or peasants'.
*Variants: Carl, Carleton, Carlson, Charles, Charlton*

## Carson

Carson is another Scottish surname that has gained currency as a first name, especially in North America. Its exact meaning is unknown but it may be of English derivation, meaning 'son of Carr', or it could have referred to someone who lived in a marsh.

## Carter

Carter comes from the Old Norse for 'cart for transporting goods' and 'driver of a cart'. It is a first name derived from a surname, which once indicated an occupational name.

## Cary

In the 20th century the name Cary became associated with the British-born American actor Cary Grant who was born Archibald Leach. Grant's stage name is thought to have more than one meaning. It was an English family name that was taken from a number of place names. It is also an Old Celtic river name and comes from the Irish for 'son of the dark one'. Its Welsh meaning is 'castle dweller'. The Latin interpretation is 'much loved' and 'costly'. As a variant of Charles, Cary means 'man'.
*Variants: Carey, Charles*

## Caspian

The British writer C S Lewis used this name for the title character of his 1951 children's novel *Prince Caspian*. The book was the second in his successful *Chronicles of Narnia* series.

The exact meaning of the name is unclear, but it is the name of the stretch of water known as the Caspian Sea.

## Cassius

Before he converted to Islam and became Muhammad Ali, the American boxer, was known as Cassius Marcellus Clay. His

Roman name has been borne by more than one personality in history. One well-known bearer was Gaius Cassius Longinus, who played an important role in the plot to assassinate Julius Caesar.

Cassius comes from the Greek for 'herb' and the Italian for 'cinnamon bark'. In Latin it means 'vain'.

*Variants: Case, Casey, Cash, Casius, Cass, Cassie, Cassy, Kas*

## Cecil

In England the name Cecil is associated with a noble family who rose to prominence during the 16th century. It has more than one meaning, both of which are rooted in the Latin language. For example, Cecil is thought to be the English form of the Old Roman family name Caecilius, which comes from the Latin for 'blind'.

The name is also thought to be the Anglicised version of a Welsh name, Seissylt. Yet this too is merely a variation of a Latin name, this time Sextilius, which comes from Sextus meaning 'sixth'. In Roman times Sextus was bestowed upon the sixth son in a family.

Cecil gained currency as a first name during the 19th century.

*Variants: Ceci, Cecile, Cecilio, Cecilius*

## Cedric

The exact origin of the name Cedric is unknown. One theory is that the name was invented by the Scottish writer Sir Walter Scott for a character in his novel *Ivanhoe* (1819). If that is the case, maybe Scott's inspiration was the name of the founder of Wessex, the Anglo-Saxon kingdom. Hence, sometimes, Cedric is taken to be a misspelling of Cerdic.

Nevertheless, despite this confusion a number of possible meanings for Cedric have emerged. They include 'welcome sight' in Welsh, 'generous pattern' in Celtic and 'friendly' in Old English. Later on in the 19th century the name was used by another writer, Frances Hodgson Burnett, in her work *Little Lord Fauntleroy*.

*Variants: Cad, Caddaric, Ced, Cedrych, Cerdic, Ceredic, Rick, Rickie, Ricky*

### Chad

Chad is the modern variant of the Old English name Ceadda, which was borne by a 7th century saint. St Ceadda was known for being humble, holy and for his role as the Bishop of York and Lichfield. The Celtic meaning of his name is 'battle' or 'warrior'. In Old English it means 'martial'.

Chad has been popular in North America since the 1980s.
*Variants: Chadd, Chaddie, Chadwick, Chaddy*

### Chandler

Such is the power of television that for a generation of channel hoppers Chandler will forever be associated with a character from the US sitcom *Friends*. However, the name existed long before the arrival of the fictitious Chandler Bing.

The name probably originally referred to someone's occupation for it comes from the French for 'candle maker' or 'seller of candles'.
*Variants: Chan, Chaney, Cheney, Shandler*

### Charles

The name Charles has long been associated with royalty. Today it is the name of the future king of England, but during the Dark Ages it was also favoured by the Frankish ruling class. For example, Carolus Magnus (Charles the Great) of Charlemagne (771 to 814) founded the Holy Roman Empire.

It was the Normans who brought this Germanic name to Britain in the 11th century and during the Stuart period it became associated with more than one monarch – Charles I, who was overthrown and beheaded, and his son Charles II. Ten French kings have borne the name as have five Swedish rulers.

Charles comes from the Old German for 'man' or 'free man'.
*Variants: Carl, Carlos, Carlton, Charlie, Charley, Chas, Charlton, Chaz, Chuck, Karl*

### Chester

Chester is both a surname and the name of an English city. When the Romans invaded England they created many fortress towns and Chester was one of them. Thus it comes from the Latin for 'fortress, castle' or 'walled town'.

Its use as a first name began during the last century.

*Variants: Caster, Castor, Chesleigh, Chesley, Chet, Ches*

## Chip

Chip is the short form of Christopher, which comes from the Greek – 'one who carries Christ'. It also comes from the name of a Native American tribe – Chippewa.

*Variants: Chipper, Christopher*

## Christian

To identify oneself as a Christian is to say that you are a follower of Jesus Christ. Naturally this is the meaning of the given name, which in Latin is 'Christianus'. However in Greek it means 'anointed one', a direct translation of the Hebrew term 'Messiah'.

Christian has been used as a first name since the Middle Ages.

*Variants: Chris, Christiaan, Christiano, Christie, Christien, Kit, Kris, Kristian*

## Christobal

Christobal is a combination of two words – 'Christ' and 'ball'. Thus it means 'dance of Christ'.

*Variants: Cristobal*

## Christopher

The 3rd century martyr St Christopher is well-known as the patron saint of travellers – and with good reason. According to tradition he acquired the name Christopher after he carried a small boy across a river. The child was unusually heavy and, when asked, explained that he was Jesus Christ who was carrying the weight of the sins of the world. Hence the name Christopher comes from the Greek for 'one who carries Christ'.

*Variants: Chip, Chris, Chrissie, Christoph, Christophe, Kester, Kit, Kristofer*

### Cicero

In Italian this name means 'learned antiquarian' or 'guide for sightseers'. The name was borne by the Roman statesman and orator Marcus Tullius Cicero, who was assassinated in 43 BC.
*Variants: Cicerone, Ciceroni, Ciro, Cyrano*

### Clark

For generations of children, be they comic book readers, cinemagoers or avid television viewers, Clark Kent is the alter ego of the hero Superman. During the 1930s the name was associated with the screen idol Clark Gable, but long before the arrival of the mass media Clark originated as an occupational name. A clerk was someone who earned his living by his ability to read or write. Indeed today a 'clerk' is still a secretary, someone who keeps records or a lay officer of a church.
*Variants: Clarke, Claxton*

### Claude

This name comes from the Roman family name Claudius, which in Latin means 'limping' or 'lame'. It has existed in Britain since the time of Roman occupation. In France its popularity grew because of a 7th century saint who bore the name. (See below.)
*Variants: Claudell, Claudian, Claudius, Claus*

### Claudius

With his limp and stutter Claudius I was an unlikely candidate for the position of Roman Emperor, but this is the role that he assumed from 41 to 54 AD. It was chosen by parents even though the name means 'limp', 'lame', 'crippled' or 'defective'.
*Variants: Claude, Claudell, Claudian, Claus*

### Claus

As a variant of Claudius, Claus means 'limp', 'lame', 'crippled' or 'defective'. (See above.) But it is also a German form of the name Nicholas, which comes from the Greek for 'people's victory'.
*Variants: Claude, Claudell, Claudian, Claudius, Klaus, Nicholas*

### Clay

The name Clay comes from the Old English word for 'clay' or 'fine-grained earth'. As a surname it would have been attached to someone who lived in an area of clay soil. Its use as a first name began in the 19th century.

In North America it is a short form of Clayton, which means 'town on clay land'.

*Variants: Clayland, Clayton, Cle, Clea, Cletus, Klay*

### Clement

Clement Attlee was the name of the leader of the Labour Party who became the British Prime Minister in 1945. His name comes from the Latin for 'kind', 'gentle', 'calm' and 'merciful'.

*Variants: Clem, Cleme, Clemen, Clemens, Clemmy*

### Clinton

In recent years the name Clinton is best known as the surname of the former President of the United States – William 'Bill' Jefferson Clinton, who lead his country from 1993 to 2001. In England the name is also associated with a noble family. Geoffrey de Clinton, who built the Castle of Kenilworth, was chamberlain and treasurer to William I. His family name comes from the Middle English for 'hilltop town'.

In North America Clinton and its variant Clint is used as a first name.

*Variant: Clint*

### Clive

Clive comes from the Old English for 'overhanging rock face', 'cliff' or 'slope'. As a surname it was derived from a number of place names in England. Its transferred use as a first name is owed to the fame of the British soldier and statesman Robert Clive who died in 1774. He was known as Clive of India because of his part in establishing British power in India. Such was his popularity with East India Company employees that some of them named their sons Clive in his honour.

Clive was also the first name of C S Lewis, the author of the series of children's novels *The Chronicles of Narnia*.
*Variants: Cleve, Cleveland, Clevey, Clevie, Cliff, Clifton*

**Clyde**
In Scotland the River Clyde runs through the city of Glasgow, but its name has the Celtic meaning 'to wash'. It also comes from the Welsh for 'heard from far away'. As well as being a place name, it is also a surname and a first name that belonged to the 1930s American bank robber, Clyde Barrow, of 'Bonnie and Clyde' fame.
*Variants: Cly, Clydesdale, Clywd*

**Cody**
In North America and Australia the name Cody is bestowed upon both boys and girls. However, it was originally an Irish surname that meant 'descendant of a helpful or cheerful person'.
*Variants: Codi, Codie*

**Colbert**
Colbert has Old French, Latin and Germanic roots. One theory suggests that it comes from the Latin for 'neck'. Another suggests that the second half of the name is derived from the Old High German for 'bright' or 'shining', while the meaning of the first half is unknown.

Whatever its origin it was brought to Britain by the Normans in the 11th century.
*Variants: Cole, Colvert, Culbert*

**Cole**
More than one meaning is attached to the name Cole. It is derived from the Middle English for 'coal', thus the name Colby means 'coal town' and Coleman refers to a 'coal miner'. However, Cole also comes from the Welsh for 'trust'. Furthermore it can be used as pet form of Nicholas, which means 'people's victory' in Greek.

The Scottish king Coel the Adulterous, who ruled during the

6th century, is said to be the inspiration for the nursery rhyme *Old King Cole*.
*Variants: Colby, Coleman, Colin, Collie, Collier, Collis, Colton, Colville, Colvin, Nicholas*

## Colin

As a short form of Nicholas, Colin comes from the Greek for 'people's victory'. But more than one theory exists to explain the origin of this popular name. It is thought to come from the Scottish Gaelic for 'youth' and 'puppy' and from the Irish Gaelic for 'young man'. 'Chieftain' is another Celtic meaning of Colin.

The name is common in Scotland where it is used as an Anglicisation of the Gaelic name 'Cailean' ('young').
*Variants: Cailean, Colan, Cole, Collie, Collin, Collins, Colly, Colyn, Nicholas*

## Connor

According to Irish legend Conchobhar was the name of the King of Ulster who planned to marry Deirdre but she eloped with Naoise instead. He took revenge on his young rival by killing him. Connor is the Anglicised form of the Gaelic name Conchobhar, which means 'lover of hounds'.
*Variants: Conn, Conor*

## Conrad

This German name was introduced to Britain during the Middle Ages. It is a combination of two Old High German words meaning 'bold', 'wise' and 'counsellor'. Thus Conrad means 'bold counsel'.
*Variants: Con, Curt, Konrad, Kurt*

## Constantine

Until 1930, Istanbul, Turkey's largest city, was known as Constantinople. It was so-named after the first Christian Roman Emperor, Constantine I or 'the Great'. His conversion to the faith in 312 marked the end of Christian persecution in the Roman Empire. His name comes from the Latin for 'to stand together', so it symbolises 'loyalty' and 'constancy'.

Constantine is another name that was brought to the British Isles by the Normans. Although its use in that country declined after the Reformation, it increased during the 19th century.

*Variants: Con, Connie, Consta, Constant, Constantin, Costa, Konstantin*

### Corbin

The exact origin of Corbin is unknown. It is thought to be derived from the Old French for 'raven' or from the Anglo-Norman for 'crow'.

*Variants: Corban, Corben, Corbet, Corbett, Corby, Corbyn, Korbin, Korby*

### Corey

In the United States Corey is bestowed upon children of both sexes, but it is especially popular for boys. Its roots stem back to the Mediterranean and to the Celtic parts of the British Isles.

The Greek meaning of Corey is 'helmet', but it is also an Irish surname that comes from the Irish and Scottish Gaelic for 'hollow dweller' or 'pool dweller'. (See also Cori in the Girls' section.)

*Variants: Cori, Cory, Correy, Corry, Korey, Kori, Kory*

### Cornelius

During the days of the Roman Empire Cornelius was the name of a talented family. One famous bearer of the name was Gaius Cornelius Tacitus, the historian whose accounts of the first century of the Roman Empire continue to be studied by history students today. His name comes from the Latin for 'cornel tree' and 'horn' or 'hard-hearted'.

*Variants: Cornell, Corney, Cornie, Cory, Neil, Neilus, Nelly*

### Cormac

Cormac comes from the Greek for 'tree trunk' but its popularity in Ireland is due to its association with a former king and bishop. The Irish Gaelic meaning of the name is 'defilement' and 'son'. It may also mean 'charioteer' and 'son of the raven'.
*Variants: Cormack, Cormick*

### Count

Count comes from the Old French for 'companion' or 'colleague'.
*Variant: Countee*

### Cosmo

St Cosmas is the patron saint of physicians, surgeons and pharmacists along with his twin brother Damian, who was also canonised by the Roman Catholic Church. Both men were early Christian martyrs who were recognised for their charitable work among the poor. They were 4th century physicians who made no charge to help the less fortunate.

The name Cosmo comes from the Greek for 'order' or 'beauty'. It was brought to Britain in the 18th century by the Scottish dukes of Gordon who had links with the ducal house of Tuscany.
*Variants: Cosimo, Cosmas*

### Craig

Craig is the Anglicised form of the Scottish Gaelic family name meaning 'from the rocks'. It was originally given to someone who lived near a cliff, but became a first name throughout the English-speaking world in the 20th century.
*Variant: Kraig*

### Cramer

Cramer comes from the Old English for 'to squeeze' or 'to fill up'. It was usually associated with cramming one's head with knowledge or filling the stomach with food.
*Variants: Cram, Kramer*

### Crispin

The saints Crispin and Crispinian were early Christian martyrs and shoemakers who were brothers. Thus they are both patron saints of shoemakers, cobblers and leatherworkers. Both names were derived from the Latin for 'curly'.
*Variants: Crispinian, Crispus, Krispin*

### Crosby

Crosby comes from the Old Norse for 'from the place with the cross' and from the Middle English for 'cross'. Therefore, it may refer to the cross that usually stood in town centres.
*Variants: Crosbey, Crosbie*

### Curtis

Although the name Curtis is more popular in North America than it is in Europe, its meaning is very much rooted in the Old World.

This surname and first name is derived from the Latin for 'courtyard'. It is also related to the Old French for 'to be or reside at court' and 'to flatter, entice or woo' or 'be courteous'.

The Middle English meaning differs from the Latin and Old French interpretations. The English family name Curtis comes from the words for 'short stockings'.
*Variants: Court, Courtenay, Courtland, Courts, Curt, Kurt, Kurtis*

### Cyril

In the 9th century the name Cyril was borne by one of the missionaries who took Christianity to Russia. His presence made a lasting impression on the region, not just because he brought with him the Biblical stories of Christ but because he made a valuable contribution to the Slavic languages. It was St Cyril who devised the Russian Cyrillic alphabet to translate the scriptures from Greek. His own name was derived from Greek and it meant 'lord' or 'ruler'.
*Variants: Ciro, Cy, Cyrill, Syril*

**Cyrus**

Cyrus was the name of the founder and first significant king of the Persian Empire. Known as Cyrus the Great, he is mentioned in the Bible. His name means 'sun' or 'throne'.
*Variants: Ciro, Cy, Cyrie, Cyro, Kir, Russ, Sy*

**Dahi**

Although Dahi is thought of as a variant of David, it is a Welsh name that comes from the Celtic for 'nimble'.

**Dalai**

Dalai Lama is the term for the Buddhist spiritual and political leader of Tibet. The name Dalai comes from the Sanskrit for 'mediator'.

**Dalbert**

Two Old High German words have been joined together to form the name Dalbert. It comes from 'tal', meaning 'valley' or 'hollow', and 'beraht', 'bright' and 'shining'. Thus Dalbert means 'bright valley'.
*Variants: Bert, Bertie, Berty, Burt, Dal*

**Dale**

In North America the name Dale is given to both boys and girls. It comes from the Old Norse for 'broad valley' and the Old English for 'valley'. As a surname it was probably first attached to someone who lived in a dale or valley. Dalton, a similar name, means 'valley town' and Dallin stands for 'from the vale'.
*Variants: Dal, Daley, Dali, Dalton, Dayle, Delles, Dillon*

**Damon**

Modern use of the name Damon seems to date back to the 1930s, but its roots are in the classical world. According to Greek mythology, Damon and Pythias were two friends who were devoted to each other. Legend has it that the tyrant Dionysius condemned Pythias to death, but allowed him to settle his affairs before facing his fate – as long as his friend stayed behind in his place. When Pythias stayed true to his word and returned rather than let Damon take his punishment, Dionysius, impressed by their loyalty, freed them both.

More than one meaning is attributed to the name Damon. They include the Greek for 'fate' or 'divine power' and the Old English for 'day'. It is also linked to the Latin for 'evil spirit' or 'demon'.
*Variants: Dame, Damian, Damiano, Damien, Dayman*

### Daniel
The Biblical tale of Daniel in the lions' den was a popular one during the Middle Ages. According to the Old Testament Daniel was an Israelite slave of an Assyrian king who was favoured by his master because he could interpret dreams. Daniel's enemies conspired against him and eventually he was thrown into a den of lions. Condemned to die, it was his faith in God that saved him from what seemed an inevitable fate.

In Hebrew the name means 'God is my judge'. Deiniol, a similar Welsh name, means 'attractive' and 'charming'.
*Variants: Dan, Dana, Dane, Daneil, Dani, Dano, Dannie, Danny, Deiniol*

### Dante
Like Daniel, the name Dante was popular during the Middle Ages. The name comes from the Italian for 'to endure, bear or be patient'. It is also the short form of the name Durante, which comes from the Latin for 'steadfast'.
*Variants: Donte, Devonte, Duran, Durante, Durant*

### Darcy
See Darcie in the Girls' section.

### Darius
Darius is a name that was borne by three kings of ancient Persia. The Persian meaning of the name is 'protector', but it also comes

from the Greek for 'wealthy' or 'rich'.
*Variants: Daare, Daren, Daria, Darian, Dario, Darien, Darren*

### Darren

The exact meaning of this name is uncertain. As a variant of Darius, Darren is derived from the Greek for 'rich' or the Persian for 'protector'. It may also have come from an Irish family name, which has the Gaelic meaning 'great' or 'small one'.
*Variants: Dar, Daren, Darien, Darin, Dario, Darius, Darnell, Daryn*

### Darwin

The name comes from the Old English for 'sea' or 'dear' and 'friend'. Hence it means 'lover of the sea'.
*Variants: Dar, Derwin, Derwyn, Durwin*

### David

King David, the father of Solomon, is one of the most revered and beloved characters of the Old Testament. As a young man, armed with a sling and pebbles, he defeated the giant Goliath in single combat. He became founder and first ruler of the united kingdom of Israel and Judah. He was also a great lover and poet, writing many of the psalms, including 'The Lord is my Shepherd'. His name is favoured by both Jews and Christians alike. Its Hebrew meaning is 'beloved'.

The name David is popular among the Welsh because it was borne by their patron saint.
*Variants: Dafydd, Dahi, Dai, Dave, Daveed, Davi, Davide, Davy*

### De Angelo

Used in North America as a first name, De Angelo comes from the Greek for 'angel' or 'messenger'.
*Variants: Angel, Angelo, DeAngelo*

### Dean

Three theories exist to explain the origin of the name Dean. The first suggests that Dean comes from the Old English for 'valley' and that originally it referred to someone who lived in a valley. Another theory points to the Middle English word 'dene', which was an occupational name for someone who served as an ecclesiastical supervisor. The name may also be derived from the Greek for 'ten'. In that case 'dean' referred to someone of high rank who was responsible for ten or more people.

There is one more, fourth suggestion about the origin of Dean. Sometimes it is the Anglicisation of the Italian name Dino, which can be a short form of the longer name Bernardino. One example of this was the Italian-American actor and singer Dean Martin who was given the Christian name Dino at birth.

*Variants: Dene, Denn, Dino*

### Declan

The exact meaning of Declan is uncertain but it may have been derived from the Irish Gaelic for 'good'. The name was borne by an early Irish saint, who was a bishop in the district of Ardmore. Declan is the Anglicised form of the Gaelic name Deaglán.

*Variant: Deaglan*

### Delmar

Delmar comes from the Latin for 'of the sea'.

*Variants: Del, Delmer, Delmore*

### Delvin

This name is derived from the Greek word 'delphis', which means 'dolphin'.

*Variants: Del, Delwin*

### Demetrius

According to Greek mythology Demeter was the goddess of the earth associated with agriculture. This Mother Nature figure was responsible for mankind and its toils, including fertility and the cultivation of the soil. The name Demetrius refers to this goddess and means either 'goddess of fertility' or 'follower of Demeter'.

The name Demetrius is mentioned in the Bible more than

once and was also borne by a 17th-century saint and bishop.
*Variants: Deems, Demeter, Demetre, Demetri*

### Dennis

Dionysus was the Greek god of wine and revelry. It is from
Dionysus that the French name Denis, or Dennis, is derived. It is
associated with St Dionysius of Paris, a 3rd century evangelist,
who was sent from Rome to Gaul as a missionary.

The Normans brought the name to Britain, where it was used
as a given name until the 1600s. Thereafter its popularity
declined until its use was revived during the 20th century.
*Variants: Deenys, Den, Denis, Denison, Dennison, Denny, Denys,
Dion, Dionysius*

### Denver

In North America, Denver is a town in Colorado, but in England
it was originally a family name derived from a reference to a
place. In Old English Denver means 'Danes' crossing' and in
Middle English it stands for 'little forested valley'. The French
interpretation is 'green'.
*Variants: Den, Dennie, Denny*

### Denzel

This is linked to the surname Denzil, which comes from the
Old Cornish place name Denzell and is from the Celtic for
'stronghold' and the Old Cornish for 'high'. In the 1980s and
1990s it became associated with the actor Denzel
Washington.
*Variants: Denzell, Denzil*

### Derby

The meaning of Derby is threefold. One suggestion is that it
comes from the Old English for 'deer'. Thus the town of Derby in
England would mean 'farmstead where deer are kept'.
Alternatively the name may be a combination of two Old English
words 'dwr' and 'by', meaning 'water' and 'village, town'.

It is also used as an Anglicised form of the Irish name Dermot, which means 'without injunction' or 'without envy'. (See also Dermot.)
*Variants: Dar, Darby, Dermot*

## Derek

The name Derek was derived from two Old High German names, both of which contain the word for 'ruler'. The first source is Hrodrick, which is a combination of two elements – 'hrod', which means 'famous', and 'richi', 'ruler', 'power' or 'wealth'. Thus, Derek means 'famous ruler'.

The name is also related to another Old High German predecessor, Theodoric. The latter, which means 'the people's ruler', was borne by the European ruler Theodoric the Great, who died in 526.

The more contemporary version, Derrick, was the name of a 17th century hangman, thus the name developed into another word for 'crane'. The French variant of Theodoric is Thierry, which developed into Terry. The Dutch interpretation is Dirk.
*Variants: Del, Derrick, Derry, Dirk, Rick, Ricky, Rik, Terry, Thierry*

## Dermot

According to Irish legend Diarmait is a romantic figure who eloped with the Queen of Tara and faced death for his actions. Dermot is the contemporary version of his name. It means 'without injunction' or 'free from envy'. (See also Derby.)
*Variants: Darby, Derby, Dermod, Dermott, Diarmid, Diarmod, Diarmuid*

## Derry

The Northern Irish city of Londonderry is sometimes referred to as Derry. The Gaelic meaning of Derry is 'red-headed', but it also comes from the Welsh for 'oak trees'. It is also a pet form of Derek.
*Variants: Dare, Darrey, Darrie, Dary, Derek*

## Desmond

The Latin meaning of Desmond is 'of or from the world'. As it originates from the word 'mundus', which means 'the universe', it implies someone who is part of creation.

Desmond also has Celtic roots. In Irish Gaelic it means 'from south Munster' or 'descendent of one from south Munster'. Munster is a province in Ireland.
*Variants: Des, Desi, Dezi*

## Devon

The name of this English county is sometimes bestowed on children of either sex. Devon is derived from the Latin name of the Celtic tribe who lived in those parts at the time of the Roman invasion.

The name can be pronounced in one of two ways – either as 'de-VON' or as 'DEV-on' with an emphasis on the first syllable. The variant Devin comes from the Celtic for 'poet'.
*Variants: Devan, Deven, Devin, Devyn*

## Dexter

Dexter is the transferred use of a surname that comes from the Latin for 'right-sided' or 'right-handed'. It has also been derived from the Old English for 'dye'.
*Variants: Decca, Deck, Dek, Dex*

## Dhani

A Hindu name, Dhani means 'person of wealth and riches'.

## Didi

Didi is the short form of the French name Didier, which is the male version of Desirée. (See Desirée in the Girls' section.) Hence it derives its meaning from the Latin for 'ardent desire', 'deep longing' and 'wish'.

Didi is also a variant of Dodo, which means 'beloved' in Hebrew or 'stupid' and 'clumsy' in Portuguese. The latter qualities were associated with the now extinct flightless bird from Mauritius.
*Variants: Didier, Didon, Didot, Dizier, Dodo*

### Diego
The name Diego is the Spanish form of the Biblical name James, which is itself a variant of the Old Testament name Jacob. All three come from the Hebrew for 'supplanter'.
*Variants: Jacob, James*

### Digby
Digby is derived from a place name in Lincolnshire, England and was later attached to a notable family. The name comes from the French for 'to dig a ditch or dike' and the Old Norse for 'ditch' and 'settlement'.

### Dirk
In Scotland 'dirk' is another word for 'dagger'. The name is also the Dutch and Flemish form of Derek, which comes from the Old High German for 'famous ruler' or 'the people's ruler'. (See also Derek.)
*Variants: Derek, Derrick*

### Dominic
Dominic was the name of the Spanish saint who founded an order of monastic priests during the 13th century. Though they became known as the Order of Preachers, they are better known as the Dominican Order or, simply, the Dominicans.

Dominic's name means 'of the Lord' in Latin and traditionally was bestowed upon boys born on a Sunday. Later, Roman Catholics gave it to their sons in honour of the saint.
*Variants: Dom, Domenic, Domenico, Domenyk, Domingo, Dominick, Nick, Nickie, Nicky*

### Donald
Donald is the Anglicised version of the Celtic name Domhnall, which means 'global or proud ruler'. It is a Scottish clan name that was borne by a number of kings of Scotland and Ireland.
*Variants: Domhnall, Don, Donahue, Donal, Donaldo, Donalt, Donn, Donne, Donnie, Donovan*

### Donnel

St Donnan was an Irish Christian who worked with a group of monks on an island in the Inner Hebrides before he was killed by a gang of locals in 617. His name comes from the Gaelic for 'hill' or 'hill-fort'. Donnel is a variant of this name.

Another Celtic name, Donald, is related to Donnel giving it the meaning 'global or proud ruler'. (See also Donald.)
*Variants: Don, Donald, Donn, Donnell, Donnelly, Donny, Dun*

### Donovan

Donovan was first used as a first name during the early 1900s. Its popularity soared during the 1960s following the success of the folk-rock singer of the same name. However, Donovan was, and still is, an Irish surname. In Gaelic it means 'descendant of Donndubhán'. Donndubhán was a personal name for someone who was dark in complexion. It also means 'dark warrior'.
*Variants: Don, Donnie, Donny, Donavan, Van*

### Dorian

*The Picture of Dorian Gray* was the only novel written by the poet, playwright and wit, Oscar Wilde. The plot is about a handsome young man who, over the years, retains his youth and beauty while the portrait of him that hangs in his attic grows old and ugly.

Wilde is thought to have taken the name from the classical world. In Ancient Greece a Dorian was someone who came from the Doris region. Doris meant 'bountiful sea' or 'sacrificial knife'. Alternatively Dorian may come from the Greek word for 'gift', 'doron'. (See also Doris in the Girls' section.)
*Variants: Doran, Dore, Dorey, Dorie, Doron, Dory*

### Dougal

The Irish Gaelic meaning of Dougal is 'dark stranger'. It was the nickname given to the invading Danes in contrast to Fingal, 'fair stranger', which was used for the lighter Norwegians.
*Variants: Doug, Dougie, Doyle, Dug, Dugard, Duggy, Dughall*

*Boys*

### Douglas

Douglas is the name of an ancient Scottish clan who acquired the earldoms of Angus and Douglas in the 8th century. Their name is derived from two Gaelic words – 'dubh' meaning 'dark colour', and 'glas', meaning 'water'. The full meaning of the name, therefore, is 'black stream'.

*Variants: Doug, Dougal, Dougie, Douglass, Dougy, Dugald, Duggie*

### Doyle

As a variant of Dougal, Doyle means 'dark stranger'. However, the name also comes from the Irish Gaelic for 'assembly' or 'gathering'.

*Variant: Dougal*

### Drake

This name comes from the Greek for 'serpent' or 'dragon'. Historically dragons have not always been viewed as negative figures. Although they were considered to be evil by Christians, they have been greatly revered by the Chinese.

### Dudley

The name Dudley comes from the Old English for 'Duddha's clearing or wood'. The exact meaning of Duddha is unclear but it may have been a nickname for a podgy man.

*Variants: Dud, Dudd, Dudly*

### Duke

Duke comes from the Latin for 'leader, conductor', 'guide' or 'commander'. It is also a hereditary title of nobility like 'earl'.

It is sometimes used as a nickname for someone who has excelled in their profession, such as Edward Kennedy Ellington – the American jazz musician best known as Duke Ellington.

### Duncan

Like Donald and Douglas, Duncan is a name associated with Scotland. It comes from the Scottish Gaelic words 'donn'

('greyish-brown') and 'chadh' ('warrior') and means 'dark-skinned warrior'. It is also thought to mean 'princely battle'.
*Variants: Dun, Dunc, Dune, Dunkie, Dunn*

**Dunstan**
Dunstan is derived from the Old English for 'greyish-brown' and 'stone' or 'hill'. Thus it means 'dark hill'. It was the first name of an Anglo-Saxon saint whose contribution to the British monarchy can still be felt. An adviser to the kings of Wessex in his day, he also devised the coronation service that is still used in Britain. He is the patron saint of blacksmiths and goldsmiths.
*Variants: Donestan, Dunn, Dunne, Dunst*

**Dustin**
The exact meaning of Dustin is uncertain. It could come from the German for 'warrior' or the Old Norse for 'Thor's stone'. Thor was the Viking god of thunder, after whom Thursday was named.
*Variants: Dust, Dustie, Dusty*

**Dwayne**
Dwayne derives its meaning from the Irish Gaelic for 'dark little one'. It gained popularity as a first name following the success of the American guitarist Duane Eddy whose work enjoyed popularity from the 1950s to the 1980s.
*Variants: Duane, Duwayne, Dwain*

**Dwight**
Dwight comes from the Old English for 'white, fair'.
*Variants: DeWitt, Dewitt, Diot, Doyt, Wit, Wittie, Witty*

**Dylan**
The exact origin of the Welsh name Dylan is uncertain but it may be derived from the Celtic word for 'sea'. In the first half of the 20th century the name was widely known through the work of the Welsh poet, Dylan Thomas.
*Variants: Dillan, Dillon*

**Eamon**

The Irish politician Eamon de Valera played a pivotal role in Ireland's independence from Great Britain. Born in New York City in 1882, he held the position of Taoiseach (Prime Minister) three times and the role of president once, before leaving public office aged 90.

His name is the Irish Gaelic form of Edmund and comes from the Old English for 'happiness', 'riches' and 'protector'. It is also a variant of Edward. (See also Edmund and Edward.)

*Variants: Eamonn, Edmund, Edward*

**Earl**

An earl is a British nobleman who ranks between Marquis and Viscount. The name means 'nobleman', 'chief', 'prince' or 'warrior' in Old English.

Earl is rarely used in Britain as a given name, but it was originally used as a nickname for someone who worked in the household of an earl. It is more commonly used as a Christian name in North America.

*Variants: Earle, Erle*

**Eaton**

Two Old English words combine to form this name – 'ea', meaning 'river' or 'running water', and 'tūn', 'town or village'. Thus Eaton means 'riverside town'.

**Eden**

Eden may be a variant of the Celtic name Aidan, which means 'little fiery one' in Irish Gaelic. Furthermore, it could come from the Old English for 'prosperity, riches' and 'bear cub'. It could also be taken from the Garden of Eden from the Book of Genesis. In North America, Eden is bestowed on baby boys and girls.

*Variants: Aidan, Ed, Edan, Eddie, Eddy*

**Edgar**

The Anglo-Saxon king Edgar the Peaceful was the grandson of

Alfred the Great. His name comes from the Old English for 'lucky spear'.
*Variants: Ed, Eddie*

### Edmund

The Old English meaning of the name Edmund is 'happy protection'. It was borne by three English kings, one of whom was the 9th century monarch and saint, Edward the Martyr. He died at the hands of the Vikings after he refused to take up arms, preferring to follow Christ's non-violent example instead.

Another saint who bore the name was Edmund of Abingdon who held the post of Archbishop of Canterbury.

The Irish form of Edmund is Eamon. (See also Eamon.)
*Variants: Eadmond, Eamon, Ed, Edmond, Eddie, Eddy, Esmund, Ned, Ted, Teddy*

### Edom

Edom is a pet form of the Biblical name Adam, which comes from the Hebrew for 'red earth'. In the Old Testament it is an alternative name for Jacob's brother, Esau, whose descendants lived in a land of the same name.
*Variants: Adam, Idumea*

### Edric

Edric is another name that begins with the Old English prefix that means 'happy' or 'riches'. The second part of the name means 'ruler'. Thus, the Old English interpretation of Edric is 'happy ruler'.
*Variants: Ed, Eddie, Eddy, Edred, Edrich, Edrick, Ric, Rick, Ricky*

### Edward

The links between Edward and the British monarchy are so strong that over the centuries England has had 10 kings bearing the name. The first was the Anglo-Saxon king of Wessex, Edward the Elder, whose father was Alfred the Great. He died in 924 and the next king with the name was eventually canonised.

Although Edward the Confessor had no children, his legacy included Westminster Abbey. Edward's death prompted the conflict over succession to the English throne. The result was William the Conqueror's defeat of Harold II at the Battle of Hastings in 1066.

Edward VIII was the most recent British monarch bearing the name. He was king briefly during 1936 before he abdicated his throne for the love of Mrs (Wallis) Simpson, a twice-divorced American woman whom he later married.

In modern times the name has been borne by the third son of Elizabeth II. Prince Edward bears a name that comes from the Old English for 'happy', 'fortunate', 'rich' and 'guardian' or 'protector'.
*Variants: Eamon, Ed, Eddie, Edison, Eddy, Eduardo, Ned, Neddie, Ted, Teddy*

### Edwin
The Scottish city of Edinburgh is said to have been named after the first Christian king of Northumbria, St Edwin. The name comes from two Old English words – 'eadig', 'fortunate, prosperous, happy', and 'wine', 'friend'. Thus, it means 'happy friend'.
*Variants: Eaduin, Ed, Edred, Edwyn, Neddie, Teddy*

### Egbert
This Anglo-Saxon name enjoyed a revival during the 19th century. It comes from the Old English for 'shining', 'famous' and 'sword, blade'. Egbert was borne by a 9th century king of Wessex.
*Variants: Bert, Bertie, Berty*

### Elan
There are three meanings for the name Elan. It is said to come from the Latin for 'spirited', the Hebrew for 'tree' and the Native American for 'friendly'.
*Variants: Ela, Elai*

### Eli
Although Eli is often used as a pet form of the names Elijah ('the

Lord is my God') and Elisha ('God is my help'), it is actually an independent name in its own right. In the Old Testament it was borne by the high priest who raised Samuel. The Hebrew meaning of his name is 'elevated', 'height' or 'Jehovah'.
(See also Elijah and Elisha.)
*Variants: El, Eloy, Ely, Ilie*

### Elijah

Elijah is a Biblical name that was favoured by the Puritan settlers in the New World of America. It was borne by an Old Testament prophet and, in Hebrew, means 'the Lord is my God'.
*Variants: El, Eli, Elia, Elias, Elliott*

### Elisha

See Elisha in the Girls' section.

### Elliott

As a variant of Elias, the Greek form of Elijah, Elliott comes from the Hebrew for 'the Lord is my God'.

Elliott is also a surname that is derived from the Old English for 'noble battle'. Another possible Hebrew meaning is 'close to God'.
*Variants: Eli, Elias, Elijah, Eliot, Ellis*

### Ellis

The 19th century English schoolboy, William Webb Ellis, was said to be the inventor of rugby. While playing a game of football at the prestigious Rugby School he picked up the ball and ran with it.

His surname is believed to have come from the Biblical name Elijah, which means 'the Lord is my God' in Hebrew. It may equally have been derived from the Welsh for 'benevolent'.
*Variants: Eli, Elias, Elie, Elis, Ellison, Elly, Elson, Elston, Ely*

### Elmer

To generations of children Elmer is the name of the Looney Tunes cartoon character Elmer Fudd, the enemy of Bugs Bunny. However, the history of the name stretches back centuries before

film or television were invented. Elmer comes from the Old English name Aethelmaer, which means 'noble' and 'famous'.
*Variants: Ailemar, Aylmer, Edmar, Edmer, Eilemar, Elma, Elmo, Elmore*

**Elmo**

As a variant of the name Elmer, Elmo comes from the Old English for 'noble' and 'famous'. However, Elmo is also the pet form of the name Erasmus, which was borne by the patron saint of sailors and people with intestinal diseases. It is said that St Elmo's intestines were wound out on a windlass. Thus the electrical discharge that is sometimes seen above the mast of a ship is known as St Elmo's fire and is taken to be a sign of his protection.

Erasmus comes from the Greek for 'beloved' or 'desired'. (See also Elmer.)
*Variants: Elmer, Erasme, Erasmus*

**Elroy**

Elroy comes from the Spanish and French for 'the king'.

**Elton**

The piano-playing singer Reginald Kenneth Dwight is better known by his stage name of Elton John. John's assumed name comes from the Old English for 'Ella's settlement' or 'noble town'. It is an English family name that was derived from a place name.
*Variants: Elden, Elsdom, Elston*

**Elvis**

Elvis Presley may be the single most important figure in American 20th century popular music. The origin of the undisputed King of Rock 'n' Roll's first name has long been disputed. It has been suggested that the Presley family, in accordance a southern tradition, made up the name.

Another possibility is that it is a variant of Elvin, which comes from the Old English for 'elf-like'.
*Variants: Alby, Alvin, Elli, Elvin, Elly*

## Emmanuel

In the Old Testament it was predicted that the Messiah would be born to a virgin girl and that her son would bear the name of Emmanuel. The Old Testament Hebrew form of this name is Immanuel. Its New Testament version is Emmanuel. Both names mean the same thing. They come from the Hebrew for 'God is with us'. This Biblical name is popular among Spanish-speakers.
*Variants: Emanuel, Emanuele, Immanuel, Mani, Manny, Manuel, Manuela*

## Emmett

Taken from the Hebrew for 'truth' and the Old English for 'ant', the name Emmett is sometimes bestowed on boys of Irish heritage in honour of Robert Emmet, the rebel who led an unsuccessful rebellion against the English in 1803.
*Variants: Emmet, Emmit, Emmitt*

## Emory

This boy's name is sometimes used as a male form of Emily, which comes from the Germanic for 'industrious' and 'hard-working'. Emory is also a version of the Old German name Emmerick, which means 'powerful' and 'noble'.
*Variants: Almery, Amory, Emmerick, Emerson, Emil, Emile, Emilio, Emlyn, Emmory*

## Emyr

This Welsh name means 'ruler, king or lord'. A 6th century Breton saint, who lived in Cornwall, bore the name.

## Erasmus

Erasmus comes from the Greek for 'beloved' and 'desired'. It was also the name of Erasmus of Rotterdam, a Dutch humanist and theologian who emphasised the importance of simple Christian faith and Bible study. Erasmus died in 1536. (See also Elmo.)
*Variants: Elmo, Erasme, Erasmo, Ras, Rastus*

### Eric

This Scandinavian name was first brought to England by the Danes before the Norman Conquest of the 11th century. Old Norse in origin, it means 'honourable ruler', 'one ruler' or 'island ruler'. The name was borne by a Norse chieftain called Eric the Red who, discovering Greenland in the 10th century, established a colony there.

Eric was increasingly given to boys during the 19th century in accordance with the Victorian trend of using Anglo-Saxon or medieval names. It has been well-known ever since.

*Variants: Erik, Eryk, Euric, Ric, Rick, Rickie, Ricky*

### Ernest

In 1895 Oscar Wilde's comedy, *The Importance of Being Earnest*, was first performed in London. Its title was a pun upon the word and name 'Earnest', both of which mean the same thing 'intense desire' or 'seriously determined'.

The name was first brought over to Britain from Germany by the Hanoverian dynasty which succeeded the House of Stuart in 1714. Indeed Ernest comes from the Old German for 'keenness in battle' or 'seriously determined'.

*Variants: Earnest, Ern, Ernie, Ernst, Erny*

### Eros

According to Greek mythology, Eros was the god of love. It is from his name that the word 'erotic' is derived. His name comes from the Greek for 'desire' or 'sexual love'.

Albert Gilbert's statue of Eros is a landmark that has stood in London's Piccadilly Circus since 1893. It shows the winged god poised to shoot an arrow that, according to legend, would strike instant passion into the heart of the recipient.

### Errol

In the early 20th century the name Errol became inextricably linked to the swashbuckling hero of the silver screen, Errol Flynn. Unfortunately the origin of the film star's name is less certain. It

could be a German form of Earl and, if so, it is the title of a British nobleman. It may also be a Scottish family name that was taken from a Scottish place name. Alternatively Errol could be a variant of the Welsh name Eryl, which means 'watcher' or 'a lookout post', or of Harold, which comes from the Old German for 'army leader'.
*Variants: Earl, Erroll, Harold, Rollo, Rolly*

## Erskine

Erskine is a Scottish surname and place name that was brought to Scotland by Irish settlers. It comes from the Gaelic for 'from the height of the cliff'.

## Esau

In the Bible, Esau is the name of Jacob's twin brother who was the son of Isaac and Rebecca. A good hunter and farmer, Esau was his father's favourite son and was to receive his blessing as his successor. He never did because his mother deceived her blind husband by dressing his other son so that he would smell and feel like his twin. Esau's name comes from the Hebrew for 'hairy'.

## Esmond

Esmond comes from the Old English for 'grace, beauty' and 'protector' and the Old Norse for 'divine protection'. Until the 19th century it was widely found as a surname.

## Ethan

The Biblical name Ethan comes from the Hebrew for 'permanent' and 'assured'. It may have been used in reference to streams that flowed throughout the year without drying up through the summer months.

In North America the name may have been used in honour of Ethan Allen, a hero of the American Revolution.
*Variants: Etan, Ethe*

## Euan

More than one theory exists to explain the origin of Euan. It is

thought to be the Welsh form of the Biblical name John, which comes from the Hebrew for 'God is gracious'. But, like Owen, it is also considered to be the Celtic version of Eugene, which is derived from the Greek for 'well-born'.
*Variants: Eugene, Ewan, Ewen, Owain, Owen*

### Eugene
As mentioned above, Eugene comes from the Greek for 'noble' or 'well-born'.
*Variants: Eugen, Eugenio, Eugenius, Ewan, Ewen, Gene, Owain, Owen*

### Ezekiel
Ezekiel is the name of the Old Testament prophet who is believed to be the author of the Book of Ezekiel in the Bible. His name comes from the Hebrew for 'may God strengthen'.
*Variants: Ezechial, Ezell, Haskell, Hehezhel, Zeke*

### Ezra
Ezra is the name of another Old Testament prophet and author. It was Ezra who established Mosaic Law in Jerusalem. His name comes from the Hebrew for 'help'.
*Variants: Azariah, Azur, Esdras, Ezar, Ezer, Ezera, Ezri*

### Fabian
Fabian comes from the Roman family name Fabianus, which is derived from the Latin for 'bean'. Quintus Fabius Maximus, who died in 203 BC, was the most famous member of the house of Fabii. His nickname was 'Cunctator' – 'the delayer' – because he defeated Hannibal's invading forces by avoiding pitched battles in favour of a war of harassment and attrition. Centuries later, in 1884, the British socialist movement, the Fabian Society, would be named after him.
*Variants: Fabe, Faber, Fabiano, Fabien, Fabio, Fabius*

### Fadil
This name comes from the Arabic for 'virtuous' and 'distinguished'.

### Fahey
Fahey comes from the Old English for 'joyful, glad' and 'happy'.

### Farley
The name Farley is thought to have been derived from one of four possible sources. The name may have been taken from the Old French for 'fair', the word for 'special place and day for a market or celebration'. Farley may have also come from the Old Norse for 'beautiful or pleasing'. Alternatively it may be derived from the Old English for 'wayside'. The Middle English word for 'meadow' is another possibility.
*Variants: Fair, Fairbanks, Fairleigh, Fairley, Far, Farl, Farlie, Farly*

### Farrell
Farrell is a variant of the Irish name Fergal, which means 'valiant man' in Gaelic. It is also a variant of Farrar, which means 'blacksmith' or 'iron' in Latin. (See also Fergal.)
*Variants: Farrel, Farris, Fergal, Ferris, Ferrol*

### Felix
Like Leo the lion or Bruno the bear, Felix is a name now commonly associated with an animal – the cat. Borne by four popes and 67 saints the name proved to be popular with early Christians. It comes from the Latin for 'happy' or 'lucky'.
*Variants: Felice, Felike*

### Felton
This name comes from the Old Norse for 'hill' and the Old English for 'village' or 'town'. Thus it means 'town on or near a hill'.
*Variants: Fell, Felt, Feltie, Felty*

### Fenn
Mainly used in America the name Fenn comes from the Old English for 'town near marshland'. Originally it may have been given to someone living in a marshy area.
*Variants: Fen, Fennie, Fenny*

### Ferdinand

This name is traditionally a favourite of the Spanish royal family. One monarch who bore it was King Ferdinand III of Castile who forced the Moors out of southern Spain in the 13th century. The name was first brought to that country in the 6th century by the Germanic Visigoths. It means either 'brave or prepared journey'. It is also thought to come from the Latin for 'wild, bold' 'courageous', 'warlike', 'gallant' and 'headstrong'.

*Variants: Ferdi, Ferdie, Fern, Nandy*

### Fergal

Ferghal was the name of an 8th century king of Ireland. Fergal is its Anglicised form. The Gaelic meaning of the name is 'man of valour'. (See also Farrell.)

*Variants: Farrell, Ferghal*

### Fergus

The fact that this name was borne by a number of Celtic saints may explain its popularity in both Scotland and Ireland. Like Fergal, Fergus could mean 'man of valour', but it is usually taken to mean 'best or manly choice' in Gaelic. An alternative meaning is 'vigorous man'.

*Variants: Feargus, Fergie, Ferguson, Fergy*

### Fidel

Fidel Castro is the name of the Cuban ruler who was instrumental in the establishment of a Communist state in his country in 1959. His name comes from the Latin for 'faithful' and 'trust'.

*Variants: Fidele, Fidelio*

### Finbar

Finbar is the Anglicised form of the Irish name Fionnbharr, which comes from the Gaelic for 'fair-headed'. Barry is said to be derived from this name.

*Variants: Barry, Fin, Findlay, Finley, Finn*

### Finlay
This Scottish surname comes from the Gaelic for 'fair-haired soldier'.
*Variants: Fin, Findlay, Findley, Finley, Finn*

### Finn
In Ireland the name is closely associated with a legendary hero called Finn mac Cumhail. This giant was a leader of the Fianna warriors and it is from him that the Fenian Brotherhood, an Irish-American revolutionary society, derived its name.

Finn comes from the Irish Gaelic for 'fair' and it is the short form of names such as Finbar and Finlay.
*Variants: Finan, Finian, Finnegan, Finnian, Fion, Fionn*

### Fitzgerald
In Ireland Fitzgerald was the name of a powerful family from Kildare. The short form Fitz means 'son' in Old English, thus the full meaning of Fitzgerald is 'son of Gerald'. The personal name Gerald comes from the Old German for 'spear rule'.
*Variant: Fitz*

### Flannan
This name comes from the Old French for 'flat metal' and the Old English for 'arrow'. It also has an Irish meaning, 'blood red'.
*Variants: Flann, Flannery*

### Fletcher
Fletcher is an English family name that was originally an occupational name for someone who made arrows.
*Variant: Fletch*

### Flint
The word 'flint' means 'hard rock' in Middle English.

### Floyd
Floyd is a variant of the Welsh name Lloyd, which means 'grey'.
*Variant: Lloyd*

**Flynn**
The Gaelic meaning of this name is 'son of the red-haired man'.
*Variants: Flin, Flinn*

**Forbes**
The Greek meaning of this name is 'any plant, except grass, that grows in a field or meadow'. The Irish Gaelic interpretation is 'field owner' or 'prosperous'.

The name is closely associated with Scotland, where it is both a surname and a place name.

**Ford**
The Old English meaning of Ford is 'shallow river crossing'.

**Forrest**
Like the vocabulary word, Forrest refers to a large area with trees and undergrowth. It is the transferred use of a surname that was originally given to someone who lived near an enclosed wood. The name also comes from the German for 'forester' or 'guardian of the forest'.
*Variants: Forest, Forester, Foster*

**Foster**
In English 'foster' means to 'promote growth or development' and in Middle English a 'foster parent' pledged to raise the child of another for a period of time. It also comes from the Middle English for 'forester', 'shearer' and 'saddle-tree maker'.
*Variants: Forest, Forester, Forrest, Forrester, Forster, Foss*

**Francis**
Although he was born Giovanni Bernardone in Italy in 1182, St Francis of Assisi was given the nickname Francesco by his friends. The name, which meant 'the little Frenchman' or 'with the airs and graces of a Frenchman', indicated that they thought he was a Francophile. Nevertheless Giovanni, who would become patron saint of animals and nature, devoted his life to God and is forever

remembered by the variant of his nickname, Francis.

In England, during the reign of Queen Elizabeth I, the name was associated with the navigator Sir Francis Drake who became the first Englishman to circumnavigate the globe.

*Variants: Franc, Francesco, Francisco, Franck, Franco, Francois Frank, Frankie*

### Franklin

The Middle English meaning of Franklin is 'freeman'. During that period the name referred to someone who was a freeholder but not a nobleman.

However the true origin of the name is rooted in 5th century Europe when a Germanic tribe known as the Franks invaded Roman-occupied Gaul. Their new home eventually became known as France and Frank meant 'free' or someone who belonged to the Frankish tribe.

*Variants: Frank, Frankie, Franklyn*

### Fraser

The exact origin of this Scottish surname, which later came into use as a first name, is unclear. It may be derived from the French word for 'strawberry'. Alternatively it may come from the French for 'charcoal cinders' or 'charcoal maker'.

*Variants: Frasier, Frazer, Frazier*

### Frederick

Brought to Britain by the Normans, the name was borne by two Holy Roman Emperors, Frederick I (also known as Frederick Red Beard) and Frederick II. The name was increasingly used in England during the reigns of the Hanoverian kings when it was borne by the father and son of George III. On the Continent 10 Danish kings bore the name, as did Frederick the Great, the 18th century King of Prussia.

The name comes from the Old High German for 'peaceful ruler'.

*Variants: Eric, Erick, Fred, Freddie, Freddy, Frederic, Frederik, Fridrich, Rick, Rickie*

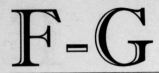

**Fulbert**
Brought to Britain by the Normans, this name comes from the Old German for 'very bright'.
*Variants: Bert, Berty, Filbert, Fulbright, Phil, Philbert, Philibert*

**Fuller**
Fuller was originally an occupational name for someone who shrinks and thickens cloth. It comes from the Latin for 'cloth-fuller'.

**Fulton**
This Scottish surname was borne by Robert Fulton (1765 – 1815), the North American engineer and inventor who designed the first commercial steamboat. His name was originally taken from a place in Ayrshire. The old English meaning of Fulton is 'town near the field'.

**Gabriel**
The Archangel Gabriel is the patron saint of diplomats, messengers, communication, radio, broadcasters and postal workers – and with good reason. In the Bible, Gabriel brought messages from God. In the Old Testament he appeared to Daniel. In the New Testament he told the priest Zachariah that his elderly wife Elizabeth would give birth to a son – John the Baptist. Shortly afterwards Gabriel appeared to the Virgin Mary, telling her that she too would have a son – God's child, the Messiah.

Unsurprisingly the Hebrew meaning of the name Gabriel is 'messenger of God' or 'my strength is God'.
*Variants: Gab, Gabby, Gabi, Gabriele, Gabrielli, Gabriello, Gabris, Gay*

**Gael**
A number of theories exist to explain the meaning of this name. One theory suggests that it comes from the Old French for 'gallant'. Other sources include the Old English for 'lively' and the Irish Gaelic for 'stranger'. Gael may also come from the Old Welsh for 'wild' via the name Gwyddel, which means 'Irishman'.

Gael is also used as a collective noun for the Gaelic-speaking people of Ireland, Scotland and the Isle of Man. Scottish Highlanders are also known by that name.

Finally, Gael is sometimes used as a male form of the female name Gail, which is a short form of the Hebrew name Abigail ('my father rejoices').
*Variants: Gale, Gail, Gaile, Gay, Gayle*

### Galil

This name is a variant of Jalal, which means 'glory' or 'greatness' in Arabic.

### Galvin

Galvin comes from the Gaelic for 'sparrow' or 'brilliant white'.
*Variants: Gal, Galvan, Galven*

### Gamal

This Arabic name means 'beauty'.
*Variants: Gamali, Gamli, Gil, Gilad, Gilead, Jammal*

### Ganesh

According to the Hindu religion the elephant-headed god Ganesh is the eldest son of the god Shiva. He is associated with prosperity and wisdom. The name Ganesh comes from the Sanskrit for 'lord of the hosts'.

### Gareth

Like many of the names taken from Arthurian legend, Gareth is said to have Welsh roots. It comes from the word for 'gentle'. Garth, a pet form of the name that is used independently, comes from the northern English for 'enclosure' or 'small cultivated area'.
*Variants: Garth, Gary, Garry*

### Garfield

In recent years this name has been associated with a cartoon character – Garfield the cat. But in the 19th century it was borne by the 20th President of the United States – James A Garfield. His surname may have been bestowed upon North American children in his honour.

The name comes from the Old English for 'triangular piece of land', 'spears' and 'open country'. Thus Garfield may have originally been used to describe someone who lived near a triangular-shaped field.
*Variants: Field, Gar, Gary*

**Garland**
The name and vocabulary word 'garland' comes from the Old French for 'ornament of gold threads'. In the modern world a garland is a wreath of flowers or leaves presented as a prize or used as a decoration during a festival.

As a first name Garland is given to both boys and girls.
*Variants: Garlen, Garlon*

**Garson**
The Old French meaning of this name is 'to protect'.
*Variant: Garrison*

**Gary**
As a variant of Gareth, Gary comes from the Welsh for 'gentle'. It may also derive its meaning from the Old German word for 'spear', 'gar'.

Gary is also a pet form of Garfield as demonstrated by the West Indian cricketer Sir Garfield Sobers who is also known by the short form. Hence, Gary may also mean 'triangular piece of land'.
*Variants: Gareth, Garfield, Gari, Garret, Garrett, Garry, Garth, Gaz*

**Gavin**
Gavin is another Arthurian name with Welsh roots. According to legend Sir Gawain was the nephew of King Arthur who also had a seat on his Round Table. The Welsh meaning of his name is 'falcon of May' or 'hawk of the plain'.

A form of this name also featured in medieval French

literature and while Gawain fell out of favour in 16th century England, it maintained currency in Scotland, which had closer cultural ties with France than with its more immediate neighbour. Gavin is a variant of this Arthurian name.
*Variants: Gauvain, Gauvin, Gav, Gawain, Gawaine, Gawen*

### Gene

This name is a short form of Eugene, which comes from the Greek for 'noble' or 'well-born'. (See also Eugene.)
*Variant: Eugene*

### Geoffrey

The exact meaning of Geoffrey is not certain. As a variant of Godfrey it has the Germanic meaning 'God's peace'. It may also come from the German for 'territory' and 'stranger' or 'pledge'. A further interpretation suggests that Geoffrey comes from the Old German for 'peaceful traveller'.

First brought to England by the Normans, the name was little used by Tudor parents, but was revived in the 19th century.
*Variants: Geoff, Godfrey, Jeff, Jefferies, Jefferson, Jeffery, Jeffries*

### George

Since George I came to the throne in 1714, the name has been associated with the British monarchy. The last king bearing the name was the father of Elizabeth II. Born Albert Frederick Arthur George in December 1895, he was not expected to succeed to the throne but was forced to do so following the abdication of his older brother, King Edward VIII, in 1936.

The name George was borne by the patron saint of England who, according to legend, slew a dragon. Thus far three Presidents of the United States have also been called George. They are George Washington, the first man to hold that position, George Bush and his son George W Bush.

Despite being associated with men of great power, the name George comes from the Greek for 'farmer'.
*Variants: Geo, Georg, Georges, Georgie, Georgio, Georgy, Jorgen*

### Geraint

This popular Welsh name was borne by Geraint who, according to legend, sat at King Arthur's Round Table. Geraint is known for his love of Enid and their story was told a series of poems by Tennyson.

Geraint's name comes from the Greek for 'old man'. It also has links to Welsh and Old English, but retains the same meaning.

### Gerald

The Germanic name Gerald was brought to England by the invading Normans. It means 'spear rule'.

Although use of the name declined in England by the 1300s, it experienced a revival in the 1800s. In the 20th century it was the first name of the American President, Gerald Ford, who took the oath of office in 1974 following the resignation of his predecessor Richard Nixon. (See also Fitzgerald and Geraldine.)

*Variants: Garald, Gerard, Geralt, Geraldo, Gerry, Jarrett, Jed, Jerald, Jerry*

### Gerard

Like Gerald, Gerard was brought to Britain by the Normans. As a variant of Gerald it shares the Germanic meaning 'spear rule'. But separate from this similar-sounding name, Gerard means 'brave or strong spear'.

*Variants: Gearad, Garrard, Gerald, Geraldo, Gerhardt, Gerry, Jarrett, Jerald, Jerrard, Jerry*

### Gervase

This is another name of disputed meaning. It is thought to mean 'spear' or 'armour bearer' in Old German or 'servant' in Celtic. A version of the name was borne by the 1st century martyr, St Gervasius.

*Variants: Gervais, Gervaise, Gervasius, Gervis, Jarvis*

### Gideon

In the Bible this name was borne by an Old Testament leader of the Israelites. The Hebrew meaning of his name is 'maimed', 'stump' or 'powerful warrior'.

Gideon was another Old Testament name favoured by the 17th century Puritans.
*Variant: Gid*

### Gil

Gil comes from the Hebrew for 'joy'. It is also the short form of Gilbert, which comes from the Old German for 'bright hostage'.
*Variants: Gili, Gill, Gilli, Gilbert*

### Gilder

'To gild' is to cover something thinly with gold. Thus the name Gilder may have been an old occupational name for someone who did this job. A variant of the name, Gildas, was borne by a hermit and saint who lived on an island in the Bristol Channel.

### Giles

According to Greek mythology Aegis was the shield of Zeus, the supreme god. It was made from animal skin and symbolised divine protection. When Zeus shook the shield, he caused a thunder-storm. The Greek word 'aegis' later became the root of the Roman name Aegidius from which Giles is derived. Thus Giles means 'kid' or 'goatskin' in Greek. It may also come from the Scottish Gaelic for 'servant'.
*Variants: Gide, Gidie, Gile, Gilean, Gill, Gilles, Gyles*

### Gilmore

Gilmore comes from the Old Norse for 'deep glen' and the Old English for 'tree root'.
*Variants: Gill, Gillie, Gillmore, Gilmour*

### Glen

Glen is a Scottish family name originally derived from a place name. It comes from the Gaelic word 'gleann', which means 'valley'.

**Godfrey**

This name is derived from two Old German predecessors – Gaufrid and Godafrid. The first meant 'district' and the second meant 'peace of God'. Godfrith was the Anglo-Saxon version of the latter, which was superseded by Godfrey, the Norman variant, in the years following their invasion of England.

**Gordon**

Gordon is an old Scottish name, borne by a clan originally named after the Gordon lands in Berwickshire, England. The Old English meaning of the first element 'gor' is 'marsh' and the Scottish Gaelic interpretation of the second part of the name is 'small wooded dell'.

The transferred use of the Gordon surname began in the late 19th century following the death of the British general, Charles George Gordon, who died defending Khartoum in Sudan, Africa, in 1885.

*Variants: Goran, Gordan, Gorden, Gordie, Gordy, Gore*

**Grady**

The Latin meaning of this name is 'step', 'position', 'degree' or 'grade'. It also comes from the Irish Gaelic for 'bright or exalted one'.

*Variant: Gradey*

**Graham**

In the Domesday Book the English town of Grantham in Lincolnshire was referred to as Grandham, Granham and Graham. In Old English the general meaning of those three names is 'gravel' and 'town'. It also means 'grey' or 'grant' or, in Latin, 'grain'.

In the 12th century William de Grantham, founder of the Scottish Graham clan, was given lands in Scotland by the monarch of that country, King David I.

*Variants: Graeham, Graeme, Grahame, Gram, Gramm*

## Gram

Although the name Gram is often used as a short form of Graham it is also a pet form of Ingram. While Graham comes from the Old English for 'gravel town', Ingram is derived from the Old Norse for 'Ing's raven' – Ing being the god of peace and fertility.

*Variants: Graham, Gramm, Ingram*

## Granger

Granger comes from the Latin for 'grain' and was used to describe either a farmhouse or granary or a person who worked on a farm. Thus it is an old occupational name.

## Grant

Grant, like Gordon and Graham, is another name that was borne by a famous Scottish clan. In America its use as a first name was influenced by the 18th President and Civil War hero, General Ulysses Grant.

It is also a vocabulary word derived from the Old French 'granter', which means 'to agree, promise or bestow'.

*Variants: Grantland, Grantley*

## Gray

In Old English the name Gray means 'bailiff' or 'grey'.

*Variants: Greg, Grey, Greyson*

## Gregory

The Greek meaning of the name Gregory is 'watchful' or 'be vigilant'. Gregory the Great was the first of 16 popes to bear the name and was the first monk to be elected to the papal office. His many achievements during his 14 years as Pope included sending missionaries to England.

Another Roman Catholic leader bearing the name was Pope Gregory XIII who adjusted the Julian Calendar in 1582, giving us the Gregorian Calendar that is used today.

*Variant: Greg*

**Guy**

Following the 1605 attempt by Guy Fawkes to blow up the Houses of Parliament in London, the name Guy swiftly fell out of favour in England.

The exact meaning of the name is unknown but it is thought to be derived from the Old German for 'wide' or 'wood'. In Latin it is associated with the word for 'lively'.

In Britain use of the name Guy was restored in the 19th century.
*Variants: Gui, Guido, Vitus, Viti*

**Gwyn**

The name Gwyn comes from the Welsh for 'blessed, holy' and 'white'. It is the masculine equivalent of Gwen.
*Variants: Gwynfor, Wyn, Wynn, Wynford*

**Hadrian**

See Adrian.

**Hal**

Hal is the short form of a variety of names including Henry, Harry and Harold. These three names all come from the Old German for 'army leader'. Hal is also a variant of Hale, which means 'safe, sound, healthy and whole' in Old English.
*Variants: Hal, Haley, Halford, Halley, Hollis, Holly*

**Hale**

As mentioned above Hale comes from the Old English word 'hal', which means 'safe, sound, healthy and whole'. It was also given to someone who lived in a nook or recess.
*Variants: Hal, Haley, Halford, Halley, Harley, Hollis, Holly*

**Ham**

As well as being a short form of Abraham ('father of many'), Ham comes from the Hebrew for 'hot' or 'swarthy'. In the Old Testament the name was borne by one of Noah's sons, who accompanied him on the Ark.

The Old English meaning of Ham is 'home', 'village' or 'town'. (See also Abraham.)
*Variant: Abraham*

**Hamal**
The Arabic meaning of Hamal is 'lamb'.

**Hamilton**
The name Hamilton has more than one Old English meaning. It means 'home' and 'lover' or 'blunt, flat-topped hill'. The name was first brought to Scotland in the 13th century and became associated with an influential family who acquired the dukedom of Hamilton. A town near Glasgow was later named after the family.

In North America the surname was given to boys as a first name in honour of Alexander Hamilton who was Secretary of the Treasury during George Washington's presidency.
*Variants: Hamel, Hamil, Hamill*

**Hamish**
Hamish is another name that is typically Scottish. It is the Anglicised spelling of Shamus, which is the Gaelic version of James. James is the New Testament version of Jacob, which means 'supplanter' in Hebrew.
*Variants: Jacob, James*

**Hank**
In North America Hank is a pet form of the name Henry, which means 'home ruler' in Old German.
*Variants: Hankin, Henry*

**Hans**
Hans is the short form of the name Johannes, which is a German version of John. The Hebrew meaning of John is 'God has favoured', 'God is gracious' or 'God is merciful'.
*Variants: Johannes, John*

# H

### Harding

The Old English family name Hearding was derived from the word 'heard', which means 'hardy, brave and strong'. Hearding eventually developed into the contemporary form Harding and was borne as a surname by the American President Warren Harding. This 20th century leader may have influenced its use as a given name.

Harding may also be a variant of Hardy, which comes from the Old French for 'to grow bold'.

*Variants: Harden, Hardy*

### Hardy

In addition to being a pet form of Harding (see above), Hardy is an independent name in its own right. It is both a given name and surname that comes from the Old French for 'to grow bold'.

*Variants: Harden, Hardin, Harding*

### Harlan

In North America the surname Harlan was first given to boys as a first name in honour of the Republican supporter of civil rights, John Marshall Harlan. Harlan, who died in 1911, was the descendant of George Harland, an English emigrant who settled in Delaware in 1687 and went on to become its governor.

Harland's surname was derived from a variety of place names in England and comes from the Old English for 'grey or hare land'.

*Variant: Harland, Harley*

### Harlequin

Two theories exist to explain the origin of Harlequin. One suggestion is that it comes from the Old English name Herla, which was borne by a king who led a troop of demon horsemen through the night. The second theory focuses on the Modern English and Old French meaning of 'harlequin'. Namely that it is a mute, colourfully dressed pantomime character who usually wears a black mask.

**Harley**

The name, which is bestowed upon children of either sex, is Old English in origin. The first element, 'har', comes from either 'haer' ('rock, heap of stones') or 'hara', which means 'hare'. The second element is derived from 'leah' – the Old English word for 'wood, meadow' or 'clearing'.

Harley also comes from the Middle Low German for 'hemp, flax'. Thus it also means 'hemp field'.

*Variants: Harl, Harlan*

**Harper**

See Harper in the Girls' section

**Harold**

In the 20th century the name Harold was borne by two British Prime Ministers – Harold Macmillan and Harold Wilson.

In 1066 the name was borne by King Harold, the last king of England before the Norman invasion. It was Harold whom William the Conqueror defeated at the Battle of Hastings. Harold not only lost the battle, and his kingdom; Hastings was also the scene of his death.

The name comes from the Old English for 'army ruler' and is derived from the Old German name Heriwald, which means 'army power'. Harold was probably brought to England by Danish invaders.

*Variants: Hal, Haldon, Halford, Harald, Hariwald, Harlow, Harry*

**Harrison**

Harrison means simply 'son of Harry'. And Harry is a short form of Harold, which comes from the Old English for 'army ruler'.

It is a surname that was borne by two American Presidents, William Henry Harrison and his grandson, Benjamin Harrison and may have been given to little boys as a first name in their honour. More recently, American actor, Harrison Ford, has increased its popularity.

*Variants: Harold, Harry*

### Harte

The Old English meaning of Harte is 'hart' or 'stag'. It is also an English family name that was derived from a variety of place names in England.

*Variants: Hart, Hartley, Hartman, Hartwell*

### Hartley

Like Harte, Hartley comes from the Old English for a 'mature male deer'. With the suffix 'ley' it also bears the meaning 'wood, meadow or clearing'. Thus Hartley means 'deer meadow'.

It is a surname that was originally the name of a number of places in England.

*Variants: Hart, Harte, Hartman, Hartwell, Heartley*

### Harvey

When the Normans invaded England in 1066 they brought the name Harvey with them. The Breton personal name means 'battle worthy'. It was borne by a 6th century blind saint. The French version of the name is Hervé.

Harvey is also an English family name.

*Variants: Ervé, Harv, Harve, Harveson, Hervé, Hervey, Hervi*

### Hassan

This Arabic name means 'handsome', 'good' or 'pleasant'. It was borne by the grandson of the Prophet Muhammad, who was called Hasan ibn Ali ibn Abu Talib.

*Variants: Asan, Hasan*

### Haydn

The name was derived from the Old High German for 'heathen' and may have originally been used as a nickname. Haydn also comes from the Old English for 'hay' and 'grassy dell'. It can be given to both boys and girls.

*Variants: Hayden, Haydon, Hayes, Hays, Haywood, Heywood*

### Heath

The Old English meaning of this name, is 'heath' or 'place where wild plants grow'.

It is an English family name originally given to someone who lived on or near a heath. It is now also used as a first name.

### Hector

The name Hector comes from the Greek for 'to restrain' or 'anchor'. According to Greek mythology it was the name of the Trojan prince who fought in the Trojan War before he was slain by Achilles.

In Scotland, where the name is especially popular, Hector is the Anglicised form of the Gaelic name Eachdonn.
*Variants: Eachann, Eachdonn, Ector, Ettore, Heck, Heckie, Hecky*

### Helmut

The Germanic name Helmut is associated with warriors, perhaps because it comes from the Old French for 'helmet' and 'strong'. It also has the Teutonic meaning 'spirited' and 'brave'.
*Variants: Helm, Helmuth*

### Henry

When the Prince and Princess of Wales named their second son Henry (Prince Harry, as he is known, is a pet form of Henry) in 1984 they were continuing a long-held association between the name and British royalty. So far there have been eight kings of England bearing the name Henry. They include Henry I, the youngest son of William the Conqueror, and Henry V who won the Battle of Agincourt in 1415. But perhaps the best known King Henry was Henry VIII, the father of Queen Elizabeth I.

In North America the name is associated with the English navigator Henry Hudson, after whom the Hudson River, Hudson Bay and the Hudson Strait were named.
*Variants: Enri, Enric, Enrico, Enrique, Hal, Hank, Harry, Heinrich, Heinz, Henri*

**Herbert**
Herbert is an Old French name of German (Frankish) origin. It means 'bright army'. An Old English version of the name existed in England but was replaced by the Norman equivalent after the Norman Conquest of 1066.
*Variants: Bert, Bertie, Herb, Herbie*

**Hercules**
The name Hercules is associated with the son of Zeus, the supreme god of Greek mythology.

Hercules was famed for performing 12 almost impossible tasks. They included the capture of a golden horned stag and the slaying of a serpent with nine heads.
*Variants: Herc, Hercule, Herk, Herkie*

**Herman**
The Old High German meaning of Herman is 'army man' or 'soldier'. Although the Normans favoured the name Herman, its use in Britain died out by the 14th century. It was revived during the 1800s. German immigrants took the name with them to North America and in France the French form Armand is used.
*Variants: Armand, Armant, Harman, Hermann, Hermie, Hermy*

**Hilal**
Hilal means 'new moon' in Arabic.
*Variant: Hilel*

**Hiram**
In the Bible Hiram was the King of Tyre who was an ally of King David and his son King Solomon. According to the Old Testament Hiram demonstrated his friendship by sending supplies, craftsmen and money to build various buildings, including the temple at Jerusalem.

The Hebrew meaning of Hiram is 'brother of the exalted one'.

### Hoffman

Hoffman is a German name that means 'courtier' or 'man of influence and flattery'. It was borne by the German romantic novelist Ernst Hoffman who died in 1822.

### Holt

The Old English meaning of the name Holt is 'wooded hill' or 'copse'.

Although used as a first name it is probably better known as a surname.

### Homer

The name Homer was given to a legendary poet believed to have lived in the 8th century BC, who composed the *Iliad* and the *Odyssey*. He was perhaps more a collective tradition than a single man.

In the first poem Homer detailed the Trojan War and in the second he recounted Odysseus' journey home afterwards.

In Greek the name Homer means 'being hostage or led'. The Old French interpretation of the name is 'helmet maker' and it also comes from the Old English for 'pool in a hollow'. The name has been found in Britain since the 19th century.

In recent years the name Homer has been linked to the US cartoon series, *The Simpsons,* an inescapable part of popular culture since the 1990s.

*Variants: Homero, Omero*

### Horace

Horace comes from the Roman family name Horatius, which was borne by the celebrated 1st century BC poet Quintus Horatius Flaccus. His name comes from the Latin for 'hour'.

In Britain use of this name increased during the Renaissance when it was the vogue to choose classical names for children. Orazio is the Italian equivalent of the name.

*Variants: Horacio, Horatio, Horatius, Orazio*

### Horatio

Horatio is a variant of the name Horace, which comes from the Latin for 'hour'. Shakespeare used the name for one of his characters in the play *Hamlet*.

Horatio was also borne by Admiral Horatio Nelson, who defeated Napoleon at the Battle of Trafalgar, a cause to which he gave his life. Horatio Nelson was killed in action in 1805.
*Variants: Horace, Horacio, Horatius, Orazio*

### Howard

In England Howard is the surname of the family that holds the hereditary title Duke of Norfolk. A number of theories exist to explain the meaning of their name. Howard may come from the Old English for 'fence-keeper' or 'hog warden'. Thus originally it was an occupational name.

The Scandinavian meaning of Howard is 'high guardian'. It also comes from the Old German for 'heart protector' and 'bold'.
*Variants: Hogg, Howey, Howie, Ward*

### Hubert

It is said that the 8th century Bishop of Maastricht, St Hubert, was converted to Christianity after seeing a vision of Christ's crucifixion between the antlers of a stag when he was out hunting. Hubert is the patron saint of hunters and a picture of a stag is his emblem.

The Normans first brought the name Hubert to England in the 11th century. It is an Old French name that is of Germanic (Frankish) origin. It means 'heart, mind, spirit' and 'bright, famous'.
*Variants: Bert, Bertie, Berty, Bart, Hubie, Huey, Hugh, Hughie, Hugi*

### Hugh

Hugh is another name that was brought to England by the invading Normans of the 11th century. In medieval Europe the name was borne by the French aristocracy and in Britain Hugh was mentioned in the Domesday Book.

The Old German meaning of Hugh is 'mind, spirit', but

another Celtic name that sounds the same – Hu, Hew – means 'fire' or 'inspiration'.
*Variants: Bert, Bertie, Berty, Hew, Hubert, Huey, Hughie, Hugo, Huw*

**Hugo**
Hugo is the German version of Hugh that was frequently used in the Middle Ages. (See Hugh and Hubert.)

**Humphrey**
Born in 1899 Humphrey Bogart was an American actor, married to the actress Lauren Bacall, who was best known for his role in the film classic *Casablanca*, in which he starred opposite Ingrid Bergman. His name comes from the Old German for 'strength' and 'peace'.
*Variants: Hum, Humfrey, Humfrid, Hump, Humph, Humphry*

**Hunter**
Hunter was originally an occupational and family name before being given to children of both sexes as their first name. First used in Scotland, it comes from the Old English word 'huntian', which meant 'to search diligently, pursue or track down'. The Old Norse meaning of the name is 'to group'.
*Variants: Huntington, Huntley, Lee, Leigh*

**Huxley**
The Old English meaning of Huxley is 'field of ash trees'.
*Variants: Haskell, Hux, Lee, Leigh*

**Hyam**
The Jewish name Hyam comes from the Hebrew for 'life'.

**Hywel**
Hywel is a name that was frequently used in the Middle Ages. It comes from the Welsh for 'eminent' or 'conspicuous' and the Old English for 'swine hill'.
*Variants: Howe, Howel, Howell, Howey, Howland*

# I

### Iago

Shakespeare gave the name Iago to a key character in his play *Othello*. It is the Spanish and Welsh version of the New Testament name James, which appears in the Old Testament as Jacob.

All three names mean 'supplanter' in Hebrew. (See also Jacob and James.)
*Variants: Jacob, James*

### Ian

Ian is the Scottish variant of the Biblical name John, which means 'God is gracious', 'God is merciful' and 'God has favoured' in Hebrew.
*Variants: Iain, John*

### Ibrahim

This is the Arabic form of the Old Testament name Abraham, which comes from the Hebrew for 'father of many' or 'father of a multitude'. (See also Abraham.)
*Variant: Abraham*

### Idris

According to Welsh legend, Idris the Giant was an astronomer and magician who was killed in 632. Cader Idris, a mountain in Wales, was said to be his observatory and the English translation of the place name is 'Idris's Chair'.

The name Idris comes from the Welsh for 'lord' and 'ardent, impulsive'. Although not a popular name in the 20th or 21st centuries, the name was often used during the Middle Ages and experienced a revival in the late 19th century.

### Ieuan

Ieuan is a Welsh version of the name John, which means 'God is gracious', 'God is merciful' and 'God has favoured' in Hebrew.
*Variants: Iefan, Ifan*

# I

### Ignatius

The exact meaning of the name Ignatius is uncertain, although it was derived from the Old Roman family name Egnatius. It is not clear where that family name came from, but during the early Christian period the first letter 'e' was replaced with an 'i' – perhaps to associate the name with the Latin word 'ignis', which means 'fire'.

Nevertheless, the name was borne by more than one saint including St Ignatius of Loyola (born Inigo Lopez de Recalde in 1491) who founded the Society of Jesus or Jesuits.

*Variants: Egnacio, Iggie, Iggy, Ignace, Ignatio, Inigo*

### Igor

According to Norse legend Ing was the god of fertility. The name Igor comes from the Old Norse for 'Ing's warrior'. It is also a variant of the Greek name George, which means 'farmer'.

*Variants: Inge, Ingmar, Ingvar*

### Ike

Ike is the short form of the Hebrew name Isaac, which means 'he laughed' or 'laughter'.

One famous 20th century Ike was the former President of the United States, Dwight D Eisenhower. Eisenhower, who was in the White House from 1953 to 1961, bore the nickname even though he was not called Isaac.

*Variant: Isaac*

### Illtyd

The Welsh name Illtyd was borne by a saint who lived during the 5th and 6th centuries. He was a well-known scholar and teacher who founded a school where a number of other Welsh saints studied. According to legend he introduced the plough to the people of Wales.

His name comes from the Welsh for 'multitude' and 'land' or 'people'.

*Variant: Illtud*

# I

### Inigo

As mentioned above, Inigo was the name of St Ignatius of Loyola. The exact meaning of the name is unknown but, as a variant of Ignatius, it may mean 'fiery'.

The name was often found in medieval Spain and is thought to be of Basque origin. Today it is little used in Spain, but in the 16th century the marriage between the English monarch, Queen Mary, and Philip of Spain may have influenced its use in England. A bearer of the name was Inigo Jones, the 16th century English architect and stage designer.

*Variants: Eneco, Ignatius*

### Ingmar

The name Ingmar is often found in Scandinavian countries. It comes from the Norse for 'famous son'.

### Ingram

According to Norse mythology Ing was the god of peace and fertility. He was known for his sword that could move by itself through the air. The name Ingram, therefore, comes from the Old Norse for 'Ing's raven'.

The name was popular throughout the Middle Ages, but fell out of favour after the Reformation. (See also Gram.)

*Variants: Gram, Ingo, Ingrim*

### Innes

Innes, a name that can be given to both boys and girls, comes from the Gaelic for 'island'. It is also a surname.

*Variant: Innis*

### Iolo

This Welsh name is a short form of Iorwerth, which means 'lord', 'value' and 'worth'. It is also the Welsh equivalent of Edward, which comes from the Old English for 'fortunate guardian'. (See also Edward.)

*Variant: Edward*

# I

### Ira

Ira is another Old Testament name that was favoured by the 17th century Puritans. In the Bible he was the captain of King David's army. The name means 'leader'.

### Irvin

Irvin is the American version of the Gaelic name Irving, which may have been derived from a number of sources. One possible meaning is 'handsome or fair'. It could also come from the Welsh for 'green, fresh' or 'white water'. Irving may have also been derived from a Scottish place name that meant 'west river'.

Irving also has Old English roots meaning 'sea' or 'boar and friend'.

*Variants: Irvine, Irving*

### Ishmael

In the Old Testament, when Sarah and Abraham could not conceive a child she encouraged her husband to have a baby with her maid Hagar. That child was called Ishmael whose name means 'God hears' or 'outcast' in Hebrew. The second meaning of his name is appropriate because after relations between Hagar and Sarah deteriorated the maid ran away. She eventually returned from her self-imposed exile in the desert and her son went on to become the father of the Arabs who were also known as the Ismailites.

*Variants: Esmael, Isamel, Ismael, Ysmael*

### Islwyn

Islwyn is a Welsh name that is also borne by a mountain located in the county of Gwent. The name means 'below the grove'.

### Isaac

According to the Bible, when God promised Abraham that he would conceive a child with his elderly wife Sarah, he laughed. As a result their son was named Isaac, which means 'he laughed' or 'laughter' in Hebrew.

Isaac was the first link in the chain that fulfilled God's promise to Abraham when he renamed him Abraham – 'father of many'. Isaac fathered the twins Esau and Jacob, and was grandfather to Jacob's 12 sons who founded the 12 tribes of Israel.
*Variants: Ike, Isaacus, Isaak, Isac, Itzik, Izaak*

## Isaiah
In the Bible the name Isaiah was borne by one of the Old Testament prophets who lived in Judah in the 8th century BC. Isaiah, who worked as a prophet for 58 years, predicted that the Messiah would be born to a virgin.
*Variants: Is, Isaias, Issa*

## Israel
In the Old Testament Israel was the name given to Jacob after he wrestled with an angel. In Hebrew his name means either 'may God prevail' or 'he who strives with God'. Jacob was also told that his descendants were to be known as the Israelites.

## Ivan
The name Ivan was borne by six Russian leaders, including Ivan the Great and Ivan the Terrible. It is the Slavic version of the Biblical name John, which in Hebrew means 'God is gracious', 'God has favoured' and 'God is merciful'.
   The name was also used by the Russian writer Leo Tolstoy in his 1886 work, *The Death of Ivan Ilyich*.
*Variants: Evo, Evon, Ivo, Vanya, Yvan, Yvon*

## Ivor
There is more than one explanation for the origin of the name Ivor. It may come from the Latin for 'ivory' or the Welsh for 'lord' or 'archer'. Another possible source is the Old Norse for 'bow made of yew' or 'army'.
*Variants: Ifor, Iomhar, Ivair, Ivar, Ive, Iver, Ivon, Yvon*

### Jabez

This name was a favourite among the 17th century Puritans. It was borne by an Old Testament character and means 'born in pain' or 'born in sorrow' in Hebrew.

### Jack

As a pet form of the name John, Jack comes from the Hebrew for 'God is gracious', 'God is merciful' and 'God has favoured'. It is also sometimes used as the pet form of the name James ('supplanter'), probably under the influence of the French form of the name, which appears as Jacques.

One person who was also known by the pet form Jack was the 1961 to 1963 President of the United States, John F Kennedy. Today the name is used independently, especially in Britain where the name is popular with parents.

*Variants: Jacob, Jacques, James, John*

### Jacob

In the Old Testament Jacob was the twin brother of Esau and the son of Isaac and Rebecca. He was also the father of 12 sons who went on to found the 12 tribes of Israel.

The name Jacob comes from the Hebrew for 'follower' or 'supplanter'. It is also said to mean 'heel grabber' because, according to the Bible, when the twins were born, Jacob was holding on to his brother's heel.

The New Testament version of the name Jacob is James and both names have spawned numerous derivatives and short forms including Jack, Jake, Iago and Jacques.

*Variants: Iago, Jack, Jacobson, Jacoby, Jacques, Jago, Jaime, Jakab, Jake, Jamie*

### Jago

Jago is a Cornish form of the name James, which is a variant of Jacob. Jago means 'supplanter' in Hebrew. (See also Jacob and James.)

*Variants: Iago, Jack, Jacobson, Jacoby, Jacques, Jaime, Jakab, Jake, James, Jamie*

**Jake**

Although the name Jake is considered to be an independent name in its own right, it originally was used as a pet form of the names John and Jacob. As a variant of John, Jake assumes the Hebrew meaning 'God is gracious', 'God has favoured' and 'God is merciful'. As a pet form of Jacob it means 'supplanter'.
*Variants: Jacob, Jacobson, Jacoby, Jacques, Jakab, James, Jamie, John*

**Jamal**

The Arabic meaning of the name Jamal is 'handsome'. Jamelia is its feminine equivalent.
*Variants: Gamal, Jahmal, Jamaal, Jamael, Jamahl, Jamall, Jameel, Jamel, Jamil*

**James**

In Britain the name James is associated with seven kings of Scotland and two kings of England. In the Bible the name was also connected with more than one person. It was the name of two of Christ's Apostles – James the son of Zebedee and James the son of Alphaeus. James was also said to be the name of Christ's own brother.

The name is derived from the same Latin source as the Old Testament name Jacob. Like Jacob it means 'supplanter' in Hebrew.

James has been such a popular name that various cultures around the world have developed their own variants. In the Scottish Highlands James appears as Hamish and the Irish equivalent is Seamus. The pet form Jamie is also given to children of either sex. Jim is also a popular derivative.
*Variants: Hamish, Jack, Jacob, Jacques, Jaime, Jamie, Jim, Jimmie, Jimmy, Seamus*

**Janus**

In Roman mythology Janus was the double-headed god of gateways, endings and beginnings. He was often pictured looking both ways. The month of January, which signals the start of a fresh year, was derived from his name.

The Latin meaning of Janus is 'passage', 'gateway' or 'arcade'.
*Variants: Januaris, Jarek*

**Jared**
The Biblical character of Jared was blessed with longevity. He lived until the age of 962 and fathered a son comparatively early on in his life (when he was 100).

The Hebrew meaning of Jared's name was 'descent' and, given that he was a descendant of Adam, it is appropriate. The name also comes from the Greek for 'rose' and, as a variant of Gerard, boasts the Germanic meaning 'brave or strong spear'.

Although the Puritans favoured the name Jared, its use eventually went into decline before it was revived in the 1960s. It is especially popular in America and Australia.
*Variants: Gerard, Jarett, Jarrad, Jarrath, Jarratt, Jarrod, Jered*

**Jarratt**
As a variant of Jared, Jarratt means 'descent' in Hebrew and 'rose' in Greek. As a variant of Gerard it means 'brave or strong spear'. (See also Jared and Gerard.)
*Variants: Garett, Gerard, Jared*

**Jarvis**
The exact meaning of the name Jarvis is unclear. It may come from the Germanic for 'spear', as a variant of Gerard. It may equally come from the Celtic for 'servant' as a variant of the Norman given name Gervaise. (See also Gerard and Gervase.)
*Variants: Gary, Gervais, Gervaise, Gervase, Jary, Jarry, Jerve, Jervis*

**Jason**
Four different Biblical characters bore the name Jason. They include the man who was believed to have written the Book of Ecclesiastes and a relative of St Paul. It is for this reason that the name was popular among the Puritans.

As a variant of the Biblical name Joshua, Jason comes from the Hebrew 'God saves'. Its Greek meaning is 'to heal'.

Indeed, Greek mythology provides perhaps the most famous early bearer of the name – the leader of the Argonauts who undertook a quest to find the Golden Fleece. His journey took him to Colchis, where he met and fell in love with the sorceress Medea. She helped Jason in his search but he betrayed her by deserting her for another woman.
*Variants: Jace, Jay, Joshua*

### Jasper

According to the Bible Jasper was the name of one of the three kings who brought gifts to the baby Jesus. Appropriately, the Persian meaning of the name is 'treasurer'. It also comes from the Arabic word for the semi-precious stone that is reddish-brown in colour.

Jasper has spawned a number of derivatives, including Caspar, the Germanic Gaspar and the French Gaspard.
*Variants: Caspar, Casper, Gaspar, Gaspard, Kasper*

### Jay

As a variant of the Biblical name James, Jay comes from the Hebrew for 'supplanter' and is also related to the Old Testament name Jacob. Jay is also a short form of a wide variety of names, all beginning with the letter 'J'.

As an independent name Jay is derived from the Latin word 'gaius', which means 'a bird's harsh chirping'. Thus to give a person the nickname Jay was to say that they were a chatterbox.
*Variants: Jacob, James, Jaye, Jey, Jeye*

### Jed

A Puritan favourite, the name Jed was originally used as a short form of Jedidiah – a name that belonged to an Old Testament character. In Hebrew Jedidiah means 'beloved of God'.
*Variants: Jedd, Jedidiah*

### Jefferson

The name Jefferson is popular in North America where it is

associated with the third President of the United States. Born in 1743, Thomas Jefferson, who was a scientist, architect and writer, drafted the American Declaration of Independence. His surname may have been given to boys in his honour.

Jefferson simply means 'son of Jeffrey'. Jeffrey is a variant of Geoffrey, which comes from the Old German for 'God's peace' and 'peaceful traveller'. (See also Geoffrey.)

**Jeffrey**
See Geoffrey.

**Jem**
As the short form of Jeremy, Jem comes from the Biblical name Jeremiah, which means 'appointed by God' in Hebrew. As a short form of James it is a variant of Jacob, which also comes from Hebrew and means 'supplanter'. (See also Jeremy.)
*Variants: Jacob, James, Jeremiah, Jeremy*

**Jeremy**
The name Jeremy is derived from the Biblical name Jeremiah which, in Hebrew, means 'appointed or exalted by God'.

Notable bearers of the name include the English philosopher, social and legal reformer, Jeremy Bentham (1748-1832) who was associated with utilitarianism.
*Variants: Gerome, Gerrie, Gerry, Jem, Jeremiah, Jerome, Jerry*

**Jeremiah**
In the Bible the name Jeremiah was borne by the Old Testament prophet and author of the Book of Lamentations. It was Jeremiah who criticised his people for their less-than-Godly actions and was upset by the destruction of Jerusalem. The Hebrew meaning of his name is 'appointed or exalted by God'.

The name Jeremiah was used in Britain during the Middle Ages and later became popular among the Puritans of the 17th century.
*Variants: Gerome, Gerrie, Gerry, Jem, Jere, Jeremia, Jeremias, Jeremy, Jerome, Jerry*

### Jermaine

Jermaine is a variant of Germaine, which comes from the Latin for 'clan brother'. The French meaning of the name is 'German'.
*Variants: Germain, Germane, Germayne, Jermain, Jermayn, Jermayne, Jerri, Jerrie, Jerry*

### Jerome

The name Jerome has been found in Britain since the 12th century. It is a variant of Gerome, which comes from the Greek for 'holy and sacred name'.

One notable bearer of the name was St Jerome, the patron saint of archaeologists, librarians and students, who was born in 342. He was the secretary of Pope Damascus, who was involved in translating the Bible into Latin.
*Variants: Gerome, Geronimus, Gerrie, Gerry, Jeromo, Jerrome, Jerry*

### Jesse

Jesse is an Old Testament name that found favour in Britain after the Reformation. In the Bible it was the name of King David's father. In North America the name was associated with the outlaw, Jesse James. More recently it has been linked to the politician Jesse Jackson. The Hebrew meaning of the name is 'gift'.
*Variants: Jake, Jess, Jessie, Jessy*

### Jesus

The name Jesus is a variant of the Old Testament name Joshua, which comes from the Hebrew for 'God saves' or 'the Lord is my salvation'. Jesus is popular in Spanish-speaking countries where it is pronounced as *'Hay-soos'*.
*Variants: Hesus, Jesous, Jesu, Jesuso, Jezus, Joshua*

### Jet

As a short form of Jethro, Jet comes from the Hebrew for 'excellence' or 'wealth'. It also means 'stone'.
*Variants: Jethro, Jett*

**Jethro**

In the Bible the name Jethro belonged to the father-in-law of Moses. As mentioned above it comes from the Hebrew for 'excellence' or 'wealth'.

In Britain the name enjoyed some currency from the 16th century and became a Puritan favourite. In particular it was the name of Jethro Tull, an English agricultural reformer born in 1674.
*Variants: Jeth, Jet, Jett*

**Joab**

The Old Testament name Joab was borne by a nephew of King David. In Hebrew it means 'God the father' and 'praise the Lord'.
*Variant: Yoav*

**Job**

To say someone has 'the patience of Job' is to say that they are able to endure great hardship or delay. This well-known saying refers to the Biblical character of Job, who patiently endured great suffering.

In the Old Testament Job was a wealthy man who fathered 10 children and was enriched with many animals and servants. He was also upright and righteous. In an attempt to prove that Job would not remain faithful to God if he underwent great tribulation, Satan afflicted him with numerous disasters. They included the deaths of his family members and a plague of boils. Throughout it all Job praised the Lord and God rewarded Job by doubling his earlier prosperity. Unsurprisingly the Hebrew meaning of Job is 'persecuted' or 'oppressed'.
*Variants: Joabee, Jobey, Joabie, Jobie, Joby*

**Jock**

Jock is often used as a nickname for a Scotsman. However, it is also the Scottish variant of the names Jack and John, both of which come from the Hebrew for 'God is gracious', 'God is merciful' and 'God has favoured'.
*Variants: Jack, John*

# J

**Joel**

The Hebrew meaning of Joel is 'Jehovah is God' and 'God is willing'. The name was a favourite among Puritans and Christian fundamentalists.

The book of Joel is in the Old Testament and is considered a 'literary jewel'.

*Variant: Yoel*

**John**

Of all the names found in the Bible and favoured by Christians, John has been a source of inspiration for parents for centuries, spawning variants and short forms around the world. Numerous saints and popes have borne the name. In the New Testament it belonged to three important characters – namely John the Baptist (the prophet, preacher and cousin of Jesus), John the Apostle (a fisherman and brother of James) and John the Evangelist (the author of the Gospel of St John, three Epistles and the Book of Revelation).

The name these three men shared also had a holy meaning that would have appealed to Christian parents. It comes from the Hebrew for 'God is gracious', 'God is merciful' and 'God has favoured'.

Unsurprisingly numerous men from history have borne the name. They include the British poets John Milton and John Keats, the English painter John Constable, the former American President, John F Kennedy and the British-born musician and former Beatle, John Lennon. The name John has also produced the short forms and variants Jack, Jock, Ian, Johannes, Sean, Ivan and Juan, among others.

*Variants: Ian, Ivan, Jack, Jock, Johannes, Jonnie, Jonny, Juan, Owen, Zane*

**Jonah**

The Biblical story of Jonah and the whale was a popular tale in the Middle Ages. Miracle plays were performed that recounted Jonah's disobedience of God. Refusing to preach in Nineveh, defiant Jonah boarded a ship and sailed in the opposite direction. God responded by creating a storm that threatened the safety of the vessel. Jonah was thrown overboard and swallowed by a 'great fish' that deposited him at the shores of Nineveh.

Jonah's name comes from the Hebrew for 'dove' or 'pigeon'. *Variants: Jonas, Yona, Yonah*

**Jonathan**
In the Old Testament the name Jonathan was borne by King Saul's son who was also a friend of King David. The Hebrew meaning of the name is 'God's gift'.
*Variants: Johnathan, Johnathon, Jon, Jonathon, Jonnie, Jonny, Jonty, Yonatan*

**Jordan**
The River Jordan plays an important role in the New Testament story of Jesus Christ. It was there that John the Baptist baptised his cousin Jesus, the Messiah. It is for this reason that medieval pilgrims who travelled to the Holy Land returned with a flask of water from the River Jordan to baptise their own offspring, some of whom would have been called Jordan as a result.

The Hebrew meaning of Jordan is 'to flow down'. The name, which is given to boys and girls, is also associated with Jordan, the Middle Eastern country.
*Variants: Jared, Jarrod, Jerad, Jordain, Jori, Jory, Judd*

**Joseph**
The name Joseph was borne by two prominent characters in the Bible. In the Old Testament it was the name of the first of Jacob and Rachel's two sons. Although Jacob had 10 more sons Joseph was his favourite and he demonstrated this by giving him an elaborate coat of many colours. In the New Testament Joseph was the name of the earthly father of Jesus, the Virgin Mary's husband. The Hebrew meaning of the name is 'God will add (another son)'.
*Variants: Jo, Joe, Joey, Jojo, José, Josephe, Yousef*

**Joshua**
In the Old Testament Joshua was the successor of Moses who led the Israelites into the Promised Land. The Hebrew meaning of his name is 'the Lord saves'.

Jason is the Greek form of the name and Jesus is the version that is used in the New Testament.
*Variants: Hosea, Jason, Jesous, Jesus, Josh*

**Joubert**
Joubert comes from the Old English for 'bright, shining'. It is a derivative of the Old English name Godbeorht, which meant 'God's radiance'.
*Variant: Jovett*

**Juan**
Juan is the Spanish version of John, which means 'God is gracious', 'God is merciful' and 'God has favoured' in Hebrew. (See also John.)
*Variants: DeJuan, John*

**Judd**
As a variant of Jordan, Judd comes from the Hebrew for 'to flow down', but as a short form of Judah it means 'praise'. It is also a surname. (See also Jordan.)
*Variants: Jordan, Judah, Jude*

**Jude**
Of the 12 Apostles of Christ, two bore the name Judas – Judas Iscariot and Judas Thaddaeus.

The first Judas was infamous for his betrayal of Jesus with a kiss. The second Judas is also known as St Jude who wrote the Epistle of Jude and is the patron saint of lost causes and desperate situations.

Like Judd, Jude is derived from Judah, which means 'praise' in Hebrew. The name has been a source of inspiration for more than one artist.

In the 19th century British novelist Thomas Hardy wrote *Jude the Obscure*.
*Variants: Jud, Juda, Judah, Judas, Judd, Judson, Yehudi*

## Jules
Jules is the short form of the name Julian, which means 'fair-skinned' in Latin. (See Julian and Julius.)
*Variants: Julian, Julius*

## Julian
Julian is taken from the name of the Roman clan, the Julii, who claimed to be direct descendents of Aphrodite, the goddess of love. The exact meaning of their name is somewhat unclear, but it is thought to come from the Latin for 'fair-skinned'.
*Variants: Giuliano, Iola, Jolin, Jolyon, Jule, Jules, Julianus, Julius, Julyan*

## Julius
Since the days of Ancient Rome the name Julius has been inextricably linked to Julius Caesar. The name Julius Caesar was borne by more than one leader of Rome. They include the military and political leader who had an affair with Cleopatra, the Queen of Egypt, and is the subject of a Shakespearean play. His adopted son, Gaius Julius Caesar Octavianus, became the first emperor of Rome.
*Variants: Jule, Jules, Julian, Julianus*

## Jun
The Chinese meaning of Jun is 'truth', and in Japan it means 'obedience'.

## Justin
The name Justin was borne by a 2nd century saint who refused to sacrifice to the gods. His name comes from the Latin for 'just'.
Iestyn and Iestin, the Welsh equivalents of the name, have been in use since the 6th century.
*Variants: Iestin, Iestyn, Justinian, Justis, Justus, Jut*

**Justus**
Justus is a variant of Justin, which comes from the Latin for 'just' or 'fair'.
*Variant: Justin*

**Kalil**
The name Kalil has more than one meaning. It comes from the Arabic for 'good friend', the Greek for 'beautiful' and the Hebrew for 'wealth' or 'crown'.
*Variants: Kahil, Kahlil, Kailil, Kal, Kallie, Khaleel, Khalil*

**Kalle**
The Scandinavian meaning of this name is 'strong' and 'manly'.

**Kamal**
Kamal comes from the Arabic for 'perfection'. In India it is the name for the lotus flower and comes from the Sanskrit for 'pale red'.

**Kamil**
Like Kamal, Kamil means 'perfection' or 'complete' in Arabic. In the Koran it is listed as one of the 99 qualities of Allah.
*Variant: Kameel*

**Kane**
More than one theory exists to explain the meaning of Kane. It is the Anglicised form of the Irish Gaelic name Cathan, which means 'warrior'. It also comes from the Celtic for 'tribute', 'battler' and 'dark'. The Welsh meaning of Kane is 'lovely'. In Japan it means 'golden' and the Hawaiian interpretation is 'man'.

Kane may also come from the Old French for 'battlefield'. As well as being an Irish surname it was also the family name of someone from the French town of Caen. Kane was especially popular in 1960s Australia.
*Variants: Kain, Kaine, Kayne*

### Karim

Karim comes from the Arabic for 'generous' and 'noble'. Like Kamil it appears in the Koran as one of the many names or qualities of Allah.
*Variants: Kareem, Kario*

### Kasimir

The Slavonic meaning of Kasimir is 'commands peace', 'proclamation of peace' or, alternatively, 'to spoil peace'. It is also a name that was popular among supporters of Polish independence. Immigrants of Polish descent took the name with them to North America.

### Kasper

Kasper is the German form of the name Jasper, which was borne by one of the three wise men who visited the baby Jesus. Thus it bears the Persian meaning of that name, 'treasurer'.
*Variants: Kaspa, Caspar, Casper, Gaspar, Gaspard, Jasper*

### Keane

The Irish Gaelic meaning of Keane is 'warrior's son'. In Old English, the name means 'wise, clever' or 'brave and strong'. It is also the Anglicised form of the Gaelic name Cian, which means 'ancient'.
*Variants: Kane, Kani, Kayne, Kean, Keen, Keenan, Kene, Keene, Kian, Kienan*

### Keegan

Keegan is the Anglicised form of the Gaelic surname MacAodhagáin.

### Keir

The Irish Gaelic meaning of Keir is 'dark-skinned' or 'spear', although it also has an Old Norse meaning – 'marshland containing brushwood'. Keir is also a Scottish surname.
*Variant: Kerr*

### Keith
The Scottish surname Keith was originally derived from a number of place names. The Scottish Gaelic meaning of the name is 'wood', while in Irish Gaelic it stands for 'battlefield'. It was not used as a first name until the 20th century.

### Kelly
See Kelly in the Girls' section.

### Kelsey
Kelsey has more than one Old English meaning. It means 'ship's keel' or 'ship' and 'victory'. It also comes from the Irish Gaelic for 'warrior'. It is given to both boys and girls.
*Variants: Kelcey, Kelley, Kelsee, Kelsie, Kelson, Kelton*

### Kelvin
First used as a given name in the 1920s, Kelvin is the name of a river that runs through Glasgow in Scotland. The Old English meaning of Kelvin is 'ship's keel' or 'friend'. It also means 'narrow stream' in Gaelic.
*Variants: Kelvan, Kelven, Kelwin*

### Kendall
In North America the name Kendall is given to both boys and girls. However, the name was originally taken from two place names in Britain – one in Cumbria and the other in Humberside.
    The Old English meaning of the name is 'royal valley'. It also boasts the Celtic meaning 'high, exalted' and 'image, effigy'.
*Variants: Ken, Kendal, Kendell, Kenn, Kennie, Kenny, Kendahl, Kendale, Kendyl, Kyndal*

### Kennedy
The Kennedy name comes from the Irish Gaelic for 'head' and 'ugly'. It also comes from the Old English for 'ruler'. As a first name it is given to both boys and girls.
    In North America the name Kennedy is associated with the

powerful political family who are of Irish descent. The Kennedys rose to prominence during the 20th century, under the guidance of the patriarch Joseph Kennedy. Joseph's second son with his wife Rose, was John Fitzgerald Kennedy who was President of the United States in the early 1960s, before he was assassinated in 1963. Their third son, Robert F Kennedy, met the same fate in 1968 when he was on the campaign trail to the White House.
*Variants: Ken, Kenman, Kenn, Kennard, Kennie, Kenny, Kent, Kenton, Kenyan*

### Kenelm
The Old English meaning of the name Kenelm is 'brave helmet'. The name was popular in the Middle Ages because of the fame of a 9th-century Mercian prince who was a saint and a martyr. The name was later borne by the 17th century diplomat, scholar and writer, Sir Kenelm Digby.
*Variants: Ken, Kennie, Kenny*

### Kenneth
Two kings of Scotland bore the name Kenneth, including Kenneth I who defeated the Picts and was the first to rule both the Picts and the Scots.

The Gaelic meaning of the name is either 'born of fire' or 'handsome'. The Old English meaning is 'royal oath'.
*Variants: Cainnech, Ken, Kene, Kenn, Kennie, Kenny, Kent, Kenton, Kenward*

### Kent
In England Kent is a southern county. It is also a family name, which shares the Old English meaning 'white', 'border' or 'coastal district'. Kent is also a short form of the name Kenton, which may come from the Old English for 'royal manor'.

As a variant of Kennedy it means 'ugly head' and as a derivative of Kenneth it means 'born of fire', 'handsome' or 'royal oath'. (See also Kennedy and Kenneth.)
*Variant: Ken, Kennedy, Kenneth, Kenton, Kenyon*

**Kern**
The Old Irish meaning of Kern is 'band of infantry'.
*Variants: Kearney, Kearny*

**Kerr**
As a variant of Keir, Kerr comes from the Irish Gaelic for 'dark-skinned' and 'spear'. It also comes from the Old Norse for 'marshland containing brushwood'. The name was originally given to someone who lived near wet ground.
*Variant: Keir*

**Kerry**
See Kerry in the Girls' section.

**Kevin**
Before the 1920s, use of the name Kevin was largely confined to Ireland, where it is associated with the patron saint of Dublin who died in 618. St Kevin's name comes from an Old Irish name that means 'handsome birth'.
*Variants: Coemgen, Kev, Kevan, Keven, Kerrie, Kerry*

**Kieran**
Like the girl's name Kiera, Kieran comes from the Irish word 'ciar', which means 'black'. Thus the name Kieran means 'dark one'.
  Several Irish saints bore the name, which may explain its popularity.
*Variants: Ciaran, Ciaren, Kiaran, Kyron*

**Killian**
Killian is another name that is closely linked to Ireland. It was borne by an Irish saint who was martyred during a mission to Germany in the 7th century. Killian's name is thought to come from the Irish word for 'strife', but it also derives its meaning from the Gaelic for 'church' or 'little warrior'.
*Variants: Cilian, Cillian, Killie, Killy, Kilmer*

### Kim

In 1901, British writer Rudyard Kipling published his book *Kim*, which told the story of a little boy who lived in India. Kim, the title character's name, was a short form of Kimball, which is derived from more than one source. The Greek meaning of the name is 'hollow vessel', but it also comes from the Old English for 'kin' or 'royal' and 'bold'. In Welsh the name means 'chief' and 'war'.

Kimball may also be a contemporary version of a name borne by an Old English ruler called Cymbeline. Cymbeline, who died in 42, ruled the area that is now Hertfordshire. His name meant 'high' and 'mighty'.

At the same time that Kipling's book was published, Britain was involved in the Boer War in South Africa and a number of soldiers were stationed at a garrison in the town of Kimberley. As a result many of them named their children – boys and girls – Kimberley. Kim is its short form.

*Variants: Kimball, Kimberley, Kimberly*

### Kingsley

The Old English meaning of this name is 'king's clearing' or 'king's wood'. It is an English family name derived from a number of English place names.

*Variants: King, Kingsleigh, Kingsly, Kingston, Kinsey*

### Kipp

Kipp comes from the Old English for 'pointed hill'.

*Variants: Kip, Kipper, Kippie, Kippy*

### Kirk

The name Kirk has roots in Old English, Scottish and Scandinavian. In all three languages Kirk has the same meaning, 'church'. In England the name was originally given to someone who lived near a church. The actor, Kirk Douglas increased the name's popularity in North America.

*Variants: Kerk, Kirby, Kirke, Kirklan, Kirkland, Kirtland, Kyrk*

**Klaus**
See Claus and Nicholas.

**Kumar**
Kumar comes from the Sanskrit for 'prince' or 'son'.

**Kushal**
Kushal is an Indian name that means 'clever'.

**Kurt**
As the short form of Conrad, Kurt comes from the German for 'brave advice' or 'bold, wise counsellor'.
*Variants: Conrad, Curt, Curtis, Kurtis*

**Kyle**
Kyle is both a surname and a Scottish place name. It comes from the Gaelic for 'narrow strait'.
*Variants: Kile, Ky*

**Lachlan**
In Scotland Lachlan was the Gaelic name given to someone from Norway. It means 'from the land of the lakes' or 'warlike'. Over time Lachlan became a family name and produced the surname MacLachlan. In Australia Lachlan is associated with a 19th century governor of New South Wales, General Lachlan Macquarie.
*Variants: Lachann, Lachie, Lachlann*

**Lal**
Lal comes from the Sanskrit for 'caress' and the Hindi for 'beloved'.

**Lamar**
A surname and a first name, Lamar comes from the French for 'the pond'.

**Lambert**
The name Lambert was borne by St Lambert of Maastricht, who

is the patron saint of children. His name comes from the Old High German for 'bright or shining land'. It also means 'pride of the nation'.

The invading Normans first brought the name to Britain.
*Variants: Bert, Bertie, Berty, Lamberto, Lammie, Landbert*

## Lamont
Mainly used in North America, the name Lamont comes from the Norse for 'law man' and the Scottish Gaelic for 'law giver'. It also comes from the French term 'la mont', which means 'the mountain'.
*Variants: Lammond, Lamond, LaMont, Lemont, Monty*

## Lance
A lance is a sharp spear used in battle by the cavalry in charging at the enemy. It comes from Lancelot, which comes from the Latin for 'lance'.

According to Arthurian legend, Sir Lancelot was a Knight of the Round Table who fell in love with King Arthur's wife, Guinevere.

The name also has the German meaning 'god'.
*Variants: Lancelot, Lancing, Lansing, Launce, Launcelot*

## Lane
The name – which comes from the Old English for 'narrow pathway between hedges or banks' – was originally given to someone who lived in or near a lane. It also has the Old Frisian meaning 'to move'. In North America the name Lane is given to both boys and girls.
*Variants: Lanie, Leney*

## Lawrence
The Latin meaning of Lawrence is 'from Laurentum' – Laurentum being the Roman name of an Italian town. The French form of the name is Laurent, the Scottish version is Lowrie and the Italian variant is Lorenzo.

Throughout history the name has been borne by a number of

notable men, including three saints. The first was a Roman martyr and deacon of Rome who lived in the 3rd century. The second was Laurence of Canterbury who accompanied St Augustine on his mission to southern England and Lawrence O'Toole, the 13th century bishop of Dublin, was the third.
*Variants: Larrance, Larry, Lars, Larse, Larson, Laurel, Laurence, Laurent, Lorenzo, Lowrie*

**Leander**
Leander is derived from two Greek words 'leon', which means 'lion', and 'andros', which means 'man'. Thus it means 'man with the strength of a lion' or 'lion man'.

According to Greek mythology Leander was the handsome lover of Hero, a priestess of Venus. He was so devoted to her that every night he swam across the Hellespont to see her. One night he drowned during a storm and the distraught Hero threw herself into the sea to join him.
*Variants: Ander, Andor, Lea, Leandre, Leandro, Lee, Leo, Leon, Maclean*

**Lee**
This name is derived from the Old English word 'leah', which means 'wood, clearing' or 'meadow'. In 19th-century North America, the name was often bestowed on children of either sex in honour of the Confederate General Robert E Lee who died in 1870.

Lee, which can be given to children of either sex, also comes from the Old English word for 'shelter' or 'cover'.
*Variants: Lea, Leigh*

**Leeland**
Leeland comes from the Old English word 'hleo', which means 'shelter' or 'cover'.
*Variants: Layland, Layton, Leighland, Leighton, Leland*

**Lennox**
Lennox was originally a place name of a Scottish district, once

known as The Levenach. It comes from the Scottish Gaelic for 'elms' and 'water'.

Now widely used as a first name, Lennox is also a Scottish surname and has been made famous lately by British boxer Lennox Lewis.

### Leo

The name Leo comes from the Latin for 'lion'. It is also one of the signs of the zodiac. The name has been popular throughout history, primarily because of its association with powerful characters. It was the name of six Byzantine emperors, several saints and 13 popes.

One such bearer of the name was Pope Leo I, who was also known as Leo the Great. He lived in the 5th century and twice saved Rome from attack. The success of actor Leo Di Caprio has helped to popularise the name since the late 1990s.

*Variants: Leander, Lee, Leon, Leonardo, Leopold, Lonnie*

### Leonard

Leonard comes from the Old High German for 'strong as a lion' or 'lion' and 'hard'. The name was borne by more than one saint, including the patron saint of prisoners and the patron saint of parish missions.

*Variants: Lenard, Lennard, Lenn, Lenny, Leo, Leon, Leonardo, Lionardo, Lonnie*

### Leopold

The conquering Normans first brought the name Leopold to England when they invaded the country in 1066. Use of the name eventually died out, although it was restored during the reign of Queen Victoria in the 19th century. The British monarch bestowed the name on one of her sons in honour of her Uncle Leopold, who was king of Belgium: the name was borne by more than one Belgian king and two Holy Roman emperors. The name comes from the Old German for 'bold or brave people'.

*Variants: Leo, Leopoldo, Leupold, Pold, Poldo*

# L

**Leroy**
A popular African-American name, Leroy comes from the French for 'the king'. It was originally a surname that was given to servants of the king of France.
*Variants: Elroy, Lee, Lee Roy, Roy*

**Leslie**
See Lesley in the Girls' section.

**Lester**
The name Lester is a contracted form of Leicester, which is the name of a town in England. The Old English meaning of Leicester is 'Roman clearing' or 'Roman fort'.
*Variants: Leicester, Les, Letcher, Leycester*

**Levi**
In the Old Testament Levi was the name of Jacob and Leah's third son. The Hebrew meaning of his name is 'attached' or 'pledged'. His mother gave him the name in the hope that her husband would be more attached to her because that she had borne him three sons.

Like his brothers, Levi became the patriarch of one of the 12 tribes of Israel. His descendants, the Levites, were a Jewish priestly caste.
*Variants: Lavey, Lavi, Lavy, Leavitt, Lev, Levey, Levy*

**Lewis**
The Old Germanic meaning of Lewis is 'famous warrior' or 'famous battle'. In the 19th century it was the pen name of the British writer, Lewis Carroll, who wrote *Alice in Wonderland*. Carroll's real name was Charles Lutwidge Dodgson.
*Variant: Lew, Lewie, Louis, Ludwig*

**Lex**
As a variant of Alexander, Lex comes from the Greek for 'defender of men' or 'warrior'. Interestingly, it may also be

derived from another Classical source as the Latin word for 'law'.
*Variants: Alexander, Laxton, Lexie, Lexton*

### Liam
Liam is the short form of the Gaelic version of William, which means 'resolute protection'. It also comes from the French for 'to bind' or 'protect'.
*Variants: Lyam, William*

### Linden
The Old English meaning of Linden is 'lime tree' or 'the hill with linden trees'. It was originally an English place name that became a surname.

In North America, as a first name, it was associated with the Democratic President Lyndon Baines Johnson, who assumed the office in November 1963 following the assassination of John F Kennedy.
*Variants: Lin, Lindon, Lindy, Lyn, Lynden, Lyndon, Lynn*

### Lindsay
See Lindsey in the Girls' section.

### Lionel
Lionel is another name connected with Arthurian legend. The French meaning of the name is 'little lion'.
*Variants: Len, Lennie, Lenny, Leo, Leon, Leonel, Lionell, Lonnell*

### Llewellyn
The name Llewellyn means 'leader', 'lion' and 'resemblance'. It was borne by two Welsh princes – although with a slightly different spelling. The first was Llywelyn the Great who was born in 1173. The second Welsh prince bearing the name was Llywelyn the Last, who died in battle with Edward I of England, which resulted in the loss of Welsh independence.
*Variants: Fluellen, Lywelyn, Llywellwyn, Lyn*

# L

**Lloyd**
Lloyd comes from the Welsh for 'brown, grey' – the implication being that the bearer is of a dark complexion.
*Variants: Floyd, Llwyd, Loy, Loyd*

**Logan**
The surname Logan was derived from a Scottish and Irish place name that means 'little hollow' in Gaelic. Logan also comes from the Middle English word 'logge', which means 'record or journal of performance'.

**Lorenzo**
Lorenzo is the Italian and Spanish form of Lawrence, which means 'from Laurentum'. (See also Lawrence.)
*Variants: Laurence, Lawrence, Loren*

**Lorimer**
The Latin meaning of Lorimer is 'harness maker'.
*Variants: Lori, Lorrie, Lorry*

**Louis**
The name Louis is closely linked to the history of France. When the Germanic tribe, the Franks, invaded Gaul in the Middle Ages they brought with them the name Hludowig or Chlodowig, which became Clovis. It is from Clovis that the name Louis was derived and, like its English derivative Lewis, it means 'famous battle or warrior'.

Eighteen kings of France bore the name including Louis XVI who was executed during the French Revolution.
*Variants: Aloysius, Clovis, Elois, Lewie, Lewis, Ludwig, Ludvig, Luis*

**Lucas**
Lucas comes from the Greek for 'from Luciana'. Luciana is a region in southern Italy.
*Variants: Luc, Lucais, Luka, Lukas, Luke*

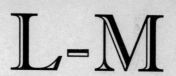
**Ludovic**
More than one theory exists to explain the origin of the name
Ludovic. Introduced to Scotland in the 17th century, the name
comes from the Gaelic for 'devotee of the Lord'.
    But, like Lewis and Louis, it also comes from the German for
'famed warrior' or 'famous battle'.
*Variants: Lewis, Louis, Ludo, Ludovick, Ludwig*

**Ludwig**
A variant of Louis and Lewis, Ludwig comes from the German
for 'famed warrior' or 'famous battle'. It was borne by the
German composer Ludwig von Beethoven and three kings of
Bavaria.
*Variants: Clovis, Lewis, Lothar, Louis, Ludovic, Ludwik*

**Luke**
Like Lucas, Luke comes from the Greek for 'from Luciana'. It
was the name of the author of the Gospel of St Luke, who is the
patron saint of doctors and painters.
*Variants: Luc, Lucais, Luka, Lukas*

**Luther**
The name Luther was borne by the founding father of the
Lutheran church, Martin Luther, who was born in 1483. This
Augustinian monk, who disapproved of papal indulgence,
launched the Protestant Reformation in 1520.
    Centuries later the name was associated with the African-
American Civil Rights leader, Martin Luther King.
    Luther comes from the Old German for 'people' and 'army'.
*Variants: Lothar, Lothario, Lother, Lother, Lutero*

**Macabee**
The Hebrew meaning of Macabee is 'hammer'. The name was
associated with the Jewish dynasty of kings, high priests and
patriots of the 2nd to 1st century BC.
*Variant: Maccabee*

*Boys*

### Mace

Mace is of Latin origin and refers to the aromatic spice of the same name, which is used in perfumes and cooking.
*Variants: Maceo, Macey, Mack, Mackey, Macy*

### Maddox

The name Maddox is both Celtic and English in origin. It means 'son of the Lord' and 'beneficent'.

### Madison

In North America the name Madison is bestowed upon children of either sex. Originally a surname it comes from the Old English for 'son of Maud', 'son of Matthew' or 'son of Magdalene'.

In the United States the name is associated with James Madison who was President during the War of 1812.
*Variants: Maddi, Maddie, Maddison, Maddy*

### Magnus

The Frankish king, Charlemagne, was commonly known by the Latin name Carolus Magnus, which in English means 'Charles the Great'. The byname Magnus was subsequently borne by a number of Norwegian kings and early saints. They include the 11th century ruler of Norway, Magnus the Good, and the 13th century king, Magnus the Law Mender.

The name was later imported to Scotland and, in Britain, was borne by the Scottish broadcaster Magnus Magnusson.
*Variant: Manus*

### Malachai

The Hebrew meaning of Malachai is 'my messenger' or 'my angel'. In the Old Testament it was borne by the last of the 12 minor prophets who predicted the coming of Christ.

Malachy is the Irish version of the name that belonged to two kings of Ireland and one saint. The saint, who lived in the 11th and 12th centuries, was the abbot of Banger, Armagh and Derry.

One of the kings who bore the name Malachy defeated the Norse invaders.
*Variants: Mal, Malachy*

## Malcolm
Generations of parents have named their children after saints or holy people. However, in the Middle Ages, it was thought to be presumptuous to do so without first using a prefix. Thus, boys who were named after the Irish monk, St Columba, were called Malcolm or 'devotee or servant of Columba'.

The name Malcolm is connected with Scotland because St Columba was the 6th century missionary who founded a monastery in Iona in 563. It was from this base that he set about converting the Scottish people.

Later, four kings of Scotland bore the name Malcolm including, it is said, Macbeth's father. In the 20th century the name was associated with the African-American activist Malcolm X, who was born Malcolm Little.
*Variants: Colm, Colum, Mal, Maolcolm*

## Malik
Malik means 'master' in Arabic.
*Variants: Mal, Mali*

## Manford
The Old English meaning of Manford is 'ford', which is the shallow part of the river that can be crossed by wading through it. People who lived near a ford were usually given the name.

## Manfred
Brought to Britain by the Normans, the name Manfred comes from the Old German for 'man of peace'. It was also the title of an 1817 poem written by Lord Byron.
*Variants: Fred, Freddie, Freddy, Manifred, Mannie, Manny, Mannye*

**Mansur**
The Arabic meaning of the name Mansur is 'divinely helped' or 'helped by God'.

**Mark**
A number of historical figures have borne the name Mark. They include St Mark, the author of the second gospel in the New Testament, who is the patron saint of lions, prisoners, lawyers and notaries. The name also belonged to Marcus Antonius (Mark Antony), the Roman political and military leader who was a follower of Julius Caesar and the lover of Cleopatra.

In North America, Mark Twain was the pen name of the writer Samuel Langhorne Clemens who produced the literary classics *The Adventures of Tom Sawyer* and *The Adventures of Huckleberry Finn*. The Venetian explorer Marco Polo bore the Italian version of the name.

Unfortunately, the exact meaning of Mark is unknown. It may come from the Latin for 'martial' as a derivative of the name Mars, the god of war.
*Variants: Marc, Marcel, Marcello, Marco, Marcus, Marques, Marquis, Mars*

**Marley**
Charles Dickens gave the name to one of the characters in his story *A Christmas Carol*. Jacob Marley was the business partner of Ebeneezer Scrooge who returned in a ghostly form to visit his friend. The name Marley means 'field near water'.

**Marlon**
The exact meaning of Marlon is unknown. As a variant of Marlow it may come from the Old English for 'pond', 'sea' and 'remnant'. But it may equally be derived from the Welsh for 'sea' and 'hill' or 'fort' as a variant of Merlin.
*Variants: Mar, Mario, Marle, Marlen, Marlin, Marlo, Marlow, Marlowe, Merlin*

### Marlow
Marlow comes from the Old English for 'pond', 'sea' and 'remnant'.
*Variants: Marle, Marlin, Marlis, Marlon*

### Marshall
Marshall is the transferred use of a surname that was originally an Old French occupational name. Historically a 'marshall' was either someone who looked after horses or a high-ranking official in the royal household.
*Variants: Marsh, Marshal, Marshe*

### Martin
The exact meaning of the name Martin is unknown. Like Mark it is thought to come from the Latin for 'martial' as a derivative of the name Mars, which belonged to the Roman god of war.

Martin Luther (1483-1546), professor of theology at Wittenberg was a leading figure in the Reformation. After him was named the African-American Civil Rights leader, Martin Luther King. The name was also borne by the son of a Roman soldier who became a pacifist and, later, a missionary and bishop, the 4th century saint, Martin of Tours. It was after this Martin that the London church, St Martin-in-the-Fields, was named.
*Variants: Mart, Martainn, Martel, Marten, Martie, Martyn*

### Marvin
The Old English meaning of the name Marvin is 'famous friend'. As a variant of Mervyn it means 'sea fort'.

In the 20th century the name was borne by legendary soul singer Marvin Gaye who died in 1984.
*Variants: Marv, Marve, Marven, Marvine, Marvyn, Mervyn, Merwin, Merwyn*

### Maskil
The Hebrew meaning of Maskil is 'educated' or 'learned'.

### Mason

Mason is an occupational name for someone who works with stone. The Old French meaning of the name is 'to make'.

### Matthew

St Matthew was the author of a gospel in the New Testament. He was also one of Christ's Apostles who used to collect tax for the Romans. Thus he is the patron saint of tax collectors, bankers, accountants and bookkeepers. The Hebrew meaning of Matthew is 'gift of God'.
*Variants: Macey, Mat, Mate, Mateus, Matiah, Matias, Matt, Mattie, Matty*

### Maurice

A Moor is a member of the Muslim people from North Africa. The Latin name used for this race of people was 'Maurus', which developed into the French name Maurice.

The name was borne by an early Byzantine emperor and by a Roman soldier who was martyred in Switzerland in 286.
*Variants: Maryse, Maur, Maurie, Morey, Morie, Morry, Morris, Morus*

### Max

As the short form of the Roman name Maximilianus, Max is derived from the Latin for 'great'. In the 15th century Emperor Frederick III bestowed a variant of the name on his first-born son Maximilian I.

As a diminutive of Maxwell, Max comes from the Scottish surname that means 'Mac's well'.
*Variants: Mac, Mack, Maks, Massimo, Maxey, Maxie, Maxim, Maximilian, Maxwell*

### Maxwell

As mentioned above Maxwell is the transferred use of the Scottish surname that means 'Mac's well'.
*Variants: Mac, Mack, Maks, Max, Maxie, Maxim, Maxime, Maxy*

**Maynard**
Keynes's middle name comes from the Old German for 'strong' and 'powerful'.

**Mel**
See Melvin.

**Melvin**
The exact meaning of Melvin is uncertain. It may come from the Old English for 'council' and 'friend' or the German for 'Amalo's settlement'. As a variant of Melville, it has the Old French meaning 'bad town'.
*Variants: Mel, Melville, Melvyn*

**Michael**
In the Old Testament the archangel Michael was seen as a messenger. In the New Testament Michael is portrayed as the leader in the war against Satan and the weigher of souls at the Last Judgement.
In Hebrew his name means 'who is like God?'.
*Variants: Michele, Mick, Mickey, Miguel, Mikael, Mike, Misha, Mitchell, Mychal*

**Milan**
A Czech name that means 'grace', Milan may also be a given as name after the Italian city.

**Miles**
The exact meaning of the name Miles is unclear. What is known is that the name was moderately popular shortly after the Norman Conquest. One suggestion is that it is a variant of the Biblical name Michael, which means 'who is like God?' in Hebrew. It may also come from the Latin for 'mils' of a thousand (mills) paces, or the Old German for 'beloved' or 'gentle'.
*Variants: Michael, Milan, Mills, Milo, Myles*

**Milo**
Milo comes from the Old Slavic for 'grace' and the Germanic for 'merciful'.
*Variants: Miles, Myles*

**Milton**
The Old English meaning of the name Milton is 'mill town' or 'middle settlement'. It is best known as the surname of the 17th century English poet John Milton who wrote *Paradise Lost* and *Paradise Regained*.
*Variants: Millard, Miller, Mills, Milt, Miltie, Milty, Mull, Muller*

**Mitchell**
Mitchell is a surname and variant of the Biblical name Michael. Thus, it means 'who is like God?' in Hebrew.
*Variants: Michael, Mitch, Mitchel*

**Montgomery**
Montgomery is a French baronial name of Old French and German origin. It is the combination of the French for 'mountain' and a German personal name that means 'power of man'.
   Montgomery is also a variant of Montague, which comes from the French and Latin for 'pointed mountain or big hill'.
*Variants: Montague, Monte, Montgomerie, Monty*

**Morgan**
See Morgan in the Girls' section.

**Mortimer**
The aristocratic surname Mortimer is taken from the French place name 'mort mer', which means 'dead sea'.
*Variants: Mort, Mortie, Morty*

**Moses**
Moses is one of the most significant characters in the Old Testament and an important figure for both Jews and Christians.

Though he never reached the Promised Land, the prophet Moses led the Israelites out of enslavement in Egypt. With God's help he performed numerous miracles including the parting of the Red Sea. God also entrusted Moses with the Ten Commandments. The Hebrew meaning of the name is 'saved from the water'. It is a fitting name for a man who, as a baby, was left in a basket among the bullrushes of the River Nile.
*Variants: Moe, Moke, Mosheh, Moss, Moy, Moyes, Moyse*

### Muhammad

Muhammad was the name of the prophet who founded the Islamic religion. Born in 570, Muhammad was a rich merchant and member of the ruling tribe in Mecca. His life was changed when he had a vision directing him to teach the true religion. He went on to conquer Mecca in 630, which is now a holy site and place of pilgrimage for millions of Muslims around the world.

The Arabic meaning of Muhammad is 'praised' or 'glorified'.

In the 1960s when the African-American boxer Cassius Clay announced he was changing his name to Muhammad Ali, it signified that he had converted to the Muslim faith.
*Variants: Mahamet, Mohamad, Mohammad, Mohamed, Mohammed*

### Murdoch

Murdoch comes from the Irish and Scottish Gaelic for 'sailor' or 'seaman'.
*Variants: Murdo, Murdock, Murtagh, Murtaugh*

### Murray

The northern Scottish district of Moray derived its name from the Old Celtic for 'settlement by the sea'. The name Murray comes from this place name.
*Variants: Murrie, Murry*

### Naaman

Naaman comes from the Hebrew for 'beautiful, pleasant'. In Arabic it means 'good fortune'.

### Nahum

In the Old Testament Nahum was a prophet who foretold the downfall of Nineveh. A Jewish name, it has been used by Christians since the Reformation.

It comes from the Hebrew for 'comforting' and was borne by the Restoration dramatist Nahum Tate who re-wrote Shakespeare's *King Lear* with a happy ending.
*Variant: Nemo*

### Naim

Naim is derived from the Arabic for 'comfortable' or 'contented'.
*Variant: Naeem*

### Namid

According to Native American legend there once existed a coyote that wanted to dance with the stars. The name Namid refers to this tale and means 'star dancer'.

### Namir

The Arabic meaning of Namir is 'leopard'.

### Naphtali

In the Old Testament Naphtali was one of Jacob's 12 sons. His mother was Bilhah, the handmaid of Jacob's co-wife Rachel.

The Hebrew meaning of the name is 'wrestler'.
*Variants: Naftali, Naftalie, Naphthali*

### Napoleon

The most famous bearer of this name was the great French commander and emporer, Napoleon Bonaparte. His name comes from the Greek for 'new town'.
*Variants: Leon, Nap*

### Naresh

Naresh comes from the Sanskrit for 'lord' or 'king'.

### Nassar

The Arabic meaning of Nassar is 'victorious'. It is listed in the Koran as one of the 99 names for God.

### Nathan

In the Bible, when King David committed adultery with Bathsheba, it was the prophet Nathan who told him that God was not happy with his actions.

In Hebrew Nathan means 'gift'. It is also a short form of Jonathan and Nathaniel, both of which mean 'God's gift'.
*Variants: Jonathan, Jonathon, Nat, Nata, Natan, Nate, Nathaniel*

### Nathaniel

In the New Testament Nathaniel was one of Christ's Apostles who was also known as Bartholomew. His name was derived from the Hebrew for 'he gave' or 'God's gift'. Nathan is its short form.
*Variants: Nat, Nata, Natal, Natan, Natanael, Natale, Nathan*

### Nav

This English gypsy name means exactly that, 'name'.
*Variants: Nev*

### Ned

As the short form of Edward, Ned is derived from the Old English for 'happiness, riches' and 'guardian'. As a diminutive of Edmund it means 'happiness, riches' and 'friend'.

Ted is now a more common short form of both these names. (See also Edward and Edmund.)
*Variants: Edmund, Edward, Neddie, Neddy, Ted, Teddie, Teddy*

### Neil

Although it is now widely used in the English-speaking world, before the 20th century Neil was primarily associated with Ireland and Scotland. This is because it is the Anglicised form of the Gaelic name Niall, which means 'cloud', 'passionate' and 'champion'.

Notable bearers of the name include the North American playwright, Neil Simon and the astronaut, Neil Armstrong and the popular singer, Neil Diamond.

*Variants: Neal, Neale, Neall, Nealson, Neely, Neill, Nelson, Niall, Nyles*

## Nelson

In the 19th century the name Nelson was often bestowed upon boys in honour of the British military hero Horatio Nelson, who defeated the powerful French navy at the Battle of Trafalgar in 1805.

In the 20th century the name became associated with the first black African President of South Africa, Nelson Mandela.

The name that both these powerful leaders shared was derived from the Old English for 'son of Neil' or 'son of Nell'. As mentioned above Neil means 'cloud, passionate or champion' in Irish Gaelic.

*Variants: Nealson, Neaton, Neil, Nils, Nilsen, Nilson*

## Nemo

As a short form of Nahum, Nemo comes from the Hebrew for 'comforting'. Its Greek meaning is 'from the glen'.

*Variant: Nahum*

## Neville

As a surname Neville was brought to England by a Norman baronial family. The French meaning of the name is 'new town or settlement'.

*Variants: Nev, Nevil, Nevile, Nevill*

## Newton

Like Neville, Newton means 'new town or settlement'. But the meaning of this name is derived from the Old English language. It is an English family name that was originally taken from a variety of locations in England.

*Variants: Newgate, Newland, Newman, Newt*

### Niall

The Irish and Scottish Gaelic form of Neil is Niall. It means 'cloud', 'passionate' and 'champion'. (See also Neil and Nelson.)
*Variants: Neil, Nelson*

### Nicholas

The name Nicholas comes from the Greek for 'victorious people'. The most well-known bearer of the name is the 4th- century saint, St Nicholas, who inpired the modern figure of Santa Claus, because of his generosity to others.
*Variants: Claus, Klaas, Klaus, Nic, Nicolai, Niccolo, Nick, Nicky*

### Nigel

As a Latinised form of the Irish Gaelic name Neil, Nigel means 'champion', 'passionate' and 'cloud'. However, a more likely source is the Old Latin for 'dark, night'. The Normans introduced the name to Britain.
*Variants: Neil, Nidge, Nigi, Nige, Niguel, Nye*

### Nir

Nir comes from the Hebrew for 'ploughed field' and is associated with industry and fruitfulness.
*Variants: Niral, Niria, Nirel*

### Noam

This Jewish name comes from the Hebrew for 'joy, delight and pleasantness'.

### Noble

Noble comes from the Latin word 'nobilis' which means 'renowned, famous' or 'born into nobility'. It is mainly used in North America.

### Noel

This Old French word for 'birthday of the Lord' is traditionally given to babies born at Christmas.
*Variants: Noël, Noëlle, Noelle*

### Nolan
Nolan is an Irish family name that comes from the Irish Gaelic for 'famous noble' or 'son of the famous one'.
*Variant: Noland*

### Norman
The Old English meaning of the name Norman was 'man from the north'. It was used in England before the arrival of the invading forces from northern France. Henceforth it came to mean 'Viking' or 'Norseman'.
*Variants: Norm, Normand, Normann, Normie*

### Norton
Norton is a surname and first name that comes from the Old English for 'north settlement'.
*Variants: Nort, Nortie, Norty*

### Nye
Born in 1897, Aneurin Bevan was a Welsh member of the Labour Party who helped to establish the National Health Service in post-war Britain. Nye is the pet form of his first name, which comes from the Welsh for 'little one of pure gold'.

Nye, however, also boasts Latin and Middle English roots. In Latin it means 'man of honour'. The Middle English interpretation is 'islander or island'.
*Variants: Aneurin, Ny, Nyle*

### Obediah
From the Hebrew 'servant', the implication being that the bearer of the name is a 'servant of God.' Obediah was one of the 12 minor prophets in the Bible.

The name was also used in Anthony Trollope's 1857 novel *Barchester Towers*, the second in the series of novels known as the *Chronicles of Barsetshire*. It was popular in the 17th and 18th centuries.
*Variants: Abdias, Obadiah, Obadias, Obe, Obed, Obie, Oby*

## Oberon

A variant of Auberon, the name is thought to be of German Frankish origin to mean 'noble' and 'bear'. The name was given by Shakespeare to the King of the Fairies in *A Midsummer Night's Dream*. (See also Auberon.)

## Octavius

A Roman family name, Octavius is Latin for 'eighth' and was traditionally given to the eighth son of a family. It was also the name of the first Roman Emperor, Augustus Caesar.
*Variants: Octave, Octavio, Otavio, Octavian*

## Oliver

An old Norse name, taken from the French for 'olive tree', Oliver was introduced into Britain by the Normans. It became popular in the Middle Ages thanks to the *Song of Roland*, about a heroic commander under Charlemagne; Oliver was the name of the hero's friend.

The name's popularity declined after the ousting of Oliver Cromwell, but it enjoyed something of a 19th century revival after the publication of Charles Dickens' 1838 novel *Oliver Twist*.
*Variants: Olivier, Ollie, Olivero*

## Olaf

From the Old Norse meaning 'ancestor' or 'remains', Olaf was brought to Britain by the Danes. Five Norwegian kings have been named Olaf, including Olaf I (995-1030), who was canonized.
*Variants: Olav, Olave, Ole, Olen, Olif*

## Omar

Arabic in origin, Omar has the meaning 'long life', 'flourishing', 'first-born son' and 'follower of the Prophet'. The name appears in the book of Genesis in the Bible.
*Variants: Omri, Oner*

### Orpheus

Derived from the Greek for 'ear' or perhaps 'darkness', the name Orpheus is associated with the Greek mythological poet whose music was so beautiful that it charmed wild beasts and moved trees and rivers to come and listen to him.

### Orrin

From the Hebrew word for 'tree', the name Orrin is mostly found in the southern states of North America. It probably has origins in the Irish name Oran, meaning 'grey-brown' or 'dark'. Oran was also the brother of St. Columba.
*Variants: Oren, Orin, Orren*

### Orson

The male form of Ursula, Orson comes from the old French for 'bear cub', Orson being a character in a medieval story who was raised by a bear in the woods.
*Variants: Sonnie, Sonny, Urson*

### Orville

A made-up name, Orville was created by novelist Fanny Burney for her 1778 work *Evelina*, which features as its hero one Lord Orville.
*Variant: Orval*

### Osbert

Taken from Old English, Osbert's meaning is 'bright' and 'gold'.
*Variants: Oz, Ozzie, Ozzy*

### Oscar

An old Norse name, Oscar means 'divine spear'. The name is a favourite with Swedish royalty, with two kings of Sweden and of Norway bearing the name.

Another notable Oscar is novelist and playwright, Oscar Wilde (1854 -1900), whose plays include: *The Importance of Being Earnest* (1895) and *An ideal Husband* (1895).
*Variants: Ossie, Ossy, Oke*

### Osmond

An English family name, Osmond derives from the old Norse for 'god' and 'protector', making the bearer of the name 'protected by God'. Saint Osmond is the protector against paralysis, toothache and insanity.

*Variants: Esmand, Osman, Osmand, Osmant, Osmen, Osmon, Osmont, Osmund, Osmundo, Oswin, Oz, Ozzie, Ozzy*

### Ossian

Originating in the Irish name meaning 'little deer', Ossian has links to Irish mythology, as Ossian was the son of Finn MacCool, who was one of the most popular heroes of Irish folklore, an Ulster tribal chieftan sometimes referred to as 'the Irish King Arthur'. According to folklore, he went on a series of adventures and bore his son Oisin (Ossian) with the goddess Sadb.

### Oswald

Oswald comes from the old English and Norse words for 'god and ruler' and 'power of wood'. The name's most positive associations were with Oswald of Winchester, a 10th century bishop of Worcester and Oswald of Northumbria, who was a close friend of St. Aidan.

*Variants: Ossie, Osvald, Oswal, Oswaldo, Oswall, Oswold, Oz, Ozzie, Ozzy, Waldo, Waldy*

### Othello

Originally from the Greek, meaning 'prosperous', the name is best-known from Shakespeare's play *Othello*, in which Othello blinded by jealousy, kills his innocent wife, Desdemona.

### Otis

Otis' origins are in the Greek for ear, as in having 'a good ear for music'/giving and taking good advice. The name was borne by James Otis, a Boston lawyer who played an integral part at the start of the American Revolution.

*Variants: Otes, Otto*

**Otto**
With its origins in the German for 'wealth' and 'prosperity', Otto arrived in Britain with the Normans as Odo, the name of William the Conqueror's brother. It was also the name of a 12th century saint and of four Roman Emperors.
*Variants: Odo, Osman, Othello, Othman, Othmar*

**Overton**
Derived from the Middle English for 'higher' or 'above' and 'town' or 'village', Overton means either 'higher of two towns' or 'hillside town'.

**Ovid**
The name Ovid is taken from the Latin for 'egg', which is seen as a symbol for life.

**Owen**
The Welsh form of 'Eugene', Owen is derived from the Greek for 'well-born' or 'lucky'.
*Variants: Bowen, Bowie, Eoghan, Eugene, Euan, Evan, Ewen, Owain, Owayne, Ovin*

**Pablo**
Pablo is the Spanish version of the name Paul, and is dervied from the Greek for 'small'. (See also Paul.)

**Paddy**
The 19th century generic name for an Irish man, Paddy is also a pet form of Patrick. (See also Patrick.)

**Paolo**
Paolo is the the Italian version of Paul and as such comes from the Greek for 'small'. (See also Paul.)

**Paris**
While Paris immediately suggests the capital of France, the

original meaning of the name Paris is uncertain. It probably derives from 'marshes of the Parisii', this being the Latin name for the Gaulish Celtic tribe. It was also the name of the Trojan prince who abducted Helen of Troy and caused the Trojan War.

### Parker
Taking its meaning from the old French for 'park-keeper', Parker as a first name is derived from an English family name, and enjoys popularity in North America.

### Parley
This name is derived from the Latin word for 'discourse'.

### Parnell
Possibly sharing 'Peter's' roots in the Greek word for 'rock', Parnell is thought to be a diminutive of Petronella, which in turn comes from the Roman family name Petronius. Parnell is also an English family name.
*Variants: Parnall, Parnel, Parnell, Pernel, Pernell*

### Pascal
Pascal is derived from the Old French word for Easter.
*Variants: Pasco, Pasqual, Pascoe, Pesach*

### Patrick
From the Latin meaning 'patrician' or a 'member of the Roman nobility', Patrick was not widely used until the 17th century due to Saint Patrick being so revered. Captured and taken to Ireland by pirates, Deacon's son Patrick became a slave herdsman, but studied religion and eventually escaped to Gaul. Training as a Bishop, he returned to Ireland as a missionary, spreading the gospel there. Patrick is the patron saint of Ireland, engineers and those who fear snakes.
*Variants: Pad, Paddie, Paddy, Padriac, Pat, Patraic, Patric, Paxton*

### Paul
Derived from the Greek for 'small', the name Paul was borne by numerous saints, the most famous being the author of Epistles in the New Testament. Originally named Saul, he was a Jewish citizen of Rome who persecuted Christians. Saul was converted after seeing a vision of Christ on the road to Damascus, changing his name to Paul to reflect his new-found humility.
*Variants: Pablo, Pal, Paolo, Pasha, Paulie, Paulino, Paulinus, Paulis, Paulo, Pol*

### Paxton
The name Paxton derives from two Latin words, 'pax', meaning peace and 'tūn', meaning 'town', hence the meaning 'town of peace'.

### Penn
Meaning 'hill' in old English, 'commander' in ancient German and 'pen' or 'quill' in Latin, Penn first appeared as an Old English surname given to someone who lived near a sheep pen.

It was popularised in North America by Sir William Penn, founder of Pennsylvania.
*Variants: Pennie, Penny, Penrod*

### Percival
Originally a Norman baronial name, Perci, the name means 'to pierce the veil'. Percival increased greatly in popularity thanks to the poet Percy Bysshe Shelley (1792-1822).
*Variants: Percy, Perceval, Perseus*

### Perry
Derived from numerous sources, Perry is either from an Old English family name, whereby it means 'pear tree', a pet form of Peregrine (meaning foreigner or stranger) or a diminutive of Peter.
*Variant: Perigrine*

**Peter**

This name is taken from the Greek for 'rock'. Saint Peter was the most prominent of the disciples during the ministry of Jesus and was charged with spreading the gospel and founding a universal church.

The name was popularised by JM Barrie's classic children's tale *Peter Pan* with its hero who never grows up.

*Variants: Pete, Perry, Pierre, Piers, Rock, Rocky*

**Philip**

The name originally derives from the Greek for 'loving horses'. It was the name of Philip of Macedonia, the father of Alexander the Great.

*Variants: Felip, Phillip, Phil, Pip, Philipot, Philippe*

**Philmore**

Philmore is aquatic, and its roots can be found both in Greek, where it means 'loving', and Welsh where it has the meaning 'lover of the sea'.

**Phoebus**

First appearing in Britain in the 16th century, Phoebus comes from the Greek for 'bright' or 'shining'.

*Variants: Feibush, Feivel, Feiwel*

**Phoenix**

See Phoenix in Girls' section.

**Piers**

This name is a French version of Peter. (See also Peter.)

**Pip**

A diminutive of Philip, the name Pip came to prominence thanks to Charles Dickens novel *Great Expectations* (1861), where the hero was named Pip.

**P**

**Plato**
Derived from the Greek word for 'broad' or 'flat', Plato is best known as the name of the celebrated Greek philosopher (428-347 BC).
*Variant: Platon*

**Poco**
This is an Italian name meaning 'little'.

**Porter**
Taken from French meaning 'to carry', the name Porter was initially bestowed upon someone who guarded a gate.

**Powell**
This name is a derivation of Howell, taken from the Old English meaning 'wild boar/domestic swine' and 'hill'.

**Pravin**
A Hindu name, meaning 'skilful' or 'able'.

**Preston**
Initially a surname, Preston probably derives from the old English for a priest's enclosure, or a village which had a priest, or a village that was built on church land.
*Variant: Prescott*

**Priestley**
Deriving its meaning from both Latin and Old English, Priestly means 'elder' or 'elder of the church'.

**Purnal**
Taken from the Latin, meaning 'pear', the purnal is a long-living tree, and a symbol of longevity in China.

**Purvis**
Purvis is derived from the Latin for 'forsee', 'look after' or 'provide'.

**Putnam**

Taken from the Latin for 'pruner' or 'one who prunes trees', Putnam was originally an English surname and place name, and means 'Putta's homestead' in Old English.

**Quentin**

Quentin comes from the Latin name Quintus, which means 'fifth'. It was traditionally bestowed upon the fifth son in a family.

In France the name is associated with a 3rd century martyr and missionary.

*Variants: Quent, Quenton, Quincy, Quinn, Quint, Quintus*

**Quincy**

In North America the name Quincy was borne by a former President of the United States, John Quincy Adams. It is also the name of a place in Massachusetts.

In France, the name is associated with a noble family from Normandy. Like Quentin, Quincy comes from the Latin for 'fifth'.

*Variants: Quentin, Quincey, Quintus*

**Quinn**

The Irish meaning of Quinn is 'descendant of Conn' – Conn being a word that meant 'leader' or 'chief'.

*Variants: Quentin, Quincy*

**Rabi**

Arabic in origin, this name means 'fragrant breeze.' It is the male form of Rabia.

**Rafferty**

Deriving from Gaelic and German roots, Rafferty means 'rich and prosperous.' It is also a surname. The name is popular in North America.

*Variants: Rafe, Raff, Rafer, Raffer*

**Raja**
This name is Arabic for 'anticipated' or 'hoped for'. Raja is the male version of Rani and means 'prince'.
*Variant: Raj*

**Raleigh**
This is an Old English name that comes from 'Ra', or 'roe deer' and 'leah' or 'grassy clearing'. It is also a surname, most famously that of Sir Walter Raleigh (1554-1618), the noted Elizabethan courtier and explorer.

**Ralph**
Taken from the German 'rand', meaning 'advice' or 'might' and 'wulf', meaning 'wolf', Ralph means 'fearless advisor'.
*Variants: Raaf, Rafe, Raff, Raffy, Randolph, Ranulf, Rauf, Rauffe, Rolf*

**Ramsey**
Ramsey, and its variant, Ramsay, have their origins in the Old English 'ram' (male sheep), and 'sey', which has the literal meaning 'land of the rams'. It is also a surname: James Ramsay MacDonald (1866-1937) was the first Labour Prime Minister of Great Britain, holding the post from 1924 to 1927 and again from 1929 to 1935.
*Variant: Ramsay*

**Randall**
A version of Randolph, which is also a surname. (See Randolph.)
*Variants: Randal, Randel, Randle, Rand, Rands, Randl*

**Randolph**
Randolph's origins are in the Old English for 'shield' and 'wolf', which come from the Norse words 'rand', meaning 'rim' or 'shield', and 'ulfr' meaning 'wolf'. Famous Randolphs include Randolph Churchill (1849-1895), father of Sir Winston Churchill.
*Variants: Dolph, Rand, Rands, Randolf, Ranulf, Randall, Randy, Randal, Rand, Randle*

### Raphael
The name of an archangel in the Bible, Raphael comes from the Hebrew for 'God has healed'. Besides the archangel, it was also the name of one of the best-known Renaissance painters.
*Variants: Raf, Rafael, Rafaelle, Rafe, Rafel, Raffael, Raphel*

### Rashad
Of Arabic origin, Rashad means 'to have good sense' or 'integrity'.

### Raul
Raul originates in the old Germanic for 'counsel' or 'might' (as in strength) and 'wolf', where it is a variant of Ralph.
*Variants: Ralph, Raolin, Raoul*

### Raven
This name means 'black bird'. Raven is a variant of the Old English 'hraefn'.

### Ravi
Ravi means 'sun', and also has origins in Hindi myth, where it was the name of the sun god. In popular culture, it is associated with Indian musician Ravi Shankar.

### Ravid
A Hebrew-derived name meaning 'jewellery' or 'adornment'.

### Ravinder
Taken from the Old French 'rapine', meaning a 'mountain stream' or 'rush of water', this name is insinuative of the power of rushing water as boundless energy and enthusiasm for life.

### Raymond
With its origins in Old German, Raymond derives from the words 'ragen' for 'wisdom', and 'mund' meaning 'guardian'; literally 'advisor and protector'. There are numerous saints with

the name, including St. Raymond of Toulouse.
*Variants: Monchi, Mondo, Mundo, Raimond, Ramond, Ramone, Raynard, Redmond, Rai, Ray*

### Raynor

Raynor has Old German/Flemish roots, coming from the Flemish words 'ragan' meaning 'wisdom' or 'advice', and 'harja' meaning 'army' or 'people'.

The derivative Rainier is popular with the Grimaldis, who are the royal family of Monaco.
*Variants: Ragnar, Rainer, Ray, Rayner, Rain, Raines, Rainier, Rains, Lee, Leigh, Rally, Rawleigh, Rawley*

### Regan

Derived from Hebrew and Old German roots, meaning 'wise', Regan and its variants are also surnames, especially in North America, where the name is associated with former US President Ronald Reagan (1911-2004).
*Variants: Reagan, Reagen*

### Redford

This name is taken from the Old English words 'red', meaning 'reedy', and 'ford', a shallow river crossing.
*Variants: Ford, Red, Redd*

### Reeves

An occupational name, Reeves is derived from the Old English for a bailiff, overseer or chief magistrate.
*Variants: Reeve, Reave*

### Reginald

This first name is derived from the Old English for 'powerful warrior'. The British singer, composer, and pianist, Sir Elton John's original name is Reginald Kenneth Dwight.
*Variants: Reg, Reggie, Rex, Ronald, Reginauld, Reinhold, Reinold, Reinwald, Renardo, Reynold, Rinardo, Nardo*

### René

This is a French name meaning 'reborn'. In France, the name is associated with René Descartes (1596-1650), the noted French philosopher and mathematician.
*Variants: Renato, Renatus, Reni*

### Reuben

Reuben is a Biblical Hebrew name, meaning 'behold, a son'.
*Variants: Rube, Ruben*

### Reuel

Derived from Hebrew, Reuel means 'friend of God'.

### Rex

This name is a diminutive of Reginald and Reynold, and is Latin for 'ruler' or 'leader'.

The name was borne by British actor Rex Harrison (1908-1990), who changed his name from Reginald Carey.
*Variants: Regino, Regis, Rexer, Rexford, Reynaud, Reyner, Ray, Rayner*

### Reynard

Reynard has roots in Flemish and French. In Flemish, it derives from 'ragin', or 'advice' and "nard', meaning 'hardy' or 'strong'. It is also the French word for fox.
*Variants: Rainardo, Ray, Raynard, Ragnard, Reinhard, Renaud, Rey*

### Rhodric

An Anglicised version of the Spanish Rodrigo, Rhodric comes from the Old German meaning 'famous ruler', 'hrod' meaning 'fame' and 'ric' meaning 'ruler'.
*Variants: Rouven, Revie, Ribbans, Rouvin, Rube, Ruben, Rubens, Rubin, Ruby, Ruvane, Ruvim, Rod, Rodd, Roddie, Rodrich, Roddy, Roderick, Roderich, Roderigo, Rodrique, Rofi, Rory, Rurih, Ruy*

# R

*Boys*

### Rider

A Middle English name, derived from the word 'ridde', meaning 'to clear' or 'to make space', Rider was often applied to someone who would clear land.

The name is associated with the British writer, Sir Henry Rider Haggard (1856-1925), who wrote the classics *King Solomon's Mines* (1885) and *She* (1887).

*Variants: Rid, Riddle, Ridgeley, Ridley, Ryder, Ryerson*

### Riordan

Of German and Gaelic origins, Riordan is derived from the words for 'royal' and 'poet'.

*Variants: Rearden, Riorden*

### Ripley

Another occupational name, Ripley is related to the Old English for 'one who would clear wooded areas'.

*Variants: Lee, Leigh, Rip, Ripp*

### Rockwell

The literal meaning is 'a well with rocks'. Rockwell comes from the Old English words 'roche' for 'rock' and 'wella' for 'well'.

*Variants: Roache, Rocco, Roch, Rocher, Rochie, Roche, Rochy*

### Roger

Roger has its roots in Old German and Old English. The English lineage derives from the word 'hodge', meaning 'a peasant labourer'. The German origin comes from 'hrod', or 'fame' and 'ger' or spear, hence a 'famous spear-carrier'.

British actor Roger Moore, of *The Saint* and James Bond fame, is a popular icon who boasts this name.

*Variants: Rog, Roggie, Rodge, Rodger, Dodge, Hodge, Rogello, Rogerio, Rogers, Roj, Rugero, Ruggerio, Rutger*

### Rollo

A variant of Roland and diminutive of Raoul, Rollo is believed

to be the Old French version of Rolf.
*Variants: Rolf, Rolly, Rolan, Roul, Rudolf, Rudolph*

**Romain**
With its literal meaning 'a citizen of Rome', Romain is essentially
French for 'Roman'.
*Variants: Roman, Romano, Romeo, Romulus*

**Roone**
An Old English name taken from 'rune', Roone means 'secret
consultation, magic or mystery'.

**Roswell**
Roswell, derived from the Old German, means 'a skilled fighting
horseman'.

**Rouel**
Rouel is a Hebrew name, meaning 'friend of God'.
*Variant: Ruel*

**Rowan**
Of Gaelic origins, Rowan means 'red haired' or 'rugged'.
*Variants: Rouan, Rooney, Rowen, Rowney, Rowan, Rowanne*

**Rhys**
Rhys is derived from the Welsh word for 'ardour', and was the
name of several Welsh rulers during the Middle Ages. It is also
a Welsh surname.
*Variants: Reece, Ray, Rees, Reese, Rey, Rhett, Rice, Royce*

**Richard**
Taken from the Germanic words meaning 'he who rules' and
'hard', the enduring popularity of the name Richard was
carried by many famous men throughout history. Among
them are three kings of England, including Richard the
Lionheart (Richard I), who lead the third Crusade. The

composer Richard Wagner is another well-known personality with this name.

*Variants: Dic, Dick, Dickie, Dicky, Ric, Ricard, Ricardo, Riccardo, Richie, Richey, Ritchie*

**Riley**

Taken from the Old English 'ryge', meaning 'rye' and 'loan',' meaning 'clearing' or 'meadow', Riley means 'rye meadow'.

*Variants: Reilly, Ryley, Royley*

**Robbie**

This name is a pet form and diminutive of Robert. (See Robert.)

*Variants: Rob, Robo, Rabbie*

**Robert**

Derived from the ancient German for 'bright' and 'famous', Robert is the name of many famous men. These include Robert the Bruce (1274-1329) who freed Scotland from British domination, two other Scottish kings and Robert Peel (1788-1850) who established the police force. More recently, it is associated with actor, Robert Redford.

*Variants: Bob, Bobbie, Hobson, Robb, Robbie, Robby, Roberto, Rory, Bert, Bertie, Robertson*

**Robin**

Robin is the original French version of Robert. Notable Robins include Robin Hood and also Christopher Robin, a character in A.A. Milne's literary works.

*Variants: Rob, Robyn*

**Rodney**

Rodney derives from the Old English, meaning 'island of reeds'.

*Variants: Rod, Rodd, Roddie, Roddy*

**Roland**

With its origins in the Old German words for 'fame' and 'land',

famous use of the name occurs in the Bible where strong-man Samson is betrayed by Delilah, and destroys the temple of the Philistines.
*Variants: Sam, Sammy, Sampson, Shimson*

### Samuel
A Biblical name of Hebrew origin, Samuel means 'asked of God' and may be a derivative of Saul.
*Variants: Sam, Sammie, Sammy, Shmuel*

### Sancho
A derivative of the Spanish for 'sincere' and 'thoughtful', as well as the Latin 'San Etus' meaning 'holy' and/or 'pure', Sancho is the male form of Sancha.

It was popularised by Miguel De Cervantes' novel, *Don Quixote* (1605-1615) where Sancho Panza was the faithful servant of the deluded title character.
*Variant: Sanchez*

### Sanford
Sanford originates in Old English, meaning 'he who dwells at a sandy river crossing' (a ford).
*Variant: Sandy*

### Sasha
Originating in Old French, Sasha means 'defender' or 'helper' as in the 'helper of mankind'. French singer Sacha Distel made the name popular in the 1960s and 70s.
*Variant: Sacha*

### Saul
Saul translates from the Hebrew for 'asked/prayed for', as in a prayed-for child. The name is also Biblical: St Paul was originally named Saul, and it was also the name of the first King of Israel.
*Variants: Shaul, Sol, Sollie, Solly, Saulo, Shane, Paul*

**Saville**
Also a surname, Saville drives from the French words, 'Sa' and 'ville', literally meaning 'his' and 'town'.

**Sawyer**
Sawyer has its origins in Middle English, and is occupational in derivation, meaning 'someone who saws'. It is also a surname, Sawyer was popularised by Mark Twain's 1876 novel *Tom Sawyer*.
*Variants: Saw, Sawyere.*

**Scott**
Of Old English derivation, Scott translates very simply as meaning 'one of Scottish origin'.
*Variant: Scot*

**Sean**
Sean is Gaelic in origin. As the Irish version of John it shares the meaning 'God is gracious'. (See John.)
*Variants: Shaughan, Shaun, Shane*

**Sear**
This name comes from an Old English word for 'battle'.
*Variants: Searle, Sears, Serle, Serlo*

**Sebastian**
Derived from the Greek for 'venerable', Sebasta was also a town in Asia Minor (now called Siva). It is also a saint's name: Saint Sebastian was a Roman soldier who was martyred when he was shot with numerous arrows, inspiring many religious paintings.
*Variants: Seb, Sebbie, Bastian, Bart, Bartiana, Barties, Sebastianus*

**Seth**
Given to the third son of Adam and Eve in the Bible, Seth is a Hebrew name meaning 'the appointed one'. In Sanskrit it also means 'bridge'.

### Seymour

In France, Seymour is derived from the old French place name of Saint-Maur, Maur meaning 'Moorish' or 'African'. In Old English, meanwhile, the name is a combination of 'sae', meaning 'sea' and 'mor' meaning marshland or moor.
*Variant: Seymore*

### Shaanan

This name is derived from the Hebrew word for 'peaceful'.
*Variants: Shanen, Shannon, Shanon*

### Shamir

Shamir's origins are in the Hebrew for 'flint'. There is a Jewish legend in which the Shamir were worms capable of cutting through the hardest substances on earth, and as such were used to cut the stones for King Solomon's temple.

### Shem

Shem's origins are Hebrew and Biblical, where Shem was one of Noah's sons, the older brother of Ham and Japeth. The Biblical Shem was supposedly born to Noah when Noah was 500 years old.
*Variants: Shammas, Shemuel*

### Shelley

Originating in the Old English for 'wood near a ledge clearing or meadow', Shelley is also an old English surname.
*Variants: Shell, Shelly*

### Sheridan

The name Sheridan is thought to be a Gaelic name meaning 'wild' or 'untamed', a development of 'Siridran'. It is also a surname, belonging to US Unionist Commander General Philip Henry Sheridan (1831-1888).
*Variants: Sheridon, Sherry*

**Sidney**
Sidney has origins in Old English, where it translates as 'of a riverside meadow', and in the Old French meaning 'of St. Denis'.
*Variants: Sid, Syd, Sydney*

**Silas**
Silas' origins are in the Greek word for 'wood', Sylvanus or Silvanus. The name became popular in the 19th century after the publication of George Eliot's novel *Silas Marner*.

**Simon**
Simon is derived from the Greek for 'snub-nosed' and the Hebrew words for 'God has heard', 'listening' and, oddly enough, 'little hyena'. The name occurs several times in the Bible, where it was the original name of St Peter. The Old Testament also features Simeon, the second son of Jacob and Leah, while the New Testament gives us no less than six Simeons.
*Variants: Cimon, Imon, Sameir, Semon, Shimone, Si, Silas, Sim, Simao, Samer, Simeon, Simi, Simion, Simkin, Simone, Simp, Simpson, Sims, Sy, Symon*

**Sinclair**
Sinclair is a contraction of Saint-Clair, the French place name borne by a Norman martyr. Clair in Old English also means 'clear', 'bright' or 'famous'. The name is also a Scottish surname.
*Variations: Clarence, Sinclaire, Sinclar*

**Sol**
Meaning 'sun' in Latin, Sol is a short form of Solomon. (See Solomon.)

**Solomon**
Derived from the Hebrew word for 'peace', 'Shalom', Solomon was most famously the name of temple-building Biblical King Solomon, who died in 980BC.

*Variants: Sol, Salaman, Salamon, Salo, Salman, Saloman, Salome, Salomo, Shelomo, Solmon.*

**Somerby**
Somerby is derived from the Middle English for 'over' and 'village or town', meaning 'town across the fields' or 'nearby town'.

**Spencer**
Derived from the Old French, it means 'dispenser of provisions' or 'administrator'.
*Variants: Spence, Spenser*

**Spike**
Taken from the Latin 'spika', meaning a spiky point, or an ear of corn, Spike's origins are given as Old English.

**Stacey**
A short form of Eustace, Stacy is derived from the Greek, meaning 'rich in corn', 'fruitful' or a 'good harvest'. Eustace is also the male form of Anastasia.
*Variants: Stacy, Stacie*

**Stanhope**
Derived from the Old English for 'stone' and 'hope', a Stanhope was a high stone one would stand on to get a good view. It was also the name of a light, open, horse-drawn carriage invented by the British clergyman Reverend Fitzroy Stanhope (1787-1864).
*Variants: Ford, Hope, Stan, Stancliff, Stanford*

**Stanley**
Taken from the old German for a 'stony clearing', where 'stan' is 'stone' and 'leah' is 'meadow' or 'grassland', Stanley is also an English surname.
*Variants: Stan, Stanford, Stanleigh, Stanly, Stanton*

### Stockton
Stockton is derived from the Old English words 'stoc' and 'tūn', meaning 'trees' and 'town' respectively. Hence Stockton's meaning is 'town near felled trees'.

### Sven
Mostly used in Sweden and Norway, Sven is Norse for 'boy'.
*Variants: Svarne, Svend, Swen*

### Sweeney
Sweeney is derived from the Gaelic word meaning 'little hero'. The name is probably best known by association with the murderous barber Sweeney Todd.

### Tad
As the Anglicised form of the Gaelic name Tadhg, Tad comes from the byname that means 'poet' or 'philosopher'.

However, it is also the short form of the name Thaddeus, which was used in the Bible to distinguish between two of Christ's Apostles, both of whom were called Judas, Judas Thaddeus and Judas Iscariot.

The exact meaning of Thaddeus is unclear but it may come from the Aramaic for 'praise, desired' or the Greek for 'gift of God'.
*Variants: Tadhg, Thaddeus, Theodore*

### Tariq
The Arabic meaning of Tariq is 'visitor'. In Hindi it means 'morning star'.

### Tarquin
Tarquin was the name of two early kings of Rome – Tarquin the Proud and Tarquin the Old.

The Roman family name, Tarquinus, was originally given to those who came from Tarquinii, an ancient town of Rome.
*Variants: Quin, Tarq*

**Tate**
The Middle English meaning of this name is 'cheerful' or 'spirited'.
It is also a surname.
*Variant: Tait*

**Terence**
The exact meaning of Terence is unknown. As a derivative of the
Roman family name Terentius, it may come from the Latin for 'to
wear out' or 'to polish'. Terentius was the name of the North
African slave and playwright who adopted the name of his
former master when he became a free man.

Terence is also the Anglicised form of the Irish Gaelic for
'initiator of an idea'.
*Variants: Tel, Telly, Terencio, Terrance, Terry, Terryal*

**Thatcher**
In the late 20th century, Thatcher was the surname of the first
woman to hold the position of Prime Minister in Britain.

The family name Thatcher can also be used as a first name,
but it was originally an occupational name. It comes from the
Old English for 'thatch'.
*Variants: Thacher, Thatch*

**Theobald**
Theobald is an Old French name that is of Germanic (Frankish)
origin. It means 'bold people'. An Old English version of the
name, Theodbeald, was already in existence in England before
the arrival of the Normans prompted the use of the German
variant.
*Variants: Tebald, Ted, Tedd, Teddie, Thebault, Theo, Thibaud, Thibault,
Tibald, Tibold*

**Theodore**
The name Theodore comes from the Greek for 'gift of God'.
*Variants: Tad, Tadd, Taddeus, Ted, Teddie, Teddy, Thadeus,
Theo, Theophilus*

**Thomas**

In the Bible Thomas was one of Christ's Apostles. He is known as 'doubting Thomas' because he would not believe that Jesus had risen from the dead until he could touch his wounds with his own hands. Thomas comes from the Aramaic and Greek for 'twin' and has been borne by numerous saints.

*Variants: Tamas, Tom, Tomas, Tome, Tomm, Tommie, Tommy*

**Thornton**

The Old English meaning of Thornton is 'thorn' and 'town', thus it was often used to refer to a town or village located near thornbushes or hawthorn trees.

*Variants: Thorn, Thorndike, Thornie*

**Timothy**

Timothy is derived from a Greek name that means 'honouring God'. In the New Testament it was borne by a young man from Asia Minor who was converted to Christianity by St Paul. He later became the Bishop of Ephesus.

*Variants: Tim, Timmie, Timofey*

**Toby**

Toby is a short form of the Biblical name Tobias. In the Old Testament Tobias was the son of Tobit who left his home and went travelling with the archangel Raphael as his companion. When he returned Tobias was wealthy, married and possessed a cure to restore his father's eyesight.

Tobias comes from the Hebrew for 'God is good'.

*Variants: Tobe, Tobey, Tobiah, Tobie, Tobin, Tobit, Tobye, Tobyn*

**Todd**

The transferred use of the surname Todd comes from the Middle English for 'fox'. As a nickname it was used for someone who either had red hair, or was known for being cunning.

*Variants: Tad, Tod, Toddie, Toddy*

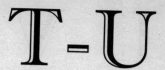
### Travis

Travis is an English family name that comes from the Old French for 'a crossing', given to someone who lived near a ford or crossroads. Alternatively original bearers of the name gathered tolls at a crossing, gate or bridge.
*Variants: Travers, Travus, Travon, Trevon*

### Trey

Originally Trey was a nickname given to a boy who bore a name that had been in his family for three generations. It comes from the Latin for 'three'. As a variant of Tremaine, it has the Cornish meaning 'the house on the rock'.
*Variant: Tremaine*

### Tyler

Tyler was an Old English occupational name given to someone who tiled roofs or made tiles.
*Variants: Tiler, Ty, Tye*

### Tyrone

The name Tyrone is derived from a Northern Irish county. Its Gaelic meaning is 'Owen's country'. Owen is the Celtic form of Eugene, which means 'well born' in Greek.
*Variants: Ty, Tye, Tyron*

### Tyson

Tyson comes from the French for 'firebrand' and was originally given to a bad-tempered person as a nickname.
*Variant: Tie, Ty, Tye, Tysen, Tysone*

### Uri

In the Bible Uriah was the name of the husband of Bathsheba, the woman with whom King David committed adultery. His name comes from the Hebrew for 'God is my light' and Uri is its short form.
*Variants: Uriah, Urie, Yuri*

### Ulysses
Ulysses was the name of the hero of the epic poem *The Odyssey*, attributed to the Greek poet Homer.

The exact meaning of the name is unknown but it is thought to come from the Greek for 'to hate'. In North America Ulysses was the first name of the American Civil War hero and President of the United States, Ulysses S Grant.
*Variants: Odysseus, Uileos, Ulick, Ulises*

### Valentine
See Valentina in the Girls' section.

### Vaughan
Vaughan comes from the Old Welsh for 'little' and the Celtic for 'small'.
*Variants: Vaughn, Vaune, Vawn, Vawne, Van, Vonn*

### Vernon
Richard de Vernon was one of the Norman conquerors of England. His name comes from the Gaulish word for 'where alders grow'. Vernon also comes from the Latin for 'belonging to the spring'.
*Variants: Vern, Verna, Verne*

### Victor
Victor, the masculine equivalent of Victoria, comes from the Latin for 'victory'. It was a popular name among early Christians who used it as a reference to Christ's victory over death and sin. In Britain use of the name was revived during the reign of Queen Victoria.
*Variants: Vic, Vick, Victoir, Viktor, Vito, Vitor*

### Vincent
Vincent derives its meaning from the Latin for 'conquering'. The name was borne by several early saints, including Vincent de Paul who founded a charitable order to help the poor.
*Variants: Vince, Vincente, Vine, Vinnie, Vinny, Vinson*

**Virgil**
The name Virgil has traditionally been given to children in honour of the Roman poet who lived during the 1st century BC. The name comes from the Latin for 'stick' and is thought to imply 'staff-bearer'.
*Variants: Verge, Vergit, Virge, Virgie, Virgilio*

**Vivian**
See Vivian in the Girls' section.

**Walker**
The Old English meaning of Walker is 'to tread'. It is a former occupational name used for 'a fuller of cloth'.
*Variant: Wal*

**Warner**
Warner is a medieval name that was brought to Britain by the Normans. It comes from the Old German for 'guard' and 'army'.
*Variants: Garnier, Warren, Werner, Wernher*

**Warren**
As a derivative of the French town name La Varenne, Warren means 'game preserve', 'wasteland' or 'sandy soil'. It was first brought to England by the Normans as Guarin or Warin.
*Variants: Varner, Ware, Waring, Warner, Warrener*

**Webster**
This is an Old English occupational name for a 'weaver'. The name is associated with the lexicographer Noah Webster after whom the Webster series of dictionaries derive their name.
*Variants: Web, Webb*

**Wesley**
The Old English meaning of Wesley is 'western wood, meadow or clearing'.
*Variants: Lee, Leigh, Wellesley, Wes, Wesleigh, Wesly, Wezley*

### Wilbur

The exact origin of the name Wilbur is uncertain, but a number of theories exist. It may come from the German and Old English for 'will' and 'defence, fortress'. It may also be derived from the Old English for 'wild boar'.

As a variant of Wilbert, Wilbur could come from the German and Old English for 'will' and 'bright'. Or it could have the Germanic meaning 'pledge or hostage' and 'bright'. Wilbur could equally mean 'servant of St Gilbert' in Scottish Gaelic.
*Variants: Gilbert, Wilbert, Wilburh, Wilburn, Wiley, Wilgburh, Willard, Willmer, Wylie*

### William

William I of England is known as William the Conqueror, after he defeated King Harold in 1066 at the Battle of Hastings. Other monarchs bearing the name include William III (William of Orange). It is also the name of the future British king, Prince William. The name means 'will, desire' and 'helmet, protection'.
*Variants: Bill, Billy, Guillaume, Liam, Wil, Wilem, Wilhelm, Williamson, Willie, Willy*

### Winston

Sir Winston Churchill was perhaps the most beloved British Prime Minister of the 20th century. The family name comes from the Old English for 'joy' and 'stone'. It also has the Old English meaning 'to win, defeat or conquer' and 'town'.
*Variants: Win, Winnie, Winton, Wynston, Wyston*

### Wycliffe

Wycliffe comes from the Old Norse for 'village near the cliff'. It was the surname of the 14th century religious reformer John Wycliffe who produced the first English translation of the Bible.
*Variants: Wyche, Wyck, Wycke*

### Xavier

In the 16th century the Spanish soldier, St Francis Xavier, spread

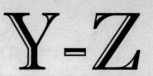
the Christian faith to lands in the Far East, including China and Japan. The patron saint of missionaries, he was also a founding member of the Jesuits. The Arabic meaning of the name is 'bright'.
*Variants: Javier, Zever*

**Yosef**
Yosef is a variant of the Biblical name Joseph, which comes from the Hebrew for 'God will add (another son)'. (See also Joseph.)
*Variant: Joseph*

**Zachary**
Zachary is a variant of the Biblical name Zachariah, which was borne by the elderly father of John the Baptist who was husband to Elizabeth. The Hebrew meaning of the name is 'remembrance of God'.
*Variants: Zachariah, Zack, Zechariah*

**Zakkai**
This name comes from the Hebrew for 'pure, innocent'.

**Zamir**
Zamir comes from the Hebrew for 'song'.

**Zeus**
In Greek mythology Zeus was the supreme god who ruled the heavens. He was also the god of weather, maintained law and order and protected earthly kings. His name comes from the Greek for 'shining', 'bright' and 'bright sky'.
*Variants: Zeno, Zenon, Zenos*

**Zion**
Zion is a name that is used in connection with Israel, Judaism, the Christian church and heaven. Rastafarians believe that it is also the name of the Promised Land.

Zion is a variant of Sion, which is the name of the hill on which the city of Jerusalem was built in King David's time.

# *African names*

**In African culture, names are of paramount importance, and a lot of work goes into their choosing.** Current events, astrology and the aspirations of parents are all taken into account, as it is generally felt that whatever name is picked, it will influence the child's life and reflect on the family. The following is a list of the more popular African names.

| FEMALE | Halima | Oni |
|---|---|---|
| | Horera | Pili |
| Adia | Imani | Pulika |
| Aisha | Imara | Rabia |
| Aliya | Ina | Rafiya |
| Ama | Jamala | Rashida |
| Amira | Jamila | Rayha |
| Asya | Jirani | Rehani |
| Azalee | Kali | Saada |
| Bashira | Kesi | Sabiha |
| Bebi | Kinah | Saburi |
| Bishara | Kioja | Safi |
| Chaniya | Kisima | Salaam |
| Chiku | Laini | Salima |
| Dafina | Latifah | Shani |
| Dalila | Lela | Suma |
| Dene | Lisha | Tabita |
| Eidi | Malaika | Talha |
| Eshe | Malia | Tamasha |
| Etana | Marjani | Tumaini |
| Fahima | Matima | Ujamaa |
| Faiza | Muna | Uzima |
| Fatima | Nadra | Wanja |
| Freya | Naima | Wema |
| Gasira | Nasra | Wesesa |
| Gerda | Neema | Yasmin |
| Gimbya | Njema | Yetunde |
| Hadiya | Noni | Yusra |
| Hafsa | Omolara | Zaina |

# African names

**MALE**

Abdul
Ahmed
Akram
Amar
Asim
Aziz
Badru
Bakari
Chandu
Chiké
Dajan
Damu
Daraja
Elimu
Eze
Ezenachi
Fahim
Fakhri
Faqihi
Fidel
Gahiji
Ghalib
Haamid
Habib
Hakim
Harun
Hasan
Hashim
Ibrahim
Iman
Islam
Ismael
Jaafar
Jafari

Jalil
Jamal
Jamil
Kadhi
Kamil
Kasim
Khalil
Kwame
Lali
Latif
Lutalo
Maalik
Mahmud
Maliki
Mandala
Mkamba
Muhammed
Mwangi
Naadir
Naeem
Nemsi
Nizam
Njama
Obaseki
Ojore
Okello
Oman
Omar
Ouma
Pandu
Petiri
Pili
Quaashie
Rafiki
Rahim
Rashaad

Rashid
Rehani
Ruhiu
Saalim
Saeed
Salaam
Salim
Sefu
Simba
Sudi
Suhuba
Taalib
Taji
Tajiri
Talib
Tarik
Ubora
Ufanisi
Umar
Usiku
Waitimu
Warui
Waziri
Weke
Wemusa
Yahya
Yasini
Yoofi
Yusuf
Zahir
Zahran
Zaid
Zende
Zuber
Zuka
Zuri

# Celtic names

There is much speculation about where exactly the Celts originated, but it is generally believed that they came from the region that is now Germany or Switzerland, and spread across Europe, settling as far afield as Ireland, Britain, Brittany, Spain, Hungary, Bohemia and Asia Minor. The original Celtic language split into two separate languages, known as Goidelic and Brythonic. Celtic names originate in both these languages, as well as in the original Celtic language, or in Celtic mythology. Following are some examples.

| FEMALE | Colleen | Kathleen |
|---|---|---|
| | Cordelia | Keelin |
| Africa | Dana | Kendall |
| Aileen | Dawn | Lorna |
| Aine | Dee | Melvina |
| Aislinn | Devnet | Meredith |
| Alanna | Deirdre | Moira |
| Alvina | Edith | Morgance |
| Annabelle | Eilis | Morgandy |
| Arden | Enid | Nola |
| Arleen | Erin | Piper |
| Arlene | Erlina | Pixie |
| Bevin | Etain | Rae |
| Birkita | Evelyn | Raelin |
| Brenna | Fainche | Rhonda |
| Bretta | Fallon | Seanna |
| Briana | Fiona | Shayla |
| Bridget | Fionn | Shea |
| Brietta | Fionnula | Shela |
| Brites | Gilda | Shylah |
| Brooke | Gwen | Tara |
| Caitlin | Gwendolyn | Treasa |
| Cara | Gwynne | Treva |
| Cary | Isolde | Ula |
| Casey | Kaie | Wilona |
| Cerdwin | Kaitlyn | Wynne |

# Celtic names

**MALE**

Abenzio
Ahearn
Ainsley
Alan
Angus
Arland
Arthur
Beacan
Bevin
Boyd
Bram
Briac
Brian
Brice
Brody
Bryant
Caedmon
Camlin
Carden
Carney
Carroll
Cary
Casey
Chadwick
Clancy
Clyde
Coalan
Cody
Colin
Con
Conan
Condon
Conner
Corey

Craig
Cullen
Dale
Dane
Davis
Dermot
Derry
Desmond
Donnelly
Driscoll
Duff
Duncan
Dunn
Edan
Egan
Erin
Evan
Farrell
Fergus
Ferguson
Ferris
Finlay
Fionn
Flynn
Frazer
Galen
Gallagher
Gilroy
Greg
Irving
Kane
Kearney
Keary
Kegan
Keir
Keith

Kelvin
Kendall
Kerwin
Maddox
Malvin
Melvin
Mannix
Marmaduke
Marvin
Melvin
Merlin
Monroe
Murray
Nevin
Palmer
Perth
Regan
Ronan
Scully
Sean
Sheridan
Sloane
Tadc
Teague
Tegan
Tiernan
Tierney
Torin
Torrance
Torrey
Trevor
Tuathal
Ultan
Urien
Varney
Vaughan

# Muslim names

In Islam, it is taught that the Prophet Mohammad requested that his followers should avoid naming their offsping with meaningless names, and should choose a name with care. The following are a selection of Muslim names.

| FEMALE | Jamila | Shahla |
|---|---|---|
| | Khadija | Shahnaz |
| Alisha | Kulsum | Shahrazad |
| Aamira | Leila | Shaliza |
| Aarifa | Lubna | Shalizar |
| Afsana | Mahjabeen | Sayeeda |
| Amani | Maimun | Shabab |
| Ameena | Malika | Shabnam |
| Azra | Marjaan | Shagufta |
| Ayesha | Mehrnaz | Shaheen |
| Aziza | Mumina | Shakeela |
| Basheera | Nadira | Shakira |
| Benazir | Nafisa | Shamina |
| Bushra | Naima | Shamshad |
| Bibi | Nargis | Shirin/Shireen |
| Darya | Nazia | Suhaila |
| Dilbar | Nazima | Suraiya/Soraya |
| Dilruba | Nazmoon | Taslima |
| Faiza | Niloufar | Wafa |
| Farida | Nusrat | Waheeda |
| Farah | Parvin | Yasmeen |
| Fatima | Rabia | Zahira |
| Firuza | Raisa | Zarin |
| Gulshan | Rashida | Zarina |
| Gulzar | Razia | Zeba |
| Habeeba | Rehana | Zeb-un-Nisa |
| Halima | Sadika | Zeenat |
| Haseena | Sakeena | Zenia |
| Husna | Salena | Zohra |
| Ismat | Salima | Zubaida |
| Jahanara | Sanaz | Zulekha |

# Muslim names

**MALE**

| | | |
|---|---|---|
| | Ibrahim | Rafi |
| | Ifran | Rahim |
| Abdul | Imran | Rashad |
| Abdullah | Iqbal | Rashid |
| Abed | Irshad | Raza |
| Ahsan | Ishrat | Rehman |
| Akbar | Izhar | Sadik |
| Alam | Izmet | Salman |
| Ali | Jalal | Selim |
| Amir | Jalil | Sayeed |
| Amzad | Jansher | Shahab |
| Aslam | Javed | Shahrukh |
| Azaad | Kamal | Shakir |
| Aziz | Karim | Shahbaz |
| Babur | Khadim | Sharif |
| Basheer | Khalid | Shamshad |
| Basit | Khan | Sherally |
| Bilal | Latif | Suhail |
| Chaghatai | Liaqat | Sultan |
| Chengiz | Mahtab | Talal |
| Dara | Mahmood | Taj |
| Dilbar | Majid | Tazim |
| Dilshad | Mohammad | Talat |
| Eijaz | Moshin | Talib |
| Faiz | Mustafa | Tariq |
| Farhad | Nabeel | Timur |
| Farookh | Nadeem | Usman |
| Fayyad | Naseem | Wahab |
| Fazil | Nasser | Wajid |
| Firouz | Nadir | Wasim |
| Ghalib | Nizam | Wazir |
| Gulzar | Omar | Yasin |
| Habeeb | Ossama | Yasir |
| Hamid | Pasha | Yusuf |
| Hassan | Qasim | Zafar |
| Hussain | Raamiz | Zahid |

# Native American names

Native American names have meanings that are usually derived from nature and/or relate to the family of the child. In many cases, the family themselves would not name a child, but rather this would be left to an important member of the tribe – often someone said to have been born with the 'gift' to be able to name children. The following are a selection of Native American names.

**FEMALE**

| | | |
|---|---|---|
| | Istaqa | Ouray |
| | Istu | Oya |
| Ahanu | Iye | Pahana |
| Ahiga | Jacy | Patwin |
| Ahiliya | Jolon | Payat |
| Anoki | Kajika | Paytah |
| Ashkii | Kele | Sakima |
| Awan | Keme | Shiye |
| Bidziil | Kitchi | Sike |
| Bimisi | Kohana | Siwili |
| Chesmu | Kono | Songan |
| Chunta | Kwahu | Sucki |
| Ciqala | Lansa | Taima |
| Delsin | Lanu | Takoda |
| Dustu | Leyati | Tse |
| Dyami | Lokni | Tupi |
| Elan | Lonato | Uzumati |
| Elki | Manipi | Viho |
| Elsu | Moki | Wahkan |
| Etu | Molimo | Waquini |
| Ezhno | Mona | Wicasa |
| Gosheven | Muata | Wuyi |
| Guyapi | Muraco | Wynono |
| Hahnee | Nahele | Yahto |
| Hakan | Nayati | Yancy |
| Hania | Neka | Yanisin |
| Helki | Nikiti | Yiska |
| Honani | Ohanko | Yuma |

# Native American names

**MALE**

Abetzi
Aiyana
Alawa
Anaba
Ankti
Ayashe
Ayita
Bena
Bly
Catori
Chenoa
Chepi
Chilaili
Chumani
Cocheta
Dena
Dyani
Ehawee
Enola
Fala
Flo
Galilahi
Haloke
Halona
Huyana
Imala
Istas
Ituha
Kachina
Kai
Kaya
Leotie
Liseli
Macawi

Mahu
Mai
Maka
Manaba
Mansi
Maralah
Mausi
Memdi
Mika
Minal
Mituna
Nahimana
Namid
Nara
Niabi
Nituna
Nova
Olathe
Onawa
Onida
Pakuna
Papina
Pavati
Powaqa
Pules
Sahkyo
Salali
Sanuye
Satinka
Shada
Shadi
Shima
Sihu
Sitala
Sitsi
Sunki

Tablita
Tadewi
Tadita
Taigi
Taini
Taipa
Takala
Takhi
Tala
Tama
Tansy
Tayanita
Tehya
Tiponi
Tiva
Tolinka
Tuwa
Una
Urika
Utina
Wachiwi
Wakanda
Waki
Waneta
Wauna
Weeko
Winema
Wuti
Wyanet
Yamka
Yazhi
Yepa
Yoki
Zaltana
Zihna
Zitkala

# Index

# Index – Girls

(v) = variant

# Index – Girls

# Index – Girls

(v) = variant

# Index – Girls

(v) = variant

# Index – Girls

# Index – Girls

(v) = variant

# Index – Girls

# Index – Girls

(v) = variant

# Index – Boys

# Index – Boys

# Index – Boys

(v) = variant

# Index – Boys

# Index – Boys

# Index – Boys

# Index – Boys

# Index – Boys

# Index – Boys

(v) = variant

# PERSONALIT

# PSYCHOLO

# AND

# INDIVID

# DIFFERE

CONNO

## DEDICATION

Thank you to all my readers. Without you, I couldn't do what I love.

# INTRODUCTION
Personality is an amazing topic.

Of course, at first, I had my doubts. I thought personality psychology was going to be boring, dull and a complete waste of my time at university.

However, after I started learning about personality psychology and everything it covered, I was hooked.

It's a great area of psychology that covers LOTS from how do we research personality to how our personalities change over time to what causes our personalities.

All the way to how do our personalities affect our religious beliefs, politics and our mental abilities.

This is a great topic that you can apply to everyday life.

1

## Who Is This Book For?

This book is for psychology students, professionals or anyone else interested in learning more about personality psychology.

If you want a great, easy to understand book that will break this topic down into manageable and FUN chunks of information. Then this IS the book for you!

This is not a boring university textbook.

## Who Am I?

I always have to know who writes the nonfiction books I read so I know they're qualified to write on the topic.

Therefore, in case you're like me then I'm Connor Whiteley an author of over 15 psychology books.

I'm a University Student doing Psychology With Clinical Psychology at the University of Kent, England.

Additionally, I'm the weekly host of The Psychology World Podcast available on all major podcast apps and YouTube. Where each week I discuss psychology news and a great psychology topic.

Finally, I'm extremely passionate about

personality psychology (not as much as Forensic Psychology) but I loved writing this book. It's filled with great information and a lot of fun stories and ideas linking it to everyday life.

Buy the book now and let's learn about the amazing area of personality psychology together!

# FUN PERSONALITY NOTES

Before we dive into a proper introduction about personality, what is and how it influences our behaviour. I thought it would be great fun to share with you some basic personality findings that will hopefully pique your interest.

I know these findings definitely piqued my interest because, at the time, I found these studies when I was doing some research for my personality psychology coursework.

Also, if you see a personality psychology term that you don't fully understand yet. You will by the end of this book. The purpose of this chapter is to show you some of the interesting research findings around personality.

As a result, Egan et al (2003) found people who scored higher on the antisocial personality factors were more interested in violent, occult and militaristic topics.

In addition, interest in violent or potentially violent topics were a feature in a wide range of personality disorders, but factors that reflected asocial and anxious disorders didn't show a reliable association between this interest in violent topics.

Therefore, it has been suggested that personality factors related to showing an interest in violent topics in people with offender characteristics and mental conditions are specific to the type of condition, and not all mental conditions.

Another interesting finding that I think shows personality in a positive and complex light is from Il et al (2015) with their study finding that not all personality dimensions are as harmful as others because personality dimensions only explained 17.6% of the variance in clinical outcomes.

Yet people with negative emotionality had the greatest impact on clinical outcomes with it explaining 43.9% of variance. Whereas the remaining personality dimensions showed a relatively minor impact.

In other words, this study showed that the influence of our personality traits differ in terms of their influence on mental conditions and the outcomes of their treatment.

This study I rather like because I feel like everyone says everything is down to your personality, and this study shows that it is not. Since there are other, sometimes more important factors that have nothing to do with your personality.

A third study that I think is rather interesting

is Deary et al (1998) when after researching over 400 undergraduates at university who filled in several personality questionnaires. The researchers found four broad factors of personality disorders that overlapped with normal personality traits. Including: an asthenic factor that was related to neuroticism; an antisocial factor associated with psychoticism; an asocial factor linked to introversion–Extroversion; and an obsessive–compulsive factor.

Overall, showing there is substantial overlap between abnormal and normal personality dimensions.

I promise you the whole thing about neuroticism and the other personality terms used in that paragraph, will become clearer. But the reason why I mentioned the study is because it debunks the layperson theory that you have *good* and *bad* personality traits. And *bad* people do it because they have *bad* personality traits.

Now, those of us who do psychology, we know that isn't true in the slightest because there are lots and lots of other social, cognitive and biological factors that influence so-called *bad behaviour*. But this study still highlights that fact.

The penultimate study I want to highlight in this chapter is Franks et al (2009) because this study found a peer led intervention to increase self-efficacy to enhance disease management only had short term effects, and the personality factors of the Five Factor Model moderated these effects.

Therefore, by measuring personality factors in chronically ill individuals, this may help facilitate targeting of self-management intervention in those people likely to respond.

In other words, the study found if we use the factors of the Five Factor Model (again we'll look at this in a few chapters time) then we can use these personality factors to help improve people's self-management in their recovery.

Finally, I really want to show you Leckelt et al (2019) because this is a great study on personality factors and wealth.

As a result, the study researched the personality factors of rich people in Germany with over one million euros in assets against a data set of nationally representative people. The researchers found that the stereotypes about rich people are exaggerated but reasonably accurate, and rich people can be characterised as stable, agentic and flexible individuals that are more focused on themselves than others.

Personally, I think this is a great study because it shows how personality factors can influence our behaviour and our success.

So, now we know some of the interesting effects personality can have on us. Let's dive into the psychology of personality!

# PART ONE: INTRODUCTION TO PERSONALITY PSYCHOLOGY

# INTRODUCTION TO PERSONALITY

Whenever people think about personality, they always tend to think they have a particular type of personality. For example, they have a hard working personality or a creative personality. This thinking is right and wrong but mostly wrong. Since we don't have a particular type of personality as we're a combination of different personality traits.

We'll return to the above thinking later on but people differ in their ways of thinking, behaving and feeling and their culturally different too. For example, you and me, we would have different opinions and beliefs around certain topics.

## Definitions of Personality:

Since personality is such an abstract concept, defining personality is very complex and difficult. But we'll try it anyway.

One rather contemporary definition is from Ashton (2013, p 27) who defined personality as the

11

following:

"A set of psychological traits and mechanisms within the individual that refer to *differences among individuals in a typical tendency to behave, think, or feel in some conceptually related ways, across a variety of relevant situations, and across some fairly long period of time.*"

This idea I quite like because it explains personality in an easy-to-understand way, and it refers to personality as the individual differences. In turn, this makes personality a lot easier to understand.

Although, a definition of what personality is, is only meaningful to the extent that it gives us, directly or indirectly, a comparison with other people. Since this is what modern personality research looks at. How does person A's and person B's personalities cause them to be so different?

And this in itself can make personality rather difficult to study and define because the psychological features that differentiate people from one another aren't always visible when you look at them.

However, people do have a predisposition to show their behaviours, thoughts, feelings and these all refer to all the different aspects of a person. You could regard these different aspects of a person as personality traits.

In addition, in some conceptual way, these

aspects are related across a wide range of situations and over a fairly long period of time. Like, we'll see in the chapter later on stability of personality over time.

Nonetheless, all this talk of aspects, individual differences and definitions, does raise a lot of questions. For example,

Personality raises a lot of questions like, what are the major personality factors?

What's the role of Individual factors in personality?

What are the real-world consequences of these differences?

What determines personality?

And all of these questions, we will look at by the end of the book.

## What Does Personality Psychology Look At?

Interestingly enough, personality psychology doesn't only look at personality traits. That is a large part of what personality psychology does, but it isn't everything.

Due to this area of psychology looks at people's styles of thinking, feeling and behaving as well.

With the overall aim of personality psychology

being to understand how and why people differ as well as how to predict similarities and differences between people in different settings.

Using personality psychology, you can investigate a lot of things. For instance, you can do what's called ideographic research. This is where you research one person in extreme detail. You typically use this research type when you want to study someone's very unique personality characteristics.

Another approach to research you could do is the nomothetic approach. This is the more typical type of research where you study large groups to find individual differences amongst other variables.

On the whole, all personality psychology research is largely correlational with a few exceptions since you can only say there is a relationship between personality trait A and behaviour B. As well as you can't get personality from one situation, so you need to test many different situations.

Evaluation of Personality Measures:

Whilst we'll look at how personality is measured in more depth later on. We need to look at how these personality measures are evaluated. Because psychology is a science.

## Reliability

The first way in which we evaluate these personality measures is by looking at their reliability. This is the degree to which a measure produces consistent results. And this overall concept of reliability can be broken down into a few subcategories.

For instance, Internal-consistency reliability is the extent to which the items of a measure are correlated with each other. This is important because we don't want your items that you think are measuring Openness to Experience, for example, to be measuring other things in addition to Openness to Experience like someone's levels of perfectionism.

We test this type of reliability using Cronbach's alpha and if the results are greater or equal to 0.70 then this is considered acceptable. Meaning your items on your measuring scale do relate to one another.

Another type of reliability, and I haven't heard of this type before I did this book, is Interrater reliability. This refers to the degree of agreement between the scores of different raters and/ or observers.

This type of reliability tends to be exclusively used by personality psychology because it's important that different observers of a person's personality get the same results.

The final type of reliability is the Test-retest reliability. Which refers to the degree of consistency between the scores across different measurement occasions or situations.

In other words, this type of reliability means the test or measure scale must produce consistent scores between people when you measure them in different situations and occasions.

It's important to know I'm saying consistent, not exact because as you'll see later in the book personality traits can vary and change over the lifespan. But not in the way you might think.

Validity

Whilst reliability focuses on producing consistent and reliable scores. Validity refers to the extent to which a test measures what it claims to measure. And as you can probably guess you can have a reliable test without it being valid, and you can have a valid test that's unreliable. This is why it's so important to test both these concepts and their different types.

The first type of validity this concept can be broken down into is content validity. Which refers to the extent a measure assesses all relevant features of the construct, and does not assess irrelevant features.

Another way of defining this type of validity is your test or measurement scale only measures what it tends to, and it measures all aspects of what you're looking at. As well as it doesn't measure anything else except what you're looking at.

Secondly, you have construct validity which is about the extent to which the measure correctly assesses what it intends to and is it the best measurement tool for the job.

In addition, construct validity can be further broken down into Convergent and discriminant validity. With convergent validity referring to how well the measurement tool measures similar and opposite characteristics to what you want to measure.

For instance, if I want to measure Agreeableness using a personality questionnaire. Then I want this questionnaire to only measure similar characteristics to Agreeableness. Because as you'll soon see Agreeableness is an overarching factor in personality. But I don't want this questionnaire to measure any other personality traits. Such as: Conscientiousness and Neuroticism.

The second subtype of construct validity is discriminant validity, and in psychology, we use these types of tests to see if factors and measures we think are unrelated actually are unrelated.

This is important because if we run a test on a new type of personality questionnaire thinking we're measuring Trait X but the questionnaire won't be contaminated by Trait Y, and we're wrong. Then our questionnaire and our results will be biased due to the influence of Trait Y.

Subsequently, the final type of validity that's important in personality psychology is criterion validity. This is another term for predictive validity meaning we can use the measure to predict the personality characteristics and behaviours of the person.

Methods of Measurement

Now we know how to evaluate these methods of measuring personality. I would like you to bear that in mind as we go together throughout this book so that will help you think about the pros and cons of each study.

Moving onto how we actually measure personality. I want to discuss the main two ways we measure personality. There are others but this is the major way that 99% of personality psychology studies used. And that is self-reports and structured questionnaires.

Here, you ask every person and participant

the exact same set of questions and there is a fixed sets of responses for every question. Because most of these questionnaires use a Likert scale so on the scale you need to indicate how much you agree or disagree with the statement.

Personality questionnaires are the most widely used method of measuring personality and most of the personality inventories assess several personality traits using this method. With each trait being assessed by several items.

This allows the questionnaire to have good reliability and content validity.

Also, in personality questionnaires, some items are reversed coded meaning the answer is the *opposite* of the trait and the answer before it. This balances the questionnaire out and prevents someone from just giving all the same answers for the questions and still giving the researchers exactly what they want.

On the whole, these two research techniques are effective, accurate and low cost. Which is always good.

Nevertheless, these two research methods say people know their behaviours, thoughts, and feelings but as I discuss in Social Psychology, people have gaps in their self-knowledge, and people might not be willing to report their behaviours, thoughts, and feelings. This links to the social desirability bias.

Also, the idea of "People know themselves better than anyone else knows them" is just plain false in most cases.

Observer reports:

"Others (sometimes) know us better than we know ourselves" (Vazire & Carlson, 2011)

These types of reports are very similar to self reports but instead of you reporting on your own personality and behaviour. Someone is providing information on you by observing you.

The person acting as the observer can be a spouse, a parent, a friend, a peer, a classmate, but they must know the 'target' of the observations fairly well.

In addition, observer reports could be more objective than self reports. One reason for this could be the impact of the social desirability boas could be weakened. Yet if the observer is a parent then their answers will still reflect some level of the social desirability bias since they would want to show off their amazing parenting. That's just one example.

You can do observer reporting by using direct observations. Which as the name suggests involves you directly watching a person's behaviour. Allowing you to see the frequency and intensity of a given behaviour that indicates a certain personality trait. As well as you can do this in their natural setting, some people call this s natural habitat but I think that sounds rather dehumanising and makes me want to do a David Attenborough impression, or you can do direct observations in an artificial setting. Like, a university laboratory.

In general, direct observations can be very informative. Yet there are limitations as there could be some aspects of personality that can never really be observed and observations are done in a limited range of contexts. As well as they're time consuming, they cost a lot of money and they involve a lot of effort.

## Biodata

This is another interesting method you can use to measure personality because this involves more objective data. As it involves life outcome data, these are records of a person's life and of course you only use data that's relevant to their personality. For example, their grade point average (another term for academic achievement), their speeding tickets and phone bills.

All of these are great examples of objective behavioural indicators but the problem with biodata is that it isn't clear what information is relevant or an accurate indicator for the personality trait of interest. For instance, you could argue that phone bills are good indicators because they potential show the size of a people's social network and a person's sociability. Hence, phone bills could relate to Extroversion.

Equally, you would need to be careful about using this data because what if the participants makes a lot of phone calls to business people or the participant calls their friends at their friends' place of work?

## Examples of Personality Inventories

I implied the use of these personality inventories in other sections in this chapter but there are lots of great personality inventories that allow us to measure personality. These inventories are all made up of questionnaires to various extents. Such as, The California Psychological Inventory (CPI) is made up of over 400 items (questions) that measure a wide range of psychological characteristics and 'everyday variables', as well as it was based on the Minnesota Multiphasic Personality Inventory (MMPI) which was intended to measure mental health difficulties and conditions.

Another example of a personality inventory is the Eysenck Personality Questionnaire (EPQ) that measures Eysenck's three basic dimensions of personality which we look at in the next chapter.

As this is an introduction, I want to keep things relatively brief but a third example of a personality inventory is The Big Five Inventory that is made up of 44 different items and this is a more condensed version of The NEO Personality

Inventory Revised (NEO-PI-R) that is made up of 240 different items and the NEO Five-Factor Inventory (NEO-FFI). This one is made up of 60 items.

Also, all of these Big Five inventories measure the following personality dimensions that will be the focus of the next chapter.

- Openness to Experience
- Conscientiousness
- Extroversion
- Agreeableness
- Neuroticism

The final example of a personality inventory that we will look at is The HEXACO Personality Inventory Revised (HEXACO-PI-R) which is very important to the next chapter and there are three different versions with different numbers of items. Like, one has 200 items, another one has 100 items and the last type has only 60 items. All of these can be found at www.hexaco.org in case you ever want to look at it in more depth.

In addition, the six personality dimensions, this personality inventory measures are as followed:

- Honesty-Humility
- Emotionality
- Extroversion

- Agreeableness
- Conscientiousness
- Openness to Experience

## Combined Use of Self- and Observer Reports

Now we know what the six major personality dimensions are and the inventories that measure them, we can continue with our evaluation of the use of self- and observer reports because it turns out there's high agreement between self- and observer reports do provide support for the construct validity of the personality inventory scale. Meaning they do accurately measure what they intend to.

With this agreement ranging from 0.40 to 0.60 for the HEXACO-PI-R according to Lee & Ashton (2013) when they conducted their study on a sample of over 600 college students. As well as the agreement is around 0.60 when the NEO-PI-R was done by spouses and observer but this agreement dropped slightly to 0.40 when it was done using friends and neighbours as the observers. Yet this could be down to friends and neighbours not knowing the 'target' as well as the family members and spouses do.

Nonetheless, one factor that could influence the validity of self- and observer reports is both the target and the observers could, and they most probably will, have some inaccurate opinions of the target's personality traits. Whilst this is perfectly normal and we all have some inaccurate ideas about our loved ones and our friends. When it comes to research this can be rather problematic. But does this affect personality research?

To test this Kolar, Funder, and Colvin (1996) conducted a study using both types of reports and their results showed each type of report showed their validity for predicting behaviour but the single observer reports were slightly better than the self-reports. As well as the reports were even more accurate when they were averaged across multiple observers.

This isn't too surprising I think when we consider the gaps people gave in their own self-knowledge and the social desirability bias. Also, we can have blind spots because we have a lack or too much information. (Varie, 2010; Vazire and Carlson, 2011)

Overall, I think we can conclude from our evaluation of personality questionnaires and reports that in some cases other people know us better than we know ourselves. But this accuracy does depend on the personality trait we're looking at.

Personally, if I ever was to conduct some sort of personality research I would use both self and observer reports as each type captures different aspects of personality. As well as by using both you're getting more data to support your conclusions with. This is very important for the credibility and reliability of your study.

Conclusion

To conclude this introductory look at personality psychology and all of its amazing features. I want to clarify and recap some things we have looked at.

After reading this chapter, we know that self- as well as observers reports show fairly high levels of agreement. Which is good because it shows self-reports are not as flawed as you would think when you consider how bad people are at knowing themselves sometimes.

In addition, people can provide fairly accurate descriptions of their own and others' personalities. As well as both self- and observer reports can predict behaviour with moderate levels of validity.

Personally, I think this is quite good because if you're read Social Psychology then you know the limitations of a person's self-knowledge. Therefore, it's refreshing and positive to see we can describe our personality well. And this makes life easier for researchers because to some extent a researcher can simply ask you about your personality.

This is further supported by recent studies that have suggested that self- and observer reports could potentially capture different aspects of personality.

Thus, if I was ever researching personality, I would recommend you might want to use both. As this would allow you to capture different aspects of the personality, and this feeds into method triangulation. This is where you use multiple methods to support your results, and this increases the creditability of your findings.

However, these self- and observer reports are *fairly* accurate, not *perfectly* accurate. Due to the various biases that can influence your results.

For example, the social desirability bias causes participants to give you socially desirable responses instead of socially undesirable responses in both self- and observer reports. Possibly leading your results to be tainted by these untrue answers.

This can be countered by establishing a rapport with the participant and by using multiple sources.

Overall, the strengths of personality questionnaires and correlational research are they allow you to study and assess a wide range of variables. As well as you can obtain the needed large samples easily.

Whereas the negatives or drawbacks of these research methods are you can't establish causality so you can only imply there's a relationship between the two variables. And there are biases that can influence your data.

Nonetheless, a partial solution for the causality problem is using longitudinal studies. Since these allow you to monitor a person throughout their life so you might be able to see causes as you follow them in their life.

# CLASSIFYING TRAITS, EYSENCK AND THE LEXICAL APPROACH

We might know what personality is and what it involves but we don't know why personality traits are classified. This is very important because if personality traits weren't grouped together then research would be extremely expensive and difficult.

Therefore, the aim of measuring personality traits is to get completeness without redundancy, and this means without missing any of the important characteristics and without measuring many very similar characteristics.

As a result, we classify all of the different personality traits into a few large groups with each group containing correlated traits. This allows us to measure personalities more efficiently and more thoroughly. Also, this could allow us to gain insights into why differences in personality exist.

This I think is extremely important because in

psychology research we need to be effective so we don't waste resources and our time. Yet we need to make sure we don't limit our depth and breadth of our research. Classifying personality traits helps with this.

## EFA- Exploratory Factor Analysis

One way to classify these personality traits together is by using exploratory factor analysis and for those of you who dislike statistics, I'm not going to go into the maths of it. All I'll say is this is a data analysis reduction technique. That aims to determine the number as well as nature of 'underlying factors' that explain a pattern of correlations between a large number of variables.

In other words, it explores patterns in your dataset. If we link this to personality, it allows researchers to find groups of personality traits that are similar to one another.

In turn, this allows researchers to create hypothesises.

Researchers test these hypothesises by using a confirmatory factor analysis by using this statistical test for model testing.

## Han J. Eysenck:

He came up with one of the earliest theories about personality and it was certainly influential and you could consider it to be the foundation for other

theories as it introduced the world to his two
superfactors in 1947.

These two superfactors were Extroversion-
introversion and Neuroticism- stability.

In addition, his theory proposed that
personality has a hierarchical structure with
Extroversion being the main superfactor that can be
broken down into sociability, activity, liveliness and
more. Then you can break it down even further by
looking at the habitual response level by specific
response levels.

In other words, the responses people give in
response to different stimuli. As an extroverted
person would enjoy more stimulation but an
introverted person would react differently.

We'll come back to this theory throughout
this chapter.

## The Idea of Lexical Approach:

Personally, I think this is a great idea and very
interesting because this is a unique way of trying to
find personality traits.

The lexical hypothesis proposes we can
generate a reasonably complete list of important
personality traits by looking at the dictionary.

This is thought to work because people will

use or invent words to describe personality traits that are important to them.

Therefore, over time these words become established in a given culture.

So by looking at a person's personality lexicon in a given language, we should be able to get a reasonably complete list.

This is called the fundamental lexical hypothesis and can be defined as "The most important individual differences in human transaction will come to be encoded as single terms in some or all of the world's language." (Goldberg, 1993, p.26)

At first this idea was proposed by Galton (1884) and lots of different researchers conducted studies to test this hypothesis. For example, Baumgarten (1933) conducted their study for the German language and Allport & Odbert (1936) did the same for the English language. The study looked at 18,000 English words and their results found approximately 4,500 personality traits, 4,500 states, 5,200 positive and negative evaluations and roughly 3,600 miscellaneous words.

Another attempt to study this was by Cattel and they found 35 traits from their first factor analysis and they found 12 traits at first and another 4 traits later on. Meaning Cattel (1949) found 16 personality factors.

## How Many Traits?

Leading us to question how many personality factors are there?

Well, over the decades there has been a lot of research done to answer this question. And here are the results of various factor Analyses.

- Tupes & Christal (1961, 1992): 5 factors

- Norman (1963, 1967): 5 factors

- Costa & McCrae (1985, 1991): 5 factors

- Goldberg (1990, 1992): 5 factors

- Different samples, ages, languages, and nations: 5 factors

Additionally, what makes this all interesting is that so many factors found the same factors using a wide range of different methods. For example, getting people to describe their traits using adjectives. Like, "quiet vs. talkative"

Another method was analysing statements when people were describing their affective experiences, cognition, and behaviours: "I really enjoy talking to people" as well as using self- and observer reports.

Then a final method was to analyse nonverbal measures. For instance, looking at cartoons and puppet interviews with young children as showed in Measelle et al (2005)

Isn't that great!

# FIVE FACTOR MODEL OF PERSONALITY AND 'THE BIG FIVE'

Of all the personality theories and models, this has to be one of the most famous as this is the main theory that personality psychology uses. And I definitely agree this model provides us with a wide range of personality traits without giving us hundreds of individual variables to study.

As a result, the Big Five personality factors are:

- Neuroticism
- Extroversion
- Openness to Experience
- Agreeableness
- Conscientiousness

Now, we'll look at these personality factors and all of the information here comes from Pervin et al (2005).

## Neuroticism:

This first personality factor assesses a person's maladjustment vs emotional stability. Meaning it finds out if people are prone to unrealistic ideas, psychological distress and excessive cravings or urges. As well as if they have any maladaptive coping responses.

## Extroversion

I think we can all agree with has to be the most famous personality factor because of its popularity in media, TV and books. And you can easily see this trait in everyday life.

In addition, this Big factor assesses the quantity and intensity of a person's capacity of joy, interpersonal relationships, activity level and need for simulation.

Since an extrovert has a high activity level with a lot of need for stimulation whereas an introvert is the opposite.

## Openness to Experience

This I think has to be one of the most interesting as it looks at a person's behaviour towards proactively seeking out as well as appreciating an experience for their own sake. And it assesses a person's tolerance for exploring the unfamiliar.

Personally, I do like this personality

dimension as I think I'm rather high in it because I love exploring new places, the woods and local areas. But to some extent, I don't really like leaving my comfort zone too often depending on the situation.

## Agreeableness

Despite the name suggesting you agree with everyone if you're high in this dimension. Agreeableness looks at how kind, gentle and sympathetic a person is.

## Conscientiousness:

The last dimension assesses an individual's degree of organisation, persistence and motivation in goal directed behaviour. As well as it contrasts people who are dependable and organised with people who are lackadaisical and sloppy.

## Mini-Conclusion

On the whole, the Big Five are important because they can help us sort out the very wide range of personality factors that various measurements have suggested there are as few as 3 and as many as 30 factors. And it gives us a great complete number that makes it a lot easier for researchers to work with these different factors.

In addition, they provide a 'compass' or mapping system for us to understand where in the personality space to place specific traits we want to know about.

## Development of the NEO-Five Factor Scales

After the initial creation of the Big Five, there were a series of different measurement scales created to try and prove its validity.

For example, you had the Neo Personality Inventory (NEO-PI) created by Costa & McCrae (1985) and this measurement tool was derived from several analyses of Cattell's 16 personality factors. Then this Inventory measured 3 scales for neuroticism, extroversion and Openness.

A second scale was the Neo- Five Factor Inventory (NEO-FFI) created by Costa & McCrae (1991) who adopted the five-factor personality model and added agreeableness and conscientiousness into their earlier Inventory. The Inventory was made up of 5 scales with 12 items each that measured neuroticism, extroversion, openness, agreeableness and conscientiousness.

The last scale was NEO Personality Inventory- Revised (NEO-PI-R) again made by Costa & McCrae (1992) that's measures 6 facets of each of the big five dimensions. This time it was made up of 30 scales with 8 items each personality dimensions. Like, neuroticism, extroversion, openness and agreeableness, conscientiousness domain and facet scores. (John & Srivastava, 1999)

## Facets

According to the Neo Personality Inventory Revised, each of the factors are made up of six facets that are like subfeatures and here they are for each of the personality dimensions.

Possible exam tip: after writing this book and doing my personality psychology exam, I want to give you a quick tip. I didn't know you can get tested on the facets since no one ever talks about these facets in research.

But if you do personality psychology at university, it would be extremely helpful if you revised the below facets.

## Neuroticism

- Anxiety
- Angry Hostility
- Depression
- Self-Consciousness
- Impulsiveness
- Vulnerability

## Extroversion:

- Warmth
- Gregariousness
- Assertiveness
- Activity

- Excitement Seeking
- Positive Emotions

Openness:

- Fantasy
- Aesthetics
- Feelings
- Actions
- Ideas
- Values

Agreeableness:

- Trust
- Straightforwardness
- Altruism
- Compliance
- Modesty
- Tender-Mindedness

Conscientiousness:

- Competence
- Order
- Dutifulness
- Achievement Striving
- Self-Discipline
- Deliberation

## Is the Five-Factor Model the final answer?

As always as much as I love this model because it's great, easy to understand and it is comprehensive. It does seem to capture Western personality language dimensions better than Eastern ones. As well as it doesn't always replicate, not even in Western cultures. Due to some studies find there are the Big 5 factors plus or minus 2.

However, on the whole, the Big Five does provide psychologists with a very useful taxonomic system of personality traits and it provides us with a common language to communicate with others about the different personality traits. As well as it does mean we have a "compass" of sorts to map and better understand personality.

So, this is useful and very good for the field of personality psychology, but could there be six factors?

# THE HEXACO MODEL OF PERSONALITY

Nonetheless, there could be a sixth factor when it comes to personality because of honesty and humility.

As a result, a lot of languages like French, Dutch, German and many more European languages rate honesty and humility as very important and a key part of their personalities. (Ashton et al., 2004)

Therefore, Ashton et al (2004) proposed the HEXACO model. Which stands for:

- H- Honesty-Humility
- E-Emotionality
- X-Extroversion
- A=Agreeableness
- C= Conscientiousness
- 0= Openness To Experience

In addition, the HEXACO model is measured using the HEXCO personality inventory. This is a questionnaire developed by Lee & Aston (2006) as well as the HEXACO model differs to the big five model in a few ways. For example, the emotionality dimension is associated with some traits from neuroticism but not others. As you'll see in a moment.

## How I And My Lecturer See This Model?

During the lecture that I learnt about this personality model, she made sure to tell us her opinion which I agree with to some extent. Since the HEXACO model is important to know and it does make a valuable contribution to research on individual differences and personality. As well as this model does explain a few personality characteristics better than the Big 5.

However, she did add that the difference between both the Big Five and the HEXACO model are often confusing and not helpful. Also, Ashton is overstating the importance of the HEXACO model due to most personality researchers continue to work within the Big Five framework.

Personally, I do completely understand where she's coming from because as you'll see below there isn't that many differences between the Facets of the two models so this can create confusion. And this model is only important if other researchers use it.

But, I do think this is important because this does cover more than the Big Five and I strongly believe that the HEXACO model is more universally applicable. Since English does not use a lot of honesty and humility traits to describe their personality. Yet a lot of other cultures do. Meaning this model is very likely to apply to their culture better than the Big Five. Of course, more research into this needs to be done. But we must consider this possibility.

## The HEXACO Facets:

As you'll see below, one reason why the HEXACO model is very important is because the Facets of the model provides us with a more in-depth look at the personality factors.

Here are the broad and narrower factors assessed by the HEXACO model:

## Honesty- humility:

- Sincerity
- Fairness
- Greed-avoidance
- Modesty

## Emotionality:

- Fearfulness
- Anxiety
- Dependence
- Sedimentary.

Extroversion:

- Social self-esteem and boldness
- Sociability
- Loneliness

Agreeableness

- Forgiveness
- Gentleness
- Flexibility
- Patience

Conscientiousness

- Organisation
- Diligence
- Perfectionism
- Prudence

Openness to experience:

- Aesthetic appreciation
- Inquisitiveness
- creativity
- Unconventionally

# PART TWO:
# THE BIOLOGICAL BASIS, GENETIC AND ENVIRONMENTAL INFLUENCES ON PERSONALITY AND DEVELOPMENTAL CHANGES AND STABILITY OF PERSONALITY

# BIOLOGICAL BASIS OF PERSONALITY: THE ANCIENT, MODERN AND NEUROTRANSMITTERS

In the next few chapters of the book, we're going to be moving onto the great topic of what causes personality. I love this area of personality psychology because I think it's great to hear about some of the explanations for how personalities develop.

And this has been thought about for thousands of years because the ancient Greeks were some of the first to think about personality and how it might be created. For example, Hippocrates and Galen believed a person's personality and temperament depended on the balance of various fluids in the body. They called these fluids 'humous'

This I think is rather interesting because even now these humous are rather influential.

Therefore, these 4 main humous are as followed:

- Blood- this makes a person very cheerful and happy as well as this is where you get the term sanguine from.
- Black bile- this makes a person very depressed, as well as sad and the term melancholic is used to describe people with a black bile imbalance.
- Yellow bile- this particular humous makes a personality angry and you would use choleric to describe them.
- Phlegm- interestingly this would make a person very calm with the term phlegmatic coming from this homus.

However, as you can guess as interesting as this idea is. There's no empirical evidence for such ideas and humouses so this has no place in modern psychology. Yet these ideas are still very influential.

For instance, the Russian psychologist Ivan Palov used this idea to propose that dogs have four types of temperaments. According to Palov dogs have:

- A weak temperament where they're inhibited from doing too much, they're anxious and basically melancholic.
- A strong unbalanced temperament where the dogs are excitable and hyperactive. Yet these dogs are still

melancholic.

- Strong balanced temperament where these dogs are slow, calm and not easily aroused.

Finally, strong balanced with these dogs being lively and eager as well as this temperament can be compared to the sanguine humous.

## Eysenck's EN Theory:

Coming back to Eysenck, his theory needs to be mentioned again because his personality dimensions about Extroversion and neuroticism are related to the four personality types from Hippocrates and Galen.

As a result of Eysenck proposing that an extroverted person with an unstable personality or emotionality would give you a choleric person.

Whereas an introvert with a stable personality would create a phlegmatic person.

I think it's always interesting to see how the same concept of theory can be applied in so many different ways.

## Modern Approaches:

Now, we need to talk about how our biology impacts our personality by looking at the modern approaches to research. Since those old ways of looking at personality are interesting but they have no research support.

Therefore, one of the main modern approaches is looking at Neurotransmitters and how they influence our personality.

I talk about them in more depth and give you a wide look at how they influence behaviour in Biological Psychology. But Neurotransmitters are chemical messengers that travel across the synaptic gap between our neurons to deliver the information across our nervous system.

Consequently, researchers have proposed the level of a particular neurotransmitter in the brain could influence someone's personality.

And this leads us onto the main theory about how Neurotransmitters affect our personality and this theory was proposed by Cloninger as well as it explores how three Neurotransmitters affect our personality.

## Dopamine and Novelty Seeking:

We're all familiar with the role of dopamine in the feelings of romantic love but dopamine isn't exclusively about sex or anything to do with things of a sexual nature.

In fact, it's all about rewards and as we find sex and romance rewarding and pleasure dopamine is released.

Therefore, dopamine facilities the transmission of reward signals in the brain in response to things that we find pleasurable and exciting.

Linking this to personality, Cloninger believed personality characteristics are related to a person's responses to pleasure and excitement. So if a person has high levels of dopamine in them then they would be high in 'novelty seeking'.

Personally, I think a better term for this is something along the lines of a desire to find something new and exciting.

As well as this 'novelty seeking' measures a person's impulsiveness, extravagantness and how exploratory, excitable and disorganised they are.

Furthermore, if a person has an under or overactive dopamine system, meaning it releases too or not enough dopamine, then this could have important effects on novelty seeking traits.

For example, Parkinson's disease leaves people extremely inactive with a lack of interest in fun or new activities as well as they have uncoordinated movements. Suggesting the condition impairs their 'novelty seeking' traits.

Whereas cocaine increases a person's dopamine activity. Making them extremely aroused and they experience an increase in novelty seeking behaviour.

Overall, this suggests there is some evidence that dopamine could influence our personality. This I think is a good idea because this could be linked to Openness to Experience. Thus, it's interesting to see how biology could cause this personality dimension.

## Serotonin and Harm Avoidance:

The second Neurotransmitter thought to influence personality is serotonin and if you're not familiar with Biological Psychology. Serotonin is associated with prosocial behaviour since serotonin inhibits the transmission of the signals of punishment. This prevents neurons from sending messages in response to things that feel harmful or unpleasant.

Leading Cloninger to believe personality characteristics are related to pain and anxiety. As well as if people have low levels of serotonin, Cloninger believed this causes them to have high harm avoidance.

Consequently, harm avoidance measures a person's levels of worry, shyness around strangers, pessimism, fatigability and fear of uncertainty.

Moreover, antidepressants like Prozac keeps the serotonin system active. Leading to the inhibition of punishment signals and the reduction of negative emotions. Such as depression and anxiety. You can read more about these two conditions in Abnormal Psychology.

On the whole, serotonin could be a good candidate for a Neurotransmitter that influences our personality since it seems to affect our ability to stay calm. Meaning it could cause the neuroticism or emotionality dimension.

## Norepinephrine and Reward Dependence:

The last neurotransmitter that is thought to influence our personality in this theory is norepinephrine. You probably have come across this neurotransmitter in psychology before but in case you haven't norepinephrine inhibits the transmission of signals to our brain that respond to stimuli that would have been associated with rewards in the past.

In other words, this neurotransmitter is involved in the signals for conditioned rewards.

As a result, this led Cloninger to propose that personality characteristics are related to people's rewards and they have been associated with pleasure.

Meaning people with low levels of norepinephrine have high reward dependences because they want that feel good feeling that comes the release in norepinephrine.

In addition, people with high reward dependency tend to have warm communication, sentimentality and dependence. Due to if a person has a very inactive norepinephrine system then this leads to the tendency for people to develop strong sentimental attachments.

Overall, the key to understanding this point or feature of the theory is if a person has low levels of norepinephrine then this makes them reward dependent.

## Research Support

Interestingly, there is some research support for Cloninger's personality dimensions. Since Comings et al (2000) investigated the role of 59 genes in personality traits. Including 7 related to dopamine, 9 related to norepinephrine and 12 related genes to serotonin.

The results showed that each set of genes were associated with more than one of Cloninger's personality dimensions.

For example, reward dependence was more associated with norepinephrine genes than any other gene.

However, there is less clear evidence for the unique relationships between harm avoidance and serotonin genes. As well as novelty seeking and dopamine.

In my opinion, I think this chapter has been an extremely interesting look at personality. From the weird and unscientific ideas of ancient Greece to Cloninger's neurotransmitter theory.

This theory is good as it draws on a lot of the research supports and facts already known to us. But it has a long way to go if the theory wants to become solid. As we still don't know how the harm avoidance and novelty seeking relationships work. Maybe you might want to research that in the future?

# GRAY'S THEORY, EYSENCK'S THEORY AND THE EVIDENCE

## Brain Structure- Gray's Theory

After looking at the neurotransmitter reasons for why personality develops, we're now going to move onto the neural or brain explanation for how personalities develop.

This theory was proposed by Gray and it's called Reinforcement sensitivity theory. With it proposing the different Brain Regions work together as a system that underlie personality.

The systems are as followed:

- The Behavioural Activation System (BAS)
- The Behavioural Inhibition System (BIS)
- The Fight-or-Flight System (FFS)

## The Behavioural Activation System (BAS)

This first system proposes that there different brain regions that are responsible for receiving signals from the nervous system. And these indicate that the person is experiencing some kind of reward.

Resulting in this being referred to as a "Go-system" as well. Since this encourages a person in their pursuit of rewards as well as the BAS is responsible for communicating the pleasurable and exciting nature of the rewards.

For example, it is the BAS that causes us to know we're excited by sex or great food.

Now, the reason why there are individual differences between us is because people differ in the sensitivity of their BAS system. Due to people with stronger or more sensitive systems have a stronger pursuit of rewards than others.

Leading to a person to become impulsive and seek pleasure and excitement.

Causing some researchers to propose a link between this system and Cloninger's Novelty Seeking dimension.

## The Behavioural Inhibition System (BIS)

Another system proposed by the theory is BIS which is the brain regions responsible for receiving signals from the nervous system which indicate that punishments are being experienced.

Leading to this system to become a "Stop-system" because the entire point of this Behavioural system is to encourage people to avoid the causes of punishment. As well as communicating the painful and frightening nature of punishments to the person.

For example, if your parents got furious with you everything you swore and they shouted and I mean REALLY shouted at you. Then this system would tell you this is an emotionally painful experience and you need to avoid swearing in the future. To avoid this punishment.

Referring back to personality and individual differences, according to this system we're all different because we all differ in the sensitivity of our BIS system. With people that have stronger or more sensitive systems having a stronger desire to avoid punishments.

In turn, this makes a person anxious and they really want to avoid pain and danger.

Again, this possibly links to Cloninger's Harm Avoidance dimension.

Another way to think of this is a good child might have a sensitive BIS because they hate punishment with a passion. So they make sure they're a good child so they maximise the chances of them avoiding the punishment.

Equally, a bad child might not have a strong system so their BIS might not be able to tell them that the punishment is an emotionally painful and frightening experience. And the system might not be able to make the bad child stop doing the behaviour that's causing the punishments.

## The Fight-or-Flight System (FFS)

The final system is extremely famous and we've all heard of our fight or flight response at one time or another. And this theory uses that idea as well as links it to personality.

Therefore, this behavioural system is made up of the regions of the brain responsible for motivating our extreme reactions. Like fighting or fleeing or freezing as a result of facing an extremely threatening situation.

If we link this to personality then people differ in the sensitivity of their Fight-Flight system. In turn this creates individual differences since people with stronger or more sensitive systems are more ready to fight or flee in case of emergency.

In terms of behaviour and personality, this makes a person have more extreme reactions. For example, they have more aggressive responses and they leave quickly. It links strongly to emotionality and neuroticism.

However, some researchers suggest that there's a negative relationship between this system and Cloninger's Reward Dependence dimension. Yet there isn't any empirical evidence showing this at the moment.

Also, we'll go into the evidence for the theory in a later section.

In my opinion, I always like learning about how our brain can impact our behaviour because some of the results are very interesting. One of the reasons why I enjoy this theory is because to some extent it works with the HEXACO model and Cloninger's theory to help explain personality. And as Gray's theory links to the other ones, it makes it easier to understand and it's great to see how all of this interconnects.

## Eysenck's Theory

Coming back to this theory, we're now going to look at how he proposed our biology influences our personality, and I have to admit something that I really like about Eysenck is that he's a multiple passionate researcher. Like, you can find this work in forensic, cognitive, biological AND personality psychology. He's a busy man!

In case you've forgotten about his personality theory (I know I did) Eysenck proposed there were two superfactors in personality in his early theory. These were Extroversion vs Introversion as well as Neuroticism vs Emotional Stability.

However, in his later theory, he added the Psychoticism personality superfactor and this renamed the theory from the EN theory to the PEN theory.

Which I think makes it a lot better!

Subsequently, if we shift gears slightly to focus on the biological perspective then in Extroversion people differ the strength of their reactions to stimulation of their senses. In turn, this is all theoretically about the arousability of their brains with extroverts preferring high levels vs low levels of stimulation.

Furthermore, extroverts actively seek out stimulation and sensation as well as they're lively, active, sociable, enjoy loud muscle, meetings and parties. Whereas introverts avoid stimulation, large groups and they prefer quieter surroundings. And this is all governed by the ARAS.

## Ascending Reticular Activating System (ARAS)

This system is located in the brain stem, where the spinal cord and the brain meet because the nervous system receives stimulation from the environment. Then the ARAS regulates the amount of stimulation that is admitted to the brain from the nervous system.

Leading us to the individual differences because if a person's ARAS allows little stimulation into their brain then they feel under aroused. making them seek out stimulation and this happens for extroverts. Yet if their ARAS allows a lot of stimulation then they feel over aroused and they avoid stimulation. As you can guess this is what happens to introverts.

Whilst, we'll look at the evidence later on for this theory. I wanted to add if there are any introverts reading this. It is perfectly okay to be introverted, you don't need to be extroverted to be successful and happy. If you're ever struggling with being an introvert, go online and you'll see lots of great articles about how brilliant introverts are.

## Neuroticism

The second superfactor according to Eysenck is neuroticism and this is how people differ in their reactions to stressful stimuli with some people being very sensitive and other people not being as sensitive.

Moreover, the people that are very sensitive to stress are classed as very neurotic and these people feel a great amount of worry and nervousness. With these people typically being moody, depressed, anxious, emotional, tense amongst other emotions. Whereas people with high emotional stability feel little stress.

As a result, the individual differences in this superfactor are governed by none other than the limbic system. Which is critical for emotion, and if you want to learn more then I recommend checking out Biological Psychology and Cognitive Psychology.

Therefore, in case you're unfamiliar with the limbic system, this is made up of several connected structures in the brain and one of its many functions is to regulate our stress responses. This links to neuroticism because if people have a limbic system that can manage stressful stimuli well then these people are higher in emotional stability. Whereas people with a limbic system that gets overwhelmed by stressful stimuli, then this leads to the person to become more neurotic.

Psychoticism

This last personality superfactor is interesting and possibly scary because it looks at how people differ in their levels of psychoticism. With people that are high in psychoticism being aggressive, cold, egocentric as well as antisocial, impersonal, tough-minded and impulsive.

In terms of behaviour, people with high levels of psychoticism are associated with criminal behaviour and mental health conditions. Yet it's associated with creativity too. Which I think is interesting, if not a little concerning.

Nonetheless, what's really interesting and links this superfactor to biology is high levels of psychoticism is associated with higher levels of testosterone and low levels of the enzyme mono-amine oxidase (MAO). This enzyme is involved in the inactivation of neurotransmitters such as serotonin and dopamine.

The whole reason I think this is extremely interesting is because it is these neurotransmitters that are associated with happiness and romantic love. The very opposite of being cold, impersonal and aggressive.

Thus, I think it's great to see another explanation how the individual differences in personality.

## Gray's and Eysenck's Dimensions: Empirical Evidence

Whilst I certainly admit this first piece of evidence is just plain weird! Please bare with me because forgive me for even mentioning this rather unscientific study.

So, Eysenck & Eysenck (1967) conducted a study using the Lemon Juice Test and if you want I don't see why you couldn't do this at home.

I think this is the only psychology study we can do at home. So take advantage!

Anyway, what the participants and yourself can do is drop lemon juice onto your tongue then you use a cotton wool ball to mop up the saliva your glands produce and you weigh it against other samples. And these other samples come from other people. For instance, you could do this with your family, friends, flatmates or work colleagues.

As a result, Eysenck proposed that the stimulation that is caused by the lemon juice is perceived more strongly by introverts than extroverts. Causing the introverts to produce more saliva.

Amazingly, this is what the results from Eysenck and Eysenck (1967) found.

I don't actually know whether to be amazed or shocked at these results because this experiment is very effective despite it being so simple.

However, I think we have to raise the question of how valid is it? Does it actually measure personality or are there other factors to explain these results?

Another piece of evidence can be found in Geen (1984) because Geen conducted a study that looked at extroversion and introversion using participants with above and below average levels of Extroversion. This was based on questionnaire scores. Then the introverts as well as extroverts had to complete a learning task whilst they were exposed to noises.

Furthermore, this study was made up of 3 conditions. The first condition was the choice condition where the participants were allowed to choose the loudness of the noise.

The second condition was an assigned-same condition where the introverts were assigned to the introvert quiet noise condition. And the extroverts were assigned to the louder condition.

In other words, the loudness of the noise matched their personalities.

Additionally, the final condition was the assigned-different condition with the introverts being assigned to the extraverted loud condition and the extroverts were assigned in the introvert quiet condition. Therefore, the conditions were believed not to match their personalities.

As interesting as this experiment sounds so far, is anyone else getting concerned about psychological distress? Or maybe that's the autism in me talking?

Anyway, Geen measured the participants' levels of arousal by measuring their levels of skin conductance and heart rate. With the research expecting the extroverts in the choice condition to prefer higher levels of stimulation and choose louder noises than the introverts in the same condition.

This was confirmed by the results because the means setting of noise intensity was 37.3 for the introverts and 54.2 for the extroverts.

Another expectation was despite the different intensity of the noise levels, the extraverts and introverts in the choice condition will show comparable arousal levels because they have chosen their optimal or preferred levels of noise.

Which I think is reasonable because there's no reason for the sympathetic nervous system to kick in if a person is used to this arousal.

In addition, the expectation for the assigned-same condition was that the introverts in the quiet condition as well as the extroverts in the loud condition would show similar results as the participants in the choice condition. At least as far as arousal levels are concerned.

The final belief Geen had about the experiment was in the assigned-different condition, the introverts in the loud condition would show higher arousal levels because they were being overstimulated. Also, the extroverts would show lower arousal levels since they were being understimulated.

Overall, the results showed when introverts were assigned to the loud condition they showed higher heart rates but the extroverts assigned to their quiet condition showed lowered heart rates. And the introverts and extroverts in the choice condition showed comparable heart rates.

In conclusion, Geen (1984) concluded the introverts prefer lower levels of stimulation than extroverts and introverts are more aroused or they react stronger than extroverts when exposed to the same levels of stimulation.

I think this is a good piece of evidence to support Eysenck's theory because it was well controlled and an effective piece of research looking at Extroversion. But on a personal note, I really wouldn't like to be in the assigned-different condition!

## Extra Evidence

Furthermore, Geen also measured how many trials participants needed to perform the learning task and the interesting thing is the research found that introverts performed better than extroverts in the quiet noise condition. But the extraverts performed better than introverts in the loud noise condition.

As a result, these findings and those of other lab experiments are broadly consistent with Eysenck's theory of the biological bases of Extroversion. Yet more research is needed to understand the brain structures that underlie personality. (More on that in the next chapter!)

## Counterevidence

Nonetheless, there is some evidence against Eysenck's theory because some studies have produced more complex patterns of results that are only partly consistent with Eysenck's theory.

For instance, Zuckerman and his colleagues

found evidence for three personality factors consistent with Eysenck's dimensions but also obtained evidence for five factors. But these are not the Big Five we looked at earlier. (Zuckerman, 1995, 2005) Suggesting there might be more to personality than Eysenck thought.

Moreover, unlike Eysenck's ideas and theories, Zuckerman suggested that each personality dimension is influenced by various complex interactions between several brain structures, neurotransmitters, and hormones. And not a single brain structure, neurotransmitter, or hormone like Eysenck believed.

In my opinion, I do have to agree with Zuckerman because as we've seen in the last two chapters and as you'll see in the next chapters, a lot of different factors influence our personality. So, the idea of personality being caused by one thing is extremely reductionist and almost certainly wrong.

# PERSONALITY AND HORMONES

Hormones are critical to so many behaviours and whilst I have an entire chapter dedicated to them and how they work in Biological Psychology. I want to quickly summarise that hormones are biological chemicals that are produced by glands in the body then they're transmitted by the bloodstream to other body parts.

The reason why we're looking at this in a personality psychology book is because hormones affect our neural activity so it's very possible that hormones affect and influence our personality.

## Testosterone

I certainly think that this is possibly the most famous hormone because it influences important behaviours in us. For example, sexual and aggressive behaviours. Thus, you'll find this hormone mentioned in a lot of my other books as well.

Anyway, testosterone is responsible for a lot of the physical characteristics of men. Like, the development of their reproductive organs, the development of their secondary sex characteristics (facial hair, body air amongst other male features) as well as testosterone is ten times higher in males than females.

In addition, our testosterone levels vary between different people but it's influenced by events and situations as well. For instance, our testosterone levels change when we experience winning and losing. (Bernhardt, Dabbs, Fielden, & Lutter, 1998)

Another massive impact this hormone had on our behaviour reason is our levels of testosterone during our early periods of development can influence behaviour later in life. For example, when girls were exposed during pregnancy to high levels of testosterone, they tended to prefer toys that are usually more preferred by boys than girls.

Testosterone and Personality:

Linking this hormone to our personality, Dabbs et al. (1996) conducted a study where in a sample of 240 members of fraternities had their testosterone levels measured.

Their results showed that fraternities with higher than average levels were more unruly, wilder and rambunctious than people with average levels of testosterone.

Equally, fraternities who had lower than

average levels of testosterone were more socially reasonable, had better academic achievement and were more successful.

Following this study, Dabbs et al (1995) ran another study made up of a sample of 692 prison inmates and they found that prisoners with higher levels of the hormone were associated with violent or sexual crimes. But higher levels were less associated with drug offences, burglaries and theft. As well as it was associated with being more likely to break the rules in prison.

Another follow up study they did look at the differences in testosterone between men and women and of course they found there was a great difference between the two genders. But there was a much, much smaller difference between the two when it came to the distribution and overlap of their personality traits. And this has been supported by other studies. Like Hyde (2005)

In other words, if testosterone was responsible for personality then this large between gender differences in the hormone should result in a large distribution of personality traits.

Overall, it's safe to say testosterone is not the only biological factor involved as we saw in the last chapter that influences personality.

Personally, I've enjoyed the look at the biological approach and especially the hormone chapter. Since testosterone does impact our behaviour in a number of ways and it's important to investigate. Yet this chapter does highlight the importance of doing follow up studies to explore behaviour in more depth. Maybe something you might want to do in the future, perhaps?

Cortisol

Then the second hormone that could be involved in personality is Cortisol and this might as well be called the stress hormone. Since it's released by the adrenal cortex and this release is triggered by stress to prepare the body for action. This results in an increase in a person's blood pressure and blood sugar. And interestingly it causes the suppression of the immune system.

which I think pretty strange because why would the body need to suppress the immune system?

Anyway, cortisol is linked to personality because some researchers believe it is the cause of emotionality or our emotional reactivity.

As supported by Loney et al (2006) who conducted a study on 100 adolescent boys and girls with high or low levels of "callous-unemotional" traits. Their results showed that among boys but not girls, the higher levels of callous-unemotional traits were associated with low cortisol levels.

Leading the researchers to conclude that having low levels of cortisol could lead to people to be more emotionally insensitive.

Yet I have to add this obviously can't be the whole story, because why weren't these results found in girls?

Another study we'll look at is Rosenblitt et al (2001) who used a sample of 143 college students and the researchers looked at the associations between testosterone, cortisol and sensation seeking scores. They broke sensation seeking down into four subscales: Boredom susceptibility, Disinhibition, Experience Seeking, Thrill and Adventure Seeking as well.

Their results showed there was no significant associations among women and there were no significant associations for testosterone. As well as the study found men with high levels of sensation seeking had significantly lower cortisol levels than other people.

Meaning this study so shows cortisol seems not to have an effect on personality in females but in men it does seem to influence Openness to Experience.

Oxytocin

I do enjoy learning about oxytocin because a part of me considers it to be the overshadowed brother to dopamine since oxytocin is critical to so many behaviours but dopamine always seems to get the credit. But I discuss this a bit more in Biological Psychology.

Therefore, oxytocin is a hormone produced in the hypothalamus and released by the pituitary gland as well as in women and female mammals, oxytocin is released when giving birth, breastfeeding and experiencing orgasms.

Also, men have oxytocin because this facilitates a man's emotional attachments to his partner and children.

Needless to say it's critical!

One study that shows its effect on behaviour is Zak et al. (2005) who got students to play a trust game involving money. The researchers found students with higher levels of oxytocin trusted other students more in how to divide some money than people with lower levels. As well as more trustworthy students, people who divided up the money equally, had higher levels of oxytocin.

However, these results couldn't be replicated by Christensen et al (2014) using a prisoner's dilemma task. Casting the results in possible doubt.

Overall, this suggests Oxytocin plays a role in people's interpersonal attachments and it could have a role in cooperative relationships, but unclear how or if the hormone determines personality differences. Since Zak et al showed us it causes differences in behaviour, but can we really link this to personality?

# DEVELOPMENTAL CHANGES AND STABILITY OF PERSONALITY

To change it up a little bit instead of a particular topic being broken down into a few chapters, this next chapter should be completely self-contained.

Therefore, in this chapter, we'll be looking at how stable our personality is over the human lifespan and if and when it changes over our lives.

This is one of those topics where at first I thought it wouldn't be very interesting but the results can be very surprising.

So, definitely read this chapter!

<u>Definition and Measurement:</u>

When it comes to defining change and stability, these are in fact two different questions that we're trying to ask.

Firstly, you have the question of how the average person changes over the course of their life. This is measured by looking for the mean difference.

Subsequently, the second question is how stable are these different personality traits between people. As well as we use this by looking at the correlation between various time points.

Furthermore, if we examine how we measure these concepts in more depth, we can measure these by using cross-sectional and longitudinal studies.

Cross-sectional studies measure personality traits at one time point using many individuals. Like, a 2020/2021 class.

This is good because it's easy to do but the results may reflect generational effects. This is where the results are influenced or tainted by a particular feature of a generation.

Another method you can use is longitude studies that use the same people at different time points.

Again, this is good because it allows researchers to measure and understand how personality changes in the same person over time. But these types of studies are difficult to do, expensive and they can reflect historical or period effects in your results.

Thus, you can see both methods have their

negatives but these can be combined.

Which I thought was amazing!

I probably thought this because these are two very different methods so I think it's impressive that you can actually combine them.

Also, this combination uses sequential designs as used in life-span developmental psychology.

Personality Change and Stability:

To introduce the topic of the chapter, I thought we would look at Robert, Walton & Wiechlbauer (2006) because they did a meta-analysis of 92 studies, and their results show a number of interesting things.

For example, they found a person's emotional stability increases from 15 years old to 30 then it levels off. As well as Openness to Experience increases a lot from 15 years old to 30 then it plateaus until it drops slightly between the ages of 50 to 65.

Furthermore, extroversion in terms of social dominance sharply increases from 15 years old to 30 then it levels off. Whereas if we look at extroversion in terms of social validity, it actually drops 15 years old to 30 then it plateaus until it drops further at about 50 to 65 years old.

The last two findings from the studies were

both agreeableness and conscientiousness increased proportionally over the course of the human lifespan.

Also, it's worth noting down that during adulthood most conscientiousness traits increase, but perfectionism doesn't.

Overall, all six personality trait domains show significant changes past the age of 30, and what's really interesting is most personality trait changes happen during young adulthood between the ages of 20-40 and not during adolescence.

This I think is surprising because I talk more about this in Developmental Psychology but during adolescence there are a lot of biological, cognitive and social changes happening to the teenager. Therefore, I'm surprised this doesn't cause a change in a given personality trait. Or is it possible it is these changes that lay the groundwork for the personality changes to occur?

Maybe an idea for future research?

Personality traits change most during young adulthood ages 20-40, not during adolescence.

Why Do We Change?

After looking at the stability of personality traits, we know that a lot of these traits change over time, but this makes us question why do these changes occur?

It turns out according to the Five Factor Theory and McCrae & Costa (1999) humans have a species-wide genetic disposition to develop in certain directions. Meaning it is because of our genetics that we develop and change our personalities.

Furthermore, this theory and study are saying that humans are hardwired to become more agreeable, socially dominant, conscientious, less open to experience as well as more emotionally stable.

However, according to the Social Investment Hypothesis or Social Roles Hypothesis by Roberts, Wood & Smith (2005) humans invest in universal tasks of social living. Like getting married. And this is what causes our personality to change so we can accomplish these tasks.

For example, if everyone had low Openness to Experience, Extroversion or Agreeableness then going out to meet and form a relationship with a potential mate would be extremely difficult.

In addition, these universal tasks are supported and encouraged in most cultures.

## Personality and Adulthood Stability:

In adults, personality traits seem to be extremely stable. As seen in Costa & McCrae (1992) that ran a study using the self-report data from adults with their age difference only being a few weeks apart. Amazingly enough their personalities, regardless of the personality dimension examined, had a correlation of 0.80. Meaning they all had very similar personalities.

Subsequently, the researchers did the same study again but this time they measured the personalities of adults that had an age gap of 6 years, in this study only- observer reports were used, and 24 years apart. Their results for the adults with 6 years apart were .70 and for the 24 years apart the correlation was .65.

Overall, you can see throughout adulthood personality changes and develops as we grow older.

## Stability of Traits In Adolescence And Young Adulthood

It's only occurred to me now that we're looking at personality from old to young but there is a critical reason for that as you'll see in a moment.

Anyway, whilst the personality traits of adults are extremely stable, when it comes to the traits of adolescents there are somewhat lower correlations between them. Meaning, the personality of teenagers are reasonably unstable.

For instance, Robins et al (2001) studied adolescents with a 4 years age gap in college to find there's only a 0.6 correlation. Which is a lot less than the adult correlation.

This is also showed in Roberts et al (2001) when they looked at young adults aged between 18-26 and these people only had an average correlation of .55.

Finally, McCrae et al (2002) studied teenagers between the ages of 12 and 16 to find an average correlation of 0.4.

Overall, adolescences and young adults have relatively unstable personality because this is most probably down to the cognitive, biological and social changes that are occurring at this stage in their development.

## Personality in Infancy and Childhood:

I mentioned there was a reason why we're looking at personality traits backwards and that's because when it comes to measuring the personality of children, it's a nightmare.

It is extremely difficult.

Mainly because when it comes to measuring the personalities of adults, we can simply ask them or get them to do a personality questionnaire.

However, when it comes to researching

personalities with children you can't really do this.

One reason is because it isn't until the age of 10 where children can start to describe themselves in terms of personality. For example, "I am smart," and "I am noisy,"

The other reason is because personality questionnaires require a level of reading comprehension that isn't reached until adolescence.

Furthermore, a lot of the behaviours that are asked about in these questionnaires aren't relevant to toddlers, children or even adolescents. As well as observer reports can be biased and problematic.

On the whole, personality measures in children are less reliable and less valid.

Yet thankfully some very clever researchers have found some ways around this since despite all these problems, there is good evidence for 4 of 5 big personality traits in children. Including Neuroticism, Extroversion, Agreeableness and Conscientiousness.

Although, there isn't so much evidence for Openness to Experience and Honesty-Humility.

For some reason though that doesn't actually surprise me because all I think about when I heard children lack Openness to Experience is: "I don't like vegetables," as children say without ever trying these new things.

Personality Changes and Relationships:

To conclude this chapter on how personality traits change over time, I really wanted to look at everyone's favourite topic of relationships!

As a result of Neyer and Lenhart (2007) studied changes in the personality of young adults from their mid-20 to early 30s with romantic relationships being the source of changes over the 8 years.

At the start of the study, most people were already in a serious relationship and others got into relationships throughout the study but some remained single throughout.

Although, the study found the people who started off as single but later got into relationships turned out to be higher in neuroticism and sociability than people who remained single throughout.

The researchers suggested being anxious and sociable could make a person more likely to go out and seek partners.

In addition, people who entered relationships tended to be less anxious, shy and higher in self-esteem, whereas these changes weren't seen in people who remained single.

Therefore, the researchers suggested on average being in a relationship makes them more secure. In turn, this increases their self-esteem. And I think it's interesting to see how personality dimensions can change over the course of a relationship.

# INTRODUCTION TO GENETIC AND ENVIRONMENTAL INFLUENCES ON PERSONALITY

We know from Biological Psychology that genes and our environments both influence our behaviour to various extents. And whilst this next section will look at how this is researched and from a personality perspective, for a more well-rounded look at how genetics influence our behaviour. I highly recommend looking at Biological Psychology for more information.

In addition, at some point or another, we've all probably heard of the nature-nurture debate. This is one of my most hated psychology arguments because it proposes that genetics OR environmental factors influence our behaviour. Which is wrong because behaviour is an interaction between environmental and genetic factors.

Thankfully, this debate has been modernised somewhat to focus on the degrees to which genetic and environmental factors influence a given behaviour. But this still doesn't stop the media and pop psychology from focusing on the old argument and wasting psychology's time.

Anyway though, from a personality psychology perspective, we need to work out how and to what extent these different factors cause these personality traits to develop. As well as we do this in a number of steps.

Firstly, researchers examine the similarities of pairs of relatives, and they do this by measuring a particular personality trait in a large number of pairs of relatives. Then they calculate the variance by calculating how much of this variance is due to the within-family and between-family differences.

Secondly, researchers compare the personality trait in different types of relatives. Like, mother, father, sister, brother, etc. This is typically done using twin studies as twin share a lot of genetic material meaning you can make links about the inheritability of personality traits. I talk more about this in Biological Psychology.

## Addictive and Non-Addictive Influences:

When I first came across this section, I thought this was talking about addiction and how genetics contribute to addiction. In fact, it's discussing the combined effects of two or more genes on personality. As well as there are different types of genes that can affect our personality.

For example, addictive genes affect each gene contributes separately. But non-addictive genetic effect influences a particular gene depending on the presence or absence of the other gene.

Consequently, this means identical twins will be more than twice as similar as fraternal or nonidentical twins when non-addictive genetic influences on a particular personality trait are involved.

Whilst this introductory look at genetics and personality might seem short, we'll return to how genetics influence particular personality traits in the next few chapters.

## Environmental Influences

These types of influences are all about how the environment we live in influences our behaviour AND interacts with your genetic factors. Also, these environmental factors can be estimated by remeasuring the similarity between biologically unrelated people raised in the same household as seen in adoption.

## Unique Environmental Influences:

When it comes to examining the environmental influences on personality, there are a number of aspects we need to consider. For instance, the common environmental factors because we need to know how the between-family environments influence us.

In addition, siblings can and do experience different environments whether it's socially or home environments and these do potentially influence their personality. As well as you need to consider the unique-unshared environmental influences since we must examine the within-family environmental influences too.

As a result, after researchers estimate the hereditary and common environmental influences the variance that is left over can be attributed to unique environmental influences.

## Real Life Examples

Now, we're going to move onto the much more fun topic of how these different influences actually affect our behaviour.

## German Twin Studies

Over the decades, there's been a lot of different twin studies done in Germany and they tend to find similar results. As seen in Riemann, Angleitner, & Strelau (1997).

One of the general findings is from self-reported data the mean correlation for the similarity between siblings in personality is .54 for identical twins and for fraternal twins .27.

In addition, these studies find the general inheritability of personality characteristics is .54. Meaning personality can be considered strongly inherited. The researchers found there were addictive genetic effects and no common environmental effects as well.

Although, when observer report data was used, the mean for identical twins dropped to .45 and for fraternal twins .20 as well as the estimated heritability of personality characteristics also dropped to .50.

However, when both self and observer reports were combined, this increased the heritability findings to .65. Meaning there is a higher level of heritability than if only one of these methods is used alone.

And as a little fun side note, Loehlin (1989) ran a twin study by comparing identical twins with fraternal twins raised together and the researcher looked at Extroversion and Neuroticism in three different countries. The surprising thing is some of the findings support the traditional assumption that neuroticism in children is caused by their parents giving the child inconsistent reinforcement or improper attachment.

After looking over this chapter so far, whilst I don't particularly care too much for the ins and outs of genetic research. I have to admit that these results are always interesting to look at, and I do like seeing how our genetics and our environment interact to produce a behaviour. This is probably why I'm a massive fan of the Diathesis Stress Model and the Biopsychosocial model in Clinical Psychology.

Religiosity

We will return to the topic of Religiosity and Political Attitudes in a later section of the book but if we look at this behaviour from a genetic and environmental perspective, this is and isn't as clear cut as you might think.

As a result, Abrahamson, Baker, and Caspi (2002) studied 650 adopted and non-adopted adolescents for their levels of religiosity. Their results showed that the adolescents' level of this behaviour did have a reasonably large effect because they correlated above .40 for both adopted and non-adopted relatives. Showing a relatively high environmental influence.

Additionally, the study found that genetics have a small effect on religiosity at .12. This only provides further evidence that religiosity is mainly caused by shared environments and environmental factors.

Nonetheless, the impact of the shared environment on religiosity did tend to decrease during adulthood as found by Koenig, McGue, Krueger, and Bouchard (2005). When they studied the religiosity level of fraternal twins and identical twins.

The results showed the levels of religiosity in nonidentical twins were around .60 during their adolescence and this dropped to around .40 in their 30s. Whereas for the identical twins, their levels of religiosity were slightly high at around .70 during their adolescence but this only decreased to around .60 in their 30s.

Yet one very surprising fact is it was the genetic tendencies of the identical twins that helped them to maintain similar religiosity levels.

So, I think after all it's interesting to say that genetics do have a stronger influence on religiosity than I previously thought. Because I knew religiosity was mainly down to environmental factors but I didn't expect to see the genetic factors helping the identical twins to maintain similar levels. Therefore, I think it's clear that genetics does play a somewhat significant role in religiosity. But more on than in a later section!

## Political Attitudes

I do love politics and as this isn't a political book, I won't mention my beliefs but when I found out personality psychology covers political beliefs and attitudes I became quite interested in learning more. Thus, whilst there's another chapter or section of the book dedicated to this area later on. It's always good to peak your interest!

To introduce you to personality and politics, let's look at Eaves et al (1997) who studied around 7000 twin pairs and the researchers measured the conservatism levels of the fraternal twins. And the results show that there was a large correlation between the similarities of the conservationism levels. With there being a correlation of around .50 during the teenage years and this only dropped slightly to around .40 after the age of 20.

However, the researchers didn't stop there because they measured the conservatism levels of identical twins as well. Finding that their levels of conservatism was around .50 during their teenage years but this actually increased the correlation to roughly .60 after the age of 20.

Therefore, the findings show that shared environments have a strong influence on political attitudes during adolescence, but this influence weakens after the age of 20. As well as the genetic influence strengthens after the age of 20.

Personally, I think that's... wow. I never would have guessed there would be an increased in similarity due to genetics. If anything I was expecting it to decrease a lot more. It just goes to show more complex genetics and behaviour can be!

## Drinking and Smoking

This is thought would be another interesting topic to look at because of how common smoking and drinking behaviour is. And in case you're currently or went to university and don't do those behaviours, it's perfectly fine. I don't drink or smoke to the dismay of others.

Anyway, these two behaviours could be down to several different personality traits, because these unhealthy behaviours could be the manifestations of different personality traits. Like, neuroticism, sensation seeking or extroversion?

To research, this Vink et al (2005) conducted a Dutch study on 1572 twins and the researchers found the heritability of smoking initiation is .44.

Furthermore, a meta-analysis (Li et al 2003) showed that the heritability of smoking persistence is .53.

As well as there are studies on the heritability of alcohol drinking that show moderate heritability ranging from .21 to .56 and studies on alcoholism showing heritability estimates of .50 or greater, up to .71.

# GENETIC AND ENVIRONMENTAL INFLUENCES ON PERSONALITY

## Are Relatives' Personality Measured Independently?

By now, I really, really wouldn't be surprised if you would starting to question the validity of twin studies or anything to do with family genetics. Since we have to ask the question of are you measuring the personalities independently from one another?

At first I didn't even think about this and it's perfectly fine if you didn't either. But now we have to consider it. Because if we don't then this non-independence could inflate or deflate the similarity between relatives and as a result bias our heritability estimates.

Another reason why this is important is because when siblings complete the same questionnaire. They may want to emphasise the differences between them instead of comparing themselves with people in general. This point very importantly refers to concepts from Social Identity Theory and Optimal Distinctiveness. (Social Psychology)

In addition, when measuring relatives' personalities the observers, like parents, might compare their children or other relatives with each other instead of with children in general. For instance, if you have two relatively nervous or anxious children, their parents might perceive one as "the nervous one" and the other as "the calm one". Resulting in researchers possibly overestimating and underestimating the nervousness levels. In turn, this would affect the emotionality ratings.

Overall, this is called The Contrast Effect.

Moreover, personality researchers need to consider the Assimilation Effect as well. This is when siblings or other relatives are still completing the questionnaire as before but this time they might consider them to be very similar or the observers perceive them as very similar. Resulting in a tendency to emphasise the similarity, as well as an overestimation of the similarity. Which has implications for the genetic findings.

How to Overcome Contrast And Assimilation Effects?

After reading that rather depressing section on the flaws of this research, let's see how we can overcome these problems.

One way of overcoming this is by obtaining observer reports from someone who knows only one of the individuals but does not know the individual's relatives very well. As seen in the German twin studies (Riemann et al. 1997)

Another way is to use direct observations where you are observing the participant's behaviour.

## The German Twin Studies:

I know I've mentioned them multiple times in this chapter and I can hear some of you asking what they are, so I'll explain them now.

There are a lot of German Twin Studies done by different people but Borkenau, Riemann, Angleitner, & Spinath (2001) studied 300 pairs of German twins and these twins took part in a variety of activities while they were being observed and video-recorded.

Some of the tasks were getting the twins to introduce themselves, arranging three photos in an order and telling the researchers an interesting story about the photos, refusing request for help by a "friend", getting the twins to mine or pantomime uses for a brick as well as solving a complex problem as fast as possible. And having a confederate solve the same problem in record time.

On a personal note, my original notes said pantomime and I was really confused by it because in the UK, we say mine or act out the actions. Language is a funny thing!

Therefore, the results from Borkenau et al (2001) showed there was a stronger similarity in the twin's personality when assessed by observations than with self- or observer reports. And the fraternal twins were more than half as similar to each other as were identical twins.

As a result, this provides us with further evidence for the impact or influence of common environment effect, as well as this supports the theory behind the occurrence of contrast effects in the personality assessment of DZ twins using self- or observer reports.

## Is There Really No Assortative Mating for Personality?

If you're like me then you do have to take a moment and remember what assortative mating is because it's a weird term.

Basically, assortative mating is two people come together and mate and both these people have similar personality and psychological traits.

In personality psychology, researchers assume that there's not a tendency for parents to be similar in their personality traits, and they're no more similar to each other than any two people chosen at random.

Yet I do believe I mentioned in Psychology of

Relationships something that doesn't support that.

Nonetheless, if we suppose for a moment that there is assortative mating in personality psychology then it would propose that if a mother's and father's levels of a personality trait were highly correlated. Then this would mean fraternal twins will share more than 50% of their genes with each other.

Consequently, if researchers compared identical and non-identical twins, this would lead to an underestimation of the heritability.

Furthermore, studies have shown that parents are not so similar in any personality characteristic in ways that would distort the results of heritability studies.

In all honesty, I think we can all see this in our daily lives because our parents and other romantic couples around us tend to have different attitudes, beliefs and cognitive abilities to their partner.

Yet in terms of personality, this means there's no tendency for mothers who are high in agreeableness to be married to fathers also high in agreeableness.

## Assumptions Of Twin-Based Heritability Studies

Like everything within psychology, twin-based studies are built on a set of assumptions and you can think of these as guiding principles that form the logic behind why we use them. But are these assumptions necessarily correct?

That's the focus for the rest of this chapter.

As I mentioned earlier the reason why twins raised apart are used is because this allows researchers to examine the environmental influences on their behaviour.

However, some researchers have objected to this idea because of two main reasons. The first is they propose twins may share some features of their early environment. This is in terms of before they were separated and after they were separated. If this is true then this puts doubt in the assumption that their differences lie in their unique environments.

The second point is these researchers argue the adopting household may differ in important ways from households in general.

This point I do understand because as we'll see in three sections time because adoptions are relatively infrequently and the placements are selective this adds to the differences between adoption family households and non-adoption households. Also, you've got the fact that not everyone wants to adopt so you got the more unique attitudes of those who do want to adopt. Personally, I do want to foster and perhaps adopt in the future as well.

In addition, people have objected to the assumption that twins raised together experience the

same environment because they believe identical
twins raised together might be treated more similarly
than fraternal twins. We'll look at this in a later
section.

## Are Twins' Early Environments Really Separate?

Going back to the second major objection to
these studies, are these early environments really
different. A lot of research has been done into this
area because in adoption studies twins are separated
at a very young age of roughly 5 months old. Yet
some people believe these 5 months of a shared
environment might influence and contribute to the
twins' similarity.

However, studies that compared early-
separated with later-separated twins found no
evidence that the shared environment during those
months together influenced the similarity between
twins.

## What About The Common Womb Environment?

Interestingly, some researchers have decided
to look at the womb as a unique and shared
environment for twins and siblings. Which I think is
sensible because both twins spend roughly 9 months
together here.

Furthermore, the consistencies across
pregnancies contribute as common
environmental influences between non-twin siblings.

Whereas changes across pregnancies are unique to the twin siblings.

Overall, some of the similarity for twins and non-twin siblings raised apart might be attributable to the common womb environment. But this hasn't been examined in heritability studies on personality traits.

I think this would be a great idea to research but I have no idea how you would do it. Do you?

## Are Twins' Adoptive Households Really Very Different?

As I touched upon a few sections ago, a major criticism for heritability studies is the assumption that adoptive households are different and offer the twins raised apart a unique environment to develop in. But are these adoptive households really that different? For instance, could one household have a more attentive and gentle parenting style than the others that influences personality development?

The thinking behind this comes from a few different strands of thinking because what if the household that adopts the twin is actually rather similar to the household the other twin lives in? For example, both households have high incomes and high educational levels.

On the whole, the main reason why this is a concern for researchers is because this limited variation among the adopting households tends to limit the estimated effect of the common environment.

Moving onto the research, McGue et al (2007) conducted their study by comparing adoptive parents with non-adoptive parents with some parents having somewhat lower levels of antisocial behaviour as well as drug and alcohol abuse, with higher socioeconomic status as well.

The study found the antisocial behaviour of the adoptive parents was completely unrelated to the antisocial behaviour of the adopted children. Therefore, the restricted variability among adoptive parents doesn't necessarily lead to an underestimation of the shared environment effects on behaviour.

Lastly for this section, the question of selective placements needs to be answered because selecting adoptive parents similar to the biological parents may underestimate the environmental influence when comparing identical twins raised apart.

However, this objection is largely unfounded because studies have shown that there's very little selective placement. Which I think we can agree can be wise in certain situations because if a child has been put up for adoption due to their abusive parents. You clearly don't want to put them with another set of parents who are likely to be abusive.

Yet I do want to add sometimes adoption can be in the interest of the child and we wouldn't blame the biological parents for putting their child up for adoption. It doesn't make them bad parents or horrible people sometimes they do it for the good of the child and that takes courage.

## Are Identical Twins Really Treated Differently By Others?

To wrap up this chapter where we have basically criticised and examined the methods and assumptions used in genetic and environmental research, I thought it would be fun to look at this question.

Since as I've implied throughout the book and in Biological Psychology, personality researchers assume that twins, be it identical or fraternal, lived in the same environment. This is known as the equal environment assumption?.

But is this *true*?

In addition, the assumption presumes that identical and fraternal twins become more similar as they develop because they both live in a similar environment. For instance, they both have the same clothes and more. Leading people to treat the twins the same.

The reason why I thought this would be good to look at is because now I've explained what the assumption really means. It does have me, don't know about you, wondering if this assumption is correct.

As a result, there are two studies that decided to look at this idea. Firstly, you have Loehlin and Nichols (1976) that conducted the study on 300 identical twin pairs from Texas, and they measured the similar versus different treatment between the twins. Their results showed that treating the twins in similar ways had little effect on the similarity of their personalities.

Secondly, you have Scarr and Carter-Saltzman (1979) and I quite like this study because the researchers decided to measure it interestingly. Since instead of measuring the similarity of the twins' treatment, they decided to measure the similarity in identical twins. BUT their parents believed these twins were fraternal twins and not identical. And they did the same for fraternal twins believed to be identical.

Very interesting!

The researchers did this because this allowed them to measure the effects of perceived similarity versus actual genetic similarity.

Consequently, the results showed personality similarity is greater for identical twins believed to be fraternal than for fraternal twins believed to be identical.

Overall, this means similarity of identical twins is not due to similar treatment.

I have to admit this has been a fun chapter, getting to examine and evaluate the assumptions and research methods used by personality psychology. I'm looking forward to the future chapters!

# EFFECTS OF UNIQUE ENVIRONMENT AND DIFFICULTIES IN HEREDITARY AND THE ENVIRONMENT

This final chapter on the genetic and environmental influences on personality will focus on how these influence behaviours but how difficult these influences are to isolate from one another.

## Parental Treatment and Peer Groups

Whilst this entire section has more or less looked at how the genetics of parents has impacted personality. We now need to look at how this links to behaviour without looking at genetics.

To investigate this, Loehlin (1997) studied 800 pairs of twins and they measured the twins' personality characteristics, different parental treatment of twins, differences in peers. The results showed the size of the personality difference was weakly correlated with the amount of differences in parental treatment and in peer groups. Overall, the researchers found the effect of the unique environment was a small correlation of .15.

In other words, the differences in how the parents treated the twins and the peer groups caused a small difference in the twin's personality.

However, this isn't the whole story because differences in personality can be caused by the differences in how peers treat each twin. For example, if school children liked one twin and supported them but they bullied the other twin. This would logically result in personality differences.

As a result, Burt, McGue, and Iacono (2009) ran a study with 450 pairs of 14 and 17 year old twins. Also, the researchers looked at the differences in the twins over a period of time for traits related to delinquency behaviour and differences in having deviant friends.

Their results show the twins who engaged in more delinquent or externalizing behaviour at age 14 tended to have more deviant friends at age 17. As well as this behaviour, which is a reflection of their personality, tended to influence the peer group more than the peer group influenced the twin's behaviour and personality.

Overall, whilst peer groups tend to have a strong impact on adolescents and differences between groups, cultures, or generations. For example, social groups can influence a person's music choice and clothes but they can influence norms related to sexual activity, delinquency and drug use.

In terms of individual differences in personality traits among different people, it seems as if the influence of friendship groups seems to be rather modest.

This I think is rather interesting because from Social Psychology we know the social group has a LOT of influence over our behaviour so I would have thought it would influence our personality too. Yet it just goes to show why it's important to conduct research because our common sense or thoughts aren't always right.

Birth Order

I read about the impact of birth order a whilst back when I was learning about sexuality at university but I didn't think about it anymore until now. Which is why we need to talk about this now because how does Birth Order influence personality?

Therefore, in terms of birth order, you can have first-born, middle-born, last-born or "only" child.

Furthermore, the first researcher we'll look at is Alfred Adler who found first born children become insecure when they lose their favourite position after their sibling or siblings is born. Also, he found that middle children are less insecure and less spoiled than last born and first born children.

Another researcher is Sulloway (1995, 1996) who researched this area but focused more on personality. They found that later born siblings had higher levels of Agreeableness and lower levels of Conscientiousness, but they had especially higher levels of Openness to experience.

The reason for this is because Sulloway believed the siblings needed to be more creative as well as unconventional to be able to impress their parents.

Which I can understand because this is the logical way to attract attention.

Also, this is further supported by other studies who asked participants to compare siblings and these other studies provide more support for higher Openness levels among later-born siblings compared to first-borns.

However, could this all just be down to the contrast effect?

It turns out yes and no because studies have assessed personality traits using self and observer reports and they show practically no difference for Openness to experience between the siblings. Yet if this was 100% true, then how did Sulloway get their results?

Overall, I truly think this emphasises the

difficulties with genetic and environmental research because we've looked at so many impacts and influences that highlights the difficulty.

But the point of this section has not been to criticise this research or the people who do genetic research. The point is I admire and appreciate the amazing people that do this research because it's hard.

So, if you want to go and do this research have fun and go and do it!

I encourage you to do what you love.

But for the rest of us, I'm very excited to move onto the next few chapters as we'll get into how personality and impact our behaviour.

Genotype-Environment Correlations

To complete our look at the genetic and environmental influences and how they're researched in personality psychology, we need to look at these things called Genotype-Environment correlations.

This is a horrific way of saying the correlation between genetics and environment and how these interact to produce a particular personality trait.

In addition, there are three types of these correlations: passive, active and reactive genotype-environment correlations. All of these we'll look at over the next few sections. But before we look at these correlations, I want to explain how these types of interactions can influence our personality. The reason why we need to look at these correlations and interactions is because the same environment can influence a person's level of a given personality trait in different ways, depending on their genetic characteristics. For example, different parenting styles can affect people differently, you only need to look at attachment theory to see this in action.

As a result, some people might be genetically inclined to behave in a certain way and have a particular level of a personality trait but others might not be as inclined. Like, a risks-averse, dependent person compared to a daring, independent person.

In addition, these interaction effects can decrease the similarities between relatives giving researchers a lower heritability correlation.

Building upon this further, so far in this section of the book, we've looked at the role of the genetic and environmental effects as if they contribute independently to the different variations in a person's personality. For instance, poor nutrition and other negative environmental factors would have the same effects on all children in the same way.

Nonetheless, there are some situational factors that might be more complicated due to their effect may be dependent on a person's genetic factors.

And I will jump in here to explain this in an

easy-to-understand way because if you're familiar with clinical psychology then you've probably heard of the Diathesis-Stress Model for mental conditions. This model proposes that people have a genetic deposition for a mental condition and the condition is triggered by environmental factors.

It is the same here. The two paragraphs above are saying that some situational factors interact with genetic factors to produce a person's level of a given personality trait.

For example, the environmental factor of having dominant parents might lead a child to become submissive or rebellious.

Equally, different genetic tendencies might lead to the child having different reactions to influences from delinquent peers, or towards opportunities for sports, music and many more.

## Passive Genotype-Environment Correlation

This type of correlation looks at how the environmental experience is influenced by parents' genetic predispositions. And it is these traits that are inherited by their children as well.

For instance, one example of this correlation is when a pair of athletic parents pass on their athleticism to their children and they create a sports-oriented home environment for them.

Personally, I prefer to describe this type of

correlation as the twins or children don't choose the environment that interacts with their genes.

## Active Genotype-Environment Correlations

This second type of correlation examines how children choose their environment as a result of their own genetic tendencies.

For example, sporty children tend to choose to take part in sport activities at school, the gym or after school clubs.

Another example is an introverted child choosing more quiet or introverted activities. Instead of loud activities with lots of people about.

Linking this back to passive correlations, these correlations are in the child's control and they can actively sure the environment in which their genes interact with.

## Reactive (Evocative) Genotype-Environment Correlations

Moving onto the final type, this type of correlation investigates how the child's genetic and environmental factors interact when the child experiences different environments depending on other people's reactions to the children's different genetic tendencies.

I know that was worded a bit strangely but one example is athletic children might be provided with more sporting opportunities because an adult has seen that they're sporty. Therefore, they respond to this by giving them access to special opportunities. Maybe with older children or 'gifted' sporty children. Hence, this all creates another environment that the child nor the parents decided.

# PART THREE:
# PERSONALITY AND
# MENTAL ABILITIES

# INTRODUCTION AND THE THEORIES OF INTELLIGENCE

When I was first taught this topic in personality psychology, I really couldn't understand the title because it was titled Mental Abilities. I know this is what I've called this section of the book, but this section is really all about Intelligence. And how personality can impact intelligence.

## What Is Mental Ability?

Personality is about the differences between people in their typical styles of thinking, behaving and feeling across different times and situations.

Whereas mental ability looks at the differences between people in their maximum performance in producing correct answers to various questions and problems.

This is also known as intelligence.

## History of Intelligence

Since it's always important to know how things began, I need to introduce how intelligence testing and the concept of intelligence came to be.

## Francis Galton:

Intelligence testing all began with Francis Galton (1822-1911) who was the first psychologist to study individual differences. As well as he found Hereditary Geniuses and he found that these differences in intelligence are determined by genetic factors.

In addition, to measure intelligence he used statistical and methodological approaches where he didn't measure mental abilities per say but he measured physical and sensory abilities. For example, a person's reaction time and sensory discrimination.

Yet he wasn't the best of people because he was clearly prejudiced insisting and trying to prove racial differences in mental abilities and that women were intellectually inferior to men.

## James McKeen Cattell (1860-1920)

Another key figure in intelligence testing is James McKeen Cattell who proposed that "Intelligence" was made up of 10 basic psychological functions. For instance, hearing, weight discrimination and tactile discrimination.

As a result, he wanted to test this by developing so-called mental tests and these tests did reliably measure individual differences in performance but they did not measure mental abilities.

## Alfred Binet (1857-1911):

Building upon the idea of the intelligence test, it was Alfred Binet who laid the foundations of modern intelligence testing because he developed a variety of tasks to measure mental abilities to help identify children with lower mental abilities and those with higher mental abilities.

Additionally, he created the first intelligence test but it didn't investigate the nature of a person's mental abilities. Instead, it measured a person's everyday practical knowledge and skills using a pragmatic approach. This is a mixed approach to research where you can use different methods.

Which as I often say is always a good thing because it increases the creditability of your findings.

## Spearman's g Factor

Now we're getting onto possibly the most important factor or theory in intelligence because Charles Spearman (1863-1945) conducted a factor analysis and other data-reduction procedures to show that different ability tests were significantly correlated. As well as they were all correlated by a single common variance, this single general factor was called: g.

Additionally, to demonstrate his idea, Spearman first showed that school grades in various courses were positively correlated with each other. Meaning the different mental abilities in each of these courses were related to each other.

## Motivation or g Factor of Intelligence?

However, how do we know intelligence and improved grades are caused by g and not a student's motivation to do well?

It turns out that other research has shown that students' scores on a number of different mental ability tasks were correlated with each other with some tasks having strong g-loadings, whereas others had weaker g-loadings.

Although, these highly g-loaded tasks could have any kind of content.

Furthermore, there are two other principles or concepts related to Spearman's g factors. Including *The principle of the indifference of the indicator.* Meaning highly g-loaded tasks demanded reasoning processes. And The education of relations and correlates.

As a result, Spearman invented the correlation

coefficient and factor analysis to help understand intelligence and these different statistical relationships. Which is whether the Spearman Coefficient comes from.

Thurstone's Primary Factors:

Nevertheless, Louis Thurstone (1887-1955) argued that the g factor doesn't explain the relations between the 3 different types of mental abilities.

Therefore, he proposed that intelligence should be conceptualised at the 'primary' level that is made up of the following seven factors:

- Memory
- Verbal fluency
- Verbal comprehension
- Spatial visualization
- Numerical facility
- Perceptual speed
- Reasoning

G+ Group Factors

On the whole, Thurstone's factors are still related to Spearman's g-factors so some researchers have decided to combine the two models into a single hierarchical model.

This works by having the g factor at the top of the model which represents intelligence as a single mental ability. Then the model shows intelligence can be broken down into Thurstone's 7 primary factors.

Afterwards, there is a final level but then you get into the nitty-gritty of each factor and that's a bit beyond the scope of this book.

Especially, as we have a lot more topics to cover in intelligence. Such as: I wonder how our biology, genetics and environment affect our intelligence?

Some of the answers might surprise you!

## Extra Information on Hierarchical Models:

## Carroll's (1993) Three Stratum Theory

In my notes here, this section looks very complex but I'm going to break it down for you.

Consequently, this theory proposes that there are three levels to intelligence: the Narrow (I), Broad (II) and General (III) levels and each of these levels differ in their degree of generality.

For example, the Broad level is made up of the basic constitutional and long standing characteristics that govern or influence a great variety of behaviours in a given domain. These broad abilities vary in differing degrees of relative emphasis on process, content, and manner of response.

The structure proposed in the CHC theory is empirically supported by mathematical (e.g., factor-analyses) as well as neurocognitive, developmental, and heritability evidence. According to Keith and Reynolds (2010), "... CHC theory offers the best current description of the structure of human intelligence. It is by no means perfect or settled ... but it functions well as a working theory ... or "periodic table" for understanding and classifying cognitive abilities

# BIOLOGICAL BASIS, GENETIC AND ENVIRONMENTAL INFLUENCES ON INTELLIGENCE

The question of what makes someone intelligent will of course be a combination of biological, genetic and environmental factors and the entire point of this chapter will be to look at these different factors. To see what influences intelligence and to what extent.

Also, I know looking at all these different factors can sometimes seem endless and sometimes they might not be the most exciting area of psychology. But there is something extremely clever and even *fun* (perhaps?) about these different factors. Since it is the job of these researchers to take these massive problems and research questions and strip them down into all these little fragments. There is something amazing in that.

So, come on, let' see what these amazing researchers have found!

## Biological Bases of Mental Ability

### Brain Size

Whilst this is the logical first thing people think of because I often hear lay people talk about the size of a smart person's brain and how wonderful it must be, but is it too obvious?

Surprisingly enough, there might be some truth to this assumption because there is a modest positive correlation with the external size of someone's head.

Which I'm pretty surprised by. And I felt as if I should add that the so-called fact that your brain doesn't grow after you're born is a MYTH. You can find out more information in my Biological Psychology book.

Moreover, McDaniel (2005) demonstrated through the use of MRI scans that brain volume shows an average correlation of .33 with intelligence. Therefore, whilst this is not a large correlation there is still a reasonable effect.

Another strand of thinking about the brain and intelligence is that some regions of the brain might be the so-called critical "intelligent" regions. Meaning some regions of the brain are responsible for our intelligence. Yet there is not an overwhelming amount of research supporting this view at the moment.

Furthermore, still thinking along the same wave length of the brain, nerve conduction velocity, or how speed nerve impulses travel, could be a factor in intelligence because this involves the speed of the electrical impulses between cells of the brain and nervous system. As well as this is sort of linked to Galton but he spoke about this in a different way. Yet the research findings to date on this nerve conduction velocity are rather inconsistent currently. Making it difficult to say if this is an actual intelligence factor.

Overall, to wrap the topic of brain size, a lot of people including myself seems to think that this idea has long been refuted by psychologists but the size of a person's brain is being looked at.

Personally, the reason why I was a little surprised by it was because I thought this idea stemmed from Phrenology (Biological Psychology) and this was a very unscientific discipline that tried to link areas of the brain to behaviour. But it had no empirical testing.

Thus, I thought the idea about brain size came from this idea, and this is what I love about psychology because it always proves positive to be questioning assumptions and helping the field to develop.

If you didn't think brain size was important, why did you doubt it?

Reaction Time and Inspection Time

This next idea sort of continues on from the concept of Nerve Conduction Velocity because both reaction time and the conduction velocity involve processing speeds.

Consequently, there is not a positive relationship between intelligence and processing speed, and this shows the complexities of statistics as it took me a moment to work out what this meant.

The correlation between reaction time and mental ability is -0.30 on simple reaction time tasks. Meaning that the speed of the brain and the nervous system is related to the g factor. As well as longer processing speeds are correlated with lower mental ability scores as it takes the person longer to process the information.

In addition, another take on reaction is Inspection time and this is the time you need to present a stimuli to a person for them to notice it. A typical experiment with this method, in short, is when you present people with two vertical lines with one line being shorter than the other. Then the participant needs to say which one is shorter but these lines only appear for a short set time.

Subsequently, over time you shorten the inspection until the person is basically guessing which line is longer. Then that is the person's inspection time.

The idea being a person with high mental abilities will need a shorter inspection time than others because their brains are faster at processing information. As well as this is supported by the research because the correlation between the two is - 0.30 on this very simple task. Showing that mental speed is related to g.

Brain Waves

The penultimate biological basis for mental ability comes from brain waves and this is measured using Electroencephalography (EEG) which measures the electrical activity of the brain using electrodes in relation to a specific stimulus. You can find out more about this research method in Biological Psychology.

Linking brain waves to intelligence, the EEG measures the amplitude, latency and string length of the brain waves as parameters. With the logic behind this basis, with the research supporting it, being that people who are high in IQ have more overall complexity to their brain waves compared to lower

IQ people.

## Brain Glucose Metabolism

Finally, the last biological basis I do like because it looks at the amount of sugar (glucose) our brains use and this is a very interesting idea.

We measure a person's metabolism using Positron Emission Tomography (PET) and this involves injecting a small amount of radioactive glucose to measure the amount of glucose being metabolized in the brain.

In addition, this relates to a person's intelligence because higher IQ scoring people tend to use less glucose in their brains during IQ tasks. Meaning their brain is more efficient than lower IQ scoring people.

I think the reason why I like this idea is because it shows that people higher in IQ have to think less or their brains don't have to work as hard as others. Meaning when people throw this idea about in conversation it's actually true to some extent.

## Genetic and Environmental Influences on Mental ability

Moving onto the last few sections of this chapter on how genetics and the environment influences our intelligence. We're now going to be

looking at genetics and some very interesting
environmental factors that might help us to explain
intelligence.

## Genetic Influences

From a previous chapter, we know
about "behavioural genetics" because both siblings
and twins are great sources of information that allow
researchers to estimate genetic effects and the effects
of shared and unique environments on different
behaviours. (In this instance personality) As well
as identical or monozygotic (MZ) twins share 100%
of their genetic material compared to only 50%
in fraternal or dizygotic (DZ) twins.

Another way to study Behavioural genetics is
to examine twins or siblings that are raised together
and apart. (adoption)

Due to there are a lot of different effects this
can have on behaviour and we'll look at some of these
throughout the book. But there are differences tye
heritability results for both children and adults.

For example, children raised together have a
behavioural heritability of .40 but thus drops slightly
to 0.35 for children raised apart.

Whereas in adulthood, the heritability for
adults that were raised together as children is 0.65 but
for the adults raised apart as children this changes
immensely to only an heritability of 0.20.

Therefore, the family context becomes less important as a person grows up as well as the extent that genes are influential changes too. Since identical twins should be more alike than fraternal twins.

Additionally, if the shared environment is influential, then siblings raised in the same family should be more similar than adopted away siblings, as this would mean they would have been raised apart.

## Womb Environment

Personally, I think this is a great idea and something that's extremely interesting to research because part of the "genetic" influence may not be genetic.

As a result of the first environmental influence on traits and mental abilities is the influence of the womb environment. Then this affects the infant's exposure to hormones, toxins and nutrients amongst other factors too.

The interesting thing about this area of research is that a number of studies have compared fraternal twins that share the womb environment with nontwins. With the age difference being statistically controlled in these studies.

As seen as in Devlin et al (1997) who looked at pairs of siblings against pairs of parents and child. Because you can still estimate the heritability from parents and their children.

Devlin et al. (1997) concluded that the heritability of mental abilities has been overestimated in twin studies.

Furthermore, according to Jacobs et al (2001), another aspect to consider when examining womb environments is the role of chorion type. This is one of the two membranes surrounding the Fetus. Two-thirds of the identical twins have the same chorion, 1/3 their own levels of hormones and nutrients. This might help to explain the differences between these groups of twins. As well as for some aspects of mental ability monochorionic MZ twins were somewhat more similar than dichorionic MZ twins.

## Nutrition

Typically, I tend to think about the topic of Nutrition in Developmental Psychology but as personality psychology is a weird combination of all these areas, I suppose it's only right to talk about Nutrition and Intelligence.

Consequently, lead poisoning, Fetal alcohol poisoning as well as severe malnutrition can all lead to a child to have a lower IQ than other children.

However, when it comes to breastfeeding, there are some interesting results. Since children who are breastfed have higher IQ scores, and in Mortensen et al (2002), this difference was as high as 9 whole IQ points.

Yet as you can probably imagine there is a problem here, a causality problem. Since Der et al (2006) found no differences between breastfed children and their non-breastfed siblings. Thus, suggesting that breastfeeding doesn't lead to higher IQ.

Could there be a cognitive cost or drawback of being a twin because both Fetuses have to share nutrients in the womb?

That's one possible explanation but there are a lot of inconsistent findings in this area. With one study showing a difference of 5 IQ points between the children (Ronalds et al., 2005) whilst more recent findings show no differences (Calvin et al., 2009)

The last two facts that link nutrition to intelligence are the child's Folate levels are weakly positively related to IQ in childhood and in old age. As well as having low Vitamin B12 is weakly related to relative cognitive decline.

In other words, please make sure your diet is okay and healthy!

Birth Order

I definitely think is a strange but surprising area of research because there is a consistent small link between birth order and mental ability. But what causes it? Biological or social influences? Is there a better womb environment for the first-born child? Or could the first-born child get undivided attention and more intellectual stimulation than other siblings? Making it more about social rank rather than birth order in a way.

To investigate this, Kristensen and Bjerkedal (2007) investigated data of 240,000 men and other second-born men that were raised as the eldest due to an unfortunately early loss of an older sibling.

Their results showed that the second-born men that were raised as the eldest scored equal to first-born men and third-borns who had moved into second place in the family had average IQ scores like second-borns, an average of 1 IQ point higher. As well as the second-born men whose older sibling had not died scored about 3 IQ points lower than first-born men.

Overall, this study is meant to show definitively that the family environment and expectations account for the intelligence boost. Leading the researchers to conclude that the findings support the social hypothesis of birth order effect.

# MENTAL ABILITY AND LIFE OUTCOMES

After looking at what influences intelligence, we have to look at how does intelligence affect our life outcomes. And whilst we will come back to the topic of personality and life outcomes as the final section of the book, I love that last section!

In this chapter, we'll focus on how our mental abilities can impact our life outcomes.

## Academic Performance

Of course, it should come as no surprise that we'll look at academic performance first as this is the most common outcome people think of when it comes to intelligence.

As a result, IQ scores are strongly correlated with school grades because there's 0.5- 0.6 correlation between intelligence and grades for elementary school children. But the reason why this isn't high, it's still massive, is because school grades also depend on the student's motivation, participation as well as teacher's perceptions of the student's attitude and effort.

Leading to an underestimation of the link between IQ and academic achievement.

Also, I should remind you that IQ is a measure of intelligence, not intelligence itself.

Resulting in some people asking is there a link between IQ and the testing of academic achievement?

Of course, there's some, at least one group of researchers who have researched it so Deary, Strand, Smith, and Fernandes (2007) conducted a 5-year prospective, longitudinal study on 70,000+ English children and they ran the correlation between $g$ at age 11 and academic achievement in 25 subjects at age 16. The results showed that having high levels of mental ability is an important advantage in doing well in schoolwork.

Nevertheless, if we back track a little bit to when I pointed out that IQ is not intelligence, this leads us onto another question. Since is there a difference between IQ tests and tests of academic achievement?

Due to IQ tests are focused on problem solving and information of a general nature yet it doesn't focus on specific skills from the school curriculum in any country. But still both of these tests involve working with numbers and words.

Consequently, it turns out that there are high correlations between IQ and academic performance tests in maths and English but these correlations are high across all subject areas.

Furthermore, non-verbal IQ tests (spatial or picture arrangement) showed high correlations with achievement.

In terms of the different stages of school life, the correlations between IQ tests and academic tests do weaken over time, but they're still strong. For example, the correlation between the two tests in secondary or high school is .50 and this drops to 0.40 when students are at university or college.

Although, another interesting factor is a person's IQ in primary or elementary school is strongly related to whether or not they turn out to be a high school drop-out.

## Job Performance, Occupational Status and Income

A number of personality traits are involved in having high job performance. For example, being disciplined, honesty, trustworthy, organised and diligent.

But how does mental ability affect your job

performance and similar aspects?

There are few reports even trying to research this area because how do you measure job performance objectively?

You could use a Personality Index, Self-reports or supervisor's reports which are basically the same as observer reports. But as we'll already seen in this book, they all have their own problems.

As a result, Hunter& Hunter (1984) decided to conduct a meta-analysis using hundreds of studies and this gave the researchers a research sample of thousands of workers.

The meta-analysis found smart workers tend to be better and there are correlations between job Performance, occupational status, and income.

For instance, the correlation between mental ability and occupational status is very large at 0.50 as well as the correlation between mental ability and income is large at 0.40.

Yet could this all be down to social class and not mental ability?

As socioeconomic status (SES) relates to education, this allows people to get potentially better jobs. Giving the person an educational and environmental advantage or advantages in the workplace.

Overall, there are correlations that say there are relationships between socioeconomic status and IQ and whilst these correlations are somewhat weaker than the others we've looked at. There are still moderately strong tendencies for smarter people to gain higher-status jobs and income (about .40) after controlling for socioeconomic status.

I think this just goes to highlight the importance of helping people with lower socioeconomic backgrounds so they can improve their education and hopefully play on a level playing field with people with higher socioeconomic backgrounds in the job market. This is especially important as we come towards the end of the COVID-19 pandemic.

## Longevity and Health

This is a major focus in psychology because we all want to live longer and everyone is looking for some tips to help them live longer. Even if we don't realise we want some of these tips.

Therefore, is a link between living longer and mental ability as shown in a few studies. For example, Whalley and Deary (2001) studied the relationship between IQ and survival by gathering data from a Scottish mental survey conducted in 1932, 2,792 Scottish children from Aberdeen and they searched the Register of Deaths from 1932 to 1997.

So as you can see the researchers were very thorough in making sure they had a lot of data to support their conclusions with.

In addition, the study found that the children with the higher IQs did tend to live longer than the children with lower IQs. But this raises the questions of Why do children with higher IQs tend to live longer than children with lower IQs?

Some of the main reasons behind this finding is a lower IQ at age 11 might reflect an "archaeological record" of prior health-related problems during their childhood or before birth. Or it could reflect a record of their bodily system integrity. This means that the child's body and brain might not be functioning very well.

Additionally, it could reflect a predictor of unhealthy behaviours that contribute to their earlier deaths. Such as, unhealthy eating behaviours, smoking, obesity, alcoholism, lack of exercise and so on. Also, it could predictor a child's inability to understand health information and health risks.

A final reason why the finding could be the lower IQ could be a predictor of the likelihood of the child going to enter an unhealthy environment. For example, a stressful occupation.

Moreover, in a later study, Deary, Whalley,

and Starr (2003) found that people with low childhood intelligence were more likely to die from lung and stomach cancer, and this could be linked to childhood social privation and unhealthy behaviour, like smoking. (Deary, Whalley, & Starr, 2003; Deary, Whiteman, Starr, Whalley, & Fox, 2004)

## Marriage: Assortative Mating

Before we wrap up this chapter with the amazing topic of criminality, we need to look at Marriage and how it links to intelligence.

Since this outcome looks at the relationship of similarity between spouses' mental ability both in intelligence and verbal ability (vocabulary) and the reason why this is important is because generally speaking people with higher IQs tend to have more varied and interesting vocabulary than those with lower IQs.

As well as in terms of relationships, research has found that there is a relationship between spouses and their verbal ability. Suggesting a possible link saying their intelligence levels could be similar. It is possible that this would give the couple more rewarding conversations. But that's more of an idea at this stage.

Another research finding has been there is a very weak correlation between the different spouses' mathematical reasoning ability but this is less important for the quality of the relationship.

Personally, none of this research has really surprised me because I think it's logical to assume that spouses would be about the same intelligence. Yet this doesn't apply to all areas of personality!

Criminality

I'll be the first to point out in Forensic Psychology the overall link between intelligence and crime is very small and I will reflect that a little bit in this section. And whilst there are some relations between IQ and crime, there are plenty of other reasons why people commit crimes. But I wanted to make it clear from the start in case there's a person why reads this and strongly believes low intelligence is why people commit crimes. For more information on this topic, please read Forensic Psychology.

Moving onto the topic, who is more likely to commit crimes? A person with low or high levels of intelligence?

It turns out there are some clear associations between crime and IQs but the main problem with this research is, do the people who commit the crimes have lower IQs or do the people who are caught for committing crimes have lower IQs?

One possible answer is from Moffit & Silva

(1988) who conducted a study by comparing three groups of young people. The first group was made up of delinquents who had been in contact with the police, the second group was made up of delinquents who had avoided contact with the police as well as the third and final group was made up of youths who had had no contact with the police and they had no delinquency.

The study found that group 3 scored higher on an intelligence test than groups 1 and 2 and between these two groups there were no differences in their scores. Hence, showing the link between lower IQ and criminality.

Moreover, there is some indication that when people with high IQs commit crimes the payoff is higher and the probability of getting arrested is lower, and "white-collar" crimes are extremely more likely to be committed by people with high IQs, because you first need to achieve a higher position to be able to commit those crimes.

On the whole, I wanted to wrap up this section and chapter by saying intelligence does have a lot of different and important impacts on the life outcomes of people. We will return to life outcomes and personality later in the book but hopefully you're more aware of how intelligence can impact our life outcomes.

However, if we return to think about criminality for a moment, I know the first study we looked at makes it seem like intelligence IS linked to criminality, but I really want to stress that it isn't. There are tens of other amazing and extremely interesting reasons for why people commit crimes. And I love Forensic Psychology so if you want to learn more, I cannot recommend reading about this area enough.

# DEVELOPMENTAL CHANGES AND STABILITY IN INTELLIGENCE

After having quite a few long chapters in the book, I thought I would break down the topic of intelligence into some smaller chapters.

Therefore, the aim of this chapter is to look at the developmental changes in a person in their mean levels of intelligence. Since we can probably guess from our own observations and ourselves that there are rapid changes in the different stages of the human lifespan.

In addition, research supports this thinking because there are a number of developmental changes in our mean levels of intelligence and for the purposes of this chapter, we're talking about the absolute levels of g.

In terms of development, a person's g or intelligence rapidly increases during their childhood and this rapid increase continues into late adolescence but a person's level of g decreases during old age.

None of these results are surprising because childhood through to late adolescence is the normal age of schooling in most countries. (And yes I know that other factors are involved in this increase) But it still doesn't answer the question of what happens in between the early and later stages of life?

To answer the question Wisdom, Mignogna, & Collins (2012) measured the differences between older adults and young adults in their scores in subtests. The results showed the levels of verbal abilities were somewhat higher for people in their 40s to 60s. Whereas the spatial ability and perceptual speeds were highest for young adults. Suggesting that some types of intelligence increase but others decrease over time.

Although, there are problems with this research because the results do possibly reflect "cohort" effects where the results are unique to this group of people and this area suffers from a lack of longitudinal research.

Meaning the overall problem of the study is that the researchers didn't use people born in different decades and they didn't measure people's intelligence over a period of time.

## Stability of Intelligence Across the Life Span:

Whilst the last section was investigating how development influences our intelligence over time, the stability of our intelligence looks at: Are individual differences in mental abilities stable across the life span despite mean level changes?

With this question looking at the relative change or stability across the life span when compared to others.

On the whole, the evidence is very clear and there does seem to have great stability of intelligence over time and a very powerful study that looks at this is Deary, Whiteman, Starr, Whalley, and Fox (2004) that administered intelligence tests to over 500 Scottish adults aged 79 or 80 but these elderly adults had completed the Stanford-Binet intelligence test 70 years earlier at aged 11.

The intelligence tests used were the Morray House Test (MHT) which is a general mental ability test showing high convergent validity with Raven's standard progressive matrices test.

Moreover, the results of the study showed that the 79- and 80-year-old participants scored on average one standard deviation higher than what they scored at age 11. Suggesting that the increase in intelligence over this time was more powerful than any decrease in their intelligence due to ageing.

Additionally, despite this increase in their intelligence overall when we look at the differences between individuals there is very high stability over their lifespan with a correlation of 0.65. And considering most correlations in human behaviour are between 0.3 to 0.6. (Source: Biological Psychology) This is massive!

In other words, the smartest 79- and 80-year-olds tended to be the smartest 11-year-olds too.

Personally, I really liked this chapter because I always think it's great to see how our behaviour can change over time. Also, I think it's good to know that if you're smart when you're young you can still be smart when you're old and you aren't doomed like all the ageist stereotypes predict.

# FLUID INTELLIGENCE, CRYSTAL INTELLIGENCE AND THE FLYNN EFFECT

## Theory Of Fluid and Crystallized Intelligence

This rather interesting theory was proposed by Raymond Cattell (1905-1998) by conducting factor analyses on the structure of and the relationship between different types of ability tests. His results found that there were 2 factors,

The first factor he found was Fluid intelligence ($Gf$) and this is the ability to learn new things and solve new problems. Regardless of the previous knowledge we have from other tasks.

For example, this type of intelligence involves tasks that measure a culture-free element of cognitive performance that require a flexible response. Such as our reasoning ability because when we encounter a new situation and we need to find the answer. We have to reason what the answer is likely to be.

The second type of factor he found was

Crystallized intelligence (*Gc*). Meaning our ability to do well on tasks that require us to have previous knowledge and this is dependent on experience and education within a culture.

In other words, we use crystallised intelligence on tasks that require us to use well-learned skills. For example, when we write essays or do psychology coursework assignments, we're using crystalised intelligence because the task relies on information we've already learnt.

Furthermore, in this section of the book so far, we've only talked about people's general intelligence. But this focus does neglect the possibility that some mental ability tasks may be differentially related to other variables.

This is where a PhD student of Spearman's comes in called: Catell because he discovered and found out more information about these different types of intelligence. Since he proposed that our Fluid abilities (Gf) drive a person's ability to think and act quickly, solve new problems as well as these abilities help us to encode our short-term memories.

Moreover, these Fluid abilities have been described as the source of intelligence that a person uses when they don't already know what to do. With Fluid intelligence being based on our biological efficiency. Resulting in the Fluid abilities being mostly independent of our education and acculturation. (Horn, 1967).

Whereas for the other factor, Crystallised

abilities, these stem from what a person has learnt both through their education and through their culture. (Acculturation) As well as this can be tested in a number of ways. For instance, in tests on knowledge, general knowledge, a person's vocabulary and a wide variety of acquired skills (Horn & Cattell, 1967).

To add a few more examples, you could test these Crystalised abilities by looking at how well a person does in exams (knowledge), quizzes (general knowledge) and other common tests from everyday life.

Linking this to personality, our crystalised abilities develop because our personality factors, motivation as well as educational and cultural opportunities are central to its development. With biological and genetic influences only having an indirect effect on them.

The Flynn Effect

When I first learnt about this effect I was very impressed and very interested.

Therefore, this effect found that people today score substantially higher on intelligence tests than people did a few generations ago. Resulting in generational increases in IQ scores across different nations.

For instance, 18-year-olds in 2000 scored on average 1 Standard Deviation higher, the equivalent of 15 IQ points, compared to 18-year-olds in 1950 when both groups took the same test.

Now, the extremely interesting thing is that if we scored people over 100 years old against our modern norms. These people would have scored 70 IQ points and by our modern standards that's the threshold for Mental Retardation.

Meaning over the past 100 years, we've experienced a MASSIVE increase in our IQ scores and by extension our intelligence.

However, these increases in intelligence are stronger for fluid intelligence than for crystallized intelligence.

Education and Test Familiarity

But why does the Flynn Effect happen?

There are a number of interesting reasons for why this might happen but no one is certain for sure. Yet education and improving education over the last century will have had an impact and should mainly influence people's verbal tests and crystallized intelligence. Possibly leading to the Flynn effect.

Another reason could be nutrition because the types and amounts of food available to us has increased over the past 50 years. (Health Psychology) And as I discuss and examine in Developmental Psychology, good nutrition is important for child development. But this can't account for all of the Flynn Effect.

The last possible reason for the effect could

be societal change because there's been an increase in technological changes as well as number of cultural changes. For example, compared to 100 years, or even 50 years, ago there's a lot more cognitively complex and more visual technology around us. For example, the internet and TV. Allowing us to learn more information.

Another subarea of this reason is parenting because parents can create more stimulating environments for their children to grow and develop in.

As well as humans are forming new habits in their minds as we train and use our brains differently than before.

Overall, the cause of the Flynn Effect is unclear and multiple factors play a role. But what I'm very interested in is to see what will people be like in 100, 200 or even 500 years' time. Will the Flynn Effect still be happening? Will humanity reach a ceiling of their IQ scores?

I don't know but it would be interesting to think about.

# ALTERNATIVE THEORIES OF INTELLIGENCE

## Alternative Theories about Mental Abilities

These last two chapters on intelligence are definitely worth a read because we're now going to look at other ideas that explain intelligence. Due to in this section of the book, we've mainly been focusing on g as the explanation of intelligence. But there are other ideas that are at least worth considering!

## Gardner's Theory of Multiple Intelligences

This theory proposes that there are 8 distinct types of intelligence compared to different levels of other theories. As well as in this theory, there is no common variable of the g factor.

In addition, these 8 types of intelligence are:

- Linguistic

- Spatial
- Musical
- Logical- mathematics
- Interpersonal- a person's ability to understand social situations.
- Intrapersonal- how well a person can understand their own feelings, thoughts and behaviour.
- Bodily- kinetic- this is related to a person's motor coordination.
- Naturalistic- the ability to classify elements in the natural world.

The logic behind this theory is that everyone can recognise their own unique strengths and weaknesses. Meaning there are different types of intelligence making up these strengths and weaknesses.

In terms of research and the purely theoretical side, not all of these distinct types are purely mental abilities. As well as no statistical factor analysis were used.

In my opinion, I can understand where the theory is coming from because if we use this as a checklist. I can easily identify my weaknesses (naturalistic, interpersonal and musical) so I can understand that these could be classed as intelligence. But I feel like these are skills more than a type of intelligence.

However, empirical studies largely contradict Gardner's theory.

## Sternberg's Triarchic Theory of Intelligence

The second alternative theory of intelligence we'll look at is by Sternberg and you might recognise him from Psychology of Relationships since he did another triangular based theory. I do enjoy his use of triangles!

As a result, he proposed that mental ability is made up of three types of intelligence.

Firstly, you have the analytical intelligence where includes academic abilities with this typically being measured by intelligence test as well as logical and critical thinking. Skills used in analytical intelligence includes comparing, contrasting things, evaluating and being good at information processing. People high in this type of intelligence tend to have good academic performance.

Secondly, you have creative intelligence, this is related to formulating new ideas and gaining original insights, and this uses skills like discovering, exploring and imagining. With people high in this ability tending to have good artistic performance.

Finally, you have practical intelligence which has been academically termed "street smarts" because this is to do with problem-solving in everyday life. Also, people high in practical intelligence tend to have a lot of real world success.

Additionally, Sternberg et al (2000) wanted to investigate practical intelligence in more depth by looking at how success is affected by 'knowing the unwritten rules or tacit knowledge of how to succeed within an organization.'

Leading the researchers to compare participant's answers with the answers of "successful" experts.

They found a higher match between the answers is related to better job performance, but still correlated with $g$.

Resulting Koke and Vernon (2003) to conclude that these 3 aspects are not independent from one another as they're all correlated with each other and correlated with general intelligent test scores. Meaning this is not some special theory that existed independently from the g factor.

Although, I do not believe we should discount this model because I strongly believe psychology could use it to build on or examine the g factor model in more depth. As this model looks at areas that the g factor model only touches on briefly.

# EMOTIONAL INTELLIGENCE

I've often heard of this term but as it was a part of pop psychology, I tended to stay far away from this topic. Since pop psychology is mostly false and this topic is no different to some extent.

Therefore, emotional intelligence was a very popular idea in the 1990s and of course, it was popularised by amazing best-selling books, tv, radio and the news. Which all suggested that emotional intelligence is more important than traditional intelligence.

And the reason why I'm rather critical in this chapter is because if you ever read my Criminal Profiling book, you tend to find that if something in psychology is hyped by the media and great books. It's probably wrong.

Sorry but that's the truth.

Moreover, Goleman (1995) defined emotional

intelligence as the ability to regulate one's emotions through the "journalistic account".

Also, emotional intelligence has been defined as having an amazing ability to have great self-control, empathy, self-confidence, trustworthiness, optimism, being achievement orientated, being great at conflict management, teamwork skills as well as a very good awareness of your own emotions.

The main problem with that definition is it's extremely broad and unclear so it doesn't really help to explain what makes up emotional intelligence.

Also, another problem is this requires us to have a very good awareness of our emotions but Cognitive Psychology shows that we don't always understand our emotions or affective states. So this is naturally very difficult.

## Four Branch Model of Emotional Intelligence

As a result to explain Emotional Intelligence better, Mayer & Salovey (1993; 1997) and Mayer, Salovey, & Caruso (2008) proposed the Four Branch Model to explain this type of intelligence in more depth.

Firstly, you have managing emotions because a person with good emotional intelligence is good at regulating their own emotions and enabling both intellectual and emotional growth.

Secondly, having good emotional intelligence

allows a person to understand emotions and emotional information, language, and other signals conveyed by emotions.

Still a little broad?

Thirdly, good emotional intelligence means a person has a good ability to use their emotions to facilitate thinking and generating the emotions that are advantageous for thought.

The final branch is good emotional intelligence allows a person to perceive their own emotions accurately in themselves and others.

Personally, there is a lot I want to say about these four branches and their problems with how they contradict modern Cognitive and Social Psychology research. But I think it's best if we continue on.

## Debate and Controversy

After my opinions on this type of intelligence, I'm sure some of you are questioning if emotional intelligence is entirely right.

So, it might not be surprising that lots of psychologists agree because emotional intelligence does raise some important questions that we'll look at later on. Like:

- Does it actually exist? And are the individual differences stable?

- Can emotional intelligence be measured? If so, is it reliable?
- Is it important? And does it show predictive validity?
- Is emotional intelligence an ability? And is it related to IQ rather than personality?
- Equally, is it more important than IQ? Also, does it have incremental validity?

## How to Measure Emotional Intelligence?

As psychology is a science, if emotional intelligence is a real construct then we need to know how to measure it. And there has been a few scales and measurement tools proposed to measure this type of intelligence.

But we first need to backtrack a little bit because emotional intelligence isn't one construct because it can be broken down into Trait Emotional Intelligence (TEI) and Ability Emotional Intelligence (AEI).

## Trait Emotional Intelligence:

With Trait emotional intelligence being related to emotion-related self-perceptions and dispositions. As well as this can be measured with self-report questionnaires because this is all to do with a person's self-perceived use of their emotional abilities.

One example of these self-reported

questionnaires is the Trait Meta-Mood Scale (TMMS) by Salovey, Mayer, Goldman, Turvey, & Palfai (1995) and the scale is divided up into different sections with different statements as seen below:

1)  Attention to Feelings

*"I don't pay much attention to my feelings"*

*"I think about my mood constantly"*

*"One should never be guided by emotions"*

2) Clarity of Feelings

*"I am usually very clear about my feelings"*

*"I am often aware of my feeling on a matter"*

*"I can't make sense out of my feelings"*

3) Mood Repair

*"When I become upset I remind myself of all the pleasures in life"*

*"Although I am sometimes sad, I have mostly optimistic outlook"*

*"No matter how badly I feel, I try to think about pleasant things*

## Ability Emotional Intelligence:

Whereas Ability emotional intelligence is a set of abilities related to the processing of emotional information that supports the adaptive use of emotions. In other words, cognitive processes. Also, you can test this using the Maximal performance test as this measures a person's ability to perform emotional problem-solving tasks.

One of these tests is called the Mayer-Salovey-Caruso Emotional Intelligence Test (MSCEIT) and this test uses two different tests for each of the four branches of Emotional Intelligence. Like to test how well a person can perceive emotions the test gets the person to identify the emotions shown in pictures of faces.

I have to admit I do quite like this test because it uses multiple tests on each branch. Hence, this would increase the reliability and creditability of the findings of the test, which is always good.

And this is a sample question with answers that are used to help measure a person's understanding of emotions.

*What feeling, when intensified and coupled with a sense of injustice, is most likely to lead a person to experience anger?*

*a) frustration*

*b) guilt*

*c) melancholy*

*d) fatigue*

Although, I must comment that this question sounds like it's built upon the Frustration Aggression Hypothesis that proposes that frustration leads to aggression. But as I talk about in Social Psychology this hypothesis isn't entirely correct and it has been reworked. Therefore, I am sceptical of the psychological validity of this question.

## Associations with the Big Five and Mental Ability

Now we understand what Emotional Intelligence is, how does it link to personality and the Big Five?

In terms of Trait Emotional Intelligence, there is a strong relationship between this trait and other socially desirable personality traits. As well as Trait Emotional Intelligence is negatively related to neuroticism and positively related to Extroversion and Conscientiousness.

However, Trait Emotional Intelligence is unrelated to grade point average and test scores. In other words, academic performance. (Brackett & Mayer, 2003; Newsome, Day, & Catano, 2000)

On the other hand, Ability Emotional Intelligence did have modest positive correlations with Agreeableness and Openness as well as verbal-based tests of mental ability.

Emotional Intelligence Conclusion:

Overall, after looking at Emotional Intelligence, I wanted to wrap this up by saying from the different scales it turns out there might be something to Emotional Intelligence. But I'm saying this because psychology still isn't sure if Emotional Intelligence is separate and unique to Traditional Intelligence.

However, it turns out that Emotional Intelligence is related to psychological health, well-being and satisfaction.

Additionally, another reason why I said there might be something to Emotional Intelligence is it turns out Emotional Intelligence-scales measure well-known personality traits particularly associated with psychological health. Thus, Emotional Intelligence isn't measuring any thing unique or traits we didn't already know about.

Then again, people with high Emotional Intelligence do tend to have better social relationships for children and adults, have better family and intimate relationships, this applies at work too and they are more positively perceived by others. And all of this is because these people tend to have better social and emotional skills than others.

Nevertheless, the main reason why Emotional Intelligence isn't unique or better than traditional intelligence is because whilst people high in Emotional Intelligence did have better academic achievement as reported by teachers. This was not related to grades or academic achievement once IQ is taken into account.

On the whole, there is not enough evidence to support all the theoretical claims about how bright Emotional Intelligence is.

I will admit Emotional Intelligence is not as bad as I initially thought but it is still far from this brilliant intelligence that you must have over traditional intelligence. And would I go out and buy a book on Emotional Intelligence to try and increase it?

No.

# PART FOUR:
# RELIGIOSITY AND
# POLITICAL ATTITUDES IN
# PERSONALITY PSYCHOLOGY

# INTRODUCTION TO RELIGIOSITY IN PERSONALITY AND RELIGIOSITY AND PERSONALITY DIMENSIONS

This section of the book will focus on a person's level of religiosity because in people's lives this brings them a lot of joy and passion but in other people's lives this can bring them a lot of conflict. Therefore, it's important that we look at this topic to understand how personality can influence this behaviour.

## A Personal Note:

I've been debating this chapter or section of the book for quite a while now and I realised I've been putting off writing it for a few reasons. But before I explain those reasons quickly, I need to say upfront I have no problem with religion and I strongly believe anti-religious attacks be it antisemitic or Islamophobic or any other type of hate crime is simply wrong and outrageous.

As a result, I wanted to write this section first and foremost in case, I come across as bias or slightly anti-religious. I am not. And if this section of this book seems a little sparse of my thoughts and opinions, it's because I don't want to offend anyone.

However, the reason why I've avoided writing this section is because I am not religious myself.

Also, when I learnt about this topic, it was the day that my Great Uncle died so I suppose there is a link between this subject and his tragic death.

## Introduction to Religiosity:

Religiosity is driven by situational factors. For example, religious socialisation, negative life events as well as positive self-transcendent experiences.

Although, religiosity is also manifested in a lot of different behaviours. Like praying, reading and attending services, and all these behaviours involve a wide range of thoughts, feelings and behaviours.

Nevertheless, it does raise the question of is religiosity a personality trait?

## Is Religiosity a Personality Characteristic?

The short answer is no because unlike personality traits, the differences that exist between different people's levels of religiosity depend on people's *beliefs,* whereas personality traits do not

14

depend on beliefs.

Due to religiosity is about the following:

- Believing
- Bonding
- Behaving
- Belonging

But different people have different motivations for their religiosity as well. Some seek community, some seek *miracles*, others seek guidance and so on.

Furthermore, there are two types of religiosity and they are "intrinsic religiosity" and "extrinsic religiosity" but for the purposes of this section we will be focusing on intrinsic religiosity.

## How is Religiosity related to the Big Five dimensions?

Linking this personality, some research has looked into this area with some interesting results. For example, Saroglou conducted a meta-analysis of 71 studies looking at people's personal religiosity. These are a person's beliefs and practices referring to a transcendent being and the extent to which these beliefs are legitimized by an established tradition or group. Such as a church or cult.

Generally speaking, when it comes to religiosity, personality has weak associations with it because it seems that the two main personality characteristics of religiousness are Agreeableness with a correlation of .19 as well as Conscientiousness at .16.

But this still doesn't explain if people high in Agreeableness and Conscientiousness are more attracted to religion or does religion make people high in Agreeableness and Conscientiousness?

According to a longitudinal study by Wink et al. (2007) that measured the personality of people during adolescence, they found that personality at this time period did predict religiosity in late adulthood.

Due to people high in Agreeableness preferred social harmony, positive qualities in their relationships with others, and the idea of a protective and loving God. As well as people high in Conscientiousness prefer to have meaningfulness of their life and the world, have a belief that there is an order in the universe through a sense of transcendence, and disciplined pursuit of valued goals.

## Religious Fundamentalism and Spirituality:

This is another major topic in religion research because fundamentalism has a massive impact on society and it can have some interesting, but tragic, effects on behaviour but that's from my own reading on this topic, and not part of this book.

Anyway, Saroglou (2010) also investigated religious fundamentalism and spirituality and how this impacts behaviour.

Therefore, religious fundamentalism is where the person has a strict obedience and unquestioning devotion to the religious figure (I'm trying to keep it open) as well as these people have authoritarian and dogmatic religious attitudes, beliefs, and practices.

Thus, it should come as no surprise that this is negatively related to Openness to Experience.

On the other end of the religious spectrum, you have spiritualism which is an emphasis on a person's individual experience, this often involves intense feeling, and this is independent of religious traditions and beliefs. So, this is positively related to openness to experience.

This is because people with high levels of Openness to Experience are inquisitive and unconventional. Making them question religious traditions, practices and rules. Also, these people are imaginative and feel connected to nature as well. Leading them to seek spirituality.

I'm not sure that I'm personally a spiritualist but I am high in Openness to Experience because I'm very unconventional and I do question a lot of traditional things.

In addition, spirituality is partially related to religiosity because both constructs do refer to transcendence.

Nonetheless, spirituality, in contemporary or modern secular societies, is distinct from religiosity because of its emphasis on the individual experience and being independent from established religious traditions and beliefs.

## Fundamentalism and Personality:

Building upon what we're already learnt about fundamentalism, we already know that this is characterized by authoritarian and dogmatic religious attitudes, beliefs, and practices. Also, the religiosity levels of the household, parents and family a person grows up in strongly correlates to the individual differences in religiosity.

Consequently, personality traits and different variables might affect this association for some very interesting reasons. As seen in McCullough, Tsang, and Brion (2003) who measured the Emotional Stability (Neuroticism) in a sample of intelligent children from 1922-23 and then the study did a follow-up in 1940-41.

The results of the study showed there was a

weaker association for children who are more confident, emotionally stable and optimistic compared to children who are described as moody, pessimistic, insecure amongst other personality variables.

The researchers believed this is the case because the emotionally unstable children might not have wanted to cause conflict between themselves and their parents or family.

Another answer might come from a perceptual change because if we view Neuroticism as both an affective and perceptual trait. Then it becomes clear that Neuroticism colours people's perceptions of negative interpersonal events in a way that they're perceived as more severe. As a result, negative life events appear to produce more negative emotional reactions among people high in Neuroticism (Gunthert, Cohen, & Armeli, 1999; Larsen & Ketelaar, 1991) than among those who are lower in Neuroticism.

Due to conflict between the child and parents can be stressful for many adolescents. Therefore, children that are particularly prone to emotional instability may experience these conflicts with their parents as more difficult with them having them coping worse.

Consequently, by the child developing a level

of personal religiousness that is consistent or similar to the level the child was raised in and having the same level as their family and parents. This could be one method for the relatively emotionally unstable adolescent to foster harmony with their parents and as a result conserve their emotional well-being.

Whereas emotionally stable adolescents might find that their affective well-being is less affected by conflicts with their parents regarding religious issues. Meaning this might allow them to choose a level of personal religiousness that is less dependent on the religious value systems of their parents.

Personally, I do understand because I am rather emotionally stable so my happiness does not depend on religion in the slightest and whilst one of my parents is slightly religious. I don't particularly care about what this family member thinks of my religious views.

Furthermore, another simple way to explain all this and doesn't require us to make assumptions about possible family conflict is that children that are low in emotional Stability might use religion and the structure it provides to foster harmony within themselves. For instance, it gives them a set of tools to use to help them cope with stressful life events or it allows them to mitigate the effects of their own affective instability.

## Religiosity and Personality Dimensions

To wrap up this chapter, there's one more study I want to examine because Altemeyer and Hunsberger (1997) conducted interviews with "Amazing Apostates". These are very non-religious people raised in a very religious household and "Amazing Believers". These are very religious people raised in a very non-religious household.

The results of the study found that these Apostates made for very good students as well as their conversion happened after a period of reason and reflection and experiencing increasing doubts about their religion.

In addition, the Believers were driven by their passion and emotion. Suggesting a strong need for a sense of community and structure with their conversion to religion being sudden followed after a time of intense personal crisis.

Consequently, I wasn't going to do a personal wrap up because I am trying to keep my opinions out of this section but I wanted to mention my personal support for these results. Since when I was in primary or elementary school I was religious because schools doctrine young people into religion. (Sorry that's the truth) But when I got to secondary or High School I started to learn about science and how the world worked, and my religious beliefs went straight out the window.

# CHANGE AND STABILITY OF RELIGIOSITY AND RELIGIOSITY AND LIFE OUTCOMES

To conclude this section of the book on religiosity, we need to look at how a person's level of personality changes and the stability of it over time. Then we need to explore the life outcomes that are related to religiosity since it can have benefits for us.

## Change and Stability in Religiosity:

The real question of this section looks at how do individual levels of religiosity change across the human lifespan?

Thankfully, McCullough et al (2005) can help us to answer this question because the researchers followed a sample of intelligent children from 1940 to 1991. Then the researchers compared the levels of religiosity in 1940 with the levels in 1991. But different patterns were detected in the results.

The first three patterns in the results were 19% of the children experienced High or increasing levels of religiosity.

Another pattern was 41% experienced Low or decreasing levels of religiosity over time.

Finally, the last pattern was 40% of the children experienced Parabolic levels of religiosity.

Parabolic in simple terms means a u shape. To explain this in this context, (But please note these are not the research findings) it means the children experienced high levels of religiosity in their childhood then this decreased for a length of time. Then as the children reached an older age, their religiosity levels increased again.

But what do these patterns mean?

Firstly, for the high or increasing growth trajectory pattern, this included people who tended to be highly religious in early adulthood and they became more with age.

Secondly, the low or declining growth trajectory group included largely nonreligious individuals who tended to, on average, become progressively less religious as they aged.

Subsequently, for the final group, the parabolic growth trajectory class, this included people

who were somewhat religious in early adulthood,
becoming more so in midlife, and then becoming less
religious through the remainder of the life course.

In conclusion, to answer the question of how
stable are individual differences in religiosity, the
answer is very high. Because McCullough et al (2005)
found people have fairly high level of stability. Since
between 1940 and 1991, which is 51 years, there was
0.55 correlation between the stability of the levels of
religiosity.

This is even supported for short spans of time
because 5 and 17 years, the correlation was still
extremely high at .61 to .92. And wow, in correlations
that's rare to get results that high.

Religiosity and Life Outcomes

The final topic on religiosity is life outcomes
and we'll look at how religiosity affects health and
longevity and life satisfaction.

For religiosity and health McCullough, Hoyt,
Larson, Koenig, and Koenig (2000) ran a Meta-
analysis that estimated the extent to which religious
involvement is significantly associated with the odds
of being alive at the time of the follow-up.

The results showed that the religious people
were about 25% less likely to die during the period of

the study.

This could be because of religious people had healthier lifestyles, more support from their religious community, like money and psychological support as well as it could be because these religious people might have better recovery from illness due to less stress and more optimism.

Nonetheless, these results do highlight the importance for everyone to have social groups and healthy lifestyles. Be it apart of a religious group or not.

Finally, in terms of life satisfaction and a person's levels of religiosity, Salsman, Brown, Brechting, and Carlson (2005) studied religious people and they found that intrinsic religiousness and prayer fulfilment were associated with greater life satisfaction. This is partly because these activities are associated with more social support and optimism.

# INTRODUCTION TO POLITICS AND PERSONALITY

I absolutely love politics. I love voting and taking part in the democratic process but please don't worry. This is not a political book and I won't be making political points at least not intentionally.

Also, because I can be rather voice-y when it comes to politics, this part of the book might lack personal opinions and thoughts.

But politics is a great topic to study because it has a massive impact on all of our lives. Yet people differ a lot in their political opinions and orientations. And this next part of the book aims to explain why this occurs through a personality lens.

<u>The Authoritarian Personality</u>

Following World War 2, Adorno, Frenkel-Brunswik, Levinson, and Sanford (1950) attempted to explain the extreme atrocities of the Nazi Regime.

Resulting in them conducting their landmark study in social and political psychology since they found Right-Wing extremism is a syndrome of an authoritarian personality.

As a result, the researchers proposed and drew upon the Psychodynamic (Freudian) theory of the development of authoritarianism to help explain these results. This theory proposes that harsh, punitive parenting as well as rigid parental values cause tension between the caregiver and the child. Since the child has both anxiety and fear of receiving the parents' disapproval but they also want to punish and are angry as well as hostile towards parents. Resulting in an "intra-psychic conflict".

Which is understandable (I'm not saying the theory is correct but still) because it is natural for children to want to impress and get approval from their parents. But the child would still be angry at them for being so punitive and harsh.

Over time this suppression of the child's impulses leads to them displacing their aggression on *safer* and *weaker* targets. Such as ethnic minorities. All because the child can't physically or afford to act out their aggressions against their caregivers for being so strict. This reflects the very interesting dynamics of authoritarian submission and aggression.

In addition, I will stop here for a moment to

add this is also rather logical since this is one idea behind bullying. As this allows the child to exercise their aggression whilst not threatening further action or disapproval from their parents.

As Sanford, Adorno, Frenkel-Brunswik, & Levinson (1950, p. 233) explains:

*"the authoritarian must, out of an inner necessity, turn his aggression against out-groups. He must do so because he is psychologically unable to attack in-group authorities, rather than because of intellectual confusion regarding the source of his frustration"*

## Linking to Politics:

If we link this theory and apply it to politics then anti-Semitic attitudes co-vary with other characteristics. For example, ethnocentrism, anti-democratic tendencies, political and economic conservatism.

Overall, Adorno et al. found positive associations between these constructs in survey studies.

Leading to the creation of the California F-scale.

## The California F-scale

Adorno created this personality scale based on interviews looking for common patterns in a person's histories, behaviours and attitudes.

The scale measures the following:

- Conventionalism: how rigidly a person sticks to traditional, middle class norms and values.
- Authoritarian submission: the extent to which a person has a submissive, uncritical attitude toward ingroup authorities.
- Authoritarian aggression: a person's support for rejection and punishment of people who violate conventional norms.
- Anti-intraception: the person's opposition to the subjective and the imaginative. In other words, non-traditional ideas.
- Superstition and stereotypy: how much a person believes in mystical determinants of a person's fate. (Interesting?)
- Pre-occupation with power and toughness: this is excessive concern with how a person scores on the dominance-submission, strong-weak, leader-follower dimensions.
- Destructiveness and cynicism: General hostility toward humanity.
- Projectivity: a person's outward projection of unconscious impulses leading them to have dangerous world beliefs.

- Pre-occupation with sex.

## Problems with the F-scale

However, this F-scale is not perfect and there are some major problems. For example, due to the fact all the items are worded in the same direction and there's no reversed coded items. It's open to the acquiescence bias. Allowing a bored student in their experiment for credit study to tick all the same boxes without it looking weird. As well as some people tend to agree with all the items regardless of what they actually say.

This isn't helped by studies that have used reversed coded items have found there's low reliability coefficients in the answers. Meaning the F-scale has low reliability.

Yet a major problem is there are problems with the theory. For example, there's no support for the 9 different factors being linked to the authoritarian personality. Also, there is no empirical evidence for these Freudian and Psychodynamic theoretical assumptions.

# RIGHT-WING AUTHORITARIANISM AND SOCIAL DOMINANCE ORIENTATION

Now we're getting into *proper* political psychology because the two concepts we're going to be exploring in this chapter and the next are so, so critical for understanding politics and personality.

## Right-Wing Authoritarianism

In an effort to improve on the F-scale, Altemeyer (1981, 1988, 1996) developed the Right-Wing Authoritarianism scale (RWA) and this is a far better authoritarianism scale based on the F-scale. Because this scale contains reverse coded items and it looks at 3, instead of 9, tendencies.

- Conventionalism: a person's adherence to social conventions endorsed by the established ingroup authorities.

- Authoritarian submission: the extent to which a person has an uncritical submission and/ or obedience to the established authorities.
- Authoritarian aggression: how much a person supports aggressiveness towards norm violators, deviants and outgroups.

In addition, some other reasons why this scale is better than the F-scale is because these tendencies are theoretically assumed to be strongly related and this scale has much better reliability.

Moreover, it's based on the social-cognitive approach and not the psychodynamic approach. Proposing that social learning occurs during adolescence with harsh punishment leading to conformity whereas tolerance leads to autonomy. With the theory saying that this conformity leads the person to become uncritical of authorities and more conventionalist as well as the other traits associated with higher levels of Right-Wing authoritarianism.

In terms of behaviour, studies have shown that high Right-Wing authoritarianism is associated with people being willing to give harsher punishments to criminals.

But I have to jump in here and say the joke is on those people. Harsher punishments don't work for criminals. In fact some research has shown that the death penalty can lead to increased crime rates and the overall effect for the death penalty is null on offending rates. You can find out more information and find out what actually works to reduce offending rates in Forensic Psychology.

I am sorry for jumping in, in a political chapter but I'm very passionate about forensic psychology.

Anyway here are some other behaviours that Right-Wing authoritarianism is associated with:

- Approval of restrictions on civil liberties.
- Ethnocentrism.
- Anti-gay/anti-lesbian attitudes.
- Traditional gender roles.
- Support for aggressive military force.
- (extreme) right-wing voting and party preferences.
- Opposition to environmental movements.

## Social Dominance Orientation

This next concept in political psychology is Social Dominance Orientation and this is critical to understand. Because it can help us to explain so much as we'll see over the next two chapters.

Therefore, it was proposed by Pratto, Sidanius, Stallworth, and Malle (1994) and according to their Social Dominance Theory, people that are high in Social Dominance prefer that a hierarchical social order is maintained through individual and institutional discrimination. As well as in terms of behaviour social dominance Orientation explains the individual differences in people's desire for hierarchical versus equal group relations in society.

Furthermore, this is measured by the SDO-scale that measures a person's support for group-based dominance and intergroup inequalities. Also, it looks at how different people differ in the extent to which they endorse attitudes, beliefs and ideologies that justify group inequalities and the oppression of some groups by others.

As seen in these silly "legitimizing myths". Such as women and black people aren't as intelligent as white men so it's fine to discriminate against them and it's for their own good.

Two other examples of these hierarchy enhancing and legitimizing myths includes the racist and sexist prejudice. For example, as women are weaker but kinder than men, they need to be protected.

Then the myth is the ideology of meritocracy. I talk about this more in Social Psychology but it's all about people who hard are at the top deserve it and the people at the bottom aren't good enough. And don't deserve to be at the top of the society.

This is all rather head shaking to be honest.

Moreover, there's extensive research evidence that shows Social Dominance Orientation is related to:

- Prejudice towards a wide range of social groups.
- Sexism, Racism, Anti-Immigrant prejudice.
- Opposition to progressive and social policies.
- Affirmative action policies.
- Support for military spending and military force.

Finally, if we link both of these topics together then both Social Dominance Orientation and Right-Wing Authoritarianism are positively interested but these relationships are too weak to suggest that both variables represent the exact same construct.

Due to Social Dominance is only weakly correlated to authoritarian submission, as well as social dominators don't necessarily value conventions and traditions. They only become interested in such things if they preserve the hierarchical societal structures.

# DUAL PROCESS MODEL OF IDEOLOGY AND PREJUDICE, ATTITUDES AND PERSONALITY AND ATTITUDES AND BEHAVIOUR TOWARDS NON-HUMAN OUTGROUPS

To wrap up this great section on personality and politics I wanted to bring everything we've learnt so far about politics together, and then apply it to some very interesting ideas. But first we need to know how exactly the two concepts we examined in the last chapter and how they relate to ideology.

## Dual Process Model of Ideology and Prejudice

In the last chapter, we looked at both Right-Wing Authoritarianism and Social Dominance Orientation and that they predict a wide range of criterion variables related to political and intergroup issues.

As a result of these two variables accounting for different aspects of why people show outgroup prejudice. With prejudice being made up of different components. Like, adherence to social norms, which can be explained by Right-Wing Authoritarianism, as well as people's preference for inequality between social groups. This can be explained by Social Dominance Orientation.

Moreover, both Right-Wing Authoritarianism and Social Dominance Orientation are complementary predictors of a person's levels of ethnocentrism and outgroup prejudice. Also what makes this interesting is when these two variables are combined they produce a correlation that is considerably higher than if you looked at prejudice and one variable alone.

## Linking to Personality:

Putting the focus on personality, both Right-Wing Authoritarianism and Social Dominance Orientation were originally introduced as 'personality' constructs but a lot of research suggests that these constructs are not personality based.

Due to both of these constructs are predicted by the core personality traits, they're influenced by contextual factors (personality traits aren't) as well as interestingly, different contextual factors and personality traits predict Right-Wing Authoritarianism and Social Dominance Orientation.

And I think we can all agree that throughout this book I have never suggested a personality trait can predict another trait. It can predict behaviour, not personality.

## Dual Process Model, Social Attitudes and Personality

Leading us to talk about the Dual processing Model by Duckitt (2001; 2002) that proposed that Right-Wing Authoritarianism and Social Dominance Orientation represent two different dimensions of social attitudes that express different types of motivational goals.

As it's the goal of Right-Wing Authoritarianism to establish and maintain societal control, stability, and cohesion. Whereas it's the goal of people high in Social Dominance Orientation to maintain their group's power as well as dominance.

To test this Sibley and Duckitt (2008) conducted a meta-analysis of 71 studies allowing them to have over 22,000 participants and they found that higher levels of Right-Wing Authoritarianism were associated with both low Openness to experience and high levels of Conscientiousness. With both of these being roughly associated with high levels of social conformity.

In terms of Social Dominance Orientation, the study found that low Agreeableness and low levels of Honesty-Humility from the HEXACO are associated with high levels of Social Dominance Orientation.

## What About Attitudes and Behaviours Towards Non-Human Animals?

I'll be the first to admit that when I first came across this topic, I was a bit unsure on it. Not because it had bad information, it doesn't. But because I wasn't sure whether or not it would be interesting. Yet after I read about it and learnt more, I have to say there are some interesting results and some of these results are very clever.

As you can probably guess, human exploiting animals and their consumption are deeply ingrained in human society in both our cultural traditions and our societal practices.

However, some researchers saw some links and asked a great question, are there parallels between the struggle for ending animal exploitation and the struggle of the human rights movement to eliminate racial discrimination?

In other words, are there psychological similarities between human-animal relationships and human intergroup relationships?

## The Role of Individual Difference Variables:

The key factor to this question is why are some people okay with the exploitation of animals but others are not? And this all comes down to different individual differences. For example, people's differences in social-ideological attitudes.

Therefore, as we're seen already a person's Social Dominance Orientation is their preference for group-based dominance and social inequality. (Pratto et al., 1994; Sidanius & Pratto, 1999) As well as Social Dominance Orientation is a great predictor of prejudice across a wide range of domains and contexts. For instance, racism, sexism, and Homophobia. (Kteily et al., 2012; Meeusen & Dhont, 2015; Sidanius & Pratto, 1999)

Moreover, what's more interesting is that high levels of Social Dominance Orientation are actually associated with people's support for greater human animal divide, stronger human-supremacy beliefs and higher speciesism. (Caviola et al., 2019; Costello & Hodson, 2010; Dhont & Hodson, 2014)

Overall, Social Dominance Orientation is strongly correlated with people's desire to have dominance over human-animal relations and this explains why some people find animal exploitation less problematic than others. (Bastian et al., 2012)

## Social Dominance Orientation and the Environment:

And this isn't unique to animals because preference for social hierarchy and general inequalities can and do apply to people wanting to dominate nature as well. Due to research has shown that people high in Social Dominance Orientation are more likely to support humanity's exploitative practices, depleting natural resources as well as to deny climate change.

This is really important to understand because these theoretical advancements have allowed us to increase our understanding of the core ideological motives that underlie people's desire to exploit animals and our world. As well as this is so important if we're going to address animal neglect and cruelty and environmental problems.

## Speciesism and Ethnic Prejudice:

Furthermore, the entire point of this chapter is to answer the question of does the idea of speciesism covary with ethnic prejudice. Therefore, suggesting a link between people's different levels of desire for group-based dominance and social inequality and does it cause this bias in both speciesism and ethnic prejudice.

The modern research and the studies we've looked at suggest they do covary. Since these studies single out social dominance orientation and they confirm that this is a key variable in explaining the connection between ethnic prejudice and speciesism.

However, the reason why this is useful is because the psychology of group-based dominance allows us to not only explain why and how different people form negative attitudes towards human outgroups. But it gives some further insight into why some people are happy to oppose the better treatment of animals and hold negative attitudes towards vegetarians and vegans. Compared to others who aim to refrain from any form of animal exploitation.

. I think this is a great area of psychology with some great results because this is a new, innovative way to approach discrimination research, and this is so important. Psychology must always be advancing and this new way of looking at intergroup relations is a great demonstration of this. Because if someone had not decided to look at speciesism and apply that to intergroup relations then this would be a blind spot in the literature. As well as we wouldn't have the extra important information we know now.

## The Social Dominance Human-Animal Relations Model

Consequently, after looking at Social Dominance and how it relates to non-human outgroups, some researchers proposed this model in an effort to explain it all.

As a result, the model proposes that Social Dominance Orientation causes the common ideological motive that results in a person's prejudicial and exploitative tendencies towards both human and animal outgroups.

In addition, the model proposes that prejudice towards human outgroup, be it racism or any other type of prejudice, and speciesism both share a common ideological motive. Which is a person's desire for group-based dominance and inequality as indicated by Social Dominance Orientation.

In relation to the research prejudice towards ethnic outgroups should be positively correlated with speciesism simply because of this common core.

Also, if this model is true or holds up to the evidence then the research should show when the relationship between ethnic prejudice and speciesism is measured when the researchers controlling for Social Dominance Orientation. The relationship should disappear because the relationship will lack this common core.

Interestingly, this is what Sidanius and Pratto (1999) and Sidanius et al (1996) found because their studies showed there was a correlation between racial prejudice and political conservatism. With this correlation being linked to Social Dominance Orientation as was the relationship between ethnic prejudice and speciesism.

Overall, these predictions of SD-HARM are consistent with what moral philosophers, like Regan (1983) Singer (1975), and activists have these saying because they've proposed that people's prejudicial attitudes towards human outgroups and animals are interconnected. And thankfully this model offers a psychological explanation as to why they are interconnected.

## The Power of Examining Them Together

I mentioned earlier that both Social Dominance Orientation and Right-Wing Authoritarianism produce much higher correlations when you examine them together.

So, whilst it's still very important to look at the unique role of Social Dominance Orientation, we still need to consider Right-Wing Authoritarianism. Since this is the construct that is (at least) conceptually the closest construct to Social Dominance Orientation. As Right-Wing Authoritarianism reflects a person's support for conventionalism, authoritarian submission, and authoritarian aggression. As well as Right-Wing Authoritarianism does predict many of the outcomes in intergroup and political domains that Social Dominance Orientation predict, as supported by Hodson & Costello (2007) Meeusen & Dhont (2015).

## Examining The Two Constructs:

However, Right-Wing Authoritarianism is still considered an alternative predictor to Social Dominance Orientation that leads to outgroup negativity and group-based inequality (Altemeyer, 1998; Duckitt, 2001; Ekehammar, Akrami, Gylje, & Zakrisson, 2004; Sibley & Duckitt, 2008). This links back to what we saw earlier with the Dual Process Model.

Furthermore, the important difference between Social Dominance Orientation and Right-Wing Authoritarianism are the worldviews and motivations that these two concepts saw people to have and allow us to predict their level of these two traits. (Duckitt, 2001; Van Hiel, Roets, & Cornelis, 2007).

Mainly because Social Dominance Orientation stems from a competitive worldview that, for lack of a better term, makes the world look like a free for all where social groups must get resources and power for themselves. Whilst they restrict and discriminate against other *weaker* groups in the process.

Subsequently, if we compare this to Right-Wing Authoritarianism then this stems from so-called dangerous worldviews. With the person believing that the world is dangerous and chaotic and only the authorities can protect us from the danger. Including any crazy liberals who want to change anything. So, we must submit to authorities and stick to our conventions. Otherwise something horrific will happen to us! (Altemeyer, 1998; Duckitt, 2001)

(And yes, I am mocking Right-Wing Authoritarianism here)

As a result of these different worldviews that the constructs stem from, low status groups and competing groups, like immigrants, become the targets of Social Dominance Orientation-based prejudice. Whereas groups perceived as threatening the group's values and norms are typically the targets of Right-Wing Authoritarianism -based prejudice. (Asbrock, Sibley, & Duckitt, 2010; Duckitt & Sibley, 2010). For instance, environmentalists and feminists.

Therefore, this line of thinking is consistent with the idea that Social Dominance Orientation is related to the acceptance of inequality in relation to hierarchy. Whereas Right-Wing Authoritarianism is about people's resistance to change and preservation of the status quo in terms of stability.

Overall, we can conclude that these two constructs are very much related but they're very distinct too. (Jost, Glaser, Kruglanski, & Sulloway, 2003).

## Examining Them Together:

Returning to the need to examine both these constructs together, I need to say that because they both deal with different domains of prejudice. All these different patterns and different yet very important things that Social Dominance Orientation and Right-Wing Authoritarianism examine. These can go unnoticed if you investigate one of these constructs without the other and at the same time.

One example of why this is critical is because if we apply the Dominance aspect as found in Social Dominance Orientation and apply it to right-wing ideologies. This allows us to investigate the impact of hierarchy and dominance on ethnic prejudice and speciesism rather than the submissive-conventional aspect reflected in Right-Wing Authoritarianism.

On the whole, we can wrap up this section of the chapter by concluding that Social Dominance Orientation strongly predicts a person's beliefs of Human supremacy and both types of sexism.

Also if we add in Social Dominance Orientation as an explanatory variable, the associations between HumSup and the sexism variables become significantly smaller, indicating that Social Dominance Orientation in part explains the connection between oppressive attitudes towards animals, nature and women.

## Perceptions Of Veganism and Vegetarians

To conclude the political part of the book, I want to wrap it up by talking about perceptions of Veganism and Vegetarians because, generally speaking, these people do have a bad stereotype. And generally people think they're just plain weird.

Now, I was no exception at first and I am sorry for that. But in 2021, I had to do a statistical project around a vegan message so we had to research veganism.

Personally, I am a fan of veganism because there are a lot of personal benefits and there is some research saying vegans live longer. I'm not sure I would ever become a full vegan but I am planning to incorporate more vegan meals into my life.

Also, despite what a lot of people think, including my own family, vegan food is actually really nice and tasty.

Anyway, now we need to look at why there are these negative perceptions of vegans and vegetarians.

Firstly, it's extremely likely that Right-Wing Authoritarianism plays a role because people with high levels of this construct stick to cultural traditions and norms. With this applying to meat consumption and how we use animals as well.

Resulting in veganism and vegetarianism being a threat to these societal norms.

Subsequently, in terms of Social Dominance Orientation, people high in this construct show a general striving for dominance and this is not restricted to human outgroups. This applies to dominance over animals and nature. Due to their human supremacy belief.

Meaning that vegetarianism as well as veganism are seen as a threat to the dominant meat culture.

Conclusion:

As a quick conclusion, we've covered a lot of great topics in this beasty chapter and whilst I've had to refrain myself from commenting on a lot of the political things. I want to say that these two constructs can be applied to so many important behaviours so they are definitely worthy of study. But I wonder what other behaviours could they apply to?

To conclude the information part of the chapter, in conclusion, Social Dominance Orientation is about a person's desire for their group to be dominant and this applies to human-animal interactions as well.

Also, ethnic prejudice, speciesism and sexism are connected as well as Social Dominance Orientation underlies many biases in both human-human and human-animal relations.

Whereas Right-wing Authoritarianism is about social conformity and traditions as well as social-cultural conservatism. Therefore, these people have negative attitudes towards people who threaten the norm. Such as: environmentalists, vegans and vegetarians. (Dhont & Hodson, 2014; Dhont, Hodson, & Leite, 2016)

Personally, I think there are a lot more important issues that need dealing with compared to what someone wants to eat! (As long as it's not human)

# PART FIVE:
# PERSONALITY AND
# LIFE OUTCOMES

# PERSONALITY AND SOCIAL LIFE OUTCOMES

After looking at a lot of different topics within personality psychology, we finally need to ask the question: how does our personality affect us in the long term?

We've seen how personality affects our beliefs and behaviour, but what about our life outcomes?

These are the type of questions we'll start to look at now. Starting off with a rather fun one and this is possibly my favourite of the outcomes we'll look at. We are going to start this section by looking at our social life outcomes!

And personality can affect these outcomes in a lot of different ways.

## Personality and Romantic Relationships

For example, in terms of our romantic relationships, results have found there's a positive but very small correlation that husband and wife personality traits are level. As showed when Malouff et al (2010) conducted a meta-analysis of 19 samples and 3848 people in intimate and heterosexual relationships. They analyzed their self-reported relationship satisfaction, and spouses self-reported personality traits.

Their results show higher marital satisfaction was associated with having a spouse who was higher in emotional stability. Meaning having a spouse that was lower in neuroticism and higher in agreeableness and conscientiousness. As well as these results are similar for both men and women.

Yet this isn't the only study to look at personality and relationships because Dyrenforth et al (2010) studied large samples of married couples from the UK and Australia. With their results showed a participant's levels of agreeableness, emotional stability and Extroversion were weakly correlated, with a Pearson's coefficient of 0.20 or lower, with their marital satisfaction.

Overall, the technical answer is neither similarity or dissimilarity between spouses are associated with higher levels of marital satisfaction.

But the normal answer is regardless if spouses are similar or not, chances of marital satisfaction are about the same. Since Dyrenforth et al (2010) showed there's a weak correlation.

I think this just goes to show how two people can be different and still be happy with each other and if you want to learn more about relationships and how we choose our romantic partners and friends, please check out Psychology of Relationships.

## Are Friends Similar in Personality?

Now this is the reason why I love this chapter because I think these results are great, and it's good to see and understand how our personality impacts our social life.

Therefore, Lee, Ashon et al (2009) conducted a number of studies on the similarity between friends and the assumed similarity between well-acquitted students for the HEXACO factors.

Their results showed for Extroversion, Emotionality, Agreeableness and Conscientiousness factors of the model, there wasn't a strong tendency for friends to be similar or different in relation to these factors. Whereas, for Openness to Experience and Honesty-Humility, friends tend to be similar for these factors.

When it came to asking the friends about how similar they believed they all were in the different personality factors. The friends didn't perceive any differences for Extroversion, Emotionality, Agreeableness and Conscientiousness dimensions.

Additionally, friends tend to perceive more similarities exist than there actually was and friends do tend to perceive friends as similar in the Openness to Experience and Honesty-Humility dimensions. The reason for this could be because these two dimensions are related to people's values about how they live their lives and relate to other people.

Nonetheless, as a side note, personality traits don't matter for the processes of forming or maintaining relationships because there are a lot of other social processes involved in that.

Also, the reason why I quite like that study is because in our friendship groups, I believe we all know that we must have similar personalities to varying extents. But we don't know how we're similar. Therefore, I like that the study above allows us to fully understand how similar we actually are to our friends.

## Personality and Social Status:

Granted it was rather difficult for me to create that subheading, but this section will look at how a child's personality affects their social status and social groups. Since Newcomb, Bukowski and Pattee (1993) conducted a meta-analysis of the differences between a child's personality and how they're liked or disliked by their peers.

Their results show for average children:

- The popular children are low in aggression and high in sociability.
- Rejected Children are high in aggression and low in sociability.
- Neglected children, the children who are liked and disliked by few, are low in both personality traits.
- Controversial children, these are the children who are liked and disliked by many, are high in both aggression and sociability.

Personally, I was quite surprised to find out controversial children existed. Did you know that?

Personality and Societal Status:

To finish up this chapter, we need to ask: how does our personality affect our societal status?

And you'll see below this is nothing like the last section.

Consequently, Anderson, John, Keltner and Kring (2001) studied the Big Five personality factors in young adult college students who were in fraternities, sororities and mixed sex dormitories.

(And for our international audience and the UK audience, fraternities and sororities are basically a society for female and males in America at university and they all live together. That's the basic version. I would comment on all the things TV teaches us about these societies, but I would like to think those things don't actually happen in real life?)

Going back to the study, the researcher measured ratings of each student's prominence, influence and respect.

The results showed that Extroversion was related to social status for men and women. As well as emotional stability was positively related to social status among men. Since toughness is admired more by men than women.

With the other 3 Big Factors not being associated with social status.

# PERSONALITY, SELF-CONTROL, THE DARK TRIAD AND OTHER LIFE OUTCOMES

Continuing on with our investigation of how personality affects our life outcomes, I've definitely saved some fun topics for this chapter. Because… there's just some great topics here I really want to explore with you.

But first I want to show you how personality can affect our overall life satisfaction then I've got some amazing topics to share with you!

<u>Personality and Life Satisfaction:</u>

<u>Life Satisfaction</u>

Life satisfaction is very important to all of us because if we don't feel happy with our lives then this can reduce and harm our mental health.

As a result, a lot of research has been done in

this area. For example, some research has examined the stability of life satisfaction over 4 years in a sample of American students, and the correlation for this was $r = .50$. A rather large correlation.

Also, the heritability of life satisfaction is large too at 0.40. (Stubbe et al, 2005)

But still, how does personality affect life satisfaction?

Furr and Funder (1998) examined how different personality traits relate to life satisfaction and the overall results show personality is positively correlated to life satisfaction. As seen below:

- Self-esteem is about .60 correlated.
- Cheerfulness is approximately .40.
- Assertiveness is roughly .30.
- Sociability is about .30.

Nonetheless, some personality traits are negatively related to life satisfaction.

- Depressiveness is roughly -.50 correlated with life satisfaction.
- Anxiety is about -.30.
- And anger is around -.30.

## Life satisfaction and Big Five Personality

In addition, if we look at life satisfaction from the viewpoint of the Big Five, life satisfaction has its strongest correlations with Extroversion and Emotional Stability.

Then life satisfaction is moderately correlated with Agreeableness and Conscientiousness.

Although, it all comes down to the fact that people with a general disposition to feel positive emotions tend to have high life satisfaction and people with a general disposition to feel negative emotions tend to have low life satisfaction.

So, please be positive, be happy and do what you love in life!

## The Role of Self-Control

When I first learnt about self-control in cognitive psychology, I never thought it could apply to personality but as personality psychology looks at people's typical ways of behaving, thinking and feeling. A person's level of self-control fits into personality psychology's remit.

Also, I know I've already said in another chapter but whilst the below does look at criminality, self-control is not the only cause and some criminals have different levels of self-control. So, this section is full of great information but I do recommend reading Forensic Psychology for a more holistic look in case you're interested in the topic.

## The Self-Control Theory of Crime

Proposed by Gottfredson and Hirschi (1990), this theory proposes that crime involves "acts of force or fraud undertaken in pursuit of self-interest" and this is a good quote because this is a logical assumption that you would think criminals only act in their own interest. Yet it doesn't look at the question *What differentiates criminals from non-criminals?* directly.

Generally speaking, and as someone who has learnt a lot about forensic psychology I do mean generally, criminals have higher levels of impulsivity, need for immediate gratification and pleasure seeking despite the negative consequences that crimes bring. As well as criminals have a failure to inhibit their selfish impulses but the motivational factors are the same for criminals and non-criminals.

As supported by Romero, Gomez-Fraguela, Luengo, and Sobral (2003) who examined impulsive behaviour in their study on Spanish university students. The researchers measured the students' personality traits of poor self-control, impulsive risk-taking, self-centeredness, "preference for simple tasks", volatile temper as well as their preference for physical activities.

Then the researchers measured the students'
criminal or delinquent activities. Such as: their
amount of aggression, theft, vandalism, academic
dishonesty and illegal drug use amongst other types of
activities.

On the whole, the results of the study show
the students' delinquent behaviour was most strongly
related to impulsive risk-taking with there being a
strong positive correlation of $r > .40$.

Showing that a willingness to take risks and
the tendency not to inhibit one's impulses influence
criminal behaviour and this is in line with the self-
control theory.

## Primary and Secondary Psychopathy

I know I would typically finish up a forensic
psychology section with a personal comment but I
love psychopathy so let's jump in.

You might not, but it's fine if you don't, that
some serious offenders and psychopaths are very
rational, coolly calculating but other serious offenders
as well as psychopaths have very poor self-control.
Leading researchers to conclude there are two types.

Also, I think this is depicted rather well on
TV programmes because I can think of a few killers
that are *too smart* for the detectives because they're so

cunning and rational. For example, Red John in *The Mentalist* and 3XK in *Castle*. Then you have others that are the stereotypical *deranged* killer. Basically, any horror film springs to mind here.

Going back to the research, Karpman (1948) created the terms *primary* versus *secondary* psychopaths with primary psychopaths being *good* or *skilled* at manipulation, deceit, callousness, grandiosity themselves, and selfishness. For example, as seen in these items from Levenson, Kiehl, & Fitzpatrick (1995):

- "For me, what's right is whatever I can get away with,"
- "I enjoy manipulating other people's feelings,"
- "Success is based on survival of the fittest, I am not concerned about the losers,"

Whereas secondary psychopaths are impulsive, suffer from a lack of planning and poor self-control and they're irresponsible. As seen below from Levenson, Kiehl, & Fitzpatrick (1995):

- "I don't plan anything very far in advance"
- "I find myself in the same kinds of trouble, time after time"

In terms of criminality, both primary and secondary psychopathy are positively correlated with delinquent activities. For example, antisocial behaviour, vandalism, thefts and intoxicated driving. As well as both are associated with a lack of self-control and they're highly manipulative and selfish.

However, there is only a moderate correlation between these two different types of psychopathy and people can score high on both factors, or low on one and high on the other factor.

One interesting finding about psychopathy is primary psychopathy can make people be exploitative and manipulative towards others but these people high in primary psychopathy can still have enough self-control to avoid criminal behaviour.

Whereas people lower on primary psychopathy but high on secondary psychopathy tend to impulsively commit a crime without the deliberate intention to harm others.

I definitely think this is a great section, because who doesn't love to learn about psychopathy?

Due to the fact, I think it's the one area of psychology that's remotely accurate on TV and psychopaths always make for good characters so this makes people interested in them. And it's always good to learn about interesting things.

## The Dark Triad

This is another epic topic and I do not use the term epic often, that might actually be the first time I've ever used it, because I remember coming across this personality trait when watching an episode of *Ransom* (a great TV show) and it really proved that people with the Dark Triad trait are the ultimate bad guy.

As a result of this personality trait is a combination of high levels of psychopathy, narcissism and machvavellism. You can imagine the *interesting* behaviour of people with this trait!

To look at the Dark Triad in a bit more depth, we're going to break down each personality trait in this combination.

Firstly, whilst in the last section I broke this down in detail, here I'm going to talk more generally. Therefore, people high in psychopathy are callous, remorseless, exploitative and manipulative. Also, they are impulsive and callous thrill-seekers, and psychopaths would tend to say the following:

- "I tend to not be too concerned with morality or the morality of     my actions"
- "I tend to lack remorse"

Secondly, narcissism as I've preluded to before in the book are people that are very high in self-esteem but it comes from an insecure place. Making these people dominant, feel superior and entitled, their exhibitionist and exploitation. Also, you can sum up narcissists as grandiose self-promoters who constantly crave attention. With these people typically saying:

- "I tend to want others to admire me,"
- "I tend to expect special favors from others,"

Additionally, if you're interested in narcissism you have to listen to episode 94 of The Psychology World Podcast because I talk about How Narcissists Use Cult Leader Tactics to Control Others.

The final personality trait in this combination is Machiavellianism and people high in this personality trait are manipulative, insincere as well as callous. Basically, master manipulators and typically say:

"I tend to manipulate others to get my way"

"I have used flattery to get my way."

## Outcomes of Dark Triad:

Personally, I really have to give these a job well done because I really would not want to meet anyone with the Dark triad because on TV they sound interesting but scary!

As a result, Furnham, Richards, & Paulhus (2013) studied the effects of the Dark triad and they found people high in this personality trait in the workplace behaviour were bad bosses, created toxic leadership and were snakes in suits.

Moreover, when the Dark triad was combined with high IQ and/or physical attractiveness, it showed some people were adaptive in some context but their behaviour was still negative. Since in education people with the Dark triad cheated and committed essay plagiarism, and their mating behaviour was toxic to say the least.

Since psychopaths had a short-term and impulsive mating strategy akin to one night stands and no commitment. Whereas Machiavellians were more strategic in their choice of a mate and had a regulated style that maintains the relationship. Yet these people were still highly prejudice in their intergroup behaviour and showed antisocial behaviour.

Furthermore, if we link this to criminality, psychopaths have reasonably high criminality, and they tend to be bullies and aggressors. Whereas Machiavellians are less impulsive and tend to commit corporate/ white-collar crimes.

After reading all that I really do believe the Dark Triad is a fascinating personality trait because it

basically combines all the major *bad* personality traits
into one negative superfactor. Which presents
personality researchers with a lot of interesting areas
to research.

But I'm not sure if I would want to meet one,
would you?

# PERSONALITY, HEALTH-RELATED OUTCOMES AND ACADEMIC ACHIEVEMENT

Moving onto the last chapter of the book, I've definitely got some fun facts for you. It's only now after writing up this section that I've realized some of these personality findings are rather dark. Including the ones below

Enjoy!

## Health-related outcomes:

### Substance Abuse

In the series, I've already spoken about a lot about substance abuse but that was mainly Health, Abnormal and Biological Psychology perspectives.

From a personality perspective, substance abuse is related to a few different dimensions and traits. For example, conscientiousness and self-disciplined as well as impulse control. With some researchers proposing these traits are related to a person's ability to resist the temptation.

Also, people who have higher neuroticism we already know are higher in anxiety, moodiness and irritability. Therefore, this increases the temptation to them to use substances to control these negative emotions.

Moving onto a study, Elkin, Kinn, McGue and Iacono (2006) conducted a study using 1000 17 years old and they were interviewed to determine their tobacco, alcohol and drug use.

Their results showed two important findings, people who used these substances at 17 years old were more likely to develop a dependency by age 20. With 30% of these people suffering from alcohol dependency, 20% from drug dependency and 30% from nicotine dependency.

The second finding showed participants who at age 17 had a substance abuse disorder were lower in conscientiousness-related traits and lower emotional stability. As well as these personality traits were predictive for developing substance abuse disorder by age 20.

Lastly, conscientiousness and emotional

stability predicted a person's likelihood of quitting smoking and drinking as well. (Tervaccvano & Caste, 2004; Bottlender & Soyka, 2004)

I think this is understandable because conscientiousness is about self-awareness and increasing self-awareness should lead to a decrease in smoking and drinking behaviour. Therefore, I think one interesting question to think about is how can we use these findings in the real world? Could you potentially put a mirror in a smoking area? In Social Psychology, I've spoken about similar things.

Just a thought.

Longevity:

We all want to live as long as possible and we generally know being healthy and exercising helps us to live longer. But how does personality influence this?

The idea behind personality influencing our longevity is people with higher levels of a particular personality trait may tend to live long and be healthier.

As a result, to study this we use data and longitudinal studies.

For instance, Friedman et al (1993) wanted to study does childhood personality predict longevity.

To study this, the researchers examined the personalities of 1,200 11 years old gifted children. Following this after 60 years they looked at the records of who were still alive and dead.

Their results showed conscientiousness played a role in longevity. Since people low in this particular personality dimension had a 35% higher chance of dying before the age of70 compared to people higher in conscientiousness.

A possible reason for this is because people high in conscientiousness are less likely to engage in health-damaging behaviour. Like, smoking or excessive drinking.

Additionally, the study found that low conscientiousness was related to drinking as well as smoking. Yet these couldn't explain the link between this personality trait and early death. (Friedman et al, 1995)

Some researchers have suggested other possible explanations. Like, social networks, a person's ability to handle stress and health-related behaviour.

Another result from Friedman et al (1993): was cheerfulness, and this is scary, because people high in cheerfulness had about a 35% higher chance of dying before the age of 70.

Now, this is scary because this wasn't related to smoking or heavy drinking behaviours (Martin et al., 2002) so the alternative explanation is these people are overoptimistic about health prospects. For example, when people say *I don't need to quit smoking. My dad smoked twenty a day and he lived to his 90s.*

In all honesty, more large scale projects are needed that use representative samples to fully understand this finding.

Personality and Heart disease

I admit I was just as surprised as you were to find out our personality and even affect our chance of getting heart disease. But William Osler (1910) said "having a keen and ambitious disposition increases the risk of heart disease"

I rather doubt this!

Leading us to talk about another one of Friedman's studies, Friedman and Rosenman (1959) looked at two unique personality types and how they caused heart disease. The study looked at "Type A" personality where these people were high in competitiveness, impatient, excessive job involvement, hostile, and they were high in time urgency. Whereas Type B was the opposite in all these personality traits.

Consequently, the study found that Type A does increase the probability of heart disease with the hostility personality traits being the most important aspect.

Due to the fact that people with a higher hostile dominance have poorer health habits, they're in more conflict which increases the amount of stress they suffer from, they receive less stress-reducing support from others as well as their greater physiological reactions to stress leads to damage in the blood vessels.

All in all, this is bad!

So, I would like to encourage you unofficially, please try and relax, don't get stressed and remember if you're hostile to other people. They wouldn't want to help you in the future. This includes being hostile towards friends and family because they won't want to help with do stress-reducing activities. Like, a day out to the zoo or whatever.

## Academic Performance

Saving the best for last in this chapter, how does our personality impact our academic outcomes?

As we saw in the last chapter, academic performance is largely down to our cognitive ability and this was explained in a lot more depth in the Mental Abilities Section of the book.

Nonetheless, linking this to personality Poropat (2009) ran a meta-analysis on more than 100 studies and they found there was a correlation between a person's level of conscientiousness and their grade point average. ($r = .25$) This was similar across different levels of education.

Moreover, personality traits related to self-discipline, diligence and organization resulted in greater effort, attention to detail and efficiency when the student was completing coursework and exams.

Penultimately, at the elementary school level (or primary school to our UK readers), there was a positive association between Agreeableness, Emotional stability, Extroversion, and Openness to Experience and academic achievement. This was found to be around .20.

Finally, I think it's fair to say personality affects everything in our lives from our social life to our academic achievements to the not so obvious health outcomes. And despite the occasionally small but present correlations between personality and a given behaviour, it's hard to deny the impact personality has on us.

So, I really hope you've enjoyed this personality psychology journey and I hope to see you soon in another book!

# REFERENCES

Ashton, M. C. (2018). *Individual differences and personality* (3rd ed.). London: Academic Press.

Ashton, M. C., Lee, K., Perugini, M., Szarota, P., de Vries, R. E., Di Blas, L., ... De Raad, B. (2004). A six-factor structure of personality-descriptive adjectives: Solutions from psycholexical studies in seven languages. *Journal of Personality and Social Psychology, 86*, 356-366.

Bernhardt, P. C., Dabbs, J. M., Fielden, J. A., & Lutter, C. D. (1998). Testosterone changes during vicarious experiences of winning and losing among fans at sporting events. *Physiology & Behavior, 65*, 59-62.

Carver, C. S., & Scheier, M. F. (2008). *Perspectives on personality* (6th ed.). Boston, MA: Pearson Education.*

Cervone, D., & Pervin, L. A. (2008). *Personality: Theory and research* (10th ed.). Hoboken, NJ: Wiley.

Corr, P. J. (2004). Reinforcement sensitivity theory and personality. *Neuroscience & Biobehavioral Reviews, 28*, 317-332.

Dabbs, J. M., Carr, T. S., Frady, R. L., & Riad, J. K. (1995). Testosterone, crime, and misbehavior among 692 male prison inmates. *Personality and Individual Differences, 18*, 627-633.

Deary, I.J., Peter, A., Austin, E. and Gibson, G. (1998), Personality traits and personality disorders. British Journal of Psychology, 89: 647-661. https://doi.org/10.1111/j.2044-8295.1998.tb02708.x

Edmonds, G. W., Goldberg, L. R., Hampson, S. E., & Barckley, M. (2013). Personality stability from childhood to midlife: Relating teachers' assessments in elementary school to observer- and self-ratings 40 years later. *Journal of Research in Personality, 47*, 505-513.

Egan, V., Austin, E., Elliot, D., Patel, D. and Charlesworth, P. (2003), Personality traits, personality disorders and sensational interests in mentally disordered offenders. Legal and Criminological Psychology, 8: 51-62. https://doi.org/10.1348/135532503762871237

Eysenck, H. J. (1947). *Dimensions of personality.*

London: Kegan Paul.

Franks, P., Chapman, B., Duberstein, P. and Jerant, A. (2009), Five factor model personality factors moderated the effects of an intervention to enhance chronic disease management self-efficacy. British Journal of Health Psychology, 14: 473-487. https://doi.org/10.1348/135910708X360700

Goldberg, L. R. (1993). The structure of phenotypic personality traits. *American Psychologist, 48*, 26-34.

ll, G., Gutiérrez, F., Peri, J.M., Gárriz, M., Ferraz, L., Baillés, E. and Obiols, J.E. (2015), Seven basic dimensions of personality pathology and their clinical consequences: Are all personalities equally harmful?. Br J Clin Psychol, 54: 450-468. https://doi.org/10.1111/bjc.12091

Hill, R. W., McIntire, K., & Bacharach, V. R. (1997). Perfectionism and the Big Five factors. *Journal of Social Behavior and Personality, 12,* 257-270.

Hyde, J. S. (2005). The gender similarities hypothesis. *American Psychologist, 60*, 561-592.

John, O. P., & Srivastava, S. (1999). The Big Five trait taxonomy: History, measurement, and theoretical perspectives. In L. A. Pervin & O. P. John (Eds.), *Handbook of personality: Theory and research* (2nd ed., pp. 102-138). New York: Guilford.

Leckelt, M., Richter, D., Schröder, C., Küfner, A.C.P., Grabka, M.M. and Back, M.D. (2019), The rich *are* different: Unravelling the perceived and self-reported personality profiles of high-net-worth individuals. Br J Psychol, 110: 769-789. https://doi.org/10.1111/bjop.12360

Maltby, J., Day, L., & Macaskill, A. (2007). *Personality, individual differences and intelligence.* Harlow, UK: Pearson Education.

McAdams, D. P. (2006). *The person: A new introduction to personality psychology* (4th ed.). Hoboken, NJ: Wiley.*

McCrae, R. R., & Costa, P. T., Jr. (1999). A five-factor theory of personality. In L. A. Pervin & O. P. John (Eds.), *Handbook of personality: Theory and research* (2nd ed., pp. 139-153). *New York: Guilford.*

McCrae, R. R., Costa, P. T., Jr., de Lima, M. P., Simões, A., Ostendorf, F., Angleitner, A., … Piedmont, R. L. (1999). Age differences in personality across the adult life span: Parallels in five cultures. *Developmental Psychology, 35,* 466-477.

Measelle, J. R., John, O. P., Ablow, J. C., Cowan, P. A., & Cowan, C. P. (2005). Can children provide coherent, stable, and valid self-reports on the Big Five dimensions? A longitudinal study from ages 5 to 7. *Journal of Personality and Social Psychology, 89,* 90-106.

Mischel, W., Shoda, Y., & Smith, R. E. (2004). *Introduction to personality: Toward an integration* (7th ed.). Hoboken, NJ: Wiley.

Navas, M.P., Maneiro, L., Cutrín, O., Gómez-Fraguela, J.A. and Sobral, J. (2021), Contributions of the dark triad to moral disengagement among incarcerated and community adults. Leg Crim Psychol. https://doi.org/10.1111/lcrp.12190

Pervin, L. A., Cervone, D., & John, O. P. (2005). *Personality: Theory and research* (9th ed.). Hoboken, NJ: Wiley.*

Roberts, B. W., Walton, K. E., & Viechtbauer, W. (2006). Patterns of mean-level change in personality traits across the life course: A meta-analysis of longitudinal studies. *Psychological Bulletin, 132*, 1-25.

Rosenblitt, J. C., Soler, H., Johnson, S. E., & Quadagno, D. M. (2001). Sensation seeking and hormones in men and women: Exploring the link. *Hormones and Behavior, 40,* 396-402.

Schaie, K. W. (1965). A general model for the study of developmental problems. *Psychological Bulletin, 64,* 92-107.

Schaie, K. W., & Baltes, P. B. (1975). On sequential strategies in developmental research.

*Human Development, 18,* 384-390.

Stöber, J. (2003). Self-pity: Exploring the links to personality, control beliefs, and anger. *Journal of Personality, 71,* 183-220.

Stoeber, J., & Corr, P. J. (2015). Perfectionism, personality, and affective experiences: New insights from revised Reinforcement Sensitivity Theory. *Personality and Individual Differences, 86,* 354-359.

Stoeber, J. (2014). How other-oriented perfectionism differs from self-oriented and socially prescribed perfectionism. *Journal of Psychopathology and Behavioral Assessment, 36,* 329-338.

Thank you for reading.

I hoped you enjoyed it.

If you want a FREE book and keep up to date about new books and project. Then please sign up for my newsletter at www.connorwhiteley.net/

Have a great day.

CHECK OUT THE PSYCHOLOGY WORLD PODCAST FOR MORE PSYCHOLOGY INFORMATION!

AVAILABLE ON ALL MAJOR PODCAST APPS.

## About the author:

Connor Whiteley is the author of over 30 books in the sci-fi fantasy, nonfiction psychology and books for writer's genre and he is a Human Branding Speaker and Consultant.

He is a passionate warhammer 40,000 reader, psychology student and author.

Who narrates his own audiobooks and he hosts The Psychology World Podcast.

All whilst studying Psychology at the University of Kent, England.

Also, he was a former Explorer Scout where he gave a speech to the Maltese President in August 2018 and he attended Prince Charles' 70th Birthday Party at Buckingham Palace in May 2018.

Plus, he is a self-confessed coffee lover!

## PERSONALITY PSYCHOLOGY AND INDIVIDUAL DIFFERENCES

All books in 'An Introductory Series':

BIOLOGICAL PSYCHOLOGY 3<sup>RD</sup> EDITION

COGNITIVE PSYCHOLOGY THIRD EDITION

SOCIAL PSYCHOLOGY- 3<sup>RD</sup> EDITION

ABNORMAL PSYCHOLOGY 3<sup>RD</sup> EDITION

PSYCHOLOGY OF RELATIONSHIPS- 3<sup>RD</sup> EDITION

DEVELOPMENTAL PSYCHOLOGY 3<sup>RD</sup> EDITION

HEALTH PSYCHOLOGY

RESEARCH IN PSYCHOLOGY

A GUIDE TO MENTAL HEALTH AND TREATMENT AROUND THE WORLD- A GLOBAL LOOK AT DEPRESSION

FORENSIC PSYCHOLOGY

THE FORENSIC PSYCHOLOGY OF THEFT, BURGLARY AND OTHER

## OTHER SHORT STORIES BY CONNOR WHITELEY

Other books by Connor Whiteley:

The Fireheart Fantasy Series

Heart of Fire

Heart of Lies

More Coming Soon!

The Garro Series- Fantasy/Sci-fi

GARRO: GALAXY'S END

GARRO: RISE OF THE ORDER

GARRO: END TIMES

GARRO: SHORT STORIES

GARRO: COLLECTION

GARRO: HERESY

GARRO: FAITHLESS

GARRO: DESTROYER OF WORLDS

GARRO: COLLECTIONS BOOK 4-6

GARRO: MISTRESS OF BLOOD

GARRO: BEACON OF HOPE

GARRO: END OF DAYS


Winter Series- Fantasy Trilogy Books

WINTER'S COMING

WINTER'S HUNT

WINTER'S REVENGE

WINTER'S DISSENSION

Miscellaneous:

THE ANGEL OF RETURN

THE ANGEL OF FREEDOM

Audiobooks by Connor Whiteley:

BIOLOGICAL PSYCHOLOGY

COGNITIVE PSYCHOLOGY

SOCIOCULTURAL PSYCHOLOGY

ABNORMAL PSYCHOLOGY

PSYCHOLOGY OF HUMAN
RELATIONSHIPS

HEALTH PSYCHOLOGY

DEVELOPMENTAL PSYCHOLOGY

RESEARCH IN PSYCHOLOGY

FORENSIC PSYCHOLOGY

GARRO: GALAXY'S END

GARRO: RISE OF THE ORDER

GARRO: SHORT STORIES

GARRO: END TIMES

GARRO: COLLECTION

GARRO: HERESY